KERNEL FUNCTIONS AND ELLIPTIC DIFFERENTIAL EQUATIONS IN MATHEMATICAL PHYSICS

Pure and Applied Mathematics

A Series of Monographs and Textbooks

EDITED BY

PAUL A. SMITH AND SAMUEL EILENBERG

Columbia University, New York, N.Y.

Volume I: ARNOLD SOMMERFELD, Partial Differential Equations in Physics, 1949
(Lectures on Theoretical Physics, Volume VI)

Volume II: REINHOLD BAER, Linear Algebra and Projective Geometry, 1952

Volume III: HERBERT BUSEMANN and P. J. KELLY, Projective Geometry and Projective Metrics, 1953

Volume IV: STEFAN BERGMAN and M. SCHIFFER, Kernel Functions and Elliptic Differential Equations in Mathematical Physics, 1953

ACADEMIC PRESS INC., PUBLISHERS
NEW YORK, N.Y.

Kernel Functions and Elliptic Differential Equations in Mathematical Physics

By

STEFAN BERGMAN AND M. SCHIFFER
Stanford University, California

1953
ACADEMIC PRESS INC., PUBLISHERS
NEW YORK, N.Y.

ACADEMIC PRESS INC.

125 East 23rd Street, New York 10, N. Y.

Library of Congress Catalog Card Number: 52—13362

TO

RICHARD VON MISES

Preface

The subject of this book is the theory of boundary value problems in partial differential equations. This theory plays a central role in various fields of pure and applied mathematics, theoretical physics, and engineering, and has already been dealt with in numerous books and articles. This book discusses a portion of the theory from a unifying point of view. The solution of a partial differential equation of elliptic type is a functional of the boundary values, the coefficients of the differential equation, and the domain considered. The dependence of the solution upon its boundary values has been studied extensively, but its dependence upon the coefficients and upon the domain is almost as important. The problem of the variation of the solution with that of the coefficients of the equation is closely related to questions of stability, which are of decisive importance in many applications. The knowledge of how the solution of a differential equation varies with a change of coefficients or domain permits us to concentrate on the study of simple equations in simple domains and to derive qualitative results from them.

When studying the relationship of a solution to the boundary values, one is led to introduce certain fundamental solutions: Green's, Neumann's, and Robin's functions. Every solution can be expressed in terms of one of these functions, and it is therefore natural to emphasize a systematic study of them. In this way, we deal only with a few well-defined functions and their interrelations and obtain a clear insight into the structure of all possible solutions of the differential equation. The fundamental solutions depend upon two argument points, are symmetric in both, and are a function of each separately. Solutions of this type are called kernels, and after linear operations extended over one variable they still represent solutions of the equation in the other variable. The systematic treatment of the various kernels and their properties is the main object of this book.

In the treatment of the fundamental solutions, certain combinations play a particularly important role. Although Green's, Neumann's, and Robin's functions possess singular points in the domain of definition, combinations of them can be found which are regular throughout the whole domain and which are, therefore, particularly amenable to theoretical and numerical treatment. For example, the difference between any two fundamental solutions is a regular kernel and possesses various important properties with respect to its boundary behavior.

The book consists of two main parts. The first part gives a survey of boundary value problems occurring in some branches of theoretical physics. The various fundamental solutions are introduced in a heuristic way, and their physical significance is studied. Various concepts can be unified by concentrating upon these particular kernels. The common mathematical background of so widely varying theories as heat conduction, hydrodynamics, electrostatics, magnetostatics, and elasticity is shown. In addition to its own intrinsic interest, the material of this part provides illustrations and adds significance to the second part of the book, which is devoted to the exact mathematical formulation of problems and the methods involved. For the sake of simplicity we have restricted ourselves in the second part to a rather special type of partial differential equation. On the other hand, we have dealt with this equation in the greatest detail and are confident that a careful reader will be able to make applications and generalizations to similar problems which may be of interest to him.

The present book is not to be considered a textbook on partial differential equations. It assumes a fair acquaintance with the standard methods of analysis provided, for example, by the excellent books of Courant-Hilbert, Frank-Mises, and Jeffreys. For this reason, an engineer or a physicist with the conventional mathematical training may possibly find some parts difficult to read. We have attempted to incorporate material which is of interest and of use to this class of readers and have tried to provide a systematic and self-contained introduction to each branch of the applications treated. On the mathematical side we have included much material which has been obtained in the researches of the last few years and which we hope may lead to further research and progress in the field of partial differential equations.

We wish to thank Dr. Philip Davis who has worked closely with us on all phases of the book. His constant help and advice has materially lightened our task.

We are further obliged to Mr. Robert Osserman for his careful reading and useful criticism of the manuscript. Various of his valuable suggestions have been incorporated into this book.

We are also obliged to Dr. G. Duff for a number of helpful remarks.

The manuscript was prepared with the support of the Office of Naval Research and the Naval Bureau of Ordnance, and we wish to express our obligation to these institutions*.

Stanford University

Stefan Bergman

Menahem Schiffer

* The ideas expressed in this book represent the personal views of the authors and are not necessarily those of the Office of Naval Research or the Naval Bureau of Ordnance.

NOTE TO THE READER

The reader's attention is called to the following notation used throughout the book:

A reference to a previous formula in a given chapter is indicated simply by quoting the formula number, e. g., (1.1), (3.5).

A reference to a formula from a previous chapter is of the form (II. 1.1), i. e., Chapter II, formula (1.1).

B.III.1, A.I.5 refer to Part B, Chapter III, Section 1, and Part A, Chapter I, Section 5, respectively.

The following conventions are used regarding print type:

Vectors are denoted by the letters of the form $\mathbf{v}$, $\mathbf{e}$, $\mathbf{q}$, $\mathbf{x}$, $\mathbf{y}$, $\mathbf{R}$, $\boldsymbol{\tau}$. Directional derivatives, however, will be indicated by the same letters in ordinary type: $\frac{\partial}{\partial v}$, $\frac{\partial}{\partial e}$, etc.

Geometrical objects (i. e., domains, curves, etc.) are denoted by B, C, D, γ, Γ, etc.

In the chapter on elasticity, A.IV, tensors are denoted by $\boldsymbol{T}$, $\boldsymbol{N}$, etc.

The capital Greek delta is used with several different meanings:

$\varDelta$ will always denote the Laplacian.

$\triangle$ denotes an increment.

A list of symbols used in Part B can be found immediately following Part B.

Numbered references refer to the bibliography at the end of the book. Square brackets refer to books, and parentheses refer to articles.

Contents

Page

Chapter III: Electro- and Magnetostatics

Chapter IV: Elasticity

Part B

Kernel Function Methods in the Theory of Boundary Value Problems

Chapter I: Properties of Solutions

Chapter II: The Kernel Functions and their Properties

PART A

Boundary Value Problems for Partial Differential Equations of Elliptic Type

In Part A, various problems of theoretical physics which give rise to boundary value problems in partial differential equations will be considered. These considerations will motivate the detailed theory of boundary value problems which will be carried out in Part B, and will provide intuitive formulations of various questions in the abstract mathematical theory in terms of physical concepts. The insight into the physical significance of the equations considered will lead us to a correct and useful formulation of the mathematical problems and will frequently yield heuristic proofs of existence and uniqueness theorems which the exact mathematical treatment will establish only after rather lengthy investigation. We are dealing with a field of applied mathematics where the interaction between mathematics and physics is highly stimulating and fruitful for both sciences.

CHAPTER I

THEORY OF HEAT CONDUCTION

1. The differential equation of heat transfer: In (x, y, z)-space let us consider a body B with the boundary surface S. Let $T(x, y, z, t)$ denote the temperature in the body at the point (x, y, z) and at the time t. The difference in temperature at various points of B creates a flow of heat represented by the vector

$$(1.1) \qquad \mathbf{q} = -\varkappa \operatorname{grad} T, \qquad \operatorname{grad} T \equiv \left(\frac{\partial T}{\partial x}, \frac{\partial T}{\partial y}, \frac{\partial T}{\partial z}\right).$$

Here $\varkappa = \varkappa(x, y, z)$ is the coefficient of heat conductivity at the point (x, y, z), and through a surface element $d\sigma$ at (x, y, z) with unit normal vector $\boldsymbol{\nu}$ the amount of heat

$$(1.2) \qquad \triangle Q = \mathbf{q} \cdot \boldsymbol{\nu}\, d\sigma \triangle t = -\varkappa \operatorname{grad} T \cdot \boldsymbol{\nu}\, d\sigma \triangle t = -\varkappa \frac{\partial T}{\partial \nu}\, d\sigma \triangle t$$

flows in the time interval $\triangle t$. Let us denote the specific heat of the material of **B** at the point (x, y, z) by $c(x, y, z)$. If we consider a portion $\mathbf{B}_1$ of the body **B** which is bounded by a surface $\mathbf{S}_1$ in **B**, the heat content of $\mathbf{B}_1$ is given by the integral

$$(1.3) \qquad Q_{\mathbf{B}_1}(t) = \iiint_{\mathbf{B}_1} c(x, y, z)\, T(x, y, z, t)\, d\tau, \qquad d\tau = dx\, dy\, dz.$$

The heat content of $\mathbf{B}_1$ can be changed only by a flow of heat through the boundary surface $\mathbf{S}_1$. This flow can be computed by means of (1.2). We see that in the time interval $\triangle t$ we have a total change of heat content,

$$(1.4) \qquad \triangle Q_{\mathbf{B}_1} = -\iint_{\mathbf{S}_1} \varkappa \frac{\partial T}{\partial \nu}\, d\sigma \cdot \triangle t\,.$$

We denote this change by $+\triangle Q_{\mathbf{B}_1}$ if $\boldsymbol{\nu}$ is understood to be the interior normal of $\mathbf{S}_1$ with respect to $\mathbf{B}_1$ and the integral (1.4) measures, therefore, the inflow of heat. Comparing (1.3) and (1.4), we obtain

$$(1.5) \qquad \iiint_{\mathbf{B}_1} c \frac{\partial T}{\partial t}\, d\tau = -\iint_{\mathbf{S}_1} \varkappa \frac{\partial T}{\partial \nu}\, d\sigma.$$

The right-hand integral in (1.5) can be transformed into a volume integral by means of Green's identity

$$(1.6) \qquad \iiint_{\mathbf{B}_1} \operatorname{div}(U \operatorname{grad} V)\, d\tau = -\iint_{\mathbf{S}_1} U \frac{\partial V}{\partial \nu}\, d\sigma$$

which is valid for any two functions U and V which are twice continuously differentiable in the closed region $\mathbf{B}_1 + \mathbf{S}_1$, and where $\boldsymbol{\nu}$ denotes the interior normal vector to $\mathbf{S}_1$ with respect to $\mathbf{B}_1$. Thus, (1.5) may be written in the form

$$(1.7) \qquad \iiint_{\mathbf{B}_1} \left(c \frac{\partial T}{\partial t} - \operatorname{div}(\varkappa \operatorname{grad} T) \right) d\tau = 0.$$

Since this formula must hold for an arbitrary choice of the portion $\mathbf{B}_1$ of the body **B**, we have the identity

$$(1.8) \qquad c \frac{\partial T}{\partial t} = \operatorname{div}(\varkappa \operatorname{grad} T),$$

$$\operatorname{div}(\varkappa \operatorname{grad} T) \equiv \frac{\partial}{\partial x}\left(\varkappa \frac{\partial T}{\partial x}\right) + \frac{\partial}{\partial y}\left(\varkappa \frac{\partial T}{\partial y}\right) + \frac{\partial}{\partial z}\left(\varkappa \frac{\partial T}{\partial z}\right)$$

valid throughout B and for all times t. This is a partial differential equation for the change of the temperature $T(x, y, z, t)$ in space and time.

The above equation is a homogeneous *linear* partial differential equation since the dependent function $T(x, y, z, t)$ occurs in it homogeneously and linearly. Within the general theory of partial differential equations, the linear differential equations play an important role. Their theory is much easier and much further developed than that of general differential equations. The main reason for this is the fact that the knowledge of two solutions T_1 and T_2 of a linear homogeneous equation immediately leads to infinitely many additional solutions $a_1 T_1 + a_2 T_2$ with arbitrary constant factors a_1, a_2. Thus, the important role of special solutions in the theory of linear partial differential equations becomes obvious. A large part of this book will be devoted to the question of how a set of special solutions may be utilized to solve the problems connected with the linear partial differential equations.

It should be pointed out that the conductivity $\varkappa$ and the specific heat c frequently depend on the temperature T of the material considered. In this case, the differential equation (1.8) is again obtained but now the dependent function T also occurs in k and c and the equation becomes *non-linear*. The theory of linear partial differential equations can be used to obtain results even in such non-linear problems.

Equation (1.8) becomes particularly simple in the case of a homogeneous isotropic body where $\varkappa$ and c are independent of (x, y, z), i. e., $\varkappa$ and c are constants. In this case, we have

$$\frac{\partial T}{\partial t} = \frac{\varkappa}{c} \Delta T, \quad \Delta = \text{div grad} = \frac{\partial^2}{\partial x^2} + \frac{\partial^2}{\partial y^2} + \frac{\partial^2}{\partial z^2}. \tag{1.9}$$

This is a well-known partial differential equation and plays a central role in the theory of diffusion as well as in heat conduction.

Bateman [2], Frank-Mises [14], Riemann-Weber [66], Sommerfeld [71], Webster [89], Webster-Szegö [90].

2. The special case of steady flow: An important special case in the problem of heat transfer is that of steady flow. Here the temperature T and heat flow $\mathbf{q}$ are stationary, i. e., independent of time. In this case, we have the simple partial differential equation for $T(x, y, z)$

$$\text{div}(\varkappa \,\text{grad}\, T) = 0 \tag{2.1}$$

which in the homogeneous case becomes Laplace's equation

$$\Delta T = 0. \tag{2.2}$$

We shall give an important normal form for equation (2.1) which leads to an easier comparison of the general case (2.1) with the homogeneous one (2.2). We start with the identity

$$\Delta (U V) = U \Delta V + 2 \operatorname{grad} U \cdot \operatorname{grad} V + V \Delta U \tag{2.3}$$

which holds for each pair of twice differentiable functions U and V. We write (2.1) in the form

$$\varkappa \Delta T + \operatorname{grad} \varkappa \cdot \operatorname{grad} T = 0. \tag{2.4}$$

Dividing (2.4) by $\varkappa^{1/2}$ and using (2.3), we obtain

$$\Delta (\varkappa^{1/2} T) - \frac{\Delta (\varkappa^{1/2})}{\varkappa^{1/2}} \varkappa^{1/2} T = 0. \tag{2.5}$$

We then introduce as a new dependent function $T^* = \varkappa^{1/2} T$ and find that it satisfies the simple differential equation

$$\Delta T^* = a (x, y, z) T^*, \qquad \Delta (\varkappa^{1/2}) = a \varkappa^{1/2}. \tag{2.6}$$

In particular, if $\varkappa^{1/2}$ is a harmonic function in **B**, equation (2.1) can be reduced to Laplace's equation by a simple change of the dependent variable.

A steady flow through a body **B** can, of course, persist only if there are sources from which the heat is coming and sinks which will absorb the flow. These sources and sinks will be situated on the boundary **S** of **B** and will be the points of inflow and outflow of heat. We can realize such a steady flow through **B** by keeping the boundary points at fixed temperatures and thus create a flow through **B** from points on **S** of higher temperature to points on **S** of lower temperature. Mathematically, this means that we are looking for a solution of the steady heat conduction equation (2.1) which has prescribed values on the boundary **S**. By physical intuition it seems obvious that to any boundary values of T on **S** there should exist a solution of the partial differential equation (2.1) which assumes these values on **S**; it also seems obvious that the boundary values will determine the solution T in a unique way.

While the exact proof of the existence of a solution of (2.1) with given boundary values on **S** requires an involved argument, we can easily establish the uniqueness of such a solution. Let, in fact, $T_1 (x, y, z)$ and $T_2 (x, y, z)$ be two solutions of equation (2.1) which on **S** have the same values. We shall show that their difference

$$d(x, y, z) = T_2 (x, y, z) - T_1 (x, y, z) \tag{2.7}$$

vanishes identically in **B**. We remark that in view of the linear and homogeneous character of the partial differential equation (2.1) the new function $d(x, y, z)$ is itself a solution of (2.1) and, by construction, vanishes identically on **S**. The proof of the general uniqueness theorem has thus been reduced to proving the following particular statement: The only solution of (2.1) which vanishes everywhere on **S** is $T(x, y, z) \equiv 0$.

We may justify this result heuristically by the following physical interpretation. Let us immerse the body **B** in a medium which is kept at the constant temperature $T = 0$, so that we always have $T = 0$ on **S**. Let us wait until a steady temperature distribution throughout **B** has been established. This distribution $T(x, y, z)$ will satisfy the equation (2.1) and have the boundary value zero on **S**. But it is also quite intuitive that it must be identically zero since there is no source or sink in **B** which might emit or absorb a flow of heat.

The mathematical proof of the uniqueness theorem is based on the identity

$$\iiint_{\mathbf{B}} \varkappa (\operatorname{grad} T)^2 \, d\tau = - \iint_{\mathbf{S}} \varkappa T \frac{\partial T}{\partial \nu} \, d\sigma \tag{2.8}$$

which is an immediate consequence of Green's identity and the partial differential equation (2.1) satisfied by T. If there were a solution $T(x, y, z)$ of (2.1) which vanished on **S**, we would have by virtue of (2.8)

$$\operatorname{grad} T = 0, \qquad (x, y, z) \text{ in } \mathbf{B}, \tag{2.9}$$

i. e., $T = \text{const.}$, and since $T = 0$ on **S** we conclude $T \equiv 0$ in **B**. This proves the uniqueness theorem.

The preceding physical and mathematical reasoning also suggests other uniqueness theorems. We easily recognize that if two solutions T_1 and T_2 of (2.1) have equal normal derivatives on **S** they can differ only by a constant. Here we have to show that the only solution of (2.1) with vanishing normal derivative on **S** is $T \equiv \text{const.}$ This follows immediately from (2.8) and (2.9). The result is also intuitive from the physical interpretation. In fact, let the body **B** be isolated thermally from its surroundings; this means that we isolate the boundary **S** and prevent the flow of heat across it, i. e., $-\varkappa \, \partial T / \partial \nu = 0$ on **S**. Clearly, the only steady state of the isolated body is a constant temperature distribution over it. We shall later prove the existence theorem: *There always exists a solution of* (2.1) *with prescribed normal derivatives on* **S**. This means that we can always obtain a steady temperature distribution T in B with a prescribed heat flow $-\mathbf{q}\cdot\boldsymbol{\nu}$ across the boundary S. There is only one restriction on the values of the normal derivatives on S; namely, since no sources or sinks exist in B, the total flow of heat through S must be zero, i. e.,

$$\iint_{\mathsf{S}} \varkappa \frac{\partial T}{\partial \nu}\, d\sigma = 0. \tag{2.10}$$

This follows immediately from (2.1) by integration over B and the application of Green's identity. But except for the restriction (2.10) the values of $\partial T/\partial \nu$ can be prescribed arbitrarily on S.

Between the two extreme cases in which the body B is isolated from its surroundings or is in perfect heat contact with it, there is the case in which the body is immersed in a thermostatic fluid of temperature 0 and the difference of temperature between the surroundings and the boundary points of S creates a flow of temperature through the boundary which is proportional to this difference. Hence, we have the boundary condition:

$$\varkappa \frac{\partial T}{\partial \nu} = \mu\, T, \qquad \mu > 0, \tag{2.11}$$

where the factor μ may in turn depend on the boundary point. In this case, too, it seems clear that the only steady state attainable is the state $T \equiv 0$. We are thus led to the following uniqueness theorem:

Let λ be a positive function on S. *If for two solutions $T_i(x, y, z)$ of* (2.1) *in* B *the expression* $\dfrac{\partial T_i}{\partial \nu} - \lambda T_i$ *has the same values on* S, *then both solutions are identical in* B.

The mathematical proof of this statement follows again from (2.8). It is sufficient to show that if for a solution T of (2.1) we have $\dfrac{\partial T}{\partial \nu} - \lambda T \equiv 0$ on S, then necessarily $T \equiv 0$. In fact, from (2.8) and the above condition we deduce

$$\iiint_{\mathsf{B}} \varkappa\, (\operatorname{grad} T)^2\, d\tau = -\iint_{\mathsf{S}} \varkappa\, \lambda\, T^2\, d\sigma. \tag{2.12}$$

Since the right-hand side is non-positive and the left-hand side non-negative, we are led to $\operatorname{grad} T \equiv 0$ in B and $T \equiv 0$ on S. Combined, these two results imply $T \equiv 0$.

The preceding uniqueness theorem can again be extended to an existence theorem: *There exists exactly one solution of* (2.1) *with prescribed values for* $\frac{\partial T}{\partial \nu} - \lambda T$ *on the boundary* **S**, *if* $\lambda > 0$.

Courant-Hilbert [13] vol. 1, Frank-Mises [14], Jeffreys [25], Kellogg [30], Murnaghan [53].

3. Point sources and fundamental singularities: Let us consider the case of a steady flow in a homogeneous body **B**. Here the temperature $T(x, y, z)$ satisfies Laplace's equation

$$\Delta T = 0. \tag{3.1}$$

Let $P \equiv (x, y, z)$ and $Q \equiv (\xi, \eta, \zeta)$ be two variable points in **B** and let $r(P,Q) = [(x-\xi)^2 + (y-\eta)^2 + (z-\zeta)^2]^{1/2}$ be the distance between them. Then, for fixed $Q \in$ **S**, the function

$$U(x, y, z) = \frac{1}{4\pi r(P,Q)} \tag{3.2}$$

is a solution of Laplace's equation and may be interpreted as a temperature distribution over **B**. However, this solution becomes infinite at the point Q and we must study its singular character there.

Let us draw a sphere $\mathbf{S}_\varepsilon$ of radius ε around Q and observe that on $\mathbf{S}_\varepsilon$

$$\operatorname{grad} U = -\frac{1}{4\pi\varepsilon^2}\boldsymbol{\nu} \tag{3.3}$$

where $\boldsymbol{\nu}$ is the exterior normal on $\mathbf{S}_\varepsilon$, i. e., directed away from the center. Thus, if we assume the constant value of the coefficient $\varkappa$ to be one, by virtue of (1.2), during each second the amount of heat:

$$\Delta Q = 1 \tag{3.4}$$

enters **B** through $\mathbf{S}_\varepsilon$. This leads to an interpretation of $U(x, y, z)$ as the temperature distribution in **B** due to a source of heat at the point Q which emits one calory of heat per second. We shall say that the source at Q has strength one.

The knowledge of the particular solution (3.2) with a point singularity at Q now permits the construction of various other types of sources. Thus, the function

$$V(x, y, z) = \frac{1}{4\pi}\iiint_{\mathbf{B}} \rho(\xi, \eta, \zeta)\,\frac{1}{r(P,Q)}\,d\tau_Q, \qquad d\tau_Q = d\xi\,d\eta\,d\zeta, \tag{3.5}$$

will represent a steady temperature distribution in **B** due to a distribution of heat sources over **B** with strength density ρ. By means of the Laplace-Poisson equation[1] we then derive the inhomogeneous partial differential equation:

$$\Delta V + \rho(x, y, z) = 0 \tag{3.6}$$

for the steady heat distribution V in a body with given source density ρ.

The solution

$$U_{Q_1Q_2} = \frac{\lambda}{4\pi}\left[\frac{1}{r(P, Q_2)} - \frac{1}{r(P, Q_1)}\right] \tag{3.7}$$

of (3.1) represents the temperature field due to a source at Q_2 and a sink at Q_1 of equal strength λ. Let $Q_1 \equiv (\xi, \eta, \zeta)$, $Q_2 = (\xi + \triangle\xi,\ \eta + \triangle\eta,\ \zeta + \triangle\zeta)$ and $\varepsilon = [(\triangle\xi)^2 + (\triangle\eta)^2 + (\triangle\zeta)^2]^{1/2}$; then by Taylor's theorem, we may write

$$U_{Q_1Q_2} = \frac{\lambda}{4\pi}\left[\triangle\xi\frac{\partial}{\partial\xi}\left(\frac{1}{r(P, Q_1)}\right) + \triangle\eta\frac{\partial}{\partial\eta}\left(\frac{1}{r(P, Q_1)}\right) + \triangle\zeta\frac{\partial}{\partial\zeta}\left(\frac{1}{r(P, Q_1)}\right)\right] + \\ + o(\varepsilon) \tag{3.8}$$

where $o(x)$ denotes a quantity such that $\lim_{x\to 0} o(x)/x = 0$. The vector $\overrightarrow{Q_1Q_2}$ with components $\triangle\xi$, $\triangle\eta$, $\triangle\zeta$ can also be represented in the form $\varepsilon\,\mathfrak{e}$ where ε measures its length, and $\mathfrak{e}$ is a unit vector describing its direction. Keeping $\mathfrak{e}$ fixed, we let $\varepsilon \to 0$ but at the same time increase the strength λ of the point sources in such a manner that $\lambda\varepsilon = \alpha$ remains constant. Thus in the limit as $\varepsilon \to 0$ we obtain a new solution of Laplace's equation

$$W(x, y, z) = \frac{\alpha}{4\pi}\,\mathfrak{e}\cdot\operatorname{grad}_Q\frac{1}{r(P, Q)}. \tag{3.9}$$

We could have deduced directly from (3.2) that W solves Laplace's equation by differentiating the original equation with respect to the parameter point Q, but our construction shows that W is the solution due to a source and sink of equal strength which have combined without cancelling each other. Such a singularity is called a dipole. $\mathfrak{e}$ is called the axis of the dipole and α its strength.

We could construct additional singular solutions of (3.1) by similar limit processes and linear operations upon the identity

$$\Delta_P\left(\frac{1}{r(P, Q)}\right) = 0 \tag{3.10}$$

[1]Kellogg [30], p. 156.

with respect to the parameter point Q. But we shall now show that the solutions (3.2) and (3.9), i. e., the point sources and the dipoles, play a particularly important role in the theory of the Laplace equation. Let $T(x, y, z)$ be an arbitrary solution of (3.1); we consider the domain $\mathbf{B}_\varepsilon^*$ which is obtained by deleting from $\mathbf{B}$ the interior of the sphere $\mathbf{S}_\varepsilon$ of radius ε around Q. We apply Green's identity with respect to $\mathbf{B}_\varepsilon^*$ in the following form:

$$\text{(3.11)} \qquad \frac{1}{4\pi}\iint\limits_{\mathbf{S}+\mathbf{S}_\varepsilon}\left[T(R)\frac{\partial}{\partial \nu_R}\left(\frac{1}{r(R,Q)}\right)-\frac{1}{r(R,Q)}\frac{\partial T(R)}{\partial \nu_R}\right]d\sigma_R = 0.$$

This takes into account that both T and $1/r$ are continuously differentiable solutions of (3.1) in the domain $\mathbf{B}_\varepsilon^*$. We observe that

$$\frac{1}{4\pi}\iint\limits_{\mathbf{S}_\varepsilon}\left[T\frac{\partial}{\partial \nu}\left(\frac{1}{r}\right)-\frac{1}{r}\frac{\partial T}{\partial \nu}\right]d\sigma = -\frac{1}{4\pi\varepsilon^2}\iint\limits_{\mathbf{S}_\varepsilon} T\,d\sigma - \frac{1}{4\pi\varepsilon}\iint\limits_{\mathbf{S}_\varepsilon}\frac{\partial T}{\partial \nu}\,d\sigma,$$

$$\text{(3.12)} \qquad d\sigma = \varepsilon^2\,d\omega$$

where $d\omega$ is the solid angle subtended at Q by the surface element $d\sigma$. Letting $\varepsilon \to 0$, we clearly obtain from (3.11):

$$\text{(3.13)} \qquad T(Q) = \frac{1}{4\pi}\iint\limits_{\mathbf{S}}\left[T(R)\frac{\partial}{\partial \nu_R}\left(\frac{1}{r(Q,R)}\right)-\frac{1}{r(Q,R)}\frac{\partial T(R)}{\partial \nu_R}\right]d\sigma_R.$$

This shows that the solution $T(Q)$ of Laplace's equation is uniquely determined in $\mathbf{B}$ by its boundary values and the values of its normal derivative. Moreover, the formal aspect of (3.13) shows that the field $T(Q)$ may be conceived as created by a distribution of sources on $\mathbf{S}$ with strength density $-\partial T/\partial \nu$ and of dipoles with their axes in the normal direction and strength density T. Thus, we have proved: *The general solution of* (3.1) *may be created by an appropriate distribution of sources and dipoles on the boundary of the domain considered.*

Since a dipole singularity can be constructed by the differentiation of the particular solution $\dfrac{1}{4\pi r(P,Q)}$, we recognize the central role of this function in the theory of Laplace's equation. It is called the fundamental singularity of this equation. There arises the problem of generalizing this concept to the case of the more general partial differential equation of steady temperature distribution:

$$\text{(3.14)} \qquad \operatorname{div}(\varkappa \operatorname{grad} T) = 0.$$

Here, in analogy to the preceding special case, we may define the fundamental singularity $S(P,Q)$ as follows:

$S(P,Q)$ is, for fixed $Q \in \mathbf{B}$, a solution of (3.14) and is continuous throughout **B** except at the point Q, where it becomes infinite. At the point Q we shall require that

$$\lim_{\varepsilon \to 0} \iint_{\mathbf{S}_\varepsilon} \left(-\varkappa \frac{\partial S(P,Q)}{\partial \nu_P} \right) d\sigma_P = 1 \tag{3.15}$$

where $\mathbf{S}_\varepsilon$ is a sphere of radius ε around Q.

$S(P,Q)$ can be interpreted as the field due to a source of strength one at the point Q. It is not uniquely determined by our requirements since we may add to it an arbitrary solution of (3.14) without changing its characteristic properties. The existence of fundamental singularities is heuristically clear; for we can realize experimentally temperature distributions due to a point source. The exact mathematical proof for the existence is by no means simple and will be given in the second part of the book. We may expect to have

$$S(P,Q) = A(P,Q)\frac{1}{r(P,Q)} + B(P,Q) \tag{3.16}$$

where $A(P,Q)$ and $B(P,Q)$ are twice continuously differentiable functions everywhere in **B** and

$$\varkappa(Q)\, A(Q,Q) = \frac{1}{4\pi}. \tag{3.17}$$

In fact, if (3.16) and (3.17) are satisfied, then clearly (3.15) will also hold. The asymptotic behavior at Q of $S(P,Q)$ as described by (3.16) and (3.17) can be established by the general theory which will be developed later.

Sommerfeld [73].

4. Fundamental solutions: Among all possible fundamental singularities connected with the partial differential equation of the steady temperature distribution certain particular ones can be distinguished by their physical significance as well as by their useful mathematical properties. We shall call them the fundamental solutions of the equation considered and define them intuitively as follows.

Consider the body **B** with a point source of strength one at the point $Q \in \mathbf{B}$ and suppose that it is immersed in a thermostatic fluid of constant temperature $T = 0$. The temperature discontinuity at the boundary **S** of the body is assumed to create an outflow of heat from the body to the exterior which is proportional to the discontinuity, i. e., we shall assume that the steady temperature finally attained satisfies the boundary condition

$$\varkappa \frac{\partial T}{\partial \nu} = \mu T \tag{4.1}$$

where μ is a positive function of the position on S. In this way, we are led to a particular fundamental singularity $S(P, Q)$ of our partial differential equation with the boundary condition (4.1). To each choice of μ such a solution can be found. We define:

Robin's function $R_\lambda(P, Q)$ *is that fundamental singularity of the equation*

$$\operatorname{div}(\varkappa \operatorname{grad} T) = 0 \tag{4.2}$$

which satisfies on S *the boundary condition*

$$\frac{\partial R_\lambda(P,Q)}{\partial \nu_P} = \lambda(P) R_\lambda(P,Q), \qquad \lambda(P) > 0, \qquad P \in \mathsf{S}. \tag{4.3}$$

By our preceding uniqueness theorem it is clear that Robin's function is defined in a unique way. The most important consequence of our choice of the fundamental singularity is the fact that Robin's function is symmetric in its argument and parameter points and therefore satisfies for fixed $P \in \mathsf{B}$ the partial differential equation (4.2) as a function of Q.

In order to prove this fact, we start with Green's identity

$$\iiint_{\mathsf{B}} \varkappa \operatorname{grad} u \cdot \operatorname{grad} v \, d\tau = -\iint_{\mathsf{S}} \varkappa u \frac{\partial v}{\partial \nu} d\sigma - \iiint_{\mathsf{B}} u \operatorname{div}(\varkappa \operatorname{grad} v) \, d\tau \tag{4.4}$$

which simplifies to

$$\iiint_{\mathsf{B}} \varkappa \operatorname{grad} u \cdot \operatorname{grad} v \, d\tau = -\iint_{\mathsf{S}} u \frac{\partial v}{\partial \nu} d\sigma \tag{4.5}$$

if v is a solution of (4.2). If both u and v satisfy (4.2), then by symmetry we derive from (4.5)

$$\iint_{\mathsf{S}} \varkappa \left[u \frac{\partial v}{\partial \nu} - v \frac{\partial u}{\partial \nu} \right] d\sigma = 0. \tag{4.6}$$

We apply this result to $u = R_\lambda(P, Q)$ and $v = R_\lambda(P, O)$. Since these functions are not continuous in B, we must at first delete from B two spheres of radius ε around the points Q and O and apply (4.6) to the remaining domain. Then letting $\varepsilon \to 0$ we obtain by a reasoning analogous to that which led to (3.13)

$$\iint_S \varkappa(P)\left[R_\lambda(P,Q)\frac{\partial R_\lambda(P,O)}{\partial \nu_P} - R_\lambda(P,O)\frac{\partial R_\lambda(P,Q)}{\partial \nu_P}\right] d\sigma_P = R_\lambda(O,Q) - R_\lambda(Q,O). \tag{4.7}$$

But now we can make use of the boundary conditions (4.3) which show that the left-hand integral vanishes. Thus, we obtain the symmetry law:

$$R_\lambda(O,Q) = R_\lambda(Q,O) \tag{4.8}$$

as was asserted.

If u is a regular solution of (4.2) in $\mathbf{B}$ and $v = R_\lambda(P,Q)$, we may apply the identity (4.6) to the domain $\mathbf{B}_\varepsilon^*$ from which the interior of the sphere $\mathbf{S}_\varepsilon$ of radius ε around Q has been deleted. Letting $\varepsilon \to 0$ and using the limit relation (3.15) which is valid for every fundamental singularity, we find quite readily that

$$u(Q) = \iint_S \varkappa(P)\left[u(P)\frac{\partial R_\lambda(P,Q)}{\partial \nu_P} - R_\lambda(P,Q)\frac{\partial u(P)}{\partial \nu_P}\right] d\sigma_P. \tag{4.9}$$

We may simplify this result by applying (4.3) and obtain

$$u(Q) = -\iint_S \varkappa(P)\, R_\lambda(P,Q)\left[\frac{\partial u(P)}{\partial \nu_P} - \lambda(P)\, u(P)\right] d\sigma_P. \tag{4.10}$$

This tells us that *the knowledge of Robin's function* $R_\lambda(P,Q)$ *enables us to determine the solution of* (4.2) *whose boundary combination* $(\partial u/\partial \nu) - \lambda u$ *is known.*

A limiting case of the above Robin's functions is the Green's function which corresponds to the value $\lambda = \infty$. From (4.1) we recognize that Green's function $G(P,Q)$ corresponds to the field of a unit source at the point Q in case of perfect heat contact with the thermostatic fluid at the boundary. In this case, we clearly have:

$$G(P,Q) = 0 \quad \text{for} \quad P \in \mathbf{S}. \tag{4.11}$$

Green's function serves for the representation of a solution of (4.2) by means of its boundary values on $\mathbf{S}$. In fact, applying (4.6) to a regular solution u and for $v = G(P,Q)$, we derive by the above limiting procedure:

$$u(Q) = \iint_S \varkappa(P)\frac{\partial G(P,Q)}{\partial \nu_P}\, u(P)\, d\sigma_P. \tag{4.12}$$

It is easily seen that *Green's function and all Robin's functions are positive in* **B**. Since a larger value of λ means a better transfer of heat out of the body, we may expect an inequality

$$R_\lambda(P,Q) \leqslant R_{\lambda'}(P,Q), \quad \text{if } \lambda > \lambda' \text{ on } \mathbf{S}, \tag{4.13}$$

and indeed such an inequality can be derived by the methods of Section B. V. 1. If we let $\lambda \to 0$, the Robin's functions will increase beyond bounds and there cannot exist a finite limit function $R_0(P,Q)$. In fact, such a function would represent the steady temperature distribution in a body **B** which is isolated from its surroundings and contains a source of heat with strength one. Clearly such a body would be heated to infinity and, hence, $R_0(P,Q)$ could not have finite values.

The same result can also be derived by calculation. The function $R_0(P,Q)$ would be, by definition, a solution of (4.2) with singularity at Q and the boundary condition $\partial R_0/\partial\nu = 0$ on **S**. Let us now apply Green's identity with respect to the domain $\mathbf{B}_\varepsilon^*$ obtained from **B** by deleting the interior of the sphere $\mathbf{S}_\varepsilon$ with radius ε around Q. We find

$$\iiint_{\mathbf{B}_\varepsilon^*} \operatorname{div}(\varkappa \operatorname{grad} R_0)\, d\tau = -\iint_{\mathbf{S}+\mathbf{S}_\varepsilon} \varkappa \frac{\partial R_0}{\partial\nu}\, d\sigma = 0 \tag{4.14}$$

since R_0 satisfies (4.2) in $\mathbf{B}_\varepsilon^*$. By the boundary condition on **S**, we thus obtain

$$\iint_{\mathbf{S}_\varepsilon} \varkappa \frac{\partial R_0}{\partial\nu}\, d\sigma = 0. \tag{4.15}$$

But this result contradicts the asymptotic formula (3.15) which R_0 must satisfy as a fundamental singularity. Thus, the assumption of a finite $R_0(P,Q)$ leads to a contradiction.

Our physical interpretation of the fundamental solutions $R_\lambda(P,Q)$ suggests the introduction of a fundamental singularity which is as near as possible to the definition of R_0. *We define Neumann's function $N(P,Q)$ as that fundamental singularity in* **B** *with unit source at Q which on* **S** *has the value of its normal derivative proportional to $\varkappa^{-1}$.* Since $N(P,Q)$ is determined by this requirement only up to an additive constant, *we complete the definition by requiring the normalization*

$$\iint_{\mathbf{S}} N(P,Q)\, d\sigma_P = 0. \tag{4.16}$$

The existence of Neumann's function appears certain from physical considerations. It is the steady temperature distribution due to a unit source at Q with constant outflow through the boundary $\mathbf{S}$. The factor of proportionality can be chosen in such a way that the loss of heat through $\mathbf{S}$ equals exactly the heat created at Q at each moment. Thus, we have the requirement

$$(4.17) \qquad \iint_{\mathbf{S}} \varkappa(P) \frac{\partial N(P,Q)}{\partial \nu_P} d\sigma_P = 1,$$

and since $\varkappa\, \partial N / \partial \nu = \text{const.}$ on $\mathbf{S}$,

$$(4.18) \qquad \varkappa \frac{\partial N(P,Q)}{\partial \nu_P} = \left[\iint_{\mathbf{S}} d\sigma \right]^{-1} = \frac{1}{A}, \qquad A = \text{surface area of } \mathbf{S}.$$

This result shows that the constant value of $\varkappa \dfrac{\partial N(P,Q)}{\partial \nu_P}$ on $\mathbf{S}$ is independent of the parameter point Q.

If we use the normalization (4.16) and the same reasoning which proved the symmetry of the Robin's functions, we can prove the symmetry of the Neumann's function

$$(4.19) \qquad N(P,Q) = N(Q,P).$$

Neumann's function plays an important role in the representation of solutions of (4.2) by means of the values of their normal derivatives on $\mathbf{S}$. We have already remarked in Section 2 that we cannot prescribe these values completely arbitrarily on $\mathbf{S}$ but for any solution $u(P)$ of (4.2) must require

$$(4.20) \qquad \iint_{\mathbf{S}} \varkappa \frac{\partial u}{\partial \nu} d\sigma = 0.$$

Furthermore, the solution $u(P)$ will not be determined uniquely by prescribing its normal derivative on $\mathbf{S}$; let us normalize it, therefore, by the additional requirement

$$(4.21) \qquad \iint_{\mathbf{S}} u\, d\sigma = 0.$$

If we prescribe $\partial u / \partial \nu$ arbitrarily on $\mathbf{S}$ except for the condition (4.20) we may always find a function $u(P)$ which satisfies (4.2), has the normalization (4.21), and has the prescribed values of the normal derivative. The representation of this function by means of the Neumann's function is easily obtained as follows. We apply the identity (4.6) to the solution u considered and to $v(P) = N(P, Q)$ with respect to the domain B_ε^*. By the usual limit procedure, we then derive:

$$u(Q) = \iint_{\mathsf{S}} \varkappa(P) \left[u(P) \frac{\partial N(P,Q)}{\partial \nu_P} - N(P,Q) \frac{\partial u(P)}{\partial \nu_P} \right] d\sigma_P. \tag{4.22}$$

Since $\varkappa \dfrac{\partial N(P,Q)}{\partial \nu_P}$ is constant on S and u is normalized by (4.21), we obtain

$$u(Q) = -\iint_{\mathsf{S}} N(P,Q) \varkappa(P) \frac{\partial u(P)}{\partial \nu_P} d\sigma_P \tag{4.23}$$

which determines the solution $u(Q)$ by means of its normal derivative on S.

Green's, Neumann's and the Robin's functions will be called the fundamental solutions of (4.2) for the domain B. Using them, we are now able to solve the principal boundary value problems connected with (4.2) and the domain B. Since every solution of (4.2) has a simple integral representation in terms of these fundamental solutions the entire analysis of the regular solutions of (4.2) can be reduced to a detailed study of these fundamental solutions.

Goursat [16], Gunther [17], Poincaré [63], Smirnoff [69].

5. Discontinuities: Let us suppose that the body B consists of two homogeneous parts B_1 and B_2 in which the coefficient of thermal conductivity has the constant values $\varkappa_1$ and $\varkappa_2$, respectively. Clearly, in each component of B a steady temperature distribution $T(x, y, z)$ must satisfy Laplace's equation. For physical reasons, the field of temperature T must be continuous in B, and the normal component of the heat flow vector must vary continuously across the surface Σ which separates the two homogeneous components. For otherwise an indefinite accumulation of heat on Σ would take place leading to infinite values of T along this separating surface. Thus, we find along Σ the condition

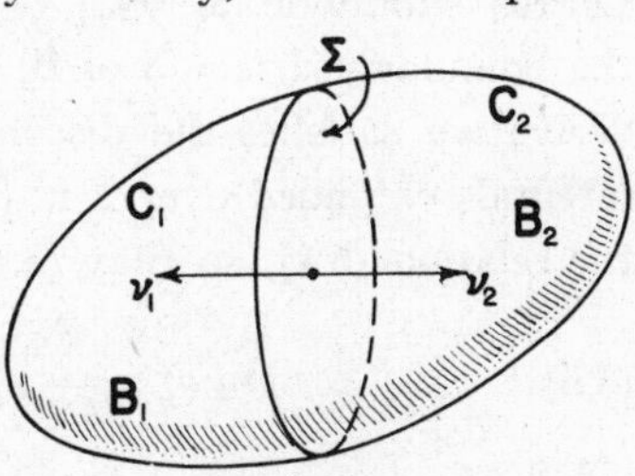

Figure 1

$$-\varkappa_1 \frac{\partial T}{\partial \nu_1} = \varkappa_2 \frac{\partial T}{\partial \nu_2} \tag{5.1}$$

where $\boldsymbol{\nu}_1$ and $\boldsymbol{\nu}_2$ denote the interior normals on Σ of B_1 and B_2, respectively.

If we prescribe the values of the solution T of the steady temperature problem on the boundary S of B, we are led to a boundary value problem of the following type: Find a solution of Laplace's equation in B with prescribed boundary values on S which is continuous in B but whose derivatives have a jump across a prescribed surface Σ of B described by (5.1).

Similarly, we may seek solutions of Laplace's equation with a prescribed discontinuity (5.1) and given values of $(\partial u/\partial \nu) - \lambda u$, $\lambda > 0$ on S. We shall show, at first, that *all these boundary value problems have at most one solution.* In fact, suppose that there were two functions u and v which on S have the same values of $(\partial u/\partial \nu) - \lambda u$, and on Σ satisfy the jump condition (5.1). Their difference $w = u - v$ would still satisfy (5.1) on Σ and, on S would satisfy

$$\frac{\partial w}{\partial \nu} - \lambda w = 0. \tag{5.2}$$

Consider then the integral

$$D\{w\} = \varkappa_1 \iiint_{\mathsf{B}_1} (\text{grad } w)^2 \, d\tau + \varkappa_2 \iiint_{\mathsf{B}_2} (\text{grad } w)^2 \, d\tau. \tag{5.3}$$

Since w is harmonic in B_1 and in B_2, we obtain by Green's identity

$$D\{w\} = -\varkappa_1 \iint_{\mathsf{S}_1} w \frac{\partial w}{\partial \nu_1} \, d\sigma - \varkappa_2 \iint_{\mathsf{S}_2} w \frac{\partial w}{\partial \nu_2} \, d\sigma \tag{5.4}$$

where S_1 and S_2 designate the boundary surfaces of B_1 and B_2, respectively. Let us subdivide $\mathsf{S}_1 = \mathsf{C}_1 + \Sigma$, $\mathsf{S}_2 = \mathsf{C}_2 + \Sigma$ so that $\mathsf{C}_1 + \mathsf{C}_2$ constitutes the boundary surface S of B. Since w is continuous on Σ and its normal derivative satisfies the discontinuity condition (5.1) there, we see that the integrals extended over Σ in (5.4) cancel each other. On C_1 and C_2 we have the relation (5.2), so that (5.4) may be put in the form:

$$D\{w\} = -\varkappa_1 \iint_{\mathsf{C}_1} \lambda w^2 \, d\sigma - \varkappa_2 \iint_{\mathsf{C}_2} \lambda w^2 \, d\sigma. \tag{5.5}$$

From definition (5.3) it is obvious that $D\{w\}$ is non-negative while (5.5) shows that the same expression is non-positive. This leads clearly to

$$w = \text{const. in } \mathsf{B}, \qquad w = 0 \text{ on } \mathsf{S} \tag{5.6}$$

and therefore

$$w \equiv 0 \quad \text{in } \mathsf{B} \tag{5.7}$$

which proves the asserted uniqueness theorem.

The mathematical tools for dealing with solutions of a given partial differential equation with prescribed discontinuities along an interior surface Σ will be developed in Sections B. III. 1—2. In this case, the functions required can also be described in terms of their boundary values and the values of their normal derivatives on the boundary by the use of the fundamental solutions for **B** and certain functions closely related to them.

Riemann-Weber [66].

6. Dirichlet's principle: In order to give uniqueness proofs for boundary value problems connected with the partial differential equation

$$\operatorname{div}(\varkappa \operatorname{grad} u) = 0 \tag{6.1}$$

we have used the integral

$$D\{u\} = \iiint_{\mathbf{B}} \varkappa (\operatorname{grad} u)^2 \, d\tau. \tag{6.2}$$

We shall now show the close formal relation between this integral expression and the partial differential equation (6.1). For this purpose we introduce the bilinear integral

$$D\{u, v\} = \iiint_{\mathbf{B}} \varkappa \operatorname{grad} u \cdot \operatorname{grad} v \, d\tau \tag{6.3}$$

and notice that by Green's identity we have

$$D\{u, v\} = -\iint_{\mathbf{S}} \varkappa v \frac{\partial u}{\partial \nu} \, d\sigma - \iiint_{\mathbf{B}} v \operatorname{div}(\varkappa \operatorname{grad} u) \, d\tau. \tag{6.4}$$

If, in particular, u satisfies (6.1) we obtain

$$D\{u, v\} = -\iint_{\mathbf{S}} \varkappa v \frac{\partial u}{\partial \nu} \, d\sigma, \tag{6.5}$$

i. e., for an arbitrary function v in **B** the expression $D\{u, v\}$ will depend only on the boundary values of v on **S**. If $v = 0$ on **S**, we have

$$D\{u, v\} = 0. \tag{6.6}$$

The bilinear integral always vanishes if one argument function satisfies (6.1) *and the other vanishes on* **S**.

The connection between $D\{u\}$ and $D\{u, v\}$ is established by the obvious identity

$$D\{u + t v\} = D\{u\} + 2t D\{u, v\} + t^2 D\{v\}, \qquad t = \text{const.} \tag{6.7}$$

which is an immediate consequence of the homogeneous quadratic dependence of $D\{u\}$ upon u. Since $D\{u + t v\} \geqq 0$, we obtain Schwarz' inequality

$$(D\{u, v\})^2 \leqq D\{u\} D\{v\} \tag{6.8}$$

by setting $t = - D\{u, v\}/D\{v\}$. Equality is possible only for $u(P) + t v(P) \equiv \text{const.}$ in B.

We may consider $D\{u\}$ as a function of the function u; it is usual to call a number which depends upon the infinitude of values of a function u in a domain B a *functional* of u. Let us now study the change of the functional $D\{u\}$ under a change $\delta u = \varepsilon v(P)$ of its argument function. We have by (6.7)

$$D\{u + \delta u\} = D\{u\} + 2\varepsilon D\{u, v\} + O(\varepsilon^2) \tag{6.9}$$

and using (6.4)

$$D\{u + \delta u\} - D\{u\} = \tag{6.10}$$
$$= -2 \iint\limits_{S} \varkappa\, \delta u \frac{\partial u}{\partial \nu} d\sigma - 2 \iiint\limits_{B} \operatorname{div}(\varkappa \operatorname{grad} u)\, \delta u\, d\tau + O(\varepsilon^2).$$

If we consider a function $F(x_1, \ldots, x_n)$ depending on n variables x_i, we have the identity

$$F(x_i + \delta x_i) - F(x_i) = \sum_{i=1}^{n} \frac{\partial F}{\partial x_i} \delta x_i + O(\varepsilon^2), \tag{6.11}$$

$$\delta x_i = \varepsilon \xi_i, \qquad \delta F(x_i) = \sum_{i=1}^{n} \frac{\partial F}{\partial x_i} \delta x_i,$$

and we call $\partial F / \partial x_i$ the partial derivative of F with respect to the variable x_i. Analogously, let us write:

$$\delta D\{u\} \equiv -2 \iint\limits_{S} \left(\varkappa \frac{\partial u}{\partial \nu}\right) \delta u\, d\sigma - 2 \iiint\limits_{B} \operatorname{div}(\varkappa \operatorname{grad} u)\, \delta u\, d\tau \tag{6.12}$$

and denote $-2 \operatorname{div}(\varkappa \operatorname{grad} u)$ *as the functional derivative of* $D\{u\}$ *with respect to the interior values* $u(P)$, *and* $-2\varkappa(\partial u/\partial \nu)$ *the functional derivative of* $D\{u\}$ *with respect to the boundary values* $u(P)$ *on* S.

The close relation between the differential expression $\operatorname{div}(\varkappa \operatorname{grad} u)$ and the quadratic integral $D\{u\}$ now becomes clear. The differential expression is essentially the functional derivative of the quadratic functional $D\{u\}$.

In the theory of functions of a finite number of variables, the extremal points of the function are characterized by the vanishing of all partial derivatives $\partial F/\partial x_i$. Analogously, we may expect some extremum property of the functional D $\{u\}$ for an argument function u in **B** for which all the functional derivatives in **B** vanish, i. e., which satisfies the partial differential equation (6.1). In fact, we have the theorem: *Each solution u of the partial differential equation* (6.1) *leads to the minimum value of the integral* (6.2) *among all functions in* **B** *with the same boundary values on* **S** *as u.* In order to prove this statement let w be an arbitrary function in **B** which on **S** has the same values as u. The difference $v = w - u$ then has the boundary values zero on **S**. Using (6.7), we have

$$\text{(6.13)} \qquad \mathrm{D}\{w\} = \mathrm{D}\{u + w - u\} = \mathrm{D}\{u\} + 2\,\mathrm{D}\{u, v\} + \mathrm{D}\{v\}.$$

Since u satisfies (6.1) and v vanishes on **S**, we obtain from (6.6)

$$\text{(6.14)} \qquad \mathrm{D}\{w\} = \mathrm{D}\{u\} + \mathrm{D}\{v\} \geqq \mathrm{D}\{u\}.$$

Equality can hold only if D $\{v\} = 0$, $w \equiv u$ in **B**. Thus, the extremal property of the solution u of (6.1) among all functions with the same boundary values on **S** has been established.

One can now try to reverse this reasoning as follows. There are surely an infinity of functions with prescribed fixed continuous boundary values on **S**. Within this class of functions one can ask for that particular function which yields the minimum value of the integral (6.2). It is easy to show that if such a function exists it must necessarily satisfy the partial differential equation (6.1). This line of reasoning has, in fact, been used in order to establish the existence of a solution of a partial differential equation of type (6.1) with prescribed boundary values. The main difficulty in this approach is the proof that there in fact exists a continuously differentiable function $u(P)$ in **B** with prescribed values on **S** which yields the minimum value for D $\{u\}$. In the last century, Lord Kelvin and Riemann attempted the first existence proof for the boundary value problem along these lines. They took for granted the existence of a minimum function, postulating its existence in the so-called "Dirichlet principle". Weierstrass objected to this reasoning and gave examples of minimum problems in the calculus of variations where no continuous function exists which solves the problem. The method of the Dirichlet principle was rehabilitated, however, by Hilbert who constructed minimum sequences and proved that uniformly convergent subsequences could be selected which converge towards a continuously differentiable limit function. This limit function was proved by Hilbert to satisfy the differential equations and the boundary conditions required. In the second part of this book, we shall base the mathematical theory of the boundary value problem upon a detailed study of one integral of the type D $\{u\}$ and also base an existence proof upon the method of orthogonal projection which is closely related to Dirichlet's principle. We shall call an integral D $\{u\}$ the *Dirichlet integral* of a given partial differential equation if it is semi-definite and if it has the partial differential equation as its functional derivative.

As we shall see on the following pages, the Dirichlet integral has physical significance in various boundary value problems. It is slightly more difficult to provide such interpretation in the case of heat conduction. But even here, some interesting observations can be made about D $\{u\}$. Consider a body **B** whose boundary **S** is kept at a fixed temperature, say $T = 0$. Let $T(x, y, z, t)$ be the temperature distribution inside **B** at the time t; then T will satisfy the partial differential equation (1.8) of heat conduction. Now, the integral

$$\text{(6.15)} \qquad \mathrm{D}\{T\} \equiv \iiint_{\mathbf{B}} \varkappa (\operatorname{grad} T)^2 \, d\tau$$

is a function of time and we may calculate its derivative with respect to t. We find:

$$\text{(6.16)} \qquad \frac{d\mathrm{D}}{dt} = 2\iiint_{\mathbf{B}} \varkappa \operatorname{grad} T \cdot \operatorname{grad}\left(\frac{\partial T}{\partial t}\right) d\tau.$$

Using Green's identity, the fact that T and, hence $\partial T/\partial t$ vanish on **S**, and (1.8) we obtain

$$\text{(6.17)} \quad \frac{d\mathrm{D}}{dt} = -2\iiint_{\mathbf{B}} \frac{\partial T}{dt} \operatorname{div}(\varkappa \operatorname{grad} T)\, d\tau = -2\iiint_{\mathbf{B}} c\left(\frac{\partial T}{\partial t}\right)^2 d\tau.$$

This result shows that during the equalization of temperature in **B**, the Dirichlet integral D is decreasing monotonically.

Courant [12], Courant-Hilbert [13], Lévy [38], Volterra [86], [87], Volterra-Pérès [88].

7. A modified heat equation: We now consider a particular problem in heat conduction which leads to a partial differential equation which will occupy our attention throughout a large part of the mathematical section of the book. Consider a body **B** with a coefficient of thermal conductivity

$\varkappa = 1$; at each point of **B** an endothermal chemical process will be assumed to take place at a rate proportional to the local temperature T. We assume that a steady state has already been attained so that T depends only on the coordinates (x, y, z) of the point $P \in \mathbf{B}$. At each point $P \in \mathbf{B}$ we have a sink for the heat and the density of these sinks at P is $p(P)\, T(P)$ where $p(P)$ is some positive function of P. Hence, in view of (3.6), the partial differential equation for the temperature distribution in this case is

$$\Delta T = p(P) \cdot T(P), \qquad p(P) > 0 \quad \text{in } \mathbf{B}. \tag{7.1}$$

The partial differential equation (7.1) is an obvious generalization of Laplace's equation and the latter can be obtained from (7.1) as the limiting case $p \to 0$ everywhere in **B**. (7.1) is associated with the Dirichlet integral

$$\mathrm{E}\{u\} = \iiint_{\mathbf{B}} [(\operatorname{grad} u)^2 + p\, u^2]\, d\tau \tag{7.2}$$

as follows immediately from the integral identity

$$\begin{aligned} \mathrm{E}\{u, v\} &\equiv \iiint_{\mathbf{B}} [\operatorname{grad} u \cdot \operatorname{grad} v + p\, u\, v]\, d\tau = \\ &= -\iint_{\mathbf{S}} v \frac{\partial u}{\partial \nu}\, d\sigma - \iiint_{\mathbf{B}} v\, [\Delta u - p\, u]\, d\tau. \end{aligned} \tag{7.3}$$

From this formula we can immediately see that the functional derivative of $\mathrm{E}\{u\}$ at the point $P \in \mathbf{B}$ is just $-2(\Delta u - p\, u)$ which vanishes for all solutions of the partial differential equation (7.1).

We can define fundamental singularities and fundamental solutions in the case of (7.1) just as we did in the case of ordinary heat conduction. One difference, however, between the equation (6.1) and (7.1) must be pointed out which shows that (7.1) is, from a mathematical point of view, more accessible than (6.1). In defining the fundamental solutions in Section 4, we can consider Green's function as a limiting case of the Robin's functions $R_\lambda(P, Q)$ for $\lambda \to \infty$ while Neumann's function has to be defined independently. For $\lambda \to 0$, the Robin's functions do not converge to a finite limit function since it is impossible to have a finite steady temperature distribution in a body which has a heat source and is isolated from its surroundings. It is heuristically clear that in the case of (7.1) the situation is essentially different. We may consider a body **B** with a heat source at the point Q and isolated from its surroundings such that the heat created by the source is absorbed by the endothermal chemical process going on everywhere in B. In this case, a finite steady heat distribution is possible in B and we may define the Neumann's function for the partial differential equation (7.1) in a much simpler way. We define:

$$N(P,Q) = \lim_{\lambda \to 0} R_\lambda (P,Q). \tag{7.4}$$

It is now clear from (4.3) that *Neumann's function is that fundamental singularity of* (7.1) *which on the boundary* S *of* B *satisfies the condition*

$$\frac{\partial N(P,Q)}{\partial \nu_P} = 0, \qquad P \in S. \tag{7.5}$$

It is easily seen from the definition and the symmetry of the Robin's function that *Neumann's function is symmetric in argument and parameter point.* Moreover, from the monotonicity of the Robin's functions with respect to λ we derive the inequality

$$N(P,Q) \geqq R_\lambda (P,Q) \geqq G(P,Q) \geqq 0. \tag{7.6}$$

It is the existence of this simple and elegant Neumann's function which distinguishes the partial differential equation (7.1) *from the equation* (6.1) *considered before.* An important consequence of this fact is the following theorem: *There exists exactly one solution $u(P)$ of the partial differential equation* (7.1) *with prescribed values of the normal derivative $\partial u / \partial \nu$ on the boundary* S *of the domain* B. *This solution can be expressed by means of the values $\partial u / \partial \nu$ and the Neumann's function in the form:*

$$u(Q) = -\iint_S N(P,Q) \frac{\partial u(P)}{\partial \nu_P} d\sigma_P. \tag{7.7}$$

In the case of the partial differential equation (6.1) we could not prescribe $\partial u / \partial \nu$ arbitrarily on S but had to satisfy the condition (4.20). If this condition were fulfilled, on the other hand, then there would be infinitely many solutions of this boundary value problem differing by an arbitrary constant. Now the only constant which solves the partial differential equation (7.1) is $u \equiv 0$ and the uniqueness of the boundary value problem considered can easily be established by the usual reasoning.

8. Formal considerations: In Section 2 we saw that the partial differential equation

$$\operatorname{div} (\varkappa \operatorname{grad} u) = 0 \tag{8.1}$$

can be transformed to

(8.2) $$\Delta v = a v$$

by means of the transformation

(8.3) $$v = k u, \qquad k = \varkappa^{1/2},$$

with

(8.4) $$a = \frac{1}{k} \Delta k.$$

We may retrace the steps of these calculations. If we start with the partial differential equation (8.2) and can find one solution of it, say k, which does not vanish in **B**, then each solution $v(P)$ of (8.2) can be transformed into a solution of the corresponding equation (8.1) by the transformation (8.3). If, in particular, we have $a(P) > 0$ in **B**, as was the case in the problem of the last section, it can be shown that such a solution $k(P) > 0$ of (8.2) exists. In Part B we shall consider the function $U(P)$ which solves (8.2) and on **S** has the boundary value one; we shall show that this function is positive throughout **B**, and it can be chosen as the solution k which serves for the transformation from (8.2) to (8.1).

We may consider the Dirichlet integral

(8.5) $$D\{u\} = \iiint_{\mathbf{B}} (k \operatorname{grad} u)^2 \, d\tau$$

for all solutions of the partial differential equation (8.1) and the integral

(8.6) $$E\{v\} = \iiint_{\mathbf{B}} [(\operatorname{grad} v)^2 + a v^2] \, d\tau$$

for all solutions of the partial differential equation (8.2). A solution u of (8.1) minimizes the integral (8.5) among all functions with the same boundary values on **S** while v solves the corresponding minimum problem with respect to (8.6). Since each u is connected with a function v by the transformation (8.3), we see that $u(P)$ simultaneously minimizes the following two integral expressions:

$$D\{u\} = \iiint_{\mathbf{B}} k^2 (\operatorname{grad} u)^2 \, d\tau, \qquad \boldsymbol{\Delta}\{u\} = \iiint_{\mathbf{B}} [(\operatorname{grad}(k u))^2 + a k^2 u^2] \, d\tau.$$

(8.7)

The question arises whether these two expressions are related to each other and if so, what the relation is. Since

$$\operatorname{grad}(k\,u) = k \operatorname{grad} u + u \operatorname{grad} k, \tag{8.8}$$

we have, in view of (8.4),

$$\boldsymbol{\Delta}\{u\} = \iiint\limits_{B} [k^2 (\operatorname{grad} u)^2 + u^2 (\operatorname{grad} k)^2 + 2\,u\,k \operatorname{grad} u \cdot \operatorname{grad} k + k\,\Delta\,k\,u^2]\,d\tau. \tag{8.9}$$

We use the identities

$$\frac{1}{2}\Delta\,k^2 = k\,\Delta\,k + (\operatorname{grad} k)^2, \qquad \frac{1}{2}\Delta\,u^2 = u\,\Delta\,u + (\operatorname{grad} u)^2 \tag{8.10}$$

and find:

$$\boldsymbol{\Delta}\{u\} = \iiint\limits_{B} \Big[\frac{1}{2}(u^2\,\Delta\,k^2 - k^2\,\Delta\,u^2) + 2\,k^2 (\operatorname{grad} u)^2 + u\,\Delta\,u\,k^2 +$$
$$+ 2\,u\,k \operatorname{grad} u \cdot \operatorname{grad} k\Big]\,d\tau = 2\,\mathrm{D}\{u\} + \iiint\limits_{B} u \operatorname{div}(k^2 \operatorname{grad} u)\,d\tau +$$
$$+ \frac{1}{2}\iiint\limits_{B} (u^2\,\Delta\,k^2 - k^2\,\Delta\,u^2)\,d\tau. \tag{8.11}$$

Finally, using Green's identity, we obtain:

$$\boldsymbol{\Delta}\{u\} = 2\,\mathrm{D}\{u\} + \iiint\limits_{B} u \operatorname{div}(k^2 \operatorname{grad} u)\,d\tau - \frac{1}{2}\iint\limits_{S}\left(u^2 \frac{\partial k^2}{\partial \nu} - k^2 \frac{\partial u^2}{\partial \nu}\right) d\sigma. \tag{8.12}$$

We have further, by (6.4),

$$\mathrm{D}\{u\} = -\iint\limits_{S} k^2\,u \frac{\partial u}{\partial \nu}\,d\sigma - \iiint\limits_{B} u \operatorname{div}(k^2 \operatorname{grad} u)\,d\tau. \tag{8.13}$$

Adding (8.13) to (8.12) and observing that $k^2\,u\,\dfrac{\partial u}{\partial \nu} \equiv \dfrac{1}{2}k^2\,\dfrac{\partial (u^2)}{\partial \nu}$, we find

$$\boldsymbol{\Delta}\{u\} = \mathrm{D}\{u\} - \frac{1}{2}\iint\limits_{S} u^2 \frac{\partial k^2}{\partial \nu}\,d\sigma. \tag{8.14}$$

We see that the quadratic functionals $\boldsymbol{\Delta}\{u\}$ and $\mathrm{D}\{u\}$ differ from each other by an expression which depends only upon the boundary values of the argument function $u(P)$. This difference is, of course, of no importance in a minimum problem where the boundary values of all functions compared are the same and it serves only as an additive constant for the functional considered.

The application of different Dirichlet integrals to the same partial differential equation will be discussed in detail in the second part of the book. It will appear that the choice of the appropriate Dirichlet integral is determined by the particular fundamental solution upon which we want to base the investigation. This fact is connected with the transformation of the fundamental solutions of the partial differential equation (8.1) into the fundamental solutions of (8.2) under the correspondence (8.3). Let $R_\lambda(P, Q)$ be a Robin's function for (8.1). Then, the fundamental singularity of (8.2)

$$P_\lambda(P,Q) = k(P)\, k(Q)\, R_\lambda(P,Q) \tag{8.15}$$

will satisfy on the boundary **S** of **B** the relation:

$$\frac{\partial P_\lambda(P,Q)}{\partial \nu_P} = \left[\lambda(P) + \frac{\partial \log k(P)}{\partial \nu}\right] P_\lambda(P,Q). \tag{8.16}$$

This shows that the Robin's functions for the partial differential equation (8.1) are transformed into Robin's functions of the partial differential equation (8.2) but with a different weight function

$$\lambda^*(P) = \lambda(P) + \frac{\partial \log k(P)}{\partial \nu}. \tag{8.17}$$

CHAPTER II

FLUID DYNAMICS

1. The fundamental equations: We study the motion of an ideal non-viscous fluid through a region **D** of (x, y, z) space. At each point of **D** and at each moment t the fluid and its motion will be described by the two scalars $\rho(x, y, z, t)$ and $p(x, y, z, t)$ which measure the density of and the pressure in the fluid and by the vector $\mathbf{q}(x, y, z, t)$ of the local flow velocity. We denote the components of $\mathbf{q}$ by u, v, and w. For the sake of simplicity we shall assume that the temperature is constant throughout the fluid and that there exists a known equation of state for the fluid which expresses the pressure p as a function of ρ,

$$p = f(\rho). \tag{1.1}$$

The mass contained in a subregion $\mathsf{B} \subset \mathsf{D}$ with boundary surface S and interior normal $\boldsymbol{\nu}$ is obviously given by

$$M(t) = \iiint_{\mathsf{B}} \rho(x, y, z, t)\, d\tau. \tag{1.2}$$

The change of mass with time is due to the flow of matter through the boundary of B. Thus, in the interval of time $(t, t + \triangle t)$ we have an increase of mass

$$\triangle M = \iint_{\mathsf{S}} \rho\, \mathbf{q} \cdot \boldsymbol{\nu}\, d\sigma \triangle t. \tag{1.3}$$

The principle of conservation of mass leads us, therefore, to the equation

$$\frac{d}{dt}\left(\iiint_{\mathsf{B}} \rho(x, y, z, t)\, d\tau\right) = \iint_{\mathsf{S}} \rho\, \mathbf{q} \cdot \boldsymbol{\nu}\, d\sigma. \tag{1.4}$$

We may transform the surface integral in (1.4) into a volume integral over B by means of Green's identity and arrive at the equation

$$\iiint_{\mathsf{B}} \left[\frac{\partial \rho}{\partial t} + \operatorname{div}(\rho\, \mathbf{q})\right] d\tau = 0 \tag{1.5}$$

which is valid for an arbitrary subregion B of D. We have, therefore, the differential equation

$$\frac{\partial \rho}{\partial t} + \operatorname{div}(\rho\, \mathbf{q}) = 0, \tag{1.6}$$

connecting the density ρ with the velocity vector $\mathbf{q}$. (1.6) is the so-called "equation of continuity" and appears as the differential formulation of the principle of conservation of matter.

Consider now the action of forces upon the elements of the fluid. We distinguish between exterior forces such as gravity and the interior pressures which act through the boundary surface of the volume element B considered. The sum total of all forces acting on B is given by

$$\mathbf{F} = \iiint_{\mathsf{B}} \rho\, \boldsymbol{\Phi}\, d\tau + \iint_{\mathsf{S}} p\, \boldsymbol{\nu}\, d\sigma \tag{1.7}$$

where $\boldsymbol{\Phi}$ is the density per mass of the exterior forces. Using the identity

$$\iint_{\mathsf{S}} p\, \boldsymbol{\nu}\, d\sigma = -\iiint_{\mathsf{B}} \operatorname{grad} p\, d\tau, \tag{1.8}$$

we may write the components of $\mathbf{F}$ in one volume integral over B and obtain:

$$(1.9)\qquad \mathbf{F} = \iiint_{\mathsf{B}} (\rho\,\boldsymbol{\Phi} - \operatorname{grad} p)\, d\tau.$$

Let $\mathbf{r}\,(t)$ be the vector to the center of gravity of the fluid element which occupies the volume B at the time t. By a fundamental theorem of mechanics, all forces acting on the matter in B create an acceleration at its center of gravity which is the same as though all the matter of B were concentrated there and all forces acted at this center. The total mass of B is given by (1.2) and we arrive, therefore, at the equation

$$(1.10)\qquad \iiint_{\mathsf{B}} \rho\, d\tau\, \frac{d^2\mathbf{r}}{dt^2} = \iiint_{\mathsf{B}} (\rho\,\boldsymbol{\Phi} - \operatorname{grad} p)\, d\tau.$$

This solution holds for an arbitrary choice of B. Let us shrink B towards one fixed point in D determined at the time t by the vector $\mathbf{r}$. In the limit we find the differential equation

$$(1.11)\qquad \rho\,\frac{d^2\mathbf{r}}{dt^2} = \rho\,\boldsymbol{\Phi} - \operatorname{grad} p,$$

where $\mathbf{r}\,(t)$ is the position vector of the fluid particle considered at the time t. Clearly, $d\mathbf{r}/dt = \mathfrak{q}$ since the point considered participates in the flow and must have the prescribed local flow velocity. But we must be careful in the calculation of $d^2\mathbf{r}/dt^2$, the change of velocity of the material point. This change is due to two factors: to the change of the local velocity $\mathfrak{q}$ in time and to the change of position of the material point due to its motion. Thus, we find

$$(1.12)\qquad \frac{d^2\mathbf{r}}{dt^2} = \frac{\partial\mathfrak{q}}{\partial t} + \frac{\partial\mathfrak{q}}{\partial x}u + \frac{\partial\mathfrak{q}}{\partial y}v + \frac{\partial\mathfrak{q}}{\partial z}w.$$

We can now put the dynamical equation (1.11) in the simple vector form:

$$(1.13)\qquad \frac{\partial\mathfrak{q}}{\partial t} + (\mathfrak{q}\cdot\operatorname{grad})\,\mathfrak{q} = \boldsymbol{\Phi} - \frac{1}{\rho}\operatorname{grad} p,$$

where we have used the operator symbol

$$(1.14)\qquad \mathfrak{q}\cdot\operatorname{grad} \equiv u\frac{\partial}{\partial x} + v\frac{\partial}{\partial y} + w\frac{\partial}{\partial z}.$$

By means of the identity

$$(1.15)\qquad (\mathfrak{q}\cdot\operatorname{grad})\,\mathfrak{q} = (\operatorname{curl}\mathfrak{q}) \times \mathfrak{q} + \frac{1}{2}\operatorname{grad}|\mathfrak{q}|^2$$

we can also put (1.13) in the form:

$$\frac{\partial \mathbf{q}}{\partial t} + \frac{1}{2} \operatorname{grad} |\mathbf{q}|^2 + (\operatorname{curl} \mathbf{q}) \times \mathbf{q} = \mathbf{\Phi} - \frac{1}{\rho} \operatorname{grad} p. \tag{1.16}$$

In equations (1.1), (1.6) and (1.16) we have five relations between the five functions p, ρ, u, v, and w which describe the fluid motion. Together with appropriate initial and boundary conditions these equations determine the motion of the fluid in space and time. Theoretical hydrodynamics coincides to a very large extent with the problem of integration of this differential system.

Cisotti [10], Frank-Mises [14], Jeffreys [25], Lamb [36], Lichtenstein [40], Milne-Thomson [48], [49], Mises-Friedrichs [51], Pérès [58], Riemann-Weber [66], Villat [84], Webster [89].

2. Stationary irrotational flow: There exist important special types of fluid flow in which the system of equations (1.1), (1.6) and (1.16) simplifies to a considerable extent. In the larger part of this section we shall deal with steady fluid flow, i. e., flows in which the five functions ρ, p, and $\mathbf{q} \equiv (u, v, w)$ do not depend on time. In this case, the first left-hand term in (1.16) vanishes.

Among the remaining terms of (1.16), the expression $(\operatorname{curl} \mathbf{q}) \times \mathbf{q}$ has by far the most complicated form. It is, therefore, understandable that the particular case of fluid flow where $\operatorname{curl} \mathbf{q} \equiv 0$ in D has been studied extensively. There is also a strong physical justification for the importance of this so-called "irrotational" case. In fact, it can be shown that if the exterior forces acting on the fluid are conservative, i. e., possess a potential $V(x, y, z)$ such that

$$\mathbf{\Phi} = -\operatorname{grad} V \tag{2.1}$$

they will create an irrotational motion of the fluid if at the time $t = 0$ the fluid was at rest. Let us, therefore, make the following two assumptions:

a) The field of exterior forces is conservative and, hence, (2.1) holds.

b) $\operatorname{curl} \mathbf{q} \equiv 0$ in D.

In this particular case, we can simplify the dynamical equation (1.16) considerably. We introduce a function of the density

$$i(\rho) = \int_{\rho_\varepsilon}^{\rho} \frac{dp}{\rho} \tag{2.2}$$

and observe that

$$\text{grad}\, i(\rho) = \frac{1}{\rho}\, \text{grad}\, p. \tag{2.3}$$

Using (2.1) and (2.3), we may put (1.16) in the form:

$$\text{grad}\left[\frac{1}{2}\mathfrak{q}^2 + V + i(\rho)\right] = 0 \tag{2.4}$$

which by integration leads immediately to Bernoulli's law:

$$\frac{1}{2}\mathfrak{q}^2 + V + i(\rho) = \text{const.} \tag{2.5}$$

The condition curl $\mathfrak{q} \equiv 0$ in **D** is equivalent to the existence of a velocity potential $U(x, y, z)$ such that

$$\mathfrak{q} = -\,\text{grad}\, U. \tag{2.6}$$

Introducing U into the continuity equation (1.6) and noticing that $\partial\rho/\partial t \equiv 0$, we obtain the differential equation for the velocity potential U:

$$\text{div}\,[\rho\, \text{grad}\, U] = 0. \tag{2.7}$$

This equation together with (2.5) which can also be written as

$$\frac{1}{2}(\text{grad}\, U)^2 + V + i(\rho) = \text{const.} \tag{2.8}$$

serves to determine the two unknown functions U and ρ. We may express ρ as a function of x, y, z and $(\text{grad}\, U)^2$ by means of (2.8) and then obtain in (2.7) a non-linear partial differential equation for the velocity potential U alone. This differential equation must be integrated under given auxiliary conditions. In order to gain a better insight into the problems arising in this connection we shall first treat the problem under an additional simplification. We shall assume that the fluid is incompressible, i. e., that it has the particular equation of state

$$\rho = \rho_0 = \text{const.} \tag{2.9}$$

Even after this long chain of simplifying assumptions with regard to the nature of the fluid and the flow, we shall still have to overcome many mathematical difficulties in the treatment of the problem.

3. Incompressible, irrotational, stationary fluid flow: In the case $\rho = \rho_0$, the differential equation (2.7) reduces to Laplace's equation

$$\Delta U = 0, \tag{3.1}$$

i. e., the velocity potential U must be harmonic in D. The function $i(\rho)$ is defined in this case by

$$i(\rho) = \frac{p}{\rho} + \text{const.}, \tag{3.2}$$

and Bernoulli's equation assumes the form

$$\frac{1}{2}\mathbf{q}^2 + V + \frac{p}{\rho} = \text{const.} \tag{3.3}$$

We must now discuss the additional conditions which will serve to make the hydrodynamical problem considered a definite one. Let C be the boundary of the flow region D; suppose that we know the flow conditions on C, specifically the influx $\mathbf{q} \cdot \boldsymbol{\nu}$ in the normal direction on C. It is heuristically evident that this condition should determine the flow within D. We must remark, however, that we are not quite free in prescribing $\mathbf{q} \cdot \boldsymbol{\nu}$ on C; in fact, we must require

$$\iint_{\mathsf{C}} \mathbf{q} \cdot \boldsymbol{\nu}\, d\sigma = 0 \tag{3.4}$$

which is the principle of conservation of matter. Using (2.6), we therefore arrive at the following boundary value problem: *To determine a solution of Laplace's equation* (3.1) *which, on the boundary* C *of the domain* D *considered, has prescribed values of the normal derivative* $\partial U/\partial \nu$. *This normal derivative must, however, satisfy the condition*

$$\iint_{\mathsf{C}} \frac{\partial U}{\partial \nu}\, d\sigma = 0. \tag{3.5}$$

This is exactly one of the boundary value problems which we encountered in the case of a steady heat flow. In Section I.4 we reduced this problem to the determination of the Neumann's function of the domain and showed that the solution U of this problem is determined up to an additive constant. This is to be expected in the hydrodynamical case, since the velocity potential is only determined up to an additive constant. Thus, the knowledge of Neumann's function for Laplace's equation and the domain D leads to the determination of the velocity field $\mathbf{q} = -\operatorname{grad} U$. By means of (3.3) we can then determine the pressure field in D and the problem is entirely solved.

We observe that the velocity field depends only on the influx through C and is independent of the exterior forces determined by V. These exterior forces, however, influence the pressure distribution in D.

The kinetic energy associated with the flow is given by the integral

$$T(U) = \frac{1}{2} \iiint_{D} \rho_0 \mathfrak{q}^2 \, d\tau = \frac{\rho_0}{2} \iiint_{D} (\operatorname{grad} U)^2 \, d\tau. \tag{3.6}$$

We see that the Dirichlet integral

$$D\{U\} = \iiint_{D} (\operatorname{grad} U)^2 \, d\tau \tag{3.7}$$

is closely related to the energy of the flow. As was shown in Section I.6 we can characterize the harmonic function U *as that function with given boundary values on* C *which leads to a minimum value of the Dirichlet integral.* In hydrodynamical problems, however, the boundary values of U have no physical meaning but the values of $\partial U/\partial \nu$ on C have. We shall therefore point out an extremum problem connected with the Dirichlet integral (3.7) where the values of $\partial U/\partial \nu$ alone enter.

Consider the vector field

$$\mathfrak{q} = -\operatorname{grad} U \tag{3.8}$$

in D. It has the property $\operatorname{div} \mathfrak{q} = 0$, i. e., it is a so-called solenoidal vector field. On C, we have

$$\mathfrak{q} \cdot \boldsymbol{\nu} = -\frac{\partial U}{\partial \nu}. \tag{3.9}$$

We now compare the particular field $\mathfrak{q}$ with all possible solenoidal vector fields $\mathbf{k}$ which on C satisfy the condition

$$\mathbf{k} \cdot \boldsymbol{\nu} = \mathfrak{q} \cdot \boldsymbol{\nu}. \tag{3.10}$$

We assert: *Among all solenoidal fields in* D *with the same normal projection* (3.10) *on* C, *the field* $\mathfrak{q}$ *leads to the minimum value of the integral*

$$I(\mathfrak{q}) = \iiint_{D} |\mathfrak{q}|^2 \, d\tau. \tag{3.11}$$

In fact, for any competing vector field $\mathbf{k}$ we have

$$
\begin{aligned}
(3.12)\qquad \mathrm{I}(\mathbf{k}) &= \iiint\limits_{D} |\mathbf{k}-\mathbf{q}+\mathbf{q}|^2\, d\tau = \iiint\limits_{D} |\mathbf{q}|^2\, d\tau + \\
&+ \iiint\limits_{D} |\mathbf{k}-\mathbf{q}|^2\, d\tau + 2\iiint\limits_{D} \big((\mathbf{k}-\mathbf{q})\cdot\mathbf{q}\big)\, d\tau.
\end{aligned}
$$

Now, using partial integration and (3.10) we obtain by virtue of (3.8):

$$
\begin{aligned}
(3.13)\qquad \iiint\limits_{D} \big((\mathbf{k}-\mathbf{q})\cdot\mathbf{q}\big)\, d\tau &= -\iiint\limits_{D} \big((\mathbf{k}-\mathbf{q})\cdot \operatorname{grad} U\big)\, d\tau = \\
&= \iiint\limits_{D} U \operatorname{div}(\mathbf{k}-\mathbf{q})\, d\tau = 0
\end{aligned}
$$

since **k** and **q** are both solenoidal. Thus, (3.12) has the simpler form:

$$
(3.14)\qquad \mathrm{I}(\mathbf{k}) = \mathrm{I}(\mathbf{q}) + \iiint\limits_{D} |\mathbf{k}-\mathbf{q}|^2\, d\tau \geqslant \mathrm{I}(\mathbf{q})
$$

and the asserted minimum property of **q** is proved. Equality in (3.14) can hold only if the vector fields **k** and **q** coincide.

In physical terms we have proved: *Among all possible flows with given influx through* C *which satisfy the law of conservation of matter* (*solenoidal*), *the actual flow leads to a minimum of kinetic energy.*[1]

Thus, in the hydrodynamical case also, Dirichlet's integral serves to characterize the required solution by a simple extremum property.

4. Sources and sinks: In the preceding section we considered a stationary, irrotational and incompressible fluid flow in a region D which was uniquely determined by its flux through the boundary C of D. Although of great mathematical interest, this problem occurs rather seldom in physical investigations. The most important situation in applications is the following: The fluid considered lies in a domain D of space which is bounded by rigid walls forming the boundary C of D. The fluid flows from given sources in D to given sinks in the same domain. We have then to determine the velocity and pressure field in the region of the flow.

In order to deal with this problem we must consider the nature of the flow at the sources and sinks. While at all other points of D the velocity field possesses a harmonic velocity potential U, this will clearly not be the

[1] Lamb [35].

case at these singular points where the law of conservation of matter is no longer fulfilled. The source points are thus singular points of the harmonic function U in D. The typical point singularity of a harmonic function is given by

$$(4.1) \qquad U_Q(P) = \frac{1}{4\pi r(P,Q)}, \qquad r(P,Q) = \overline{PQ}.$$

This function is harmonic in P everywhere in space except at the point Q where it becomes infinite. Interpreted as a velocity potential, it creates the velocity field

$$(4.2) \qquad \mathbf{q} = -\operatorname{grad} U = \frac{1}{4\pi r^3}\mathbf{r}, \qquad \mathbf{r} = \overrightarrow{QP},$$

the stream lines of which are the radii emerging from the point Q. Through any sphere S of radius R and center Q there passes per unit time the amount of matter

$$(4.3) \qquad \rho_0 \iint_{\mathsf{S}} \mathbf{q}\cdot\boldsymbol{\nu}\, d\sigma = \frac{1}{4\pi R^2}\rho_0 \cdot 4\pi R^2 = \rho_0.$$

Let us assume for sake of simplicity that the constant density of the fluid is $\rho_0 = 1$. Then, we see that the velocity potential (4.1) represents a source with strength one.

We may now construct complicated flow patterns of the form

$$(4.3) \qquad U(P) = \sum_{\nu=1}^{N} \lambda_\nu U_{Q_\nu}(P)$$

which possesses sources of strength λ_i at the points Q_i, or

$$(4.4) \qquad U(P) = \iiint_{\mathsf{D}} \mu(Q)\, U_Q(P)\, d\tau_Q$$

which represents a continuous source distribution over D with strength density μ. Other types of singularities may be created by processes of differentiation on $U_Q(P)$ with respect to the coordinates of the source point Q. The most important singularity obtained in this way is the dipole singularity

$$(4.5) \qquad W(P) = \frac{1}{4\pi}\mathbf{e}\cdot\operatorname{grad}_Q \frac{1}{r(P,Q)}.$$

As was shown in Section I.3 this singularity may be interpreted as the limiting case of a source and a sink of great equal strength which lie very near to the point Q and such that the vector from the sink to the source has the direction of the vector $\mathfrak{e}$. If $P = (x, y, z)$, $Q = (\xi, \eta, \zeta)$ and $\mathfrak{e} = (\alpha, \beta, \gamma)$, we have

$$W(x, y, z) = \frac{1}{4\pi r^3}[\alpha(x-\xi) + \beta(y-\eta) + \gamma(z-\zeta)]. \tag{4.6}$$

We need some additional remarks in the important case that the domain **D** of the flow is unbounded and contains the point at infinity. We shall study the possible singularities of a harmonic function U at the point of infinity. For this purpose, we transform the neighborhood of the point at infinity into a finite domain by means of a transformation by reciprocal radii

$$x' = \frac{x}{r^2}, \quad y' = \frac{y}{r^2}, \quad z' = \frac{z}{r^2}, \quad r = (x^2 + y^2 + z^2)^{1/2}. \tag{4.7}$$

It is easy to invert this transformation:

$$x = \frac{x'}{r'^2}, \quad y = \frac{y'}{r'^2}, \quad z = \frac{z'}{r'^2}, \quad r' = (x'^2 + y'^2 + z'^2)^{1/2} = \frac{1}{r}. \tag{4.8}$$

Lord Kelvin made the important observation that if $U(x, y, z)$ is harmonic in the neighborhood of infinity then $U'(x', y', z') = r\,U(x, y, z)$ will be harmonic in the image domain near the origin of the (x', y', z')-coordinates. This result can be easily verified by formal differentiation.[1] Conversely, every harmonic function $U'(x', y', z')$ near the finite point $x' = y' = z' = 0$ will lead to a harmonic function

$$U(x, y, z) = r'\,U'(x', y', z') \tag{4.9}$$

defined near infinity in the (x, y, z)-space.

We shall use this result in order to transform the above singularities defined at finite source points into singularities near infinity. Let us start with the basic singularity $1/(4\pi r')$ which represents a unit source at the origin of the (x', y', z')-space. By (4.9), we arrive at the harmonic function $U = 1/(4\pi)$ near infinity. We shall make the following convention: *a function will be called regular harmonic at infinity if it corresponds to a regular harmonic function at the origin by* (4.9). We recognize that a non-zero constant is not a regular harmonic function at infinity; however, its singularity does not lead to a source at infinity. On the other hand, the

[1] Kellogg [30], p. 232.

function $U' = 1/(4\pi)$ which is regular at the origin gives rise to the function $U = \frac{r'}{4\pi} = 1/(4\pi r)$ which is by definition regular at infinity and can easily be interpreted as a sink of unit strength at infinity. Consider next the dipole potential

$$W'(x', y', z') = \frac{1}{4\pi r'^3}(\alpha x' + \beta y' + \gamma z'). \tag{4.10}$$

By means of (4.8) and (4.9), this leads to the harmonic function near infinity

$$W(x, y, z) = \frac{1}{4\pi}(\alpha x + \beta y + \gamma z). \tag{4.11}$$

This linear function leads to the velocity field

$$\mathfrak{q} = -\frac{1}{4\pi}\mathfrak{e}, \qquad \mathfrak{e} \equiv (\alpha, \beta, \gamma) \tag{4.12}$$

which represents a uniform flow in the direction of the vector $-\mathfrak{e}$. Since the flow comes from infinity and goes to infinity we may consider it as due to a dipole at infinity.

In a similar way, from every type of singularity for harmonic functions at a finite point we may create new types of singularities at infinity. We remark further that in view of (4.9) and $r' = 1/r$ every regular harmonic function at infinity must vanish there at least to the same order as $1/r$; similarly, it can easily be seen that its derivatives must go to zero at infinity at least of the order of $1/r^2$. These remarks are of great importance when one wants to apply Green's identity to domains which contain the point at infinity. They guarantee the convergence to zero of certain integrals over a sequence of spheres whose radii go to infinity.

5. Fundamental solutions and flow patterns: Let us consider a finite domain D. Denote the boundary of D by C and its interior normal by $\boldsymbol{\nu}$. Neumann's function $N(P, Q)$ of D is defined by the following three requirements:

a) $N(P, Q)$ is regular harmonic for $P \in \mathsf{D}$, except at the point Q.

b) Near the point Q, the function $N(P, Q) - \dfrac{1}{4\pi r(P, Q)}$ is regular harmonic.

c) On the boundary C of D, Neumann's function has a constant normal derivative $\frac{\partial N(P,Q)}{\partial \nu_P} = \text{const.}$

This definition agrees with the definition of the Neumann's function given in Section I.4 for the case of the more general partial differential equation (I.4.2). Neumann's function is the velocity potential of an incompressible fluid flow with a source of unit strength at the point Q. Hence, the flow through the boundary C of D per unit of time must equal one, i. e.,

$$\iint_C \frac{\partial N(P,Q)}{\partial \nu_P} d\sigma_P = 1. \tag{5.1}$$

Since $\frac{\partial N(P,Q)}{\partial \nu_P}$ is constant on C by definition, we obtain the equation

$$\frac{\partial N(P,Q)}{\partial \nu_P} = A^{-1}, \quad A = \text{surface area of C}. \tag{5.2}$$

This shows that *the constant value of the normal derivative of Neumann's function is also independent of the source point* Q, a fact of great importance in the sequel.

The above definition of Neumann's function still leaves undetermined an additive constant which may depend on the parameter point Q. We determine Neumann's function uniquely by the requirement

$$\iint_C N(P,Q)\, d\sigma_P = 0. \tag{5.3}$$

By the methods of Section I.4 it is readily shown that Neumann's function satisfies the symmetry relation:

$$N(P,Q) = N(Q,P) \tag{5.4}$$

and is, therefore, a harmonic function of its parameter point also.

We now take n points $Q_\nu \in$ D $(\nu = 1, 2, \ldots, n)$ and n real numbers λ_ν whose sum vanishes. Consider the flow with the velocity potential

$$U(P) = \sum_{\nu=1}^{n} \lambda_\nu N(P, Q_\nu). \tag{5.5}$$

This represents the flow of an incompressible fluid in D with sources at the points Q_ν of strength λ_ν. On the boundary C of D, we have by (5.2)

(5.6) $$-\mathfrak{q}\cdot\boldsymbol{\nu} = \frac{\partial U}{\partial \nu} = \sum_{\nu=1}^{n} \lambda_\nu A^{-1} = 0.$$

Thus, no fluid passes through the boundary C of D. The velocity potential (5.5) represents the flow in the domain D bounded by rigid walls C due to a source distribution at the points Q_ν with strength λ_ν. The restriction

(5.7) $$\sum_{\nu=1}^{n} \lambda_\nu = 0$$

is a natural and a necessary one since, in view of the incompressibility and steady character of the flow, the total strength of all sources must be zero. But except for this restriction we may prescribe the location and strength of the sources and always construct a flow which on the rigid boundary C of D satisfies the necessary condition $\mathfrak{q}\cdot\boldsymbol{\nu} = 0$. We see that *the problem of determining the flow of a fluid in a walled-in region with given simple sources and sinks is solved if the Neumann's function of this region has been determined.* Thus, in the problem mentioned at the beginning of Section 4 as well as in the problem of Section 3, the Neumann's function plays a decisive role.

The Neumann's function can also be used in order to find flows which are created by more complicated singularities. Consider, for example, the velocity potential

(5.8) $$W(P) = \mathfrak{e}\cdot \text{grad}_Q N(P,Q).$$

This is obviously a regular harmonic function of $P \in$ D, except at the point Q where it behaves like a dipole (4.5) with axis $\mathfrak{e}$. If we apply the gradient operation to the identity (5.2) with respect to Q we recognize that $\text{grad}_Q N(P,Q)$ has a vanishing normal derivative in P on C. Thus, the velocity potential (5.8) represents a flow in the domain D with an impenetrable boundary C due to a dipole at Q with prescribed axis $\mathfrak{e}$.

The preceding reasoning can be extended considerably; by applying linear operations on the Neumann's function with respect to the source point Q, we may create flows in D with very general singularities and which do not cross the boundary C of D. Let, for example, $\mu(Q)$ be continuous in D and satisfy

(5.9) $$\iiint_{D} \mu(Q)\, d\tau_Q = 0.$$

Then, the function

$$V(P) = \iiint_{D} N(P, Q)\, \mu(Q)\, d\tau_Q \tag{5.10}$$

will represent the velocity potential of a flow in D due to a continuous source distribution in D with strength density $\mu(Q)$ which satisfies the boundary condition $\partial V / \partial \nu = 0$. In this example, as in the general case, one has only to take care that the total strength of all sources in D be zero.

6. Infinite domains: Many of the previous results do not hold in the case of a domain D which contains the point at infinity as an interior point. Let us consider the following boundary value problem: To determine a regular harmonic function $U(P)$ in D with prescribed values $\partial U / \partial \nu$ for the normal derivative on the boundary C of D.

In the case of finite domains D this problem does not always possess a solution, but if there exists one function U satisfying the requirements, there will exist an infinity of such functions, namely all functions $U + \text{const.}$ This is no longer the case in a domain D which contains infinity since the only constant which is regular at infinity is the constant zero. *There can therefore exist only one solution of the boundary value problem considered and it must vanish at infinity to the order of* $1/r$ since it is regular at infinity. On the other hand, there are no restrictions on the values of $\partial U / \partial \nu$ on C. While in the case of a finite domain we had necessarily

$$\iint_{C} \frac{\partial U}{\partial \nu}\, d\sigma = 0 \tag{6.1}$$

this need not hold for an infinite domain. For a function may be regular harmonic at all points of D but can have an arbitrary source at infinity. Thus, we have greater freedom in posing the boundary value problem and less freedom in choosing the solution.

It is also intuitively clear that we may now define Neumann's function for a finite source point Q as follows:

a) $N(P, Q)$ is a regular harmonic function for $P \in D$, except at $P = Q$.

b) $N(P, Q) - (4\pi r(P, Q))^{-1}$ is regular harmonic at the point Q.

c) For $P \in C$, we have $\dfrac{\partial N(P, Q)}{\partial \nu_P} = 0$.

By the above definition, the Neumann's function for an infinite domain represents the velocity potential of a steady incompressible fluid flow around the impenetrable walls C which has a source of unit strength at the finite point $Q \in \mathsf{D}$ and a sink of unit strength at infinity. The above definition is possible since a simple source at infinity does not affect the regularity of the corresponding velocity potential.

The above definition determines the Neumann's function uniquely. By the methods of Section I.4 one easily derives the law of symmetry

$$N(P,Q) = N(Q,P). \tag{6.2}$$

From this result we can extend the definition of the Neumann's function consistently to the case in which the parameter point lies at infinity. In fact, letting $Q \to \infty$ and using the fact that a regular harmonic function must vanish at infinity, we deduce from (6.2):

$$N(P,\infty) = 0. \tag{6.3}$$

Thus, the Neumann's function with parameter point at infinity describes the fluid at rest; this was to be expected since source and sink of strength unity now both lie at infinity and cancel each other.

Also in the case of an infinite domain *the Neumann's function* $N(P,Q)$ *has the property of being non-negative in* D. In fact, suppose there existed a point P where $N(P,Q)$ had a negative value; there would then exist a whole subdomain D_- of D in which the Neumann's function would be negative. This domain has a boundary in D on which N is zero, and a part of its boundary might possibly coincide with a part of C, so that $\partial N/\partial \nu = 0$ holds there. Hence, the expression $N(\partial N/\partial \nu)$ will be zero on the entire boundary C_- of the domain D_-. The Neumann's function is regular harmonic in D_- since at the singular point Q, $N(P,Q)$ becomes positively infinite and Q cannot therefore lie in D_-. But integrating by parts,

$$\iiint_{\mathsf{D}_-} [\operatorname{grad}_P N(P,Q)]^2 \, d\tau_P = -\iint_{\mathsf{C}_-} N(P,Q) \frac{\partial N(P,Q)}{\partial \nu_P} \, d\sigma_P = 0. \tag{6.4}$$

We conclude that the Neumann's function is constant over the entire domain D_- and, since it vanishes on the part of C_- which lies in D, it must be identically zero in D_-. Hence, there are no points in D where the Neumann's function is negative.

We may draw the following inference from the non-negative character of the Neumann's function. Let $u(P)$ be regular harmonic in D; we derive by Green's identity just as in Section I.4 the formula

$$u(P) = -\iint_{\mathsf{C}} N(P,Q) \frac{\partial u(Q)}{\partial \nu_Q} \, d\sigma_Q. \tag{6.5}$$

Since $N(P, Q) \geqq 0$, this tells us that a regular harmonic function in D with positive values of the normal derivative on C is non-positive in D. This result could also have been derived from the well-known principle that a harmonic function in an infinite domain attains its maximum either at infinity or on the boundary of the domain. Since $u(P)$ has a positive normal derivative on C it cannot have its maximum on the boundary. Hence, it attains its maximum at infinity; but there it must vanish as a regular harmonic function. Thus, $u(P)$ is negative at all other points of D.

If the domain D contains the point at infinity, there exists a regular harmonic function $v(P)$ which has a constant normal derivative on C, say

$$\frac{\partial v}{\partial \nu} = -1 \quad \text{on C.} \tag{6.6}$$

By means of (6.5) this function may be represented in the form

$$v(P) = \iint_{C} N(P, Q)\, d\sigma_Q. \tag{6.7}$$

It is positive in D and is the velocity potential of a flow from a source at infinity with the strength A (A = surface area of C) and a constant outflow over the entire boundary. It may be used as a comparison function for all regular harmonic functions $u(P)$ in D. In fact, suppose that on C we have the estimate

$$m \leqq \frac{\partial u}{\partial \nu} \leqq M. \tag{6.8}$$

Then, the functions $(u + m\, v)$ and $-(u + M\, v)$ will be regular harmonic in D and possess positive normal derivatives on C. Hence, by our previous result both functions will be negative in D and this leads to the estimate

$$-M\, v \leqq u \leqq -m\, v. \tag{6.9}$$

It should be remarked that in the case of an infinite domain the value of the velocity potential has a physical significance. For we normalize this potential in such a way that it has the value zero at infinity. Thus, the value of the velocity potential may also be interpreted as the drop of potential towards infinity.

We are now able to construct the velocity potential due to a dipole at infinity of a flow which does not cross the boundary C of the flow region D.

Let us use the coordinates x_i $(i = 1, 2, 3)$ and construct the velocity potentials which at infinity behave like x_i. Thus, we define three functions

$$\Phi_i(P) = x_i + \varphi_i(P) \tag{6.10}$$

which are harmonic in D except at infinity (where $\varphi_i(P)$ is still regular harmonic) and which on the boundary C of D satisfy the conditions

$$\frac{\partial \Phi_i(P)}{\partial \nu} = 0, \qquad P \in \mathrm{C}. \tag{6.11}$$

Clearly, the general velocity potential in D due to a dipole at infinity will behave there like $\sum_{i=1}^{3} a_i x_i$ and can be represented in the form $\sum_{i=1}^{3} a_i \Phi_i$. The functions $\varphi_i(P)$ are regular harmonic in D, and on C we know their normal derivatives:

$$\frac{\partial \varphi_i}{\partial \nu} = - \frac{\partial x_i}{\partial \nu}. \tag{6.12}$$

Hence, according to (6.5), we can express them by means of the Neumann's function and obtain

$$\varphi_i(Q) = \iint_{\mathrm{C}} N(P,Q) \frac{\partial x_i}{\partial \nu} d\sigma_P. \tag{6.13}$$

Thus, *the knowledge of the Neumann's function leads immediately to the velocity potentials with dipole singularities at infinity.*

There exists an interesting relation between the velocity potentials Φ_i and the series development of the Neumann's function near infinity. Let us develop the function $N(P,Q)$ near infinity in a series of the form[1]

$$N(P,Q) = \frac{A(Q)}{r} + \sum_{i=1}^{3} \frac{a_i(Q)\, x_i}{r^3} + O(r^{-3}), \qquad r^2 = \sum_{i=1}^{3} x_i^2, \tag{6.14}$$

which is always possible for a regular harmonic function. We assume that the origin of our system of coordinates lies outside the domain D so that $1/r$, x_ν/r^3 are regular harmonic functions in D. It is easily shown that

$$A(Q) = \frac{1}{4\pi}. \tag{6.15}$$

[1] Kellogg [30], p. 144.

In fact, consider the domain D_R bounded by C and a sufficiently large sphere S_R $(r = R)$; we assume that $Q \in \mathsf{D}_R$ and use Green's identity to obtain

$$\iint_{\mathsf{S}_R} \frac{\partial N(P,Q)}{\partial \nu_P} d\sigma_P = \iint_{\mathsf{C}+\mathsf{S}_R} \frac{\partial N(P,Q)}{\partial \nu_P} d\sigma_P = 1. \tag{6.16}$$

Now inserting the development (6.14) into (6.16) and letting $R \to \infty$ we obtain (6.15).

We next use the series (6.14) in order to evaluate the integral (6.13). Applying Green's identity to the domain D_R and letting $Q = (\xi_1, \xi_2, \xi_3) \in \mathsf{D}$, we find

$$\iint_{\mathsf{C}+\mathsf{S}_R} \left(N(P,Q) \frac{\partial x_i}{\partial \nu} - x_i \frac{\partial N(P,Q)}{\partial \nu_P} \right) d\sigma_P = -\xi_i. \tag{6.17}$$

Hence, in view of (6.13), we have

$$\varphi_i(Q) = -\xi_i - \iint_{\mathsf{S}_R} \left(N(P,Q) \frac{\partial x_i}{\partial \nu} - x_i \frac{\partial N(P,Q)}{\partial \nu_P} \right) d\sigma_P. \tag{6.18}$$

Now, we insert the series (6.14) in place of N. Using $\dfrac{\partial x_i}{\partial \nu} = -\dfrac{x_i}{R}$ on S_R and the fact that

$$\iint_{\mathsf{S}_R} x_i x_k \, d\sigma = \frac{4\pi}{3} R^4 \delta_{ik}$$

one easily computes

$$\iint_{\mathsf{S}_R} \left(\frac{1}{r} \frac{\partial x_i}{\partial \nu} - x_i \frac{\partial}{\partial \nu} \left(\frac{1}{r} \right) \right) d\sigma = 0, \quad \iint_{\mathsf{S}_R} \left(\frac{x_k}{r^3} \frac{\partial x_i}{\partial \nu} - x_i \frac{\partial}{\partial \nu} \left(\frac{x_k}{r^3} \right) \right) d\sigma = -4\pi \delta_{ik}.$$

$$\delta_{ik} = \begin{cases} 1 \text{ if } i = k, \\ 0 \text{ if } i \neq k, \end{cases} \tag{6.19}$$

and hence

$$\varphi_i(Q) = -\xi_i + 4\pi a_i(Q) + O\left(\frac{1}{R}\right). \tag{6.20}$$

Letting $R \to \infty$ and using definition (6.10), we finally arrive at

$$a_i(Q) = \frac{1}{4\pi} \Phi_i(Q). \tag{6.21}$$

Thus, the velocity potentials $\Phi_i(Q)$ are the coefficients in the development of the Neumann's function near infinity:

$$N(P, Q) = \frac{1}{4\pi}\left(\frac{1}{r} + \sum_{i=1}^{3} \frac{\Phi_i(Q)\, x_i}{r^3} + \ldots\right). \tag{6.22}$$

In a similar way, the higher coefficients of this development may be identified as velocity potentials of flows in the region D with rigid walls C which have higher order singularities at infinity.

Schiffer-Szegö (S 6).

7. Virtual mass: Let B be a rigid body with boundary surface C which is immersed in an infinite incompressible fluid with density ρ_0. Suppose that the body B is translated with constant velocity c in the direction of the unit vector $\mathfrak{e} = (\alpha_1, \alpha_2, \alpha_3)$ and that the fluid is at rest at infinity. The motion of the body creates a fluid flow. An observer referring to a set of axes in the body B will ascribe the motion of the fluid to a time-independent velocity potential $\Phi(P)$ which satisfies the boundary condition

$$\frac{\partial \Phi}{\partial \nu} = 0 \quad \text{on } \mathsf{C}, \tag{7.1}$$

and at infinity behaves like the function

$$W \equiv c\,(\alpha_1 x_1 + \alpha_2 x_2 + \alpha_3 x_3). \tag{7.2}$$

In fact, since the fluid is at rest at infinity it will move with the velocity vector $-c\,\mathfrak{e}$ relative to the body B and clearly we shall have

$$\mathfrak{q} = -\operatorname{grad} W = -c\,\mathfrak{e}. \tag{7.3}$$

We may express the velocity potential Φ by means of the potentials Φ_i of the last section and obtain

$$\Phi(P) = c \sum_{i=1}^{3} \alpha_i \Phi_i(P). \tag{7.4}$$

At each fixed moment the field of the absolute velocities differs from the field of relative velocities by the vector $\mathfrak{q}$ and can be derived from the velocity potential

$$\varphi(P) = c \sum_{i=1}^{3} \alpha_i \varphi_i(P), \tag{7.5}$$

which is regular harmonic at infinity.

The kinetic energy connected with the fluid motion is given by the integral

$$T_0 = \frac{1}{2}\rho_0 \iiint\limits_{D} |\operatorname{grad}\varphi|^2 d\tau = \frac{1}{2}\rho_0 c^2 \sum_{i,k=1}^{3} a_i a_k \iiint\limits_{D} (\operatorname{grad}\varphi_i \cdot \operatorname{grad}\varphi_k)\, d\tau. \tag{7.6}$$

Here D is the exterior of the body B and the integrals over this infinite region are convergent since the functions φ_i are regular harmonic at infinity. We define the matrix, based on the Dirichlet product between the different φ_i's:

$$w_{ik} = \iiint\limits_{D} (\operatorname{grad}\varphi_i \cdot \operatorname{grad}\varphi_k)\, d\tau = \mathrm{D}\,\{\varphi_i, \varphi_k\}, \tag{7.7}$$

and observe from (7.6) that it determines the dynamical behavior of the body B moving through the fluid. In fact, if the mass of B is M, then the kinetic energy of its motion through the fluid in direction $\mathfrak{e}$ with velocity c will be given by

$$T = \frac{1}{2} M c^2 + \frac{1}{2}\rho_0 \sum_{i,k=1}^{3} a_i a_k w_{ik} c^2. \tag{7.8}$$

Thus, the presence of the fluid increases the inertia of the body by an amount

$$\mu = \rho_0 \sum_{i,k=1}^{3} a_i a_k w_{ik} \tag{7.9}$$

which is called *the virtual mass of the body in the direction* $\mathfrak{e}$. This quantity is obviously independent of the particular choice of the system of coordinates. Hence, the elements of the matrix $((w_{ik}))$ transform like the components of a tensor. The tensor w_{ik} is called the tensor of the virtual mass of the body B.

We can relate the tensor w_{ik} with the coefficients of the series development of the harmonic functions $\varphi_i(P)$ at infinity. Let us write

$$\varphi_i(P) = \sum_{k=1}^{3} \frac{d_{ik} x_k}{r^3} + \cdots \tag{7.10}$$

as the development near infinity. Because the fluid is incompressible, there cannot occur a term a/r in this development of $\varphi_i(P)$, since it would correspond to a source of fluid at infinity. Mathematically, this follows from the fact that

$$\iint \frac{\partial \Phi_i}{\partial \nu}\, d\sigma = \iint \frac{\partial \varphi_i}{\partial \nu}\, d\sigma = 0$$

over any closed surface in the flow region. We shall show that the coefficient scheme d_{ik} forms a tensor closely related to w_{ik}.

We start with the definition (7.7) of the w_{ik} and apply Green's identity:

$$w_{ik} = -\iint_{C} \varphi_i \frac{\partial \varphi_k}{\partial \nu}\, d\sigma = \iint_{C} \varphi_i \frac{\partial x_k}{\partial \nu}\, d\sigma \tag{7.11}$$

by virtue of (6.12). The function x_k is harmonic in **D** but not regular at infinity. We introduce, therefore, the domain D_R bounded by **C** and a sufficiently large sphere S_R of radius R around the origin. Now, Green's identity applied to D_R yields:

$$\iint_{C} \left(\varphi_i \frac{\partial x_k}{\partial \nu} - x_k \frac{\partial \varphi_i}{\partial \nu} \right) d\sigma = -\iint_{S_R} \left(\varphi_i \frac{\partial x_k}{\partial \nu} - x_k \frac{\partial \varphi_i}{\partial \nu} \right) d\sigma. \tag{7.12}$$

Inserting the development (7.10) in the right-hand side of (7.12) we find by (6.19):

$$\iint_{C} \left(\varphi_i \frac{\partial x_k}{\partial \nu} - x_k \frac{\partial \varphi_i}{\partial \nu} \right) d\sigma = 4\pi\, d_{ik} + O\left(\frac{1}{R}\right). \tag{7.13}$$

Now letting $R \to \infty$, we obtain

$$w_{ik} = \iint_{C} \varphi_i \frac{\partial x_k}{\partial \nu}\, d\sigma = \iint_{C} x_k \frac{\partial \varphi_i}{\partial \nu}\, d\sigma + 4\pi\, d_{ik}. \tag{7.14}$$

The first right-hand term can be simplified by means of the boundary condition (6.12) for φ_i. We have by Green's first identity applied to the complement **B** of **D**:

$$\iint_{C} x_k \frac{\partial \varphi_i}{\partial \nu}\, d\sigma = -\iint_{C} x_k \frac{\partial x_i}{\partial \nu}\, d\sigma = -\iiint_{B} (\operatorname{grad} x_k \cdot \operatorname{grad} x_i)\, d\tau = -V\, \delta_{ik}, \tag{7.15}$$

where V is the volume of the body **B** considered. Thus, we finally obtain the result:[1]

$$w_{ik} = 4\pi\, d_{ik} - V\, \delta_{ik}. \tag{7.16}$$

[1] G. I. Taylor (T 1).

This formula shows that the coefficient matrix $4\pi d_{ik}$ differs from the tensor of the virtual mass only by a multiple of the unit tensor and is, therefore, itself a tensor. Since w_{ik} is by definition (7.7) symmetric, the same holds for the tensor d_{ik}. Relation (7.16) shows that the tensor of the virtual mass can be obtained from a series development of the Φ_i at infinity, and hence, ultimately from a development of the Neumann's function there. We shall show that the tensor d_{ik} has various important properties which lead to interesting applications for the tensor of virtual mass.

As an illustrative example we mention the case of the sphere of radius R around the origin. One can easily verify that the velocity potentials $\Phi_i(P)$ have the form

$$\Phi_i(P) = x_i + \frac{1}{2} R^3 \frac{x_i}{r^3}, \qquad r^2 = x_1{}^2 + x_2{}^2 + x_3{}^2. \tag{7.17}$$

Hence, the tensor d_{ik} has the simple form

$$d_{ik} = \frac{1}{2} R^3 \delta_{ik} \tag{7.18}$$

and the tensor of the virtual mass

$$w_{ik} = \left(2\pi R^3 - \frac{4\pi}{3} R^3\right) \delta_{ik} = \frac{2\pi}{3} R^3 \delta_{ik}. \tag{7.19}$$

Thus, the inertia of a sphere moving in the fluid is increased by half the mass of the fluid which has been displaced by the sphere. For reasons of symmetry the tensor w_{ik} must be a multiple of the unit tensor.

8. Dirichlet identities: In many problems of mathematical physics there arises the problem of constructing a harmonic function which satisfies simple conditions at the boundary of its domain of definition and has prescribed singularities at given interior points of the domain. We have already met such questions in the preceding sections; the Neumann's function and the velocity potentials Φ_i were required to have the normal derivative zero on the boundary C of the domain D considered and to have a simple source or dipole singularity respectively at a specified point of D. In such cases it is useful to write the required function $F(P)$ in the form

$$F(P) = S_F(P) + f(P) \tag{8.1}$$

where $S_F(P)$ is the prescribed singularity term and $f(P)$ the regular corrective term which must be added to $S_F(P)$ in order to satisfy the boundary conditions.

Thus, we may write:

$$N(P,Q) = \frac{1}{4\pi r(P,Q)} + n(P,Q) \tag{8.2}$$

and

$$\Phi_i(P) = x_i + \varphi_i(P). \tag{8.3}$$

The singularity term being given, the whole problem of determining the function $F(P)$ reduces to the calculation of the regular part $f(P)$. This latter function is determined by its harmonicity and the boundary conditions it must satisfy which can be derived from the given conditions on $F(P)$. Thus, we have:

$$\frac{\partial n(P,Q)}{\partial \nu_P} = -\frac{1}{4\pi}\frac{\partial}{\partial \nu_P}\left(\frac{1}{r(P,Q)}\right), \qquad P \in \mathsf{C} \tag{8.4}$$

and

$$\frac{\partial \varphi_i(P)}{\partial \nu} = -\frac{\partial x_i}{\partial \nu}, \qquad P \in \mathsf{C}. \tag{8.5}$$

There exists an important technique for the investigation of the regular harmonic functions $f(P)$ which is based on the use of the Dirichlet integral. We have already applied this method in Section 7 when we calculated the tensor of virtual mass w_{ik}. The principle of this method is the following: Let $F(P)$ and $H(P)$ be two harmonic functions with prescribed boundary conditions and singularities. We represent them in the form (8.1) as

$$H(P) = S_H(P) + h(P). \tag{8.6}$$

Now construct the Dirichlet integral

$$\mathrm{D}\{f,h\} = \iiint_{\mathsf{D}} (\operatorname{grad} f \cdot \operatorname{grad} h)\, d\tau = -\iint_{\mathsf{C}} f \frac{\partial h}{\partial \nu}\, d\sigma = -\iint_{\mathsf{C}} h \frac{\partial f}{\partial \nu}\, d\sigma. \tag{8.7}$$

This integral can be evaluated now by using the fact that the boundary values for f and h or their normal derivatives are known. On the other hand, the Dirichlet integral has various important properties which in turn lead to results concerning the functions f and h.

We shall illustrate these general remarks by the following particular cases: Let $F(P) = N(P,Q)$ and $H(P) = N(P,Q')$ where Q and Q' are any two points in D. Accordingly, we have to consider the Dirichlet integral

$$\mathrm{D}\{n(P,Q), n(P,Q')\} = -\iint_{\mathsf{C}} n(P,Q') \frac{\partial n(P,Q)}{\partial \nu_P}\, d\sigma_P. \tag{8.8}$$

Using the boundary condition (8.4) we obtain

$$D\{n(P,Q), n(P,Q')\} = \frac{1}{4\pi}\iint_C n(P,Q')\frac{\partial}{\partial\nu_P}\left(\frac{1}{r(P,Q)}\right)d\sigma_P. \tag{8.9}$$

Thus, one of the unknown functions has been replaced by the normal derivative of the elementary function $1/r$. If the boundary conditions had now determined $n(P,Q')$ in a simple way our work would be finished. But in the problem which we are considering, only $\partial n(P,Q')/\partial\nu_P$ is given in an elementary manner. In order to utilize this fact, we apply Green's identity, and using the fact that $1/4\pi r(P,Q)$ is harmonic in **D**, except for $P = Q$ where it represents a source of unit strength, we obtain

$$\frac{1}{4\pi}\iint_C n(P,Q')\frac{\partial}{\partial\nu_P}\left(\frac{1}{r(P,Q)}\right)d\sigma_P = \frac{1}{4\pi}\iint_C \frac{1}{r(P,Q)}\frac{\partial n(P,Q')}{\partial\nu_P}d\sigma_P + n(Q,Q'). \tag{8.10}$$

Now, we may express $\dfrac{\partial n(P,Q')}{\partial\nu_P}$ according to (8.4) and find:

$$D\{n(P,Q), n(P,Q')\} = n(Q,Q') - \frac{1}{16\pi^2}\iint_C \frac{1}{r(P,Q)}\frac{\partial}{\partial\nu_P}\left(\frac{1}{r(P,Q')}\right)d\sigma_P. \tag{8.11}$$

We remark that $\dfrac{1}{r(P,Q)}$ and $\dfrac{1}{r(P,Q')}$ are regular harmonic functions in the complement **B** of **D** and we may therefore express the right-hand integral in (8.11) as follows.

$$I(Q,Q') \equiv \frac{1}{16\pi^2}\iint_C \frac{1}{r(P,Q)}\frac{\partial}{\partial\nu_P}\left(\frac{1}{r(P,Q')}\right)d\sigma_P =$$

$$= \iiint_B \left(\operatorname{grad}\frac{1}{4\pi r(P,Q)}\cdot\operatorname{grad}\frac{1}{4\pi r(P,Q')}\right)d\tau. \tag{8.12}$$

The integral $I(Q,Q')$ can be calculated from the elementary functions $\dfrac{1}{r(P,Q)}$ and $\dfrac{1}{r(P,Q')}$ by processes of differentiation and integration. These processes may be rather complicated from a numerical point of view but they are elementary when compared to the processes necessary for solving boundary value problems in the theory of harmonic functions.

Thus, the term $I(Q, Q')$ is more elementary than $n(Q, Q')$ which can be determined only by solving a boundary value problem. In dealing with boundary value problems for partial differential equations we shall consider expressions elementary in character if they can be calculated by processes of finite algebra, finitely many differentiations and finitely many integrations over given domains. Terms calculated in this way will be called *geometric terms*. In contradistinction, we frequently have to deal with expressions which are defined by a partial differential equation and by boundary conditions. Such terms are the main object of our study and will be called *potential-theoretic terms*. For instance, $I(Q, Q')$ is a geometric term, while $n(Q, Q')$ is potential-theoretic. Our aim is to express potential-theoretic terms by a series of geometric terms or to estimate terms of this type by geometric terms.

As a first application, we remark that $D\{n(P, Q), n(P, Q)\}$ is positive and, therefore, we have the inequality

$$n(Q, Q) > I(Q, Q) > 0. \tag{8.13}$$

Let Q_i be a set of m arbitrary points in D and let λ_i be m arbitrary real numbers. We consider the Dirichlet integral

$$\begin{aligned} D\left\{\sum_{i=1}^{m} \lambda_i n(P, Q_i), \quad \sum_{i=1}^{m} \lambda_i n(P, Q_i)\right\} &= \\ = \sum_{i,k=1}^{m} \lambda_i \lambda_k D\{n(P, Q_i), n(P, Q_k)\} &= \\ = \sum_{i,k=1}^{m} \lambda_i \lambda_k \big(n(Q_i, Q_k) - I(Q_i, Q_k)\big). \end{aligned} \tag{8.14}$$

We observe that the left-hand term is non-negative by definition of the Dirichlet integral and that also

$$\sum_{i,k=1}^{m} \lambda_i \lambda_k I(Q_i, Q_k) = \iiint_{B} \left(\sum_{i=1}^{m} \lambda_i \operatorname{grad}\left(\frac{1}{4\pi r(P, Q_i)}\right)\right)^2 d\tau \geqq 0. \tag{8.15}$$

Hence, we obtain the inequality

$$\sum_{i,k=1}^{m} \lambda_i \lambda_k n(Q_i, Q_k) \geqq \sum_{i,k=1}^{m} \lambda_i \lambda_k I(Q_i, Q_k) \geqq 0. \tag{8.16}$$

Thus, the matrices $n(Q_i, Q_k)$ $(i, k = 1, \ldots, m)$ lead to positive definite quadratic forms which can be estimated in terms of the corresponding quadratic forms based on the geometric matrices $I(Q_i, Q_k)$.

If we choose $m = 2$, we find that

$$\lambda^2 [n(P,P) - I(P,P)] + 2\lambda [n(P,Q) - I(P,Q)] + [n(Q,Q) - I(Q,Q)] \geqq 0 \tag{8.17}$$

and this leads to the discriminant condition

$$[n(P,Q) - I(P,Q)]^2 \leqq [n(P,P) - I(P,P)]\,[n(Q,Q) - I(Q,Q)]. \tag{8.18}$$

Similarly, we derive from (8.16)

$$(n(P,Q))^2 \leqq n(P,P)\, n(Q,Q). \tag{8.19}$$

In problems in which an incompressible fluid is moving in a domain with rigid walls, we always deal with boundary value problems for harmonic functions utilizing the values of the normal derivative. In fact, the gradient of the velocity potential, i. e., the velocity vector, is the significant quantity and hence only the derivatives of the potential will enter into the boundary conditions. For the theoretical understanding of the problems, it is, however, useful also to consider the Green's function of the domain D which plays a central role in the boundary value problem of the first kind for harmonic functions, i. e., where the boundary values of the potential are prescribed on the boundary C.

We write Green's function in the form

$$G(P,Q) = \frac{1}{4\pi r(P,Q)} - g(P,Q) \tag{8.20}$$

where we require that $G(P,Q)$ shall vanish for $P \in \mathsf{C}$ and that $g(P,Q)$ be regular harmonic in D. The symmetry of Green's function can again be proved by the method of Section I.4.

At first we remark that Green's function is non-negative in D. In fact, it vanishes at infinity for it is regular harmonic there. It vanishes on C and becomes positive infinite for $P = Q$. Since G cannot take on its minimum at an interior point of D it is necessarily non-negative. Consider next the function

$$g(P,Q) = \frac{1}{4\pi r(P,Q)} - G(P,Q). \tag{8.20'}$$

It is positive on C, regular harmonic throughout D and hence by the minimum principle it must be non-negative in D. Finally, the function

$$K(P,Q) = N(P,Q) - G(P,Q) = n(P,Q) + g(P,Q) \tag{8.21}$$

is regular in D and non-negative on C. Hence, again by the minimum principle, we conclude

$$K(P,Q) \geqq 0 \qquad \text{for} \qquad P, Q \in \mathsf{C}. \tag{8.22}$$

We now study the Dirichlet product between the functions $g(P,Q)$ and $n(P,Q')$. By Green's identity we obtain immediately

$$\mathrm{D}\{g(P,Q), n(P,Q')\} = -\iint_{\mathsf{C}} g(P,Q) \frac{\partial n(P,Q')}{\partial \nu} d\sigma. \tag{8.23}$$

Now using (8.4) and the boundary condition

$$g(P,Q) = \frac{1}{4\pi r(P,Q)} \qquad \text{for} \qquad P \in \mathsf{C}, \tag{8.24}$$

we obtain in view of (8.12):

$$\mathrm{D}\{g(P,Q), n(P,Q')\} = I(Q,Q'). \tag{8.25}$$

Next, we compute

$$\begin{aligned} \mathrm{D}\{g(P,Q), g(P,Q')\} &= -\iint_{\mathsf{C}} \frac{1}{4\pi r(P,Q)} \frac{\partial g(P,Q')}{\partial \nu} d\sigma_P = \\ &= g(Q,Q') - \frac{1}{16\pi^2} \iint_{\mathsf{C}} \frac{1}{r(P,Q')} \frac{\partial}{\partial \nu}\left(\frac{1}{r(P,Q)}\right) d\sigma_P. \end{aligned} \tag{8.26}$$

Hence, using (8.12) again we arrive at

$$\mathrm{D}\{g(P,Q), g(P,Q')\} = g(Q,Q') - I(Q,Q'). \tag{8.27}$$

The identities (8.11), (8.25), and (8.27) lead to numerous inequalities between the various potential theoretical quantities. The method for deriving them is always based upon the definite character of the Dirichlet integral $\mathrm{D}\{\varphi, \varphi\}$ which can be utilized in numerous ways. We do not enter here in a detailed study of these inequalities since we shall consider similar inequalities for more general partial differential equations in Part B.

It is useful to observe that the Dirichlet integral of two harmonic functions is particularly simple if the boundary values of the one function and the normal derivatives of the other are prescribed on C. In this case, one application of Green's identity will yield a geometric expression for the Dirichlet integral. One example of this is the computation of the Dirichlet integral (8.25). Functions with prescribed normal derivatives occur in problems of hydrodynamics while, as we shall see in Chapter III, most electrostatic problems lead to harmonic functions with prescribed boundary values. We can then expect certain interrelations between quantities arising in hydrodynamics and corresponding electrostatic quantities. As a first example, we consider the Dirichlet product

$$\text{(8.28)} \quad D\left\{\sum_{i=1}^{m} \lambda_i g(P,Q_i), \sum_{i=1}^{m} \lambda_i n(P,Q_i)\right\} = \sum_{i,k=1}^{m} \lambda_i \lambda_k I(Q_i,Q_k).$$

Using Schwarz' inequality, (8.11), and (8.27), we obtain

$$\text{(8.29)} \quad \left(\sum_{i,k=1}^{m} \lambda_i \lambda_k I(Q_i,Q_k)\right)^2 \leqslant$$

$$\leqslant \left(\sum_{i,k=1}^{m} \lambda_i \lambda_k \big(g(Q_i,Q_k) - I(Q_i,Q_k)\big)\right)\left(\sum_{i,k=1}^{m} \lambda_i \lambda_k \big(n(Q_i,Q_k) - I(Q_i,Q_k)\big)\right).$$

Inequality (8.29) couples the excess of the quadratic form based on $n(P,Q)$ over the quadratic form of $I(P,Q)$ with the corresponding excess of the g-form. We shall later see the central role played by the Green's function in electrostatic conductor problems.

Let us next define harmonic functions $\psi_i(P)$ in the following way: let

$$\text{(8.30)} \quad \Psi_i(P) = x_i - \psi_i(P),$$

where $\psi_i(P)$ is regular harmonic in the infinite domain D and let

$$\text{(8.31)} \quad \Psi_i(P) = 0, \qquad \text{i.e.,} \qquad \psi_i(P) = x_i \qquad \text{for} \qquad P \in \mathsf{C}.$$

The potentials $\Psi_i(P)$ play a role in the problem of electrostatic polarization and will be treated in Section III.6. Let their development near infinity be given by

$$\text{(8.32)} \quad \Psi_i(P) = x_i - \frac{A_i}{r} - \sum_{k=1}^{3} \frac{e_{ik}\, x_k}{r^3} + O\left(\frac{1}{r^3}\right).$$

The matrix $((e_{ik}))$ is closely analogous to the matrix $((d_{ik}))$ defined in (7.10) which is related to the tensor of the virtual mass. It has the same relation to the polarization tensor which will be defined in III.6. Let us consider the Dirichlet integrals:

(8.33) $$D\{\psi_i, \psi_k\} = -\iint_C \psi_i \frac{\partial \psi_k}{\partial \nu} d\sigma = -\iint_C x_i \frac{\partial \psi_k}{\partial \nu} d\sigma.$$

By the same calculations as those which led to (7.13), we derive

(8.34) $$\iint_C \left(\psi_k \frac{\partial x_i}{\partial \nu} - x_i \frac{\partial \psi_k}{\partial \nu}\right) d\sigma = 4\pi\, e_{ki}.$$

Hence, we find

(8.35) $$D\{\psi_i, \psi_k\} = 4\pi\, e_{ki} - \iint_C \psi_k \frac{\partial x_i}{\partial \nu} d\sigma = 4\pi\, e_{ki} - \iint_C x_k \frac{\partial x_i}{\partial \nu} d\sigma.$$

Reasoning again as in (7.15), we then obtain:

(8.36) $$D\{\psi_i, \psi_k\} = 4\pi\, e_{ki} - V\,\delta_{ik} = 4\pi\, e_{ik} - V\,\delta_{ik},$$

since the symmetry of the matrix $((e_{ik}))$ is obvious from this formula. The matrix

(8.37) $$p_{ik} = 4\pi\, e_{ik} - V\,\delta_{ik}$$

is the polarization tensor of the body **B**.

Let us now study the Dirichlet product between any φ_i and any ψ_k. According to our preceding general remarks we can expect a particularly simple result. In fact, we find by (6.12) and (8.31)

(8.38) $$D\{\varphi_i, \psi_k\} = -\iint_C \psi_k \frac{\partial \varphi_i}{\partial \nu} d\sigma = \iint_C x_k \frac{\partial x_i}{\partial \nu} d\sigma = V\,\delta_{ik}$$

where V again denotes the volume of the body **B**.

Let α_i and α'_i, $(i = 1, 2, 3)$, denote the components of two arbitrary unit vectors and let us construct the harmonic function

(8.39) $$h(P) = \sum_{i=1}^{3} (\alpha_i \varphi_i + \lambda\, \alpha'_i\, \psi_i).$$

In view of (7.7), (7.16), (8.36), and (8.38), we obtain

$$\begin{aligned} D\{h, h\} = \sum_{i,k=1}^{3} a_i a_k (4\pi d_{ik} - V \delta_{ik}) + 2\lambda \sum_{i=1}^{3} a_i a'_i V + \\ + \lambda^2 \sum_{i,k=1}^{3} a'_i a'_k (4\pi e_{ik} - V \delta_{ik}). \end{aligned} \tag{8.40}$$

Since this expression is non-negative for arbitrary choice of the parameter λ, we obtain the discriminant condition:

$$\left(\sum_{i=1}^{3} a_i a'_i\right)^2 V^2 \leqslant \left(4\pi \sum_{i,k=1}^{3} d_{ik} a_i a_k - V\right)\left(4\pi \sum_{i,k=1}^{3} e_{ik} a'_i a'_k - V\right). \tag{8.41}$$

Putting $a_i = a'_i$, we obtain in particular:

$$V^2 \leqslant W W_P \tag{8.42}$$

where

$$W = 4\pi \sum_{i,k=1}^{3} d_{ik} a_i a_k - V \tag{8.43}$$

is the virtual mass of the body **B** in the direction of the unit vector (a_i), for density $\rho_0 = 1$, and

$$W_P = 4\pi \sum_{i,k=1}^{3} e_{ik} a_i a_k - V \tag{8.44}$$

is the polarization of **B** in the same direction.

Since for a given body **B** it is more convenient to determine electrostatic quantities by measurement than hydrodynamic ones, inequality (8.42) leads to a useful way of estimating the virtual mass of **B**.

We observe finally for later reference the two identities

$$W = D\left\{\sum_{i=1}^{3} a_i \varphi_i\right\} \tag{8.45}$$

$$W_P = D\left\{\sum_{i=1}^{3} a_i \psi_i\right\}, \tag{8.46}$$

which follow from (7.7), (7.16), and (8.36).

9. Virtual mass as an extremum: In the preceding section we applied the Dirichlet integral to harmonic functions. It is often useful to consider the wider class of functions $f(P)$ which are continuously differentiable in D and which possess a finite Dirichlet integral $D\{f, f\}$. If $f(P)$ and $h(P)$ are two such functions, then by virtue of the Schwarz inequality

$$(D\{f, h\})^2 \leqslant D\{f, f\} \cdot D\{h, h\}, \tag{9.1}$$

we can also assert the existence of the bilinear expression $D\{f, h\}$.

For an arbitrary $f(P)$ with finite Dirichlet integral which is continuously differentiable in the closed domain D, we consider the integral

$$D\left\{f, \sum_{i=1}^{3} a_i \varphi_i\right\} = -\iint_{\mathsf{C}} f \frac{\partial}{\partial \nu}\left(\sum_{i=1}^{3} a_i \varphi_i\right) d\sigma, \qquad \sum_{i=1}^{3} a_i^2 = 1. \tag{9.2}$$

Using the known boundary values of $\partial\varphi_i/\partial\nu$, we may write this integral in the form

$$D\left\{f, \sum_{i=1}^{3} a_i \varphi_i\right\} = \iint_{\mathsf{C}} f \cdot \frac{\partial}{\partial \nu}\left(\sum_{i=1}^{3} a_i x_i\right) d\sigma. \tag{9.3}$$

This result shows that we know the Dirichlet product of $\Sigma a_i \varphi_i$ with an arbitrary function $f(P)$ even if we have not yet determined the potentials $\varphi_i(P)$. Let us next apply the Schwarz inequality to (9.3):

$$\left(\iint_{\mathsf{C}} f \frac{\partial}{\partial \nu}\left(\sum_{i=1}^{3} a_i x_i\right) d\sigma\right)^2 \leqslant D\{f\} \cdot D\left\{\sum_{i=1}^{3} a_i \varphi_i\right\}. \tag{9.4}$$

This inequality is sharp; it becomes an equality for $f = A \sum_{i=1}^{3} a_i \varphi_i + B$.

We next apply the formulas (7.7) and (7.16) and obtain:

$$\frac{\left(\iint_{\mathsf{C}} f \frac{\partial}{\partial \nu}\left(\sum_{i=1}^{3} a_i x_i\right) d\sigma\right)^2}{D\{f\}} \leqslant 4\pi \sum_{i,k=1}^{3} d_{ik}\, a_i a_k - V = W, \tag{9.5}$$

where W is the virtual mass in the direction of the unit vector (a_i). The left-hand side of this inequality can be computed for each given function

$f(P)$ by elementary processes and provides in each case a lower bound for the virtual mass W. For an appropriate choice of f, namely $f = \sum_{i=1}^{3} a_i \varphi_i$, the inequality becomes an equality. Thus, we may define[1]

$$W = \max \frac{\left(\iint_C f \frac{\partial}{\partial \nu} \left(\sum_{i=1}^{3} a_i x_i \right) d\sigma \right)^2}{D\{f\}} \tag{9.6}$$

and base a Ritz procedure for approximation of W on this definition.

The computation of the virtual mass will become more convenient if we can also provide upper bounds for it. We shall now show that W can also be defined as the minimum of an energy integral which will lead to estimates for W from above. Consider in D an arbitrary solenoidal vector field $\mathfrak{q}$, i. e.,

$$\operatorname{div} \mathfrak{q} = 0 \qquad \text{in } \mathsf{D} \tag{9.7}$$

which on the boundary C satisfies the condition

$$\mathfrak{q} \cdot \boldsymbol{\nu} = -\frac{\partial}{\partial \nu} \left(\sum_{i=1}^{3} a_i x_i \right). \tag{9.8}$$

The velocity field

$$\mathfrak{D} = \operatorname{grad} \left(\sum_{i=1}^{3} a_i x_i \right) + \mathfrak{q} \tag{9.9}$$

will then represent the motion of an incompressible fluid in D which has everywhere on the boundary C a vanishing normal velocity. We then have the result:

$$W = \min \iiint_{\mathsf{D}} |\mathfrak{q}|^2 \, d\tau \tag{9.10}$$

and the minimum is attained for $\mathfrak{q} = \operatorname{grad} \left(\sum_{i=1}^{3} a_i \varphi_i \right)$.

---

[1] Diaz-Weinstein (D 3).

In fact, we have by virtue of (7.16)

$$\iiint_D \left| \mathfrak{q} - \text{grad} \sum_{i=1}^{3} a_i \varphi_i \right|^2 d\tau = \tag{9.11}$$
$$= \iiint_D |\mathfrak{q}|^2 d\tau + W - 2 \iiint_D \left(\mathfrak{q} \cdot \text{grad} \sum_{i=1}^{3} a_i \varphi_i \right) d\tau.$$

The last integral can be transformed by means of Green's identity; by virtue of (9.7), we find that we can write it as follows:

$$\iiint_D \text{div} \left(\mathfrak{q} \sum_{i=1}^{3} a_i \varphi_i \right) d\tau = - \iint_C \mathfrak{q} \cdot \boldsymbol{\nu} \sum_{i=1}^{3} a_i \varphi_i \, d\sigma = \tag{9.12}$$
$$= \iint_C \left(\frac{\partial}{\partial \nu} \left(\sum_{i=1}^{3} a_i x_i \right) \right) \sum_{i=1}^{3} a_i \varphi_i \, d\sigma = W.$$

Thus, we conclude that for an arbitrary vector field $\mathfrak{q}$ which satisfies (9.7) and (9.8) the following equality holds:

$$\iiint_D \left| \mathfrak{q} - \text{grad} \sum_{i=1}^{3} a_i \varphi_i \right|^2 d\tau = \iiint_D |\mathfrak{q}|^2 d\tau - W. \tag{9.13}$$

Hence:

$$W \leqq \iiint_D |\mathfrak{q}|^2 d\tau \tag{9.14}$$

with equality only for $\mathfrak{q} = \text{grad} \sum_{i=1}^{3} a_i \varphi_i$, as was asserted.

We have given upper and lower estimates for the virtual mass in terms of geometric integrals. In both cases, use was made of the energy integral. In the first case, we estimated the energy of the flow for all irrotational flows with the prescribed boundary conditions, while in the second case all solenoidal flows were compared. In both cases, the irrotational incompressible flow led to the extremum and to the equality sign in the estimates.

The reasoning which led to the characterization of the virtual mass as the maximum value of a given extremum problem can be extended to all boundary value problems of the second kind for harmonic functions. Let us define a harmonic function $h(P)$ in the domain D considered, which on the boundary C of D satisfies

$$\frac{\partial h}{\partial \nu} = \mu(P), \qquad P \in \mathsf{C}, \tag{9.15}$$

$\mu(P)$ being a continuous function on C. Let $f(P)$ be an arbitrary continuously differentiable function in the closed region $\mathsf{D} + \mathsf{C}$ and consider the Dirichlet integral

$$\mathrm{D}\{f, h\} = -\iint_{\mathsf{C}} f \frac{\partial h}{\partial \nu}\, d\sigma = -\iint_{\mathsf{C}} f \mu \, d\sigma. \tag{9.16}$$

Applying Schwarz' inequality, we obtain

$$\left(\left(\iint_{\mathsf{C}} f \mu \, d\sigma \right)^2 / \, \mathrm{D}\{f\} \right) \leqq \mathrm{D}\{h\} \tag{9.17}$$

and equality obviously holds only for $f(P) = \alpha\, h(P) + \beta$. Thus, we may characterize the harmonic function $h(P)$ with the boundary condition (9.15) within the class of all functions $f(P)$ which are continuously differentiable in $\mathsf{D} + \mathsf{C}$ by the property of its yielding the maximum value in the left-hand side of (9.17).

In Section I.6 we characterized the solution of a boundary value problem of the first kind by a minimum problem with respect to the Dirichlet integral. Now we have analogously characterized the solution of a boundary value problem of the second kind by a maximum problem which again involves the Dirichlet integral.

10. Variational formulas: In many investigations the following problem arises. Suppose that the flow pattern has been determined for a given domain D and for a known distribution of sources and sinks; how will this pattern be affected by a slight change of the boundary C of the domain D? This question can best be studied by deriving the formula for the variation of the Neumann's function under a deformation of the boundary C of D.

For the sake of simplicity, we shall deal with the case where D contains the point at infinity so that the Neumann's function has particularly simple properties. We consider a subdomain D' of D with boundary C' and make the following assumption: a one-to-one correspondence can be established between the points $P \in \mathsf{C}$ and $P' \in \mathsf{C}'$ by erecting at P the interior normal $\boldsymbol{\nu}$ and following it to the first intersection with C', the point of intersection being P'. The distance $\overline{PP'}$ will be given by

$$\overline{PP'} = \delta \nu (P) = \varepsilon v (P) \tag{10.1}$$

where $\varepsilon > 0$ is a smallness parameter and $v(P)$ is a twice continuously differentiable function on C. It can then be seen that the angle between the normal $\boldsymbol{\nu}$ at P on C and the normal $\boldsymbol{\nu}'$ at P' on C' is also of the order of magnitude ε. We shall say that the surfaces C and C' are in an ε-neighborhood of each other. Let $N'(P,Q)$ be the Neumann's function of the domain D'. It can be shown that for fixed $Q \in \mathsf{D}'$ we have uniformly for $P \in \mathsf{D}' + \mathsf{C}'$ the estimate

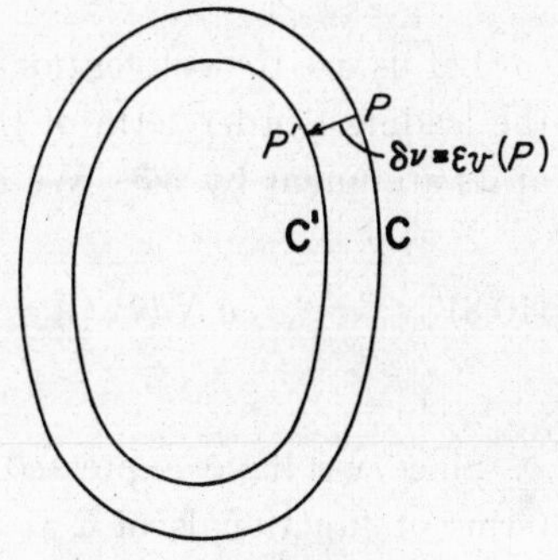

Figure 2

$$N'(P,Q) - N(P,Q) = O(\varepsilon), \qquad |\mathrm{grad}\,(N'(P,Q) - N(P,Q))| = O(\varepsilon). \tag{10.2}$$

Our aim is to obtain further information about this difference term.

We consider the function

$$d(P,Q) = N(P,Q) - N'(P,Q), \qquad Q \in \mathsf{D}' \tag{10.3}$$

which is harmonic and regular in D' since the poles at $P = Q$ of N and N' have cancelled by subtraction. We know the normal derivative of d on C':

$$\frac{\partial d(P,Q)}{\partial \nu'_P} = \frac{\partial N(P,Q)}{\partial \nu'_P}, \qquad P \in \mathsf{C}'. \tag{10.4}$$

Hence, by virtue of (6.5), we obtain:

$$d(P,Q) = -\iint_{\mathsf{C}'} N'(P,Q') \frac{\partial N(Q',Q)}{\partial \nu'_{Q'}} \, d\sigma_{Q'}. \tag{10.5}$$

Now, it is easily seen that

$$\frac{\partial N(Q',Q)}{\partial \nu'} = O(\varepsilon) \qquad \text{on } \mathsf{C}', \tag{10.6}$$

since the surfaces C and C' lie in an ε-neighborhood of each other and since $\partial N / \partial \nu$ vanishes on C. If, therefore, we replace the Neumann's function

$N'(P,Q)$ by $N(P,Q)$ in (10.5), then by (10.2) we only incur an error of order $O(\varepsilon^2)$. Thus, we find:

$$N'(P,Q) - N(P,Q) = \iint_{C'} N(P,Q') \frac{\partial N(Q',Q)}{\partial \nu'_{Q'}} d\sigma_{Q'} + O(\varepsilon^2). \tag{10.7}$$

Let us use the conventional notation of functional analysis which denotes the leading ε-order term of the change of a functional Φ under an ε-change of its argument by $\delta\Phi$. We then have:

$$\delta N(P,Q) = \iint_{C'} N(P,Q') \frac{\partial N(Q',Q)}{\partial \nu'_{Q'}} d\sigma_{Q'}. \tag{10.8}$$

Since we have expressed the variation of the Neumann's function in terms of functionals of C it is natural to eliminate the surface C′ entirely from (10.8). For this purpose, we notice that $N(P,Q)$ is regular harmonic in D — D′ since Q is assumed to lie in D′. Hence, we may apply Green's identity to (10.8) and find

$$\delta N(P,Q) = \iiint_{D-D'} \left(\operatorname{grad} N(P,Q') \cdot \operatorname{grad} N(Q',Q)\right) d\tau_{Q'}. \tag{10.9}$$

We split the volume integration into an integration over the surface C and an integration normal to it; we consider volume elements

$$d\tau_{Q'} = \delta\nu_{Q'}\, d\sigma_{Q'} \tag{10.10}$$

and obtain within the ε-precision required:

$$\delta N(P,Q) = \iint_{C} \left(\operatorname{grad} N(P,Q') \cdot \operatorname{grad} N(Q',Q)\right) \delta\nu_{Q'}\, d\sigma_{Q'}. \tag{10.11}$$

This is the variational formula for the Neumann's function which we set out to derive. It has been derived under the assumption that the domain D′ lies entirely within D, in other words that the function $v(P)$ in (10.1) is always non-negative. It is easy to extend the formula (10.11) to the more general case in which the surface C′ is obtained from C by shifting each point $P \in C$ along the interior normal $\boldsymbol{\nu}$ by an amount $\delta\nu = \varepsilon\, v(P)$ which may be positive or negative. The only requirement on $v(P)$ is that it be twice continuously differentiable on C.

To prove this statement, we introduce a domain D'' with boundary C'' which contains D and D' and such that C and C' lie in an ε-neighborhood of C''. Let $N''(P,Q)$ be the Neumann's function of D''; we denote by $\delta\nu_1$ and $\delta\nu_2$ the normal shifts which transform C'' into C and C', respectively. Applying formula (10.11) first to N'' and N and then to N'' and N', we find:

$$N''(P,Q) - N(P,Q) = -\int\!\!\int_{\mathsf{C}''} \big(\operatorname{grad} N''(P,Q') \cdot \operatorname{grad} N''(Q'Q)\big)\,\delta\nu_1\, d\sigma_{Q'} + O(\varepsilon^2),$$

$$N''(P,Q) - N'(P,Q) = -\int\!\!\int_{\mathsf{C}''} \big(\operatorname{grad} N''(P,Q') \cdot \operatorname{grad} N''(Q',Q)\big)\,\delta\nu_2\, d\sigma_{Q'} + O(\varepsilon^2).$$

(10.12)

Hence, subtracting the second from the first equation, we find:

$$\delta N(P,Q) = \int\!\!\int_{\mathsf{C}''} \big(\operatorname{grad} N''(P,Q') \cdot \operatorname{grad} N''(Q',Q)\big)(\delta\nu_2 - \delta\nu_1)\, d\sigma_{Q'}. \tag{10.13}$$

But it is easily seen that

$$\delta\nu = \delta\nu_2 - \delta\nu_1. \tag{10.14}$$

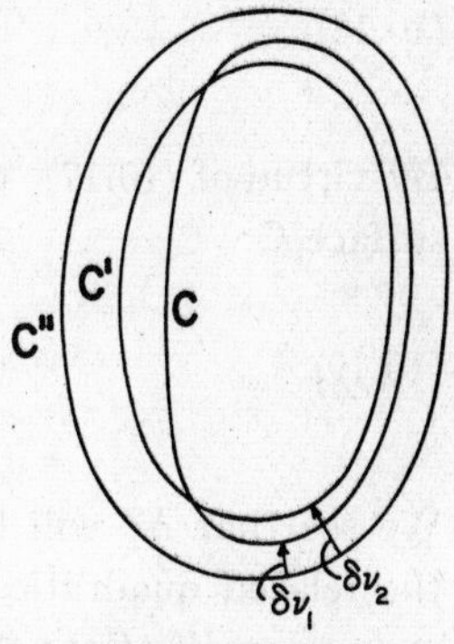

Figure 3

Using the second estimate (10.2), we then finally obtain (10.11) which has thus been proved for arbitrary smooth variations of the surface C. Another proof of this variational formula will be given in B. III.6 in the case of a more general differential equation. In the same place, we shall also indicate how the higher variational terms for the fundamental solutions can be determined. Here, we shall give some applications of the variational method to problems of fluid mechanics.

We introduce the series development (6.22) of the Neumann's function near infinity into (10.11). Comparing the coefficients of x_i/r^3 on both sides, we derive the new variational formula:

$$\delta\Phi_i(Q) = \int\!\!\int_{\mathsf{C}} \big(\operatorname{grad} \Phi_i(Q') \cdot \operatorname{grad} N(Q',Q)\big)\,\delta\nu_{Q'}\, d\sigma_{Q'}. \tag{10.15}$$

As was to be expected, the variational formula for the Neumann's function leads immediately to a corresponding result for the dipole potentials $\Phi_i(Q)$. We can repeat this reasoning by using the series development of $\Phi_i(Q)$ near infinity. By virtue of (6.10) and (7.10), we have near infinity

$$\Phi_i(Q) = \xi_i + \sum_{k=1}^{3} \frac{d_{ik}\,\xi_k}{\rho^3} + \ldots, \qquad \rho^2 = \sum_{k=1}^{3} \xi_k^2; \tag{10.16}$$

substituting (6.22) with respect to $N(Q, Q')$ for Q near infinity in (10.15), and comparing the coefficients of ξ_k/ρ^3, we obtain:

$$\delta d_{ik} = \frac{1}{4\pi} \iint_{\mathsf{C}} (\operatorname{grad} \Phi_i \cdot \operatorname{grad} \Phi_k)\, \delta\nu\, d\sigma \tag{10.17}$$

a variational formula for the coefficients d_{ik} which are closely related to the tensor of virtual mass.

We can frequently use variational formulas to establish the monotonic change of a functional with its domain. Consider, for example, the unit vector $\mathfrak{e} = (\alpha_1, \alpha_2, \alpha_3)$ and the quadratic form

$$Z = 4\pi \sum_{i,k=1}^{3} \alpha_i \alpha_k d_{ik}. \tag{10.18}$$

By virtue of (10.17), we have for a variation of the body B enclosed by the surface C:

$$\delta Z = \iint_{\mathsf{C}} \left(\sum_{i=1}^{3} \alpha_i \operatorname{grad} \Phi_i \right)^2 \delta\nu\, d\sigma. \tag{10.19}$$

We see that δZ will be positive if $\delta\nu > 0$. Thus, if the body B increases, the related quadratic form Z will increase. This is not true for the whole expression W of the virtual mass in the direction $\mathfrak{e}$. We have by (7.16)

$$W = Z - V \tag{10.20}$$

and the increase of Z by expansion of B may be compensated by the gain of volume thus obtained. We know that

$$\mathfrak{q} = -\sum_{i=1}^{3} \alpha_i \operatorname{grad} \Phi, \tag{10.21}$$

is the field of relative velocities if the body B moves with unit speed in the direction $\mathfrak{e}$. Since by virtue of (10.19) and (10.20) we have

$$\delta W = \iint_{\mathsf{C}} (|\mathfrak{q}|^2 - 1)\, \delta\nu\, d\sigma \tag{10.22}$$

we see that the virtual mass will increase if the body **B** is expanded at a point with $|\mathbf{q}| > 1$ and will decrease if the body is expanded at a point where $|\mathbf{q}| < 1$.

Let V' denote the volume of the largest sphere contained in the solid **B** and let V'' be the volume of the smallest sphere containing **B**. Since we have shown in (7.18) that for a sphere of radius R

$$Z = 2\pi R^3, \tag{10.23}$$

we deduce from (10.20) and the monotonicity of Z with respect to the solid that

$$\frac{3}{2} V' - V \leqq W \leqq \frac{3}{2} V'' - V. \tag{10.24}$$

Thus, the monotonicity of the quadratic form Z leads to simple estimates for the virtual mass of a solid **B**.

It is easy to construct additional functionals which have the same monotonic property. We notice that in view of (8.2) we may write

$$\delta N(P, Q) = \delta n(P, Q) \tag{10.25}$$

and obtain, in particular, from (10.11):

$$\delta n(Q, Q) = \iint_C (\operatorname{grad} N(P, Q))^2 \, \delta \nu_P \, d\sigma_P. \tag{10.26}$$

Thus, $n(Q, Q)$ also increases monotonically with the solid **B**. Additional interesting monotonic functionals can also be obtained. Let c be an arbitrary real number; consider the expression

$$E(Q) = 4\pi c^2 \sum_{i,k=1}^{3} a_i a_k d_{ik} + 2c \sum_{i=1}^{3} a_i \Phi_i(Q) + n(Q, Q). \tag{10.27}$$

By virtue of (10.15), (10.17), and (10.26), we find:

$$\delta E(Q) = \iint_C \left(\sum_{i=1}^{3} c\, a_i \operatorname{grad} \Phi_i(P) + \operatorname{grad}_P N(Q, P) \right)^2 \delta \nu_P \, d\sigma_P. \tag{10.28}$$

Thus, the functional $E(Q)$ will increase with the body **B**.

This result has a simple hydromechanical interpretation. Suppose that a dipole flow with speed c at infinity and in the direction opposite to the unit vector $\mathfrak{c} \equiv (a_1, a_2, a_3)$ moves past the body B, and that, in addition, a source of unit strength is situated at the point Q. The field of velocities is given by

$$\mathfrak{q} = -\operatorname{grad}\left(c \sum_{i=1}^{3} a_i \Phi_i(P) + N(P,Q)\right). \tag{10.29}$$

If no body were present in the flow we would have a velocity field

$$\mathfrak{q}_0 = -\operatorname{grad}\left(c \sum_{i=1}^{3} a_i x_i + \frac{1}{r(P,Q)}\right). \tag{10.30}$$

The presence of the solid creates a field of velocity differences $\mathfrak{q} - \mathfrak{q}_0$, and it can be shown that the energy of this velocity field is closely related to the expression (10.27). Thus, (10.28) appears as a natural generalization of the variational formula for the quadratic form Z connected with the virtual mass. We may again use spheres of comparison lying entirely inside B or containing B in order to obtain estimates for $E(Q)$.

Hadamard [18], Lévy [38], Volterra [86], [87]; Schiffer-Szegö (S 6)

11. Free boundaries, discontinuity surfaces, and virtual mass: Let a solid B be immersed in an incompressible irrotational fluid which flows past B under the influence of a dipole in the x_i-direction at infinity. We have shown in Section 6 that the velocity potential of this motion is given by the function $\Phi_i(P)$. This potential describes a fluid motion in which each particle of the fluid participates; there are no regions in the domain D outside of B where grad Φ_i vanishes. For this would imply that Φ_i is constant in a subregion of D and being harmonic everywhere in D (except at infinity) this would lead to $\Phi_i = \text{const.}$ throughout D by analytic continuation. But near infinity Φ_i must behave like x_i and become arbitrarily large. This would contradict the assumption that Φ_i is constant in D and, hence, there are no subregions of D which are at rest during the flow.

It was pointed out by Helmholtz that a part of the fluid might be at rest in a flow if the velocity potential were discontinuous along certain surfaces and that such occurrences can actually be observed in fluid motion. Thus, besides the uniquely determined velocity potentials Φ_i there may exist additional solutions to the flow problem which shall be considered now.

Suppose that a flow issues from infinity in the direction of the positive x_i-axis, passes along the solid B and leaves a region B* at rest behind the solid. The fluid region B^* is called a dead water region of B. If the composite domain $\mathsf{B} + \mathsf{B}^*$ were known the velocity potential Φ of the motion would be again uniquely determined. The function Φ must be harmonic in the complement D^* of $\mathsf{B} + \mathsf{B}^*$ with the prescribed dipole singularity at infinity and vanishing normal derivative on the boundary C^* of D^*. Let us decompose

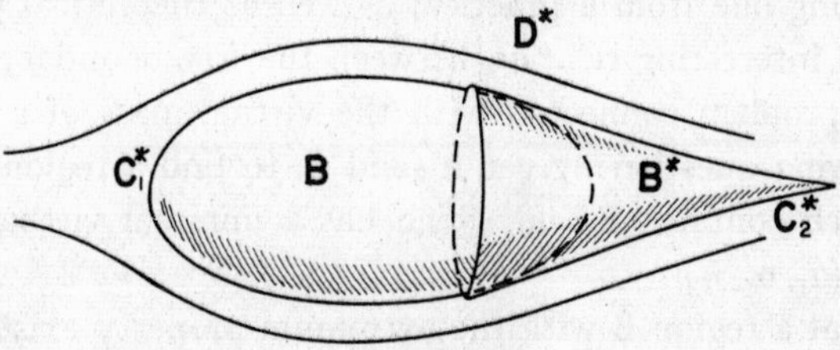

Figure 4

C^* into two parts: C_1^* consisting of points of C^* lying on the boundary C of B and C_2^* consisting of boundary points of B^*. We shall now show that the velocity potential Φ must satisfy additional conditions on C_2^*.

To this end we apply Bernoulli's law (3.3) but observe that since there are no exterior forces the potential V of the exterior forces may be omitted. Thus, we have in D^*:

$$\frac{1}{2}|\mathfrak{q}|^2 + \frac{p}{\rho_0} = \frac{1}{2}(\operatorname{grad}\Phi)^2 + \frac{p}{\rho_0} = \text{const.} \tag{11.1}$$

The same formula holds in the dead water region B^*; but since $\mathfrak{q} \equiv 0$ in B^*, it reduces to simply

$$p = \text{const.} \qquad \text{in } \mathsf{B}^*. \tag{11.2}$$

On the boundary C_2^* between the fluid at rest and the moving fluid, the pressure is necessarily a continuous function and therefore, $p = \text{const.}$ in C_2^*. Hence:

$$|\operatorname{grad}\Phi| = \text{const.} \qquad \text{on } \mathsf{C}_2^*. \tag{11.3}$$

This equation shows clearly the mathematical problem connected with the determination of a dead water region B^*. For any domain B^* adjacent to B the potential Φ is determined in a unique way, and condition (11.3) will, in general, not be fulfilled since the conditions $\partial\Phi/\partial\nu = 0$ and $|\operatorname{grad}\Phi| = \text{const.}$ overdetermine the potential Φ. But there exist distinguished domains B^* for which the two requirements for $\partial\Phi/\partial\nu$ and $|\operatorname{grad}\Phi|$ become compatible. Helmholtz, Kirchhoff, and Levi-Civita gave numerous examples of such dead water regions in the case of two-dimensional flows.

Villat, Weinstein, Leray, and Schauder dealt with the problem of existence of such regions for given solids B. The discontinuity surface between the fluid at rest and the moving fluid is called a free boundary of the flow in contradistinction to the rigid boundaries given by the walls of the solids in the fluid. The problem of determining free boundaries in a flow is a highly interesting one from a practical as well as theoretical point of view.

There is an interesting relation between the free boundary problem and an extremum problem connected with the virtual mass of a solid B. We raise the following question: given a solid B, to find a region $\tilde{B}$ with given volume V which contains B and which has a minimal virtual mass in the direction $\mathfrak{e} = (\alpha_1, \alpha_2, \alpha_3)$.

Suppose that a region $\tilde{B}$ with the extremum property exists and that its boundary is regular enough to allow our variational formulas to be applied. Let us try to characterize the extremum region by means of our variational formulas which allow us to compare $\tilde{B}$ with nearby regions. We again divide the boundary $\tilde{C}$ of $\tilde{B}$ into two parts: $\tilde{C}_1$ consists of boundary points of $\tilde{B}$ while $\tilde{C}_2$ consists of the rest of $\tilde{C}$. If we wish to vary the boundary $\tilde{C}$ we shall have to take care that even after the variation the region still contains the solid B and has the prescribed volume $\tilde{V}$. Thus, the normal shift of a point $P \in \tilde{C}_1$ must always be positive, i. e., away from the solid. However, we are much freer in variations on C_2.

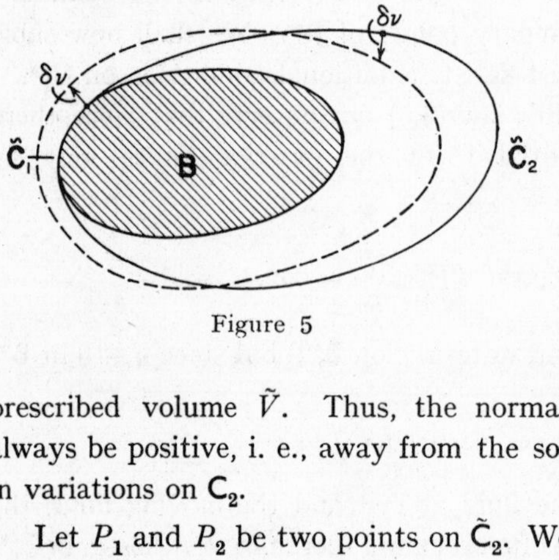

Figure 5

Let P_1 and P_2 be two points on $\tilde{C}_2$. We deform the region $\tilde{B}$ by shifting a neighborhood of P_1 and of P_2 according to the function $\delta\nu\,(P)$. We obtain a change of volume

$$\delta \tilde{V} = \iint_{\tilde{C}_2} \delta\nu \, d\sigma \tag{11.3}$$

and according to (10.22) a change of virtual mass in the direction $\mathfrak{e}$:

$$\delta W = \iint_{\tilde{C}_2} \left(\left(\sum_{i=1}^{3} \alpha_i \operatorname{grad} \tilde{\Phi}_i \right)^2 - 1 \right) \delta\nu \, d\sigma, \tag{11.4}$$

where $\tilde{\Phi}_i$ is the potential defined in (6.10) but with respect to the body $\tilde{\mathsf{B}}$. Since $\delta\nu$ is different from zero only near P_1 and P_2, we may use the mean value theorem of the integral calculus and put (11.4) in the form:

$$\delta W = \left[\left(\sum_{i=1}^{3} a_i \operatorname{grad} \tilde{\Phi}_i\right)^2 - 1\right]_1 \iint_{\mathsf{n}_1} \delta\nu \, d\sigma +$$

(11.5)

$$+ \left[\left(\sum_{i=1}^{3} a_i \operatorname{grad} \tilde{\Phi}_i\right)^2 - 1\right]_2 \iint_{\mathsf{n}_2} \delta\nu \, d\sigma.$$

Here $[A]_i$ denotes an intermediate value of A in the neighborhood n_i of the point P_i. Since we assume that the volume is unchanged, we must require by (11.3)

$$\delta\tilde{V} = \iint_{\mathsf{n}_1} \delta\nu \, d\sigma + \iint_{\mathsf{n}_2} \delta\nu \, d\sigma = 0, \tag{11.6}$$

and we may put (11.5) in the form:

$$\delta W = \left(\left[\left(\sum_{i=1}^{3} a_i \operatorname{grad} \tilde{\Phi}_i\right)^2 - 1\right]_1 - \left[\left(\sum_{i=1}^{3} a_i \operatorname{grad} \tilde{\Phi}_i\right)^2 - 1\right]_2\right) \iint_{\mathsf{n}_1} \delta\nu \, d\sigma.$$

(11.7)

If $\tilde{\mathsf{B}}$ were an extremum region, we should necessarily have $\delta W \geqq 0$ for our variation above inasmuch as this variation transforms $\tilde{\mathsf{B}}$ into a region of equal volume and still contains the solid B. Hence the new virtual mass cannot be less than that of $\tilde{\mathsf{B}}$. But we are quite free in choosing the sign of $\iint_{\mathsf{n}_1} \delta\nu \, d\sigma$. Hence, $\delta W \geqslant 0$ is only possible if

$$\left[\left(\sum_{i=1}^{3} a_i \operatorname{grad} \tilde{\Phi}_i\right)^2\right]_1 = \left[\left(\sum_{i=1}^{3} a_i \operatorname{grad} \tilde{\Phi}_i\right)^2\right]_2. \tag{11.8}$$

Since we can choose the neighborhoods of P_1 and P_2 as small as we please, we can conclude: *In the case of an extremum domain* $\tilde{\mathsf{B}}$, *the expression*

$$|\mathfrak{q}| = \left|\sum_{i=1}^{3} a_i \operatorname{grad} \tilde{\Phi}_i\right| \tag{11.9}$$

is constant along the tree boundary $\tilde{\mathsf{C}}_2$.

The function

$$\tilde{\Phi} = -\sum_{i=1}^{3} a_i \tilde{\Phi}_i$$

represents the velocity potential of a flow past the body B which has the direction $\mathfrak{e}$ at infinity. On $\tilde{\mathsf{C}}$ it satisfies the boundary condition $\partial\tilde{\Phi}/\partial\nu = 0$ and by (11.9) leads to a constant velocity on the part $\tilde{\mathsf{C}}_2$ of the boundary of $\tilde{\mathsf{B}}$ which does not lie on B. Thus, $\tilde{\Phi}$ represents a flow past the solid B with a free boundary $\tilde{\mathsf{C}}_2$.

We can further characterize the flow with the potential $\tilde{\Phi}$ by carrying out other variations of $\hat{\mathsf{B}}$ and using the extremum property of the region. In fact, let Q be a point on the boundary $\tilde{\mathsf{C}}_1$ of $\tilde{\mathsf{B}}$. We choose another point P on boundary $\tilde{\mathsf{C}}_2$; we vary $\tilde{\mathsf{C}}$ in a neighborhood $\mathfrak{n}_Q$ of Q and a neighborhood $\mathfrak{n}_P$ of P in such a manner that a new permissible region is obtained. For this purpose, we have to make two requirements:

$$\delta\nu > 0 \quad \text{in} \quad \mathfrak{n}_Q \tag{11.10}$$

and

$$\iint_{\mathfrak{n}_Q} \delta\nu\, d\sigma + \iint_{\mathfrak{n}_P} \delta\nu\, d\sigma = 0. \tag{11.11}$$

This will guarantee that the new region still contains the solid B and that its volume is unchanged. Because of the minimum property of $\tilde{\mathsf{B}}$ we are then sure that $\delta W \geq 0$ under this variation also. Using (11.4) and proceeding as before, we deduce from (11.10) and (11.11) the inequality:

$$|\mathfrak{q}|_Q \geq |\mathfrak{q}|_P \quad \text{for} \quad Q \in \tilde{\mathsf{C}}_1 \quad \text{and} \quad P \in \tilde{\mathsf{C}}_2. \tag{11.12}$$

Thus: *the flow obtained by our extremum problem leads to velocities which are higher at each point of the rigid flow boundary than the constant velocity along the free boundary.* By Bernoulli's law (11.1) we can formulate the result also in the form: *the fluid pressure is higher on the free than on the rigid boundary.*

We have shown that if a solution of the extremum problem exists it will lead to a flow past the solid with free boundaries. Conversely, it is clear that each flow with free boundaries represents a region $\hat{\mathsf{B}}$ whose virtual mass is stationary under volume-preserving variations. This relation can lead to existence proofs and construction procedures for free boundary flows; in fact, this method has been applied successfully in the theory of two-dimensional flows in order to establish the existence of certain free boundary flows for an extended class of solids B. A numerical procedure based upon the extremal property of the free boundary flow would approximate the correct free boundary by starting from one chosen tentatively and varying the boundary continuously in such a manner that the volume enclosed is preserved and the virtual mass decreases. For this procedure, the variational formula (10.22) is of central importance.

We consider next the following extremum problem involving the tensor d_{ik} which was defined in (7.10). Let B be a given solid with boundary C and complement D; let γ be a curve in D whose endpoints lie on C. Determine a solid $\tilde{B}$ containing B and γ whose complement $\tilde{D}$ is simply connected and which minimizes $4\pi \sum_{i,k=1}^{3} \tilde{d}_{ik}\, a_i\, a_k$ for fixed $\mathfrak{a} = (a_1, a_2, a_3)$.

We shall again assume that an extremal solid $\tilde{B}$ exists and that its boundary is sufficiently regular to permit the use of the variational formula (10.19) for the quadratic form Z. We remark at first that $\tilde{B}$ — B cannot have interior points; for, otherwise, we could decrease the solid B without changing the connectivity of its complement $\tilde{D}$ and in view of the monotonic dependence of $\tilde{Z}$ upon $\tilde{B}$ we could decrease the value of the quadratic form; but this would contradict the extremum property of $\tilde{B}$. We thus recognize that $\tilde{B}$ is obtained from B and γ by spanning an appropriate surface between B and γ which makes the complement of the body obtained simply connected. We shall characterize the best possible surface Σ by means of our variational formula (10.19). Let P be a point on Σ; the velocity potentials $\tilde{\Phi}_i$ of $\tilde{B}$ will have, of course, different values and different derivatives at P on both sides of Σ. If we shift a neighborhood n of P by an amount $\delta\nu(P)$ in the direction of the interior normal on one side of Σ, this must be considered as a shift $-\delta\nu(P)$ of the other side of Σ with respect to *its* interior normal. Hence, (10.19) will lead to the result:

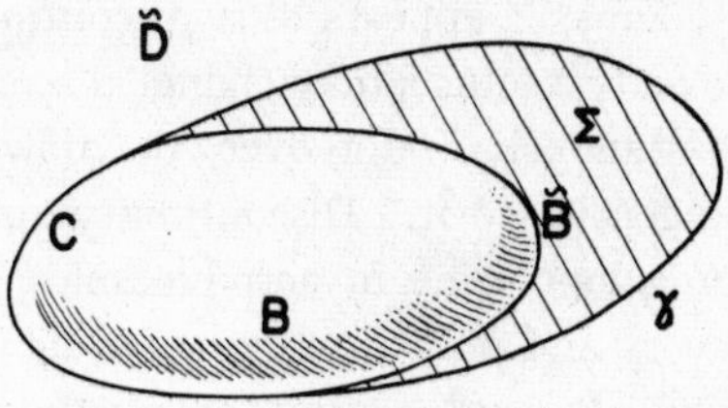

Figure 6

$$(11.13)\qquad \delta\tilde{Z} = \iint_{\mathfrak{n}} \left(\left[\sum_{i=1}^{3} a_i \operatorname{grad} \tilde{\Phi}_i \right]_2^2 - \left[\sum_{i=1}^{3} a_i \operatorname{grad} \tilde{\Phi}_i \right]_1^2 \right) \delta\nu\, d\sigma,$$

where $[A]_1$ denotes the value of A on one side of Σ and $[A]_2$ on the other. Since the sign of $\delta\nu$ can be chosen arbitrarily and since the minimum property of $\tilde{\mathsf{B}}$ implies $\delta\tilde{Z} \geqslant 0$, we obtain the necessary extremum condition:

$$\left[\sum_{i=1}^{3} a_i \operatorname{grad} \tilde{\Phi}_i\right]_2^2 = \left[\sum_{i=1}^{3} a_i \operatorname{grad} \tilde{\Phi}_i\right]_1^2. \tag{11.14}$$

The velocity potential

$$\tilde{\Phi} = -\sum_{i=1}^{3} a_i \tilde{\Phi}_i$$

represents a flow past $\tilde{\mathsf{B}}$ which at infinity has the direction $\mathfrak{e} = (a_1, a_2, a_3)$. On $\tilde{\mathsf{C}}$ it satisfies the boundary condition $\partial\Phi/\partial\nu = 0$. Moreover, on the surface Σ which forms part of $\tilde{\mathsf{C}}$ we have the condition

$$|\mathfrak{q}_1|^2 = [\operatorname{grad} \tilde{\Phi}]^2{}_1 = [\operatorname{grad} \tilde{\Phi}]^2{}_2 = |\mathfrak{q}_2|^2, \tag{11.15}$$

i. e., the absolute value of the velocity vector $\mathfrak{q}$ must be the same on both sides of the surface Σ. According to Bernoulli's law the pressure upon Σ will be equal on both sides.

Thus, Σ appears as a discontinuity surface in the flow along which the velocity vector $\mathfrak{q}$ may change discontinuously but where the pressure changes continuously. Moreover, the flow does not cross the surface but remains tangential to it. Discontinuity surfaces of this type have been considered for a long time in aerodynamics. They appear as vortex sheets in wing theory and play an important role in the theory of lift of a three-dimensional wing. It is interesting that they occur in a simple extremum problem where the existence of an extremal surface Σ seems intuitive. Again it seems hopeful to base an existence theory and a construction procedure for discontinuity surfaces upon this extremum property.

In all the preceding examples, we dealt with free boundaries or discontinuity surfaces in a flow originating from dipoles at infinity. It is easy to devise extremum problems which lead to the same phenomena but with respect to other types of singularity for the flow. As an example, let us deal with the following question: *Given a body* B. *To find a larger body* $\tilde{\mathsf{B}}$ *with given volume* $\tilde{V}$ *which contains* B *and leads to a minimum for the expression* $\tilde{E}(Q)$, *as defined in* (10.27). The same reasoning as before shows that the extremum body $\tilde{\mathsf{B}}$ possesses velocity potentials $\tilde{\Phi}_i$ and $\tilde{N}(P, Q)$ such that on that part $\tilde{\mathsf{C}}_2$ of the boundary $\tilde{\mathsf{C}}$ of $\tilde{\mathsf{B}}$ which does not belong to the boundary C of B the following holds:

$$(11.16) \qquad \left| \operatorname{grad} \left(c \sum_{i=1}^{3} a_i \tilde{\Phi}_i (P) + \tilde{N} (P, Q) \right) \right| = \text{const.} \qquad P \in \mathbf{C}_2.$$

The velocity potential

$$(11.17) \qquad \tilde{\Phi} (P) = c \sum_{i=1}^{3} a_i \tilde{\Phi}_i (P) + \tilde{N} (P, Q)$$

represents a flow around the solid $\tilde{\mathbf{B}}$ due to a dipole with strength c and direction $\mathfrak{e} \equiv (\alpha_1, \alpha_2, \alpha_3)$ at infinity plus a source of unit strength at Q. It is obvious from (11.16) that the part $\tilde{\mathbf{C}}_2$ of $\tilde{\mathbf{C}}$ represents a free boundary in this flow. In this way, we can deal with the free boundary problem in the presence of a dipole and an ordinary source.

In this section we have shown how the variational treatment of the Neumann's function and the allied potentials Φ_i leads to important and difficult problems of fluid dynamics. This result again justifies the methodological principle of this book: to reduce the treatment of the solutions of a partial differential equation to the study of a few central fundamental solutions.

Cisotti [10], Courant-Hilbert [13], Frank-Mises [14], Villat [84].

12. Two-dimensional flows: The theory of the motion of an incompressible and irrotational steady fluid flow represents a great idealization and simplification of the real flow problem. But, from a mathematical point of view, it still leads to problems of sufficient complexity that a further simplifying step has been found to be of great advantage. The treatment of a partial differential equation is easier if the number of independent variables occurring in it is smaller. Thus, it is natural to study fluid motions which depend only on two instead of three coordinates. We assume that the velocity vector $\mathfrak{q}$ of the motion has only two non-vanishing components, say u and v and that these components depend only on x and y. Thus, each point in the three dimensional (x, y, z)-space moves parallel to the (x, y)-plane and its motion is uniquely determined by its coordinates x and y. In order that such a flow be possible we must assume, of course, that the boundaries $\mathbf{C}$ of the flow domain are cylindrical with generators in the z-direction and that the singularities lie along straight lines in the same direction.

It will be sufficient to study the fluid motion in a representative plane, say, the plane $z = 0$. The boundary surfaces will appear here as two-dimensional curves and the singularity lines as point singularities. We shall deal with the two velocity components $u(x, y)$ and $v(x, y)$ and we may express the system of fundamental differential equations as follows. We have the condition of irrotationality:

$$\text{(12.1)} \qquad \operatorname{curl} \mathfrak{q} = 0, \qquad \text{i. e.,} \qquad \frac{\partial u}{\partial y} = \frac{\partial v}{\partial x};$$

the continuity equation for an incompressible fluid:

$$\text{(12.2)} \qquad \operatorname{div} \mathfrak{q} = 0, \qquad \text{i. e.,} \qquad \frac{\partial u}{\partial x} + \frac{\partial v}{\partial y} = 0$$

and the Bernoulli equation

$$\text{(12.3)} \qquad \frac{1}{2}(u^2 + v^2) + V + \frac{p}{\rho} = \text{const.}$$

The last equation may be used to compute the pressure field in the fluid and the influence of the external forces with the force potential V. The first two equations, on the other hand, form a closed system of differential equations which, together, with the singularity and boundary conditions, determines the velocity field $\mathfrak{q}$.

The most important tool in the theory of plane fluid motion is the theory of analytic functions of a complex variable. With each point (x, y) we associate the complex variable $z = x + i y$ and consider complex-valued functions

$$\text{(12.4)} \qquad f(z) = a(x, y) + i b(x, y)$$

of z. We call such a function analytic in a domain D of the z-plane if at every point of this domain it possesses a complex derivative

$$\text{(12.5)} \qquad f'(z) = \lim_{\Delta z \to 0} \frac{f(z + \Delta z) - f(z)}{\Delta z} = \frac{df(z)}{dz}$$

which is itself a continuous complex-valued function of z. It is easily shown that this condition of analyticity is equivalent to the condition that the functions a and b be continuously differentiable in D and satisfy the Cauchy-Riemann differential equations there:

$$\text{(12.6)} \qquad \frac{\partial a}{\partial x} = \frac{\partial b}{\partial y}, \qquad \frac{\partial a}{\partial y} = -\frac{\partial b}{\partial x}.$$

Comparing these equations with (12.1) and (12.2), we see that

$$\text{(12.7)} \qquad \overline{f(z)} = u(x, y) - i v(x, y)$$

is an analytic function of the complex variable $z = x + i\,y$. $f(z)$ is called the *velocity function* of the flow. The well-developed theory of complex numbers and analytic functions will provide a very convenient formalism for the treatment of incompressible, irrotational steady flows in a plane.

Each real component $a(x, y)$ and $b(x, y)$ of an analytic function satisfies Laplace's equation

$$\Delta a = 0, \qquad \Delta b = 0 \tag{12.8}$$

as can be easily derived from the Cauchy-Riemann equations (12.6). Conversely, every harmonic function $a(x, y)$ may be completed to an analytic function $f(z) = a + i\,b$. $a(x, y)$ and $b(x, y)$ are called conjugate functions and the conjugate function to $a(x, y)$ is determined to within an additive constant.

The velocity potential $\varphi(x, y)$, for which

$$u = -\frac{\partial \varphi}{\partial x}, \qquad v = -\frac{\partial \varphi}{\partial y} \tag{12.9}$$

holds, is by (12.2) a harmonic function. There exists, therefore, a conjugate function $\psi(x, y)$ which satisfies the Cauchy-Riemann equations

$$\frac{\partial \varphi}{\partial x} = \frac{\partial \psi}{\partial y}, \qquad \frac{\partial \varphi}{\partial y} = -\frac{\partial \psi}{\partial x} \tag{12.10}$$

such that

$$F(z) = \varphi(x, y) + i\,\psi(x, y) \tag{12.11}$$

is an analytic function of the complex variable z. $\psi(x, y)$ is called the *stream function* of the fluid motion considered. In view of (12.9) and (12.10) we have:

$$u = -\frac{\partial \psi}{\partial y}, \qquad v = \frac{\partial \psi}{\partial x}. \tag{12.12}$$

Consider a particle which travels with the fluid flow and has, therefore, at each moment the velocity

$$\frac{dx}{dt} = u(x, y), \qquad \frac{dy}{dt} = v(x, y). \tag{12.13}$$

Integrating this system of ordinary differential equations, we obtain $x = x(t)$ and $y = y(t)$, i. e., the motion of the particle as a function of time. The curve $x(t)$, $y(t)$ is called a *stream line* of the flow.

We study now the dependence of the function $\psi\big(x(t), y(t)\big)$ on the parameter t of the stream line. Differentiation leads to the result:

$$\frac{d\psi\big(x(t), y(t)\big)}{dt} = \frac{\partial \psi}{\partial x}\cdot\frac{dx}{dt} + \frac{\partial \psi}{\partial y}\cdot\frac{dy}{dt} = \frac{\partial \psi}{\partial x}u + \frac{\partial \psi}{\partial y}v = 0. \tag{12.14}$$

Thus, the function $\psi(x, y)$ is constant along each stream line; it is an integral of the system of differential equations (12.13). This interpretation shows the usefulness of the stream function for the study of the fluid motion.

The function $F(z)$ is called the *complex potential* of the flow. It is easily seen that the velocity function $f(z)$ is related to $F(z)$ by the simple formula

$$\overline{f(z)} = -\frac{dF(z)}{dz}. \tag{12.15}$$

Any given analytic function of the complex variable z may be interpreted either as the complex potential or velocity function of an incompressible irrotational flow. Thus, function theory yields numerous examples of plane flows and leads to instructive illustrations of the theory.

Let us take the fundamental singularity of Laplace's equation in two variables

$$\varphi_Q(P) = \frac{1}{2\pi}\log\frac{1}{r(P,Q)}, \qquad r = [(x-\xi)^2 + (y-\eta)^2]^{1/2}. \tag{12.16}$$

If $z = x + iy$ and $\zeta = \xi + i\eta$ denote the complex coordinates of the points $P \equiv (x, y)$ and $Q \equiv (\xi, \eta)$, respectively, we may complete φ_Q to the analytic function:

$$F_\zeta(z) = \frac{1}{2\pi}\log\frac{1}{z-\zeta} = \frac{1}{2\pi}\left(\log\frac{1}{|z-\zeta|} - \arg(z-\zeta)\right). \tag{12.17}$$

Here, $\arg(z-\zeta)$ denotes the angle between the radius vector $\overrightarrow{QP}$ and the positive x-axis. It is now very easy to characterize the flow connected with the velocity potential $\varphi_Q(P)$; its stream lines satisfy the equation

$$\psi_Q(P) = -\frac{1}{2\pi}\arg(z-\zeta) = \text{const.}, \tag{12.18}$$

i. e., are rectilinear rays issuing from the parameter point Q. Thus, the flow considered has a simple source at Q. For any curve C enclosing the source, the following holds:

$$\oint_{\mathsf{C}} \frac{\partial \varphi_Q}{\partial \nu}\, ds = 1, \tag{12.19}$$

i. e., the strength of the source is unity. The flow is defined and regular in the whole complex plane; but at infinity the complex potential again becomes infinite and one recognizes that the point at infinity is a sink of unit strength for the flow.

Just as in the three-dimensional case we can derive dipole singularities from the simple source potential by differentiation with respect to the coordinates of the source point. Thus:

$$\chi_Q(P) = \lambda\left(\alpha \frac{\partial \varphi_Q(P)}{\partial \xi} + \beta \frac{\partial \varphi_Q(P)}{\partial \eta}\right), \qquad \alpha^2 + \beta^2 = 1, \qquad \lambda > 0, \tag{12.20}$$

will represent a dipole with strength λ and axis $\mathbf{e} \equiv (\alpha, \beta)$. We may complete this harmonic function to a complex potential as follows:

$$H_\zeta(z) = \frac{\lambda}{2\pi} \frac{A}{z - \zeta}, \qquad A = \alpha + i\beta. \tag{12.21}$$

Dipoles at infinity have the somewhat different complex potential:

$$H_\infty(z) = \lambda A z, \qquad A = -\alpha + i\beta, \qquad |A|^2 = \alpha^2 + \beta^2 = 1, \qquad \lambda > 0. \tag{12.22}$$

In fact, the real part of this analytic function is the velocity potential

$$\chi_\infty(P) = -\lambda(\alpha x + \beta y) \tag{12.23}$$

which leads to the velocity field

$$\mathbf{q} \equiv (u, v) \equiv \lambda(\alpha, \beta) \tag{12.24}$$

which is a uniform flow with velocity λ in the direction of the unit vector (α, β).

We make the obvious remark that if $f(z) = a + i\,b$ is an analytic function; then $i\,f(z) = -b + i\,a$ will also be an analytic function. Thus, any pair of conjugate harmonic functions φ and ψ leads to two different flow patterns. We may interpret φ as velocity potential and ψ as stream function, but we may also take $-\psi$ as velocity potential and φ as its stream function. Let us apply this reasoning to the analytic function (12.17). We are led to a flow with the velocity potential

$$\varphi(P) = \frac{1}{2\pi} \arg(z - \zeta) \tag{12.25}$$

and the stream function

$$\psi(P) = \frac{1}{2\pi} \log \frac{1}{|z - \zeta|}. \tag{12.26}$$

The new velocity potential is now a multivalued function and increases by integer values if z turns around the singular point ζ. But its first derivatives are single-valued functions and since they have a physical significance as velocity components, the function $\varphi(P)$ is an acceptable potential. The stream lines of the flow in question are given by the equation $\psi = \text{const.}$, i. e., satisfy the condition $|z - \zeta| = \text{const.}$ and are, therefore, circles with center ζ. The flow described by the velocity potential (12.25) is called a circulation or a vorticity around the point ζ, and ζ is called the vortex point of the motion. Isolated vortex points can only occur in two-dimensional motion; for, in two dimensions a multivalued potential possesses a branch point which is just the vortex point while in space a multivalued function possesses a branch line for topological reasons. Indeed, we must remember that a point singularity in a plane flow is the representation of a singular line in space. One can study the theory of multivalued velocity potentials in space with arbitrarily given closed curves as branch lines; but the resulting theory of vortex rings is rather complicated and because of the arbitrariness of the branch line also somewhat vague. Thus, the vortex point in the plane flow represents a distinguished and particularly simple phenomenon of a singularity for a multivalued velocity potential.

Hurwitz-Courant [23].

13. Boundary value problems and fundamental solutions in plane flows: Let Γ be an open or closed smooth curve in the (x, y)-plane and s its length parameter. We may represent Γ in parametric form as $z = z(s)$; then $z' = dz/ds = x'(s) + i\,y'(s)$ will be a complex unit vector in the tangential direction with respect to Γ. The vector $i\,z'(s)$ will be orthogonal to $z'(s)$ and is obtained from the tangent vector by a rotation in the positive sense. It determines the normal vector $\boldsymbol{\nu}$ of Γ at $z(s)$. Thus, $\boldsymbol{\nu}$ has the components $(-y'(s), x'(s))$. Similarly, let $\boldsymbol{\tau} = (x', y')$ denote the tangent vector.

Again let

$$f(z) = a(x, y) + i\,b(x, y) \tag{13.1}$$

be an analytic function of z. Let us compute the directional derivative of $a(x, y)$ in the tangential direction at a point $z \in \Gamma$. We find:

$$\frac{\partial a(x, y)}{\partial s} = \frac{\partial a}{\partial x}\cos(\boldsymbol{\tau}, \mathbf{x}) + \frac{\partial a}{\partial y}\cos(\boldsymbol{\tau}, \mathbf{y}) = \frac{\partial a}{\partial x}x' + \frac{\partial a}{\partial y}y'. \tag{13.2}$$

Applying now the Cauchy-Riemann differential equations (12.6) and the determination of the normal vector $\mathbf{v}$, we may transform the above expression as follows:

$$\frac{\partial a}{\partial s} = \frac{\partial b}{\partial y} \cos(\mathbf{v}, \mathbf{y}) + \frac{\partial b}{\partial x} \cos(\mathbf{v}, \mathbf{x}) = \frac{\partial b}{\partial \nu}. \tag{13.3}$$

Similarly, we find:

$$\frac{\partial b}{\partial s} = -\frac{\partial a}{\partial \nu}. \tag{13.4}$$

We may consider the pair of equations (13.3) and (13.4) as the generalization of the Cauchy-Riemann equations to two arbitrary orthogonal directions $\boldsymbol{\tau}$ and $\mathbf{v}$. Their role in the general theory of harmonic functions in the plane is of great importance.

In the treatment of the three-dimensional case, we saw that in hydrodynamics one has to deal with the problem of determining a harmonic function from the values of its normal derivative on the boundary of the domain considered. The decisive tool is the Neumann's function of the domain. In problems of electrostatics one has to characterize harmonic functions by their boundary values and for this purpose one needs the Green's function of the domain. The two types of boundary value problems are essentially different and so are the fundamental solutions, i. e., the Neumann's and the Green's function. We shall now show that in the plane problem the situation is quite different and that the two boundary value problems are equivalent.

In fact, let a harmonic function $b(x, y)$ be given in a domain D with a smooth boundary curve C and let its normal derivative $\partial b/\partial \nu$ be known on C. We determine its conjugate harmonic function $a(x, y)$ so that $a + ib$ is an analytic function in D. By virtue of (13.3), we can express the value of $\partial a/\partial s$ and hence of $a(x, y)$ on C if the value of $\partial b/\partial \nu$ is known. Thus, instead of determining $b(x, y)$ by means of its normal derivative on the boundary (second boundary value problem), we may calculate its conjugate function $a(x, y)$ in terms of its values on the boundary (first boundary value problem). It is easy to find $b(x, y)$. once its conjugate function has been determined. It is therefore sufficient to know one fundamental solution for a domain D in order to treat hydrodynamical as well as electrostatic problems. Since the Green's function is more accessible than the Neumann's function we shall reduce our problems to it.

We define the Green's function $G(z, \zeta)$ of a plane domain D with smooth boundary C by the following three requirements:

a) $G(z, \zeta) = \dfrac{1}{2\pi} \log \dfrac{1}{|z - \zeta|} + g(z, \zeta)$ is a regular harmonic function of z in D, except at $z = \zeta$.

b) Near $z = \zeta$ the function $g(z, \zeta)$ is regular harmonic in z.

c) $G(z, \zeta)$ is continuous in the closed region $\mathsf{D} + \mathsf{C}$ and has the boundary value zero on C.

It is easy to show that the Green's function is symmetric in both arguments.

As an example of our general statement let us find the relation between the Neumann's function $N(z, \zeta)$ of the domain D and the Green's function. We put

(13.5) $$N(z, \zeta) = \frac{1}{2\pi} \log \frac{1}{|z - \zeta|} + n(z, \zeta)$$

and require that $N(z, \zeta)$ be harmonic for $z \in \mathsf{D}$ except at the point $z = \zeta$ where $n(z, \zeta)$ shall be harmonic. On the boundary C of D we require

(13.6) $$\frac{\partial N(z, \zeta)}{\partial \nu_z} = \text{const.} \qquad \text{for} \qquad z \in \mathsf{C}$$

and since by Green's theorem we have

(13.7) $$\int_{\mathsf{C}} \frac{\partial N}{\partial \nu} \, ds = 1,$$

we calculate that the constant value of the normal derivative on C is $1/L$ where L is the length of C. Our requirements determine the Neumann's function to within an additive constant. We may complete our definition by prescribing:

(13.8) $$\int_{\mathsf{C}} N(z, \zeta) \, ds_z = 0.$$

This normalization has the advantage of insuring the symmetry

(13.9) $$N(z, \zeta) = N(\zeta, z)$$

of the Neumann's function in analogy to the results of Section 5.

For the sake of simplicity let us assume that the domain **D** is finite and simply connected. Then, the regular harmonic function $n(z, \zeta)$ of z possesses a regular and single valued conjugate function, say $m(z, \zeta)$. By virtue of (13.5) and (13.6), we have the boundary condition for $n(z, \zeta)$:

$$\frac{\partial n(z,\zeta)}{\partial \nu_z} = \frac{1}{L} + \frac{1}{2\pi}\frac{\partial \log|z-\zeta|}{\partial \nu_z}. \tag{13.10}$$

Thus, by virtue of (13.3), and putting $b = n$, $a = m$, we obtain:

$$\frac{\partial m(z,\zeta)}{\partial s_z} = \frac{1}{L} + \frac{1}{2\pi}\frac{\partial \log|z-\zeta|}{\partial \nu_z}. \tag{13.11}$$

Now, we notice that $\log|z-\zeta| + i\arg(z-\zeta)$ is an analytic function of z and, hence, by (13.4):

$$\frac{1}{2\pi}\frac{\partial \log|z-\zeta|}{\partial \nu_z} = -\frac{1}{2\pi}\frac{\partial \arg(z-\zeta)}{\partial s_z}. \tag{13.12}$$

Thus, we may integrate (13.11) and find the boundary values for $m(z, \zeta)$:

$$m(z,\zeta) = \frac{s}{L} - \frac{1}{2\pi}\arg(z-\zeta) + k, \qquad k = \text{const.} \tag{13.13}$$

Since m is defined only up to an additive constant, we may put $k = 0$. We remark that these boundary values form a single-valued function on **C**, in spite of the fact that s/L and $(1/2\pi)\arg(z-\zeta)$ are multivalued there.

By means of the Green's function $G(z, \zeta)$ we may express every harmonic function $h(z)$ in **D** in terms of its boundary values on **C** as follows:

$$h(z) = \int_{C} \frac{\partial G(z,t)}{\partial \nu_t} h(t)\, ds_t. \tag{13.14}$$

Thus, for $m(z, \zeta)$ we find the expression:

$$m(z,\zeta) = \int_{C} \frac{\partial G(z,t)}{\partial \nu_t}\left[\frac{s_t}{L} - \frac{1}{2\pi}\arg(t-\zeta)\right] ds_t. \tag{13.15}$$

Knowing $m(z, \zeta)$ we can determine $n(z, \zeta)$ from the Cauchy-Riemann equations by simple integration and this leads us finally to the Neumann's function of **D**. In most problems, however, it will not even be necessary to compute the Neumann's function; it is always possible to reduce the problem directly to the Green's function.

In this section we shall continue to restrict ourselves to simply-connected domains **D**, and for the sake of subsequent applications we shall assume that the domain contains the point at infinity. According to the celebrated theorem of Riemann on conformal mapping, there exists exactly one function with a series development

$$w = f(z) = a z + b + \frac{c}{z} + \frac{d}{z^2} + \dots, \qquad a > 0 \tag{13.16}$$

at infinity which maps the domain **D** upon the exterior $|w| > 1$ of the unit circle in the w-plane. We recognize from (13.16) that the points at infinity correspond to each other in this map. The coefficients $a, b, \dots,$ are well-determined functionals of the domain **D**; in particular, a plays an important role in many applications and a^{-1} is called the mapping radius of **D**. The reason for this name is the fact that the function

$$\frac{f(z)}{a} = z + \frac{b}{a} + \frac{c}{a z} + \frac{d}{a z^2} + \dots \tag{13.17}$$

which is normalized at infinity to have the derivative one there, maps **D** upon the exterior of a circle of radius a^{-1}.

There exists a simple relation between the mapping function (13.16) of the domain **D** and its Green's function $G(z, \zeta)$. In fact, we assert that

$$G(z, \zeta) = \frac{1}{2\pi} \log \left| \frac{1 - f(z)\overline{f(\zeta)}}{f(z) - f(\zeta)} \right|. \tag{13.18}$$

We prove this identity by verifying that the right-hand side has all the characteristic properties of the Green's function of **D**.

a) Since $\frac{1}{2\pi} \log \left(\frac{1 - f(z)\overline{f(\zeta)}}{f(z) - f(\zeta)} \right)$ is an analytic function of z, except for $z = \zeta$, its real part, i. e., the right-hand side of (13.18), is harmonic for z in **D**, except for $z = \zeta$.

b) Clearly we may write

$$\frac{1}{2\pi} \log \left| \frac{1 - f(z)\overline{f(\zeta)}}{f(z) - f(\zeta)} \right| = \frac{1}{2\pi} \log \frac{1}{|z - \zeta|} + \tag{13.19}$$
$$+ \frac{1}{2\pi} \log \left| \frac{\left(1 - f(z)\overline{f(\zeta)}\right)(z - \zeta)}{f(z) - f(\zeta)} \right|$$

and the last right-hand term is regular harmonic even for $z = \zeta$. For, the function $f(z)$ provides a one-to-one map of D on the exterior of the unit circle and, hence, $f'(z) \neq 0$ in D. This verifies the singular behavior at ζ which is required of the Green's function.

c) For $z \in \mathsf{C}$, we have $|f(z)| = 1$ since the boundaries of the two domains in question correspond to each other. We thus obtain:

$$(13.20) \qquad f(z)\,\overline{f(z)} = 1, \qquad \frac{1}{f(z)} = \overline{f(z)} \qquad \text{for} \qquad z \in \mathsf{C}.$$

Thus, we may write:

$$(13.21) \qquad G(z, \zeta) = \frac{1}{2\pi} \log |f(z)| + \frac{1}{2\pi} \log \left| \frac{\overline{f(z)} - \overline{f(\zeta)}}{f(z) - f(\zeta)} \right| \qquad \text{for} \qquad z \in \mathsf{C}.$$

It is easy to see that the absolute value of $\overline{A}/A$ is one for each complex number $A \neq 0$. Thus, (13.21) shows that $G(z, \zeta) = 0$ for $z \in \mathsf{C}$ and this verifies the third and most restrictive requirement for the Green's function.

Formula (13.18) establishes an important relation between the theory of conformal mapping and the boundary value problem in harmonic functions. One often makes use of a known mapping function $f(z)$ in order to solve the boundary value problem for a given domain D; but it is also sometimes necessary to use the numerical methods devised for the calculation of the Green's function in order to calculate the mapping function $f(z)$. In any case it will be useful to introduce the function $f(z)$ instead of the Green's function for a plane simply-connected domain inasmuch as Green's function depends on two arguments, while $f(z)$ depends only on one and expresses, nevertheless, the Green's function.

Let us consider the following example. Let the domain D be the exterior of a circle of radius R, i. e., the domain $|z| > R$. In this case, we evidently have

$$(13.22) \qquad w = f(z) = \frac{z}{R}$$

for the mapping function $f(z)$ and, hence, by virtue of (13.18):

$$(13.23) \qquad G(z, \zeta) = \frac{1}{2\pi} \log \left| \frac{R^2 - z\,\overline{\zeta}}{R(z - \zeta)} \right| = \operatorname{Re} \left(\frac{1}{2\pi} \log \frac{R^2 - z\,\overline{\zeta}}{R(z - \zeta)} \right)$$

as a representation for the Green's function of a circle with radius R. We can use this formula in order to solve explicitly the boundary value problem for the circle. Let $h(z)$ be harmonic in the infinite domain $|z| > R$. We may represent the vàlues of this function at interior points $z \in \mathbf{D}$ in terms of its boundary values by means of (13.14). We put $t = Re^{i\varphi}$, $z = re^{i\psi}$, $ds = R\, d\varphi$, $\dfrac{\partial G(t)}{\partial \nu} = \dfrac{\partial G(\rho e^{i\varphi})}{\partial \rho}\Big|_{\rho=R}$. Thus, we find:

$$\frac{\partial G(z,t)}{\partial \nu} = \frac{1}{2\pi} \operatorname{Re}\left(-\frac{e^{i\varphi}\,\bar{z}}{(R^2 - t\bar{z})} - \frac{e^{i\varphi}}{t - z} \right) \tag{13.24}$$

and since $t\bar{t} = R^2$, i. e., $R^2/t = \bar{t}$, we may put (13.24) in the form:

$$\frac{\partial G(z,t)}{\partial \nu_t} = -\frac{1}{2\pi} \operatorname{Re}\left(\frac{\bar{z}}{R(\bar{t} - \bar{z})} + \frac{t}{R(t - z)} \right) = -\frac{1}{2\pi R} \frac{|t|^2 - |z|^2}{|t - z|^2}. \tag{13.25}$$

Thus, we may write (13.14) in the form:

$$h(re^{i\psi}) = \frac{1}{2\pi} \int_0^{2\pi} \frac{(r^2 - R^2)}{R^2 + r^2 - 2rR\cos(\varphi - \psi)} h(Re^{i\varphi})\, d\varphi. \tag{13.26}$$

This is the well-known Poisson formula which solves the boundary value problem for harmonic functions in the case of the exterior of a circle with radius R.

14. Obstacles in a plane flow: Let us consider a cylindrical solid in the (x, y, z)-space whose generators have the direction of the z-axis. This cylinder cuts the plane $z = 0$ in a domain $\mathbf{B}$ bounded by a curve $\mathbf{C}$. We suppose that $\mathbf{C}$ is a closed and smooth curve and we denote the complement of $\mathbf{B}$ in the (x, y)-plane by $\mathbf{D}$. A flow in space around the solid which is everywhere parallel to the plane $z = 0$ and which depends only on the coordinates x, y will be represented by a plane flow in the (x, y)-plane past the closed contour $\mathbf{C}$.

Suppose that the flow originates from a dipole at infinity and that its velocity potential $\varphi(x, y)$ has at infinity the leading term $-\lambda(\alpha x + \beta y)$, $\alpha^2 + \beta^2 = 1$. This means that the flow behaves at infinity like a uniform flow in the direction of the unit vector $\mathbf{e} \equiv (\alpha, \beta)$ with the velocity λ. Then, we have the representation for φ:

$$\varphi(x, y) = -\lambda(\alpha x + \beta y) + \gamma(x, y) \tag{14.1}$$

where $\gamma(x, y)$ is regular harmonic in $\mathbf{D}$; on the boundary $\mathbf{C}$ of the flow region $\mathbf{D}$ we have the condition:

$$\mathbf{q} \cdot \boldsymbol{\nu} = -\frac{\partial \varphi}{\partial \nu} = 0, \qquad (x, y) \text{ on } \mathbf{C}, \tag{14.2}$$

since no fluid can cross the boundary of the solid obstacle. We will obtain a simpler boundary condition if we introduce the stream function $\psi(x, y)$, conjugate to $\varphi(x, y)$. It has the form

$$\psi(x, y) = \lambda(\beta x - \alpha y) + \delta(x, y) \tag{14.3}$$

where $\delta(x, y)$ is the harmonic function conjugate to $\gamma(x, y)$. In fact, the complex potential can now be written in the form:

$$F(z) = \varphi(x, y) + i\psi(x, y) = Az + \chi(z), \qquad A = -\lambda(\alpha - i\beta), \tag{14.4}$$
$$\chi(z) = \gamma(x, y) + i\delta(x, y),$$

and $\chi(z)$ is a regular analytic function of $z \in \mathsf{D}$ since $\gamma(x, y)$ and $\delta(x, y)$ are regular harmonic and conjugate. By virtue of (13.4), the boundary condition (14.2) on φ implies for the stream function

$$\frac{\partial \psi}{\partial s} \equiv 0 \quad \text{on } \mathsf{C}. \tag{14.5}$$

Since ψ is only determined up to an additive constant, we may now fix the stream function in a unique way by integrating (14.5) such that:

$$\psi(x, y) = 0 \quad \text{on } \mathsf{C}. \tag{14.6}$$

The best characterization of the two basic functions φ and ψ of the flow is obtained if one considers them together in the complex potential $F(z)$. This is an analytic function which possesses a pole of first order at infinity, is elsewhere regular analytic in D and has real values on the boundary C of D. We shall prove that $F(z)$ is univalent in D, i. e., $F(z_1) = F(z_2)$ and $z_1 \in \mathsf{D}$, $z_2 \in \mathsf{D}$ implies that $z_1 = z_2$. For this purpose we apply the following well-known result of function theory: let $g(z)$ be meromorphic in D but have no poles or zeros on the boundary C of D; then

$$\frac{1}{2\pi i} \oint_{\mathsf{C}} \frac{g'(z)}{g(z)}\, dz = Z - P \tag{14.7}$$

where the integral is taken in the positive sense with respect to D and where Z and P are integers representing the number of zeros and poles of $g(z)$ in D, respectively.

Now let w be an arbitrary complex value; consider the expression

$$Y(w) = \frac{1}{2\pi i} \oint_{\mathsf{C}} \frac{F'(z)}{F(z) - w}\, dz. \tag{14.8}$$

Since $F(z)$ is bounded for $z \in \mathsf{C}$, it is clear that the function $g(z) = F(z) - w$ has for sufficiently large values of w no zeros or poles on the curve **C**. Hence, the above theorem becomes applicable and the value of the integral must be an integer for large enough absolute value of w. But for the same large values of w the integrand in (14.8) becomes arbitrarily small in absolute value; hence $Y(w)$ can only coincide with the integer zero for large enough values of w. As w varies, $Y(w)$ will change continuously as long as w does not take on one of the values of $F(z)$ on **C**, for only this would lead to a singularity of the integrand in (14.8). Now, $F(z)$ has the property of taking on real values on **C**. Hence, if w_0 is any point in the complex plane which is not a value taken on by $F(z)$ on **C**, we may connect it by a parallel to the imaginary axis with the point at infinity without meeting a point w which is taken on by $F(z)$ on **C**. Thus, we conclude that the integer $Y(w)$, which is zero near infinity and which changes continuously with w, must be zero for all points w not taken on by $F(z)$ on **C**. But the function $F(z) - w$ has exactly one pole in **D**: for $z = \infty$; from $Y(w) = Z - P = 0$ we may conclude then that it has exactly one zero in **D**. Thus, we have shown: *the function $F(z)$ maps the domain* **D** *univalently upon the w-plane with the exception of a set of points on the real axis which corresponds to the boundary* **C** *of* **D**. Since the function $F(z)$ still is continuous on **C** the image of the boundary in the w-plane is connected and forms a segment of finite length on the real axis. Thus: $w = F(z)$ maps the domain **D** univalently upon the w-plane slit along a finite segment of the real axis. Since the existence of a fluid flow past a given contour **C** and with a given dipole singularity at infinity is intuitively obvious, we may consider the preceding result as a heuristic proof for a mapping theorem of function theory. This result is equivalent to Riemann's mapping theorem and it was, indeed, hydrodynamical considerations which led mathematicians to the formulation of this mapping theorem.

It is simple to show that the pole at infinity and the mapping property of $F(z)$ determine this function up to a real additive constant. In fact, suppose there were a second function

$$F_1(z) = A z + \chi_1(z) \tag{14.9}$$

with the same mapping property. The difference function $F(z) - F_1(z)$ would be regular analytic in **D** and real valued on **C**. Its imaginary part would be regular harmonic in **D** and vanish on the boundary. Thus, by the maximum-minimum principle for harmonic functions, it would be identically zero in **D**. But then we conclude immediately from the Cauchy-Riemann equations that the real part of $F(z) - F_1(z)$ is a constant which proves our assertion.

The last remark is important since we are able to construct a function of the character of $F(z)$ by means of the function $f(z)$, defined in the last section, which maps **D** upon the exterior of the unit circle. In fact, consider the function

$$F_1(z) = \frac{1}{a}\left(A f(z) + \bar{A}\left(f(z)\right)^{-1}\right). \tag{14.10}$$

($1/a =$ mapping radius of **D**). Near the point at infinity this function has the development

$$F_1(z) = A z + \frac{A b}{a} + \left(\frac{A c}{a} + \frac{\bar{A}}{a^2}\right)\frac{1}{z} + \ldots, \tag{14.11}$$

as can easily be computed from (13.16). It has, therefore, the same pole at infinity as the complex potential $F(z)$. For $z \in \mathbf{C}$ we have $\overline{f(z)} = \left(f(z)\right)^{-1}$; hence

$$F_1(z) = \frac{1}{a}\left(A f(z) + \overline{A f(z)}\right) = \frac{2}{a}\,\mathrm{Re}\left(A f(z)\right) \tag{14.12}$$

is real on **C**. Since $F_1(z)$ has the same pole at infinity as $F(z)$ and is real on the boundary **C** of the domain **D** it coincides with $F(z)$ up to an additive real constant. Since this constant is inessential for the complex potential, we may write simply:

$$F(z) = \frac{1}{a}\left(A f(z) + \bar{A}\left(f(z)\right)^{-1}\right). \tag{14.13}$$

If we know the function $f(z)$ mapping the exterior **D** *of the obstacle* **B** *upon the exterior of the unit circle, we can determine the complex potential of all flows due to a dipole at infinity past* **B**.

It is now easy to calculate the virtual mass of **B** in any direction $\mathfrak{e}$. If **B** moves with unit speed in the direction opposite to $\mathfrak{e} \equiv (\alpha, \beta)$ it will create in the fluid a flow whose complex potential relative to it is $F(z)$, with $A = -\alpha + i\beta$. The field of absolute velocities is then derived from the complex potential

$$h(z) = [F(z) - A z] = k(x, y) + i\,l(x, y). \tag{14.14}$$

These considerations are entirely analogous to those of Section 7 in the three-dimensional case. Let us now compute the kinetic energy connected with the flow described by (14.14). We have by definition (up to a factor ρ_0),

$$T = \frac{1}{2} \iint\limits_{D} \left[\left(\frac{\partial k}{\partial x} \right)^2 + \left(\frac{\partial k}{\partial y} \right)^2 \right] d\tau = -\frac{1}{2} \oint\limits_{C} k \frac{\partial k}{\partial \nu} ds. \tag{14.15}$$

Using (13.4), we may replace $\frac{\partial k}{\partial \nu}$ by $-\frac{\partial l}{\partial s}$ and obtain:

$$T = \frac{1}{2} \oint\limits_{C} k\, dl = \frac{1}{8i} \oint\limits_{C} [h(z) + \overline{h(z)}]\, [dh(z) - d\overline{h(z)}]. \tag{14.16}$$

The integration over C is to be understood as taken in the positive sense with respect to the domain D. Now, clearly

$$\oint\limits_{C} h\, dh = \oint\limits_{C} \bar{h}\, d\bar{h} = 0 \tag{14.17}$$

since h is a single-valued function on C. Hence, there remains:

$$T = \frac{1}{8i} \oint\limits_{C} (\bar{h}\, dh - h\, d\bar{h}) = \frac{1}{4i} \oint\limits_{C} \overline{h(z)}\, dh(z) \tag{14.18}$$

since by integrating by parts, we have

$$\oint\limits_{C} h\, d\bar{h} = -\oint\limits_{C} \bar{h}\, dh. \tag{14.19}$$

In order to evaluate the integral in (14.18) we must make use of the characteristic properties of $F(z)$. Using (14.14) and bearing in mind that $F(z)$ is real on C, we find:

$$T = \frac{1}{4i} \oint\limits_{C} (F(z) - \bar{A}\bar{z})\, (dF - A\, dz). \tag{14.20}$$

We can evaluate each of the four terms into which (14.20) can be decomposed as follows.

$$\oint\limits_{C} F\, dF = 0 \tag{14.21}$$

since F is single-valued on **C**. From (14.11) and the residue theorem, we conclude

$$\frac{1}{4i}\oint_C F(z)\,dz = -\frac{\pi}{2}\left(\frac{Ac}{a} + \frac{\bar{A}}{a^2}\right). \tag{14.22}$$

By integration by parts, we find

$$\frac{1}{4i}\oint_C \bar{z}\,dF = -\frac{1}{4i}\oint_C F\,d\bar{z} = \overline{\frac{1}{4i}\oint_C F\,dz} = -\frac{\pi}{2}\left(\frac{\overline{Ac}}{a} + \frac{A}{a^2}\right). \tag{14.23}$$

Finally, we have

$$\frac{1}{4i}\oint_C \bar{z}\,dz = \frac{1}{4i}\oint_C (x\,dx + y\,dy) + i\,(x\,dy - y\,dx) = -\frac{1}{2}\Lambda \tag{14.24}$$

where Λ is the area of **B**. Collecting all terms and using $|A| = 1$, we obtain:

$$T = \frac{1}{2}\left[2\pi\left(\mathrm{Re}\left(\frac{A^2 c}{a}\right) + \frac{1}{a^2}\right) - \Lambda\right]. \tag{14.25}$$

Let τ be the angle between the direction of the flow at infinity and the real axis; we have then $A = -e^{-i\tau}$ and in analogy to (7.9) and (7.16) we may define

$$W = 2\pi\left(\frac{1}{a^2} + \mathrm{Re}\left(\frac{c\,e^{-2i\tau}}{a}\right)\right) - \Lambda \tag{14.26}$$

as the virtual mass of **B** for a flow in the direction $e^{i\tau}$ at infinity. Thus, the virtual mass of **B** is easily computed in terms of its area and the first coefficients of the function $f(z)$ which maps its exterior upon the exterior of the unit circle.

Let us next calculate the force exerted by the field pressure upon the obstacle **B**. At each boundary point, we have according to Bernoulli's law the pressure:

$$p = \rho_0\left[c - \frac{1}{2}\mathfrak{q}^2\right], \qquad c = \text{const.} \tag{14.27}$$

in the direction of the normal $-\boldsymbol{\nu}$, i. e., exterior with respect to **D**. On a line element ds of **C** there acts a force dk with the components

$$dk_x = -p\cos(\boldsymbol{\nu}, \mathbf{x})\,ds, \qquad dk_y = -p\cos(\boldsymbol{\nu}, \mathbf{y})\,ds. \tag{14.28}$$

Let us combine these two components into the complex force vector $dk = dk_x - i\,dk_y$:

$$dk = -p\,[\cos(\mathbf{\nu}, \mathbf{x}) - i\cos(\mathbf{\nu}, \mathbf{y})]\,ds = i\,p\,d\bar{z} \tag{14.29}$$

by virtue of the relation $i\,dz/ds = \cos(\mathbf{\nu}, \mathbf{x}) + i\cos(\mathbf{\nu}, \mathbf{y})$. The total force acting on **B** is then given by the integral

$$k = i\oint_C p\,d\bar{z} = i\,\rho_0 \oint_C \left(c - \frac{1}{2}\mathfrak{q}^2\right) d\bar{z} = -\frac{1}{2}\,i\,\rho_0 \oint_C (\varphi_x{}^2 + \varphi_y{}^2)\,d\bar{z} =$$

$$= -\frac{1}{2}\,i\,\rho_0 \oint_C |F'(z)|^2\,d\bar{z} = -\frac{1}{2}\,i\,\rho_0 \oint_C F'(z)\,d\bar{F} = -\frac{1}{2}\,i\,\rho_0 \oint_C F'^2\,dz. \tag{14.30}$$

This is the "Blasius formula" expressing the force on **B** in terms of the complex potential. The last integral can immediately be evaluated by the residue theorem. We have

$$\oint_C (F'(z))^2\,dz = \oint_C \left(A - \left(\frac{A\,c}{a} + \frac{\bar{A}}{a^2}\right)\frac{1}{z^2} + \ldots\right)^2 dz = 0 \tag{14.31}$$

since only a $1/z$-term can contribute to a residue. Thus, *we have proved that every flow with a dipole singularity at infinity will exert zero force upon an obstacle.* This result which seems to contradict experience and intuition is called the "paradox of D'Alembert."

If we wish to utilize our theory of incompressible, irrotational, and steady plane flow in order to give an account of the forces created, we shall have to consider flows with additional singularities at infinity. For this purpose we shall use singularities of the vortex type considered in Section 12.

For the obstacle **B** with given boundary **C** and known mapping function $f(z)$ we construct the complex potential:

$$F(z) = -q\frac{1}{a}\left(e^{-i\tau} f(z) + \frac{e^{i\tau}}{f(z)}\right) + i\frac{\Gamma}{2\pi}\log f(z), \quad q > 0, \quad \Gamma \text{ real.} \tag{14.32}$$

This function is regular analytic in the complement **D** of **B**, except for the point at infinity where it has the development:

$$F(z) = -q\,e^{-i\tau} z + i\frac{\Gamma}{2\pi}\log z + \text{power series in } \frac{1}{z}. \tag{14.33}$$

Its real part has the form

$$(14.34)\quad \varphi(x, y) = -q(x\cos\tau + y\sin\tau) - \frac{\Gamma}{2\pi}\arg z + \text{regular harmonic terms}$$

and therefore represents the velocity potential of a dipole having the direction $e^{i\tau}$ and strength q combined with a vortex around infinity with strength Γ. Γ is called the *circulation* constant of the vortex.

It is easily seen that because $|f(z)| = 1$ on **C** the complex potential $F(z)$ is real on the boundary of the flow domain. Hence, by the Cauchy-Riemann equations in the form (13.4) we conclude that $\partial\varphi/\partial\nu = 0$ on **C**. Thus, we may interpret $F(z)$ as the complex potential of a fluid flow past **B** which has at infinity the velocity q and the direction $e^{i\tau}$, and a circulation around infinity of strength Γ.

Let us calculate the force upon **B** exerted by the flow determined by (14.32). By using the residue theorem we find from (14.30)

$$(14.35)\quad \begin{aligned} k &= -\frac{i\rho_0}{2}\oint_{C}\left(-q e^{-i\tau} + i\frac{\Gamma}{2\pi z} + \text{terms in } \frac{1}{z^2} \text{ at least}\right)^2 dz = \\ &= \rho_0 q e^{-i\tau}\Gamma i = \rho_0 \overline{w}_\infty \Gamma i \end{aligned}$$

where w_∞ is the complex vector representing the velocity of the dipole flow at infinity in magnitude and direction. Putting $w_\infty = u_\infty + i v_\infty$, we obtain in view of the definition $k = k_x - i k_y$

$$(14.36)\quad k_x = \rho_0 \Gamma v_\infty, \qquad k_y = -\rho_0 \Gamma u_\infty .$$

We recognize that the force acting on **B** is perpendicular to the direction of the flow at infinity. The above formulas are due to Kutta and Joukowski and play an important role in the theory of lift for an infinite cylindrical wing.

For the sake of completeness, let us also compute the moment of the pressures acting on **B**. For this purpose, we have to evaluate the integral

$$(14.37)\quad M = \oint_{C}(y\,dk_x - x\,dk_y) = \operatorname{Im}\left(\oint_{C} z\,dk\right).$$

Using (14.29) and (14.27), we obtain

$$M = \operatorname{Im}\left(i\rho_0\oint_{C} z\left(c - \frac{1}{2}\mathfrak{q}^2\right)d\bar z\right) = \operatorname{Im}\left(i\rho_0 c\oint_{C} z\,d\bar z - \frac{i\rho_0}{2}\oint_{C} z\,\mathfrak{q}^2\,d\bar z\right).$$

(14.38)

Since c is a real constant and since by (14.24) the integral

$$\frac{1}{2i}\oint_C z\,d\bar{z} = A \tag{14.39}$$

is also real, the first term in (14.38) does not contribute anything to the imaginary part. Hence, there remains only:

$$M = \operatorname{Im}\left(-\frac{i\rho_0}{2}\oint_C z\,|F'(z)|^2\,d\bar{z}\right) = \operatorname{Re}\left(-\frac{\rho_0}{2}\oint_C z\,F'(z)\,d\bar{F}\right) \tag{14.40}$$

and since dF is real on C, we obtain finally:

$$M = \operatorname{Re}\left(-\frac{\rho_0}{2}\oint_C z(F'(z))^2\,dz\right). \tag{14.41}$$

This is the Blasius formula for computing the moment of the fluid forces on B in terms of the complex potential.

We can evaluate the above integral if we calculate the series development of $F'(z)$ near infinity by means of (14.32) and (13.17). We find easily:

$$F'(z) = -q\,e^{-i\tau} + \frac{i\Gamma}{2\pi z} + q\left(e^{-i\tau}\frac{c}{a} + \frac{e^{i\tau}}{a^2} - \frac{b}{2\pi a q}\frac{i\Gamma}{}\right)\frac{1}{z^2} + \dots. \tag{14.42}$$

Hence, the residue theorem applied to (14.41) leads to

$$M = -\operatorname{Re}\left(2\pi i\rho_0\left(\frac{\Gamma^2}{8\pi^2} + q^2 e^{-i\tau}\left(\frac{c}{a}e^{-i\tau} + e^{i\tau}\cdot\frac{1}{a^2}\right)\right) + \frac{b}{a}\rho_0\,q\,e^{-i\tau}\,\Gamma\right). \tag{14.43}$$

We may introduce into this formula the complex force k determined in (14.35) and obtain finally:

$$M = \operatorname{Im}(c\,e^{-2i\tau})\cdot 2\pi\rho_0\frac{q^2}{a.} + \operatorname{Re}\left(i\frac{b}{a}k\right). \tag{14.44}$$

The force and the moment of a fluid flow past the body B can thus be expressed in a simple way in terms of the coefficients of the development of the mapping function $f(z)$ near infinity.

The physical interpretation of (14.44) is obvious. The term $\operatorname{Re}(i\,(b/a)\,k)$ represents the moment of the lifting force k; it can be removed if we choose the origin of the z-plane in such a way that $b = 0$, i. e., if we introduce as a new complex variable $\zeta = z + b/a$ in (13.17) and all later formulas. On the other hand

$$(14.44') \qquad M_0 = \operatorname{Im}(c\,e^{-2i\tau}) \cdot 2\pi\rho_0\,\frac{q^2}{a}$$

represents the force couple created by the fluid pressure; it is unchanged under a shift of the point of reference. If the moment of the pressure forces is mentioned without explicitly stating the point of reference, the moment M_0 is usually meant.

While the moment of the pressure forces on the obstacle is independent of the circulation constant Γ of the flow, the force k depends on it. In principle, every real value Γ is possible for this constant and the question arises as to which factors determine the circulation in an actual flow. An answer can be given in many problems by considering the velocity field of the flow, described by the analytic function

$$(14.45) \qquad F'(z) = \left(-\frac{q\,e^{-i\tau}}{a} + \frac{q\,e^{i\tau}}{a\big(f(z)\big)^2} + \frac{i\Gamma}{2\pi f(z)}\right) f'(z).$$

Since $|f(z)| > 1$ in D this represents a regular analytic function in D and leads to bounded velocities. If C is a smooth curve, as has been heretofore assumed, $f'(z)$ will be continuous in the closed region $\mathsf{D} + \mathsf{C}$ and so will $F'(z)$. Let us suppose now that C is smooth everywhere, except for a point z_e where it has a sharp corner. It can easily be seen that $f'(z)$ will be continuous everywhere on C, except at z_e where it will become infinite. Thus, $F'(z)$ would become infinite there, too, provided the factor of $f'(z)$, i. e., the term in parentheses in (14.15) does not vanish; this would lead to infinite velocity of the flow at z_e. Joukowski enunciated the following principle: the flow will attain that circulation Γ such that a finite velocity field is established. This means that the circulation constant Γ has to be determined in such a way that the factor of $f'(z)$ vanishes at the point z_e, i. e.,

$$(14.46) \qquad \Gamma = \frac{2\pi q}{a} \cdot \frac{1}{i}\left(f(z_e)\,e^{-i\tau} - e^{i\tau}\big(f(z_e)\big)^{-1}\right).$$

Thus, Joukowski's principle determines the flow in a unique way if the boundary of the obstacle B has exactly one sharp corner. In the construction of wing profiles one takes care to use this type of boundary curve in order to fix the circulation constant Γ for a given flow direction $e^{i\tau}$.

Let us return to the case of a smooth curve C and consider the function $w = f(z)$ which maps the closed curve continuously upon the unit circumference. On the circle we have $f(z) = e^{i\sigma}$ and σ varies continuously with $z \in$ **C**. We recognize from (14.45) that the analytic function $F'(z)$ vanishes exactly twice on **C**. In fact, $f'(z) \neq 0$ because of the univalence of $f(z)$ and the smoothness of **C**; hence, $F'(z)$ will vanish only if

$$\frac{q}{a}\left(e^{i(\sigma-\tau)} - e^{i(\tau-\sigma)}\right) = \frac{i\Gamma}{2\pi}, \tag{14.47}$$

i. e., if

$$\sin(\sigma - \tau) = \frac{a\Gamma}{4\pi q}. \tag{14.48}$$

For fixed τ this leads to two values

$$\sigma_1 \quad \text{and} \quad \sigma_2 = \pi + 2\tau - \sigma_1 \tag{14.49}$$

which satisfy the equation; these values correspond to two points z_1 and z_2 on **C**. At these points we have $F'(z) = 0$, i. e., the velocity components vanish and the fluid is at rest at z_1 and z_2. These two points are called the stagnation points of the flow. They can also be interpreted in the following way: the stream line $\psi = 0$ issues from infinity and approaches the boundary **C** of the obstacle; since we have on **C**, $\psi = 0$, this stream line must split into two parts which enclose **B** between them and unite behind the body to form one single stream line $\psi = 0$, returning to infinity. The stagnation points z_1 and z_2 correspond to the points where the stream line $\psi=0$ splits and reunites, respectively. For at any point with non-vanishing $F'(z)$ the direction of the flow and, hence, the tangent to the stream line is uniquely determined. Thus, the branching of a stream line can occur only at a stagnation point.

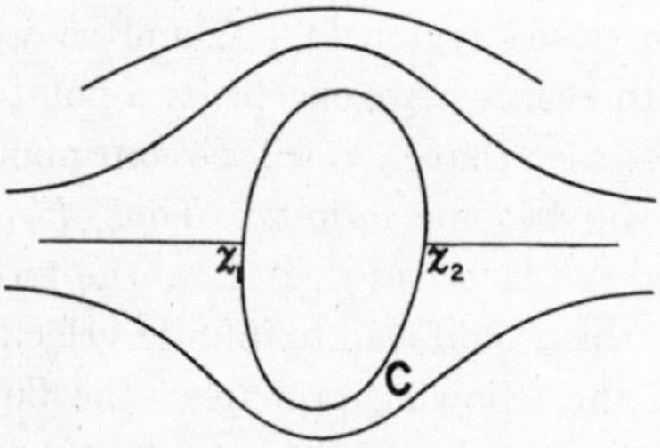

Figure 7

We have seen that the velocity of the dipole flow at infinity and the circulation constant Γ determine the stagnation points z_1 and z_2. We will now show that we may conversely choose any two points z_1 and z_2 on the boundary **C** of **B**, prescribe a speed q of the dipole flow at infinity and find a complex potential (14.32) for which the points z_1 and z_2 appear as stagnation points. We determine the points $f(z_1) = e^{i\sigma_1}$ and $f(z_2) = e^{i\sigma_2}$

which correspond to z_1 and z_2 under the conformal map of D upon the exterior of the unit circle. We determine τ by the equation

$$\tau = \frac{1}{2}(\sigma_1 + \sigma_2 - \pi) \tag{14.50}$$

which follows from (14.49). Next, we determine Γ by (14.48) and (14.50):

$$\Gamma = 4\pi q \frac{1}{a} \sin\left(\frac{\pi}{2} + \frac{1}{2}(\sigma_1 - \sigma_2)\right) = 4\pi q \frac{1}{a} \cos\left(\frac{\sigma_1 - \sigma_2}{2}\right). \tag{14.51}$$

Let us formulate the result obtained: consider a body B with boundary C and with mapping radius $r = a^{-1}$; on C we select an arc γ with the two end points z_1 and z_2. If we map the exterior D of B upon the exterior of the unit circle the arc γ becomes a circular arc subtending an angle $\omega = \sigma_1 - \sigma_2$. There exists a dipole flow with circulation at infinity which has just the endpoints z_1 and z_2 of γ as stagnation points. Its circulation constant has by (14.51) the value

$$\Gamma = 4\pi q r \cos\frac{\omega}{2}. \tag{14.52}$$

The force on B is perpendicular to the direction of the dipole flow at infinity and has by (14.35) the magnitude

$$|k| = 4\pi \rho_0 q^2 r \cos\frac{\omega}{2}. \tag{14.53}$$

Formula (14.53) expresses the lift force upon the body B in terms of the physical constants ρ_0 and q and the conformal geometric quantities r and ω. We shall call

$$l = r \cos\frac{\omega}{2} \tag{14.54}$$

the lift factor of the arc γ with respect to the obstacle B. It is a quantity which depends only upon the geometry of B and γ and will be investigated later on by means of the theory of Green's function. Its significance for problems of wing theory is obvious.

Bieberbach [8], Milne-Thomson [49], v. Mises [50], (M 2), Villat [84].

15. The variation of the Green's function: In the preceding sections we have seen that a large part of potential theory in a simply-connected domain D may be reduced to the determination of the function $f(z)$ which maps D upon the exterior of the unit circle. In particular, the Green's function of the domain D can easily be expressed in terms of $f(z)$. In spite of the fact that Green's function which depends on two complex variables is more complicated from a numerical point of view than $f(z)$ which depends only on one complex variable, it is advantageous to consider the Green's function as the more fundamental one. This becomes quite clear if one wishes to extend the theory to multiply-connected domains where no $f(z)$ exists but Green's function is still defined. But even in the case of a simply-connected domain the numerous theoretical properties of the Green's function will lead to new results for the mapping function $f(z)$.

As an illustration let us study the dependence of the mapping function $f(z)$ upon the domain D or its boundary curve C which it has to transform into the unit circumference. We shall study how $f(z)$ varies with slight deformations of the boundary curve C. It appears that the simplest way to do so is to investigate the corresponding variational behavior of the Green's function and to derive the variation of $f(z)$ from it. Let us start with a finite or infinite domain D in the complex plane with a smooth boundary curve C. If s is the length parameter along C, we define a positive, twice continuously differentiable function $v(s)$ on C and shift every boundary point $t(s)$ in the direction of the interior normal $\boldsymbol{\nu}$ of D by an amount

$$\delta\nu = \varepsilon\, v(s) \tag{15.1}$$

where $\varepsilon > 0$ is a smallness parameter. For sufficiently small values of ε the points so obtained will form a new curve C^* which is smooth, lies entirely in D and bounds a new domain $\mathsf{D}^* \subset \mathsf{D}$. We shall determine the Green's function $G^*(z, \zeta)$ for this new domain in terms of the Green's function $G(z, \zeta)$ of D, up to an error of the order of ε^2.

For this purpose we consider the difference function

$$d(z, \zeta) = G^*(z, \zeta) - G(z, \zeta) \tag{15.2}$$

which is harmonic and regular in D^* since the singularities of the two Green's functions cancel each other. On the boundary C^* of D^*, $d(z, \zeta)$ has the boundary value $-G(z, \zeta)$ since by definition G^* vanishes on C^*. Hence, we can represent $d(z, \zeta)$ by means of formula (13.14), applied to the domain D^*:

$$d(z, \zeta) = -\oint_{\mathsf{C}^*} G(t, \zeta) \frac{\partial G^*(t, z)}{\partial \nu_t}\, ds_z. \tag{15.3}$$

We now make use of the fact that we have, for fixed $\zeta \in \mathsf{D}^*$ the uniform estimate

(15.4) $G(z, \zeta) - G^*(z, \zeta) = O(\varepsilon), \qquad |\text{grad}\,[G(z, \zeta) - G^*(z, \zeta)]| = O(\varepsilon),$
$$z \in \mathsf{D}^* + \mathsf{C}^*.$$

Since G^* vanishes on C^*, $G(t, \zeta)$ is obviously of the order ε on this curve and if we replace in (15.3) G^* by G, we commit an error only of order ε^2. Thus, we find:

$$G^*(z, \zeta) - G(z, \zeta) = -\oint_{\mathsf{C}^*} G(t, \zeta) \frac{\partial G(t, z)}{\partial \nu_t} ds_t + O(\varepsilon^2). \tag{15.5}$$

Applying Green's identity to the difference domain $\mathsf{D} - \mathsf{D}^*$ and using the fact that G vanishes on C, we obtain:

$$G^*(z, \zeta) - G(z, \zeta) = -\iint_{\mathsf{D}-\mathsf{D}^*} \text{grad}\, G(t, \zeta) \cdot \text{grad}\, G(t, z)\, d\tau + O(\varepsilon^2). \tag{15.6}$$

On C grad $G(t, z)$ has the direction of the interior normal $\boldsymbol{\nu}$ and the absolute value $\dfrac{\partial G(t, z)}{\partial \nu_t}$. Hence, referring all terms to the length parameter s of C and putting

$$d\tau = \delta\nu\, ds, \tag{15.7}$$

we may write (15.6) in the notation already used in Section 10:

$$\delta G(z, \zeta) = -\oint_{\mathsf{C}} \frac{\partial G(z, t)}{\partial \nu_t} \frac{\partial G(t, \zeta)}{\partial \nu_t} \delta\nu_t\, ds_t. \tag{15.8}$$

This formula has been derived under the assumption that $\delta\nu$ is everywhere positive on C. By the reasoning of Section 10 it may be extended to the case in which $\delta\nu = \varepsilon\, v(s)$ where $v(s)$ is still twice continuously differentiable but which is no longer restricted in sign. Formula (15.8) was derived by Hadamard and is of great importance in the theory of the Green's function. It may readily be extended to the case of domains of higher connectivity, to a higher number of dimensions and to more general types of partial differential equations. It stands in complete analogy to the variational formula (10.11) for the Neumann's function and to the variational formulas which will be derived in B. III.

In order to derive a variational formula for the mapping function $f(z)$ of D from (15.8), we remark that if in (13.18) we let $\zeta \to \infty$, we have $f(\zeta) \to \infty$ and, hence, the following limit formula obtains:

$$G(z, \infty) = \frac{1}{2\pi} \log |f(z)|. \tag{15.9}$$

Let, therefore, $\zeta \to \infty$ in (15.8). By virtue of (13.18) we find:

$$\delta\left(\frac{1}{2\pi}\log|f(z)|\right) = -\oint_C \frac{\partial}{\partial\nu_t}\left(\frac{1}{2\pi}\log\left|\frac{1-f(z)\overline{f(t)}}{f(z)-f(t)}\right|\right)\frac{\partial}{\partial\nu_t}\left(\frac{1}{2\pi}\log|f(t)|\right)\delta r_t\, ds_t.$$
(15.10)

Clearly, $\delta\left(\frac{1}{2\pi}\log f(z)\right)$ is an analytic function of z with real part $\delta\left(\frac{1}{2\pi}\log|f|\right)$. We will, therefore, obtain the variation of $\log f(z)$ if we complete the harmonic functions on both sides to analytic functions; for two analytic functions which have the same real parts can differ only by an imaginary constant. Thus, we find:

$$\delta \log f(z) = -\frac{1}{2\pi}\oint_C \frac{\partial}{\partial\nu_t}\left(\log\left(\frac{1-f(z)\overline{f(t)}}{f(z)-f(t)}\right)\right)\frac{\partial}{\partial\nu_t}(\log|f(t)|)\,\delta\nu_t\, ds_t + i\,k.$$
(15.11)

In order to determine the constant k and to adapt the result to the notation of the theory of analytic functions, we subject (15.11) to a few transformations. We observe at first that the directional derivative of an analytic function may be expressed in a simple way by means of its derivative

$$(15.12)\quad \frac{\partial f}{\partial\tau} = \frac{\partial f}{\partial x}\cos(\boldsymbol{\tau}, \mathbf{x}) + \frac{\partial f}{\partial y}\cos(\boldsymbol{\tau}, \mathbf{y}) = f'(z)\,[\cos(\boldsymbol{\tau}, \mathbf{x}) + i\cos(\boldsymbol{\tau}, \mathbf{y})].$$

Hence, if $e^{i\tau}$ is the complex unit vector in the direction $\boldsymbol{\tau}$, we have simply:

$$(15.13)\quad \frac{\partial f}{\partial\tau} = f'(z)\, e^{i\tau}.$$

Similarly, we derive for the directional derivative of an anti-analytic function

$$(15.14)\quad \frac{\partial\bar{f}}{\partial\tau} = \overline{f'(z)}\, e^{-i\tau}.$$

If $t(s)$ is the parametric representation of $\mathbf{C}$ in terms of its length parameter, $\boldsymbol{\tau} = t'(s)$ will be the unit vector in the tangential direction and $\boldsymbol{\nu} = i\,t'(s)$ the unit vector in the normal direction. Thus, we find:

$$(15.15)\quad \frac{\partial}{\partial\nu_t}\left(\log\left(\frac{1-f(z)\overline{f(t)}}{f(z)-f(t)}\right)\right) = \frac{f(z)\overline{f'(t)}\cdot\overline{i\,t'}}{1-f(z)\overline{f(t)}} + \frac{i\,t'\,f'(t)}{f(z)-f(t)}.$$

Let us recall that

$$f(t(s)) = e^{i\sigma(s)} \tag{15.16}$$

since $f(z)$ maps the curve C upon the unit circumference. Hence:

$$\frac{t' f'}{f} = i\sigma'(s), \qquad \frac{1}{f} = \bar{f}. \tag{15.17}$$

Therefore, we may simplify (15.15) as follows:

$$\frac{\partial}{\partial \nu_t}\left(\log\left(\frac{1-f(z)\overline{f(t)}}{f(z)-f(t)}\right)\right) = \sigma'(s)\left(\frac{f(t)+f(z)}{f(t)-f(z)}\right). \tag{15.18}$$

By virtue of the generalized Cauchy-Riemann equation (13.4), we have

$$\frac{\partial \log |f(t)|}{\partial \nu} = -\frac{\partial \arg f(t)}{\partial s} = -\sigma'(s) \tag{15.19}$$

by (15.15). Thus, (15.11) may be put in the form:

$$\delta \log f(z) = \frac{1}{2\pi}\oint_C \frac{f(t)+f(z)}{f(t)-f(z)}(\sigma'(s_t))^2\,\delta\nu_t\,ds_t + ik. \tag{15.20}$$

Using the development (13.16) for $f(z)$ near infinity, we have

$$\log f(z) = \log z + \log a + \frac{b}{az} + \left(\frac{c}{a} - \frac{b^2}{2a^2}\right)\frac{1}{z^2} + \cdots. \tag{15.21}$$

Hence, we find by varying this formula:

$$\delta \log f(z) = \delta \log \mathrm{a} + \delta\left(\frac{b}{a}\right)\cdot\frac{1}{z} + \delta\left(\frac{c}{a} - \frac{b^2}{2a^2}\right)\frac{1}{z^2} + \cdots \tag{15.22}$$

as the series development of $\delta \log f(z)$ near infinity. Now let $z \to \infty$; comparing (15.20) with (15.22), we obtain:

$$\delta \log a = -\frac{1}{2\pi}\oint_C (\sigma'(s))^2\,\delta\nu\,ds + ik. \tag{15.23}$$

But we have normalized $f(z)$ in such a way that a is positive. Thus, we have necessarily $k = 0$ and (15.20) reduces to

$$\delta \log f(z) = \frac{1}{2\pi}\oint_C \frac{f(t)+f(z)}{f(t)-f(z)}|f'(t)|^2\,\delta\nu_t\,ds_t \tag{15.24}$$

since from (15.17) we derive $|f'(t)| = |\sigma'(s)|$ by taking the absolute value on both sides of the equation. Formula (15.24) was obtained by Julia from the Hadamard variation formula.

We note that $a = r^{-1}$ where r is the mapping radius of D. Thus, (15.23) leads to the variational formula for the mapping radius:

$$\frac{\delta r}{r} = \frac{1}{2\pi} \oint_{C} |f'(t)|^2 \, \delta\nu \, ds. \tag{15.25}$$

Hadamard [18], Julia (J 2), Lavrentieff-Shabat [37], Lévy [38], Schiffer (S 3).

16. Lavrentieff's extremum problem for lift: We shall use the variational formula for the mapping function $f(z)$ of a domain D in order to study the lift factor l which was defined at the end of Section 14. In particular, we shall consider the following extremum problem proposed by Lavrentieff: *Let z_1 and z_2 be two given points in the complex plane. Draw a closed curve* C *through these two points such that they determine on* C *an arc* γ *with maximal lift factor* l. In our investigation we shall see that the curve C must be subjected to certain auxiliary conditions in order to make the problem significant. But, in the beginning let us use the variational formula for $f(z)$ in order to derive a corresponding variational formula for l. This will lead to sufficient insight into the problem in order to treat the problem of Lavrentieff correctly.

We have by definition (14.54)

$$\delta l = \delta r \cos\frac{\omega}{2} - \frac{1}{2} r \sin\frac{\omega}{2}\, \delta\omega. \tag{16.1}$$

The variation of the mapping radius r is expressed by (15.25) and there remains only the problem of deriving the variation δw from (15.24). Let $f(z_1) = e^{i\sigma_1}$ and $f(z_2) = e^{i\sigma_2}$. In Section 14 we defined

$$\omega = \sigma_1 - \sigma_2; \tag{16.2}$$

we may assume, without loss of generality, that $\sigma_1 > \sigma_2$. Thus, we have

$$\omega = \frac{1}{i}\big(\log f(z_1) - \log f(z_2)\big). \tag{16.3}$$

Let us perform a variation of the curve C such that the points z_1 and z_2 are not moved, i. e., let $\delta\nu = 0$ in intervals near z_1 and z_2. Then, we have by (16.3) and (15.24):

$$\delta\omega = \frac{1}{2\pi i}\oint_C \left[\frac{f(t)+f(z_1)}{f(t)-f(z_1)} - \frac{f(t)+f(z_2)}{f(t)-f(z_2)}\right] |f'(t)|^2\, \delta\nu_t\, ds_t. \tag{16.4}$$

The integrand on the right remains bounded despite the fact that z_1 and z_2 lie on C since $\delta\nu = 0$ in intervals around these points. Let us put $f(t) = e^{i\tau}$. We find:

$$\delta\omega = -\frac{1}{2\pi}\oint_C \frac{2\sin(\omega/2)}{\cos(\omega/2) - \cos\left(\tau - \dfrac{\sigma_1+\sigma_2}{2}\right)} |f'(t)|^2\, \delta\nu_t\, ds_t. \tag{16.5}$$

Finally using (15.25) and (16.1), we obtain:

$$\delta l = \frac{1}{2\pi}\oint_C r\, \frac{1 - \cos\dfrac{\omega}{2}\cos\left(\tau - \dfrac{\sigma_1+\sigma_2}{2}\right)}{\cos\dfrac{\omega}{2} - \cos\left(\tau - \dfrac{\sigma_1+\sigma_2}{2}\right)} |f'(t)|^2\, \delta\nu_t\, ds_t. \tag{16.6}$$

In order to discuss this formula, we denote by γ the arc $z_1 z_2$ of C which is mapped upon the arc of angle $\omega \leqslant \pi$ on the unit circumference and its complement we denote by $\tilde{\gamma}$. Since except for $\delta\nu$ and

$$n(\tau) = \cos\omega/2 - \cos\left(\tau - \frac{\sigma_1+\sigma_2}{2}\right),$$

all factors in the integrand of (16.6) are positive, we may reduce the whole theory of the change of l to a study of the signs of these two expressions. Let us assume that we have chosen $\delta\nu$ to be always positive or zero. Then, the sign of δl will be determined by the sign of $n(\tau)$. The function $n(\tau)$ has two zeros in the interval $0 \leqslant \tau \leqslant 2\pi$ and they are $\tau = \sigma_1$, and $\tau = \sigma_2$. It has, therefore constant and opposite sign inside the arcs which correspond to γ and to $\tilde{\gamma}$. The point $(\sigma_1+\sigma_2)/2$ corresponds to a point of γ; at this point $n(\tau) = \cos\omega/2 - 1$ is negative and, hence, we conclude: $n(\tau)$ is positive on $\tilde{\gamma}$ and negative on γ.

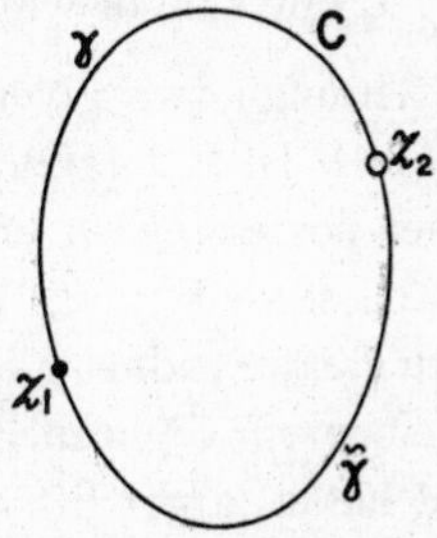

Figure 8

Using the known sign of $n(\tau)$ on C and the formula (16.6), we can now make the following statement: *The lift coefficient l of the arc γ will increase if we let C expand over $\tilde{\gamma}$ and will decrease if we let C expand over γ.* Thus, the lift coefficient of the arc γ with respect to the curve C varies monotonically with C but in the inverse sense on the two components γ and $\tilde{\gamma}$ of C. We now recognize why our initial statement of Lavrentieff's extremum problem was incomplete. There can never be a finite curve C leading to a maximum for l; for we can always expand a curve C over the arc $\tilde{\gamma}$ and increase the lift factor a little more. We need some restricting auxiliary conditions which exclude such continued deformations.

Lavrentieff adopted the requirement that the curvature of C be bounded by some upper bound P^{-1}. In this case it is clear that for the maximum curve the arc $\tilde{\gamma}$ of C must have everywhere a constant curvature P^{-1}; for if there were a point $z \in \tilde{\gamma}$ where $\tilde{\gamma}$ had a curvature less than P^{-1} we could expand $\tilde{\gamma}$ over this point z and still keep the curvature less than P^{-1}. This would lead to an increase of the lift factor in contradiction to the maximum property of C.

The same reasoning applies also to the curve γ itself. If there were some point $z \in \gamma$ where γ had a curvature less then P^{-1} we might push the contour C in at z without creating a larger curvature than P^{-1} on γ. But since the lift factor l decreases if C expands over the arc γ, it will increase if we push C in over the arc γ. This again contradicts the maximum property of C and thus we conclude: *the extremum lift factor is obtained if* C *consists of two circular arcs* γ *and* $\tilde{\gamma}$ *of radius* P *through the points* z_1 *and* z_2. These two arcs may also coincide so that C becomes one circular arc through z_1 and z_2 one side of which corresponds to $\tilde{\gamma}$ and the other to γ.

Through two given points z_1 and z_2 one can put two circular arcs of radius P $\left(\text{if } P > (1/2)\,|z_1 - z_2|\right)$, one possessing an angle less than π and the other possessing an angle larger than π. Let us suppose that $\tilde{\gamma}$ is an arc of the second type; we could put another circular arc through z_1 and z_2 with greater radius, i. e., smaller curvature, near to $\tilde{\gamma}$ and inside the domain D. The contour C* formed by the new arc and γ would be a permissible contour and has a larger lift coefficient. Hence, the original contour C could not have been an extremal one. Continuing this reasoning for all possible cases, one finds that the only configuration which does not lead by variation to a greater lift factor is the following: C *is the circular arc of radius* P *through* z_1 *and* z_2 *whose angle is less than* π; γ *is the inner* (*concave*) *side of the arc and* $\tilde{\gamma}$ *the outer* (*convex*) *side.* One verifies that this type of contour is the only possible maximum configuration.

It should be remarked, however, that the maximum thus obtained is only a local one. It is easy to see that there are other contours with larger lift factor, l, although they cannot be obtained from C by continuous variation which increases all the time and preserves the maximum curvature condition. In fact, let us replace the arc $\tilde{\gamma}$ by the circular arc through z_1 and z_2 with radius P which has the larger opening, but let us keep γ unchanged. Since we can obtain this new contour C^* by pushing $\tilde{\gamma}$ continuously into the outside D of C, its lift factor l^* will be greater than l. We may now deform C^* by pushing γ in continuously until it coincides with the concave side of the arc $\tilde{\gamma}$ on C^*; we arrive at a contour C^{**} consisting of the circular arc of radius P through z_1 and z_2 with opening larger than π and the outer side being $\tilde{\gamma}$, the inner side γ. The lift factor l^{**} of C^{**} is larger than l^* of C^* since we have decreased the interior of C^* over its γ-arc. We have further seen that we can deform C^{**} continuously such that the curvature of its arcs is less than P^{-1} and that its lift factor keeps growing. Thus, our extremum arc C represents purely a local maximum configuration.

It is also easily seen that this arc through z_1 and z_2 of radius P with opening less than π leads to the absolute maximum for the lift coefficient among all contours C through z_1 and z_2 with maximal curvature P^{-1} which lie inside the circle through z_1 and z_2 with diameter $(z_1 z_2)$.

Other extremum problems for the lift factor l can be treated in a similar way by means of the variational formula (16.6). Moreover, it provides a useful tool for studying the question of stability in wing theory in the sense that the influences of slight deformations of the contour C upon the effect of the performance of the wing can be estimated.

Lavrentieff (L 2), Lavrentieff-Shabat [37].

17. Free boundaries in plane flow: Extremum problems may be formulated for certain functionals connected with the fundamental solutions and variational theory used in order to characterize the extremal domain. As in Section 11, we shall formulate the extremal conditions in a hydrodynamical form.

At first we derive some variational formulas for the coefficients of the mapping function $f(z)$ of a given domain D upon the exterior of the unit circle. Using the development (15.22) for $\delta \log f(z)$ near infinity and developing the right-hand side of (15.24) in another power series of z by means of (13.16), we obtain by comparing the coefficients

(17.1) $$\delta \log a = -\frac{1}{2\pi} \oint_{\mathsf{C}} |f'(t)|^2 \, \delta\nu \, ds,$$

(17.2) $$\delta\left(\frac{b}{a}\right) = -\frac{1}{2\pi} \oint_{\mathsf{C}} \frac{2}{a} f(t) \, |f'(t)|^2 \, \delta\nu \, ds,$$

(17.3) $$\delta\left(\frac{c}{a}-\frac{b^2}{2a^2}\right)=\frac{1}{2\pi}\oint_C \frac{2}{a^2} f(t)\left(b-f(t)\right)|f'(t)|^2\,\delta\nu\,ds.$$

Since clearly $\delta\left(\frac{b^2}{2a^2}\right)=\frac{b}{a}\,\delta\left(\frac{b}{a}\right)$, we obtain from the last formula:

(17.4) $$\delta\left(\frac{c}{a}\right)=-\frac{1}{2\pi}\oint_C \frac{2}{a^2} f(t)^2\,|f'(t)|^2\,\delta\nu\,ds.$$

Let us now study the variation of the following composite expression:

(17.5) $$\Omega=q^2\left[\frac{1}{a^2}+\mathrm{Re}\left(\frac{c}{a}e^{-2i\omega}\right)\right]+\frac{\Gamma q}{\pi}\,\mathrm{Im}\left(\frac{b}{a}e^{-i\omega}\right)-\frac{\Gamma^2}{4\pi^2}\log a.$$

We deduce, at first, from (17.1) and (17.4):

(17.6) $$\delta\left[\frac{1}{a^2}+\mathrm{Re}\left(\frac{c}{a}e^{-2i\omega}\right)\right]=\frac{1}{2\pi}\oint_C \frac{2}{a^2}\left(1-\mathrm{Re}\left(e^{-2i\omega}f(t)^2\right)\right)|f'(t)|^2\,\delta\nu\,ds.$$

Since $|f|=1$ on C, we may write this formula in the form:

(17.7) $$\delta\left[\frac{1}{a^2}+\mathrm{Re}\left(\frac{c}{a}e^{-2i\omega}\right)\right]=-\frac{1}{2\pi}\oint_C \frac{1}{a^2}\left(e^{-i\omega}f(t)-\frac{e^{i\omega}}{f(t)}\right)^2|f'(t)|^2\,\delta\nu\,ds.$$

Next, we have by (17.2):

(17.8) $$\delta\,\mathrm{Im}\left(\frac{b}{a}e^{-i\omega}\right)=-\frac{1}{2\pi i}\oint_C \frac{1}{a}\left(f(t)\,e^{-i\omega}-\frac{e^{i\omega}}{f(t)}\right)|f'(t)|^2\,\delta\nu\,ds.$$

Thus, combining (17.1), (17.7), and (17.8), we obtain:

(17.9) $$\delta\Omega=-\frac{1}{2\pi}\oint_C\left(-\frac{q}{a}\left(e^{-i\omega}f(t)-\frac{e^{i\omega}}{f(t)}\right)+\frac{i\Gamma}{2\pi}\right)^2|f'(t)|^2\,\delta\nu\,ds.$$

Obviously, the integrand is a negative number; since $|f(t)|=1$, we may write (17.9) in the form:

(17.10) $$\delta\Omega=\frac{1}{2\pi}\oint_C\left|\left(-\frac{q}{a}\left(e^{-i\omega}-\frac{e^{i\omega}}{f(t)^2}\right)+\frac{i\Gamma}{2\pi f(t)}\right)f'(t)\right|^2\delta\nu\,ds.$$

We now recall the definition of the function (14.32):

(17.11) $$F(z)=-\frac{q}{a}\left(e^{-i\omega}f(z)+\frac{e^{i\omega}}{f(z)}\right)+\frac{i\Gamma}{2\pi}\log f(z)$$

which represents the complex potential of a flow in the domain D with a rigid wall C due to a dipole of strength q and direction ω and a circulation of strength Γ at infinity. We may now put (17.10) in the simple form:

$$\delta\Omega = \frac{1}{2\pi} \oint_{\mathsf{C}} |F'(t)|^2 \, \delta\nu \, ds. \tag{17.12}$$

This elegant variational formula and the applications we are going to make of it justify the definition of the rather complex term Ω. We observe that by means of (14.26) the expression $(1/a^2) + \operatorname{Re}\left((c/a)\, e^{-2i\omega}\right)$ is closely related to the concept of virtual mass in the direction ω.

In analogy to the problem of Section 11 we now raise the following question: let a curve C enclose a body B; consider all bodies $\tilde{\mathsf{B}}$ with given area $\tilde{V}$ and boundary $\tilde{\mathsf{C}}$ which contain the body B. We ask for that body $\tilde{\mathsf{B}}$ with minimum value for $\tilde{\Omega}$ where $\tilde{\Omega}$ is defined for fixed values q, Γ, and ω analogously to Ω but with respect to the exterior $\tilde{\mathsf{D}}$ of the body $\tilde{\mathsf{B}}$.

If we assume the existence of a sufficiently regular curve $\tilde{\mathsf{C}}$ which solves the extremum problem posed above, we shall be able to apply our variational method. We shall draw conclusions from the extremum property and translate them into hydrodynamical terms. It will appear that $\tilde{\mathsf{C}}$ is the boundary of a domain in an incompressible fluid flow consisting of the body B and fluid at rest and in equilibrium with the hydrodynamical pressures of the flow on $\tilde{\mathsf{C}}$. $\tilde{\mathsf{B}} - \mathsf{B}$ will represent, consequently, a dead water zone behind the body B under a flow due to a dipole and a vortex at infinity with prescribed direction and strength. Later we shall indicate how this reasoning can be extended to an existence proof for dead water regions.

Suppose there exists an extremum body $\tilde{\mathsf{B}}$ and that its boundary $\tilde{\mathsf{C}}$ is sufficiently smooth so that the variational formulas derived are applicable to it. We divide $\tilde{\mathsf{C}}$ into two parts: $\tilde{\mathsf{C}}_1$ consists of those boundary points of $\tilde{\mathsf{B}}$ which lie on the boundary C of B; we cannot vary the boundary $\tilde{\mathsf{C}}$ at these points arbitrarily but only in the exterior direction, if we want the new body still to contain B. $\tilde{\mathsf{C}}_2$ consists of the remaining points of $\tilde{\mathsf{C}}$; since these are separated from the body B and its boundary C, we may make near these points small, but otherwise arbitrary deformations of C without violating the condition that the larger body contains B entirely. We may call $\tilde{\mathsf{C}}_2$ the free boundary of the extremum body $\tilde{\mathsf{B}}$. Under an arbitrary variation of the boundary $\tilde{\mathsf{C}}$, we obtain the change of area $\tilde{V}$:

(17.13) $$\delta \tilde{V} = \oint_{\tilde{C}} \delta v \, ds.$$

If we deform only the free boundary $\tilde{C}_2$ of $\tilde{B}$, the only auxiliary condition to be met is that $\delta \tilde{V} = 0$. Reasoning as in Section 11 we then derive from the minimum property of $\tilde{B}$

(17.14) $$|F'(t)|^2 = \text{const.} = K \qquad \text{on } \tilde{C}_2.$$

Let us next vary the part $\tilde{C}_1$ of the boundary; here we have to keep $\delta v \geqslant 0$ if we do not want to penetrate the body B. In order to keep $\delta \tilde{V} = 0$, we must compensate for the variation of $\tilde{C}_1$ by an additional variation of $\tilde{C}_2$. Because of the minimum property of $\tilde{B}$, the total variation must lead to an increase of Ω. This is possible only if we have the inequality

(17.15) $$|F'(t)|^2 \geqslant K \qquad \text{on } \tilde{C}_1.$$

We come now to the hydrodynamical interpretation of our result. Let

(17.16) $$F(z) = \varphi(x, y) + i\,\psi(x, y).$$

We have

(17.17) $$|F'(z)|^2 = \varphi_x^2 + \varphi_y^2 = \mathfrak{q}^2$$

where $\mathfrak{q} = -\operatorname{grad} \varphi$ is the velocity vector connected with the complex potential $F(z)$. Thus, $F(z)$ represents a flow outside the body B with a dipole and circulation at infinity. This flow leaves the region $\tilde{B}$ at rest, and at those boundary points of $\tilde{B}$ which are not boundary points of B the fluid pressure is constant by virtue of (17.14), (17.17), and Bernoulli's equation (12.3). Thus, $\tilde{B}$ — B represents a dead water region behind the body B with a free boundary $\tilde{C}_2$ for a flow with the prescribed dipole and circulation at infinity.

So far, the reasoning was based on the assumption that a smooth curve $\tilde{C}$ exists which solves the extremum problem. It was shown that this curve solves at the same time an important hydrodynamical question. We shall now indicate briefly how the existence of a minimum curve $\tilde{C}$ can be proved and how certain smoothness properties can be derived for it. It is always possible to construct a minimum sequence of curves $\tilde{C}_n$ for which the corresponding values $\tilde{\Omega}_n$ converge to the greatest lower bound possible under the given side conditions. One can select them in such a way that they converge towards a limit curve $\tilde{C}$. It will be shown that this limiting curve is by its very construction rectifiable. In order to use our rather elementary method of variation, we shall have to prove that $\tilde{C}$ is even smooth. This latter part of the proof will be omitted since standard methods of variations have been developed in order to bridge the gap between rectifiable and smooth curves in extremum problems. We have inserted the proof of the rectifiability of $\tilde{C}$ since this proof has not yet been published and since it gives the reader an indication of the finer methods in the treatment of extremum problems.

In order to eliminate at least one restrictive auxiliary condition we reformulate our minimum problem as follows: *Given a body* B *with area* $V > 0$. *To determine a body* $\tilde{B}$ *containing it such that the expression* $\tilde{\Omega} - \lambda \log \tilde{V}$ *is a minimum* ($\lambda > 0$, *a given constant*).

It is easily seen that the conditions on the extremum body $\tilde{B}$ are in this case exactly the same as in the previous problem. However, we are now permitted to use variations which do not preserve the area $\tilde{V}$ of $\tilde{B}$.

It can be shown that among all contours with area V, the circle with this area (i. e., with the radius $(V/\pi)^{1/2}$) has the least mapping radius $r = a^{-1}$. Since the mapping radius of a circle is its own radius, we thus have Poincaré's inequality:

$$a^{-1} \geqslant \left(\frac{V}{\pi}\right)^{1/2}, \qquad -\log a - \frac{1}{2}\log V \geqslant -\frac{1}{2}\log \pi. \tag{17.18}$$

If we therefore choose $\lambda < \Gamma^2/8\pi^2$, we derive from the fact that $\tilde{V} > V > 0$, from the boundedness of the coefficients of the schlicht functions $\dfrac{f(z)}{a}$ and from (17.5), that the expression to be minimized is bounded from below; it can also be seen readily that the lower bound is not attained by a sequence of bodies $\tilde{B}_n$ which grow in area or in mapping radius beyond any limit. Let now $\mu = \inf(\tilde{\Omega} - \lambda \log \tilde{V})$ and consider a sequence of domains $\tilde{B}_n$ whose corresponding functionals $\tilde{\Omega}_n - \lambda \log \tilde{V}_n$ converge towards the lower limit μ. Let $f_n^{-1}(w)$ be that univalent function defined in the exterior of the unit circle which maps $|w| > 1$ upon the exterior $\tilde{D}_n$ of the body $\tilde{B}_n$. It is easy to show that these univalent functions form a normal family and that we can select, therefore, a subsequence which converges uniformly in each closed subdomain $|w| \geqslant r > 1$ to the univalent function $f^{-1}(w)$. Without loss of generality we may assume a priori that the sequence $f_n^{-1}(w)$ is itself convergent. Let $\tilde{D}$ be the domain upon which $f^{-1}(w)$ maps the domain $|w| > 1$ and let $\tilde{B}$ be its complement. Then, $\tilde{D}$ will be the kernel[1] of the domain sequence $\tilde{D}_n$ and the boundary

[1] Bieberbach [8], lst ed., p. 12; Bolza [9].

$\tilde{\mathsf{C}}$ of $\tilde{\mathsf{B}}$ will be the limit in the Fréchet sense of the boundary curves $\tilde{\mathsf{C}}_n$ of the $\tilde{\mathsf{B}}_n$. $\tilde{\Omega}$ will be the limit of the $\tilde{\Omega}_n$ and if we denote the exterior (outer) area of $\tilde{\mathsf{B}}$ by $\tilde{V}$, then we also have $\tilde{V} = \lim_{n=\infty} \tilde{V}_n$. Thus, we have found a domain $\tilde{\mathsf{D}}$ for which $\tilde{\Omega} - \lambda \log \tilde{V}$ takes on the lower limit μ.

The complement $\tilde{\mathsf{B}}$ of $\tilde{\mathsf{D}}$ may, however, be of a very complicated structure and might contain prime end continua and curves with a finite exterior area. The variational formulas derived at the beginning of this section may be inapplicable for the limit contour $\tilde{\mathsf{C}}$. We shall now show that $\tilde{\mathsf{C}}$ can always be chosen to be a rectifiable curve. For this purpose we consider the limit domain $\tilde{\mathsf{B}}$; $w = f(z) = a z + b + c/z + \ldots$ maps its exterior $\tilde{\mathsf{D}}$ upon the exterior of the unit circle. Let $\tilde{\mathsf{D}}_R \subset \tilde{\mathsf{D}}$ be the domain which corresponds to the domain $|w| > R > 1$, and let $\tilde{\mathsf{B}}_R$ be its complement. Since the function $w = (1/R) f(z) = (a/R) z + b/R + c/R \cdot 1/z + \ldots$ maps $\tilde{\mathsf{D}}_R$ upon $|w| > 1$, we can readily compute

$$\tilde{\Omega}_R = q^2 \left(\frac{R^2}{a^2} + \operatorname{Re} \left(\frac{c}{a} e^{-2i\omega} \right) \right) + \frac{\Gamma q}{\pi} \operatorname{Im} \left(\frac{b}{a} e^{-i\omega} \right) - \frac{\Gamma^2}{4\pi^2} \log \frac{a}{R} =$$

$$(17.19) \qquad = \tilde{\Omega} + q^2 \frac{R^2 - 1}{a^2} + \frac{\Gamma^2}{4\pi^2} \log R.$$

We denote by $\tilde{V}_R$ the area of $\tilde{\mathsf{B}}_R$; $\tilde{\mathsf{B}}_R$ has an analytic boundary $\tilde{\mathsf{C}}_R$ and by definition we have on $\tilde{\mathsf{C}}_R$ the equality:

$$(17.20) \qquad G(z, \infty) = \frac{1}{2\pi} \log |f(z)| = \frac{1}{2\pi} \log R,$$

where $G(z, \infty)$ is the Green's function of $\tilde{\mathsf{D}}$. On the contour $\tilde{\mathsf{C}}_{R+\Delta R}$ we have correspondingly

$$(17.21) \qquad G(z', \infty) = \frac{1}{2\pi} \log |f(z')| = \frac{1}{2\pi} \log (R + \triangle R).$$

Now let z' lie at a distance $+ \delta\nu$ on the normal at z to $\tilde{\mathsf{C}}_R$; subtracting (17.20) from (17.21), we find

$$(17.22) \qquad \frac{\partial G(z, \infty)}{\partial \nu} \delta\nu = \frac{1}{2\pi} \frac{\triangle R}{R} + O(\triangle R^2).$$

The difference in area $\tilde{V}_{R+\Delta R} - \tilde{V}_R$ can be expressed by the formula:

$$(17.23) \qquad \triangle \tilde{V} = \oint_{\tilde{\mathsf{C}}_R} \delta\nu \, ds = \frac{\triangle R}{2\pi R} \oint_{\tilde{\mathsf{C}}_R} \frac{ds}{(\partial G/\partial \nu)} + O(\triangle R^2)$$

whence

$$\frac{d\tilde{V}_R}{dR} = \frac{1}{2\pi R} \oint_{\tilde{C}_R} \frac{ds}{(\partial G/\partial \nu)}. \tag{17.24}$$

Since further, by Green's identity,

$$\oint_{\tilde{C}_R} \frac{\partial G}{\partial \nu} ds = 1 \tag{17.25}$$

we have

$$\frac{d\tilde{V}_R}{dR} = \frac{1}{2\pi R} \oint_{\tilde{C}_R} \frac{ds}{(\partial G/\partial \nu)} \cdot \oint_{\tilde{C}_R} \frac{\partial G}{\partial \nu} ds \geqslant \frac{1}{2\pi R} \left(\oint_{\tilde{C}_R} ds \right)^2 \tag{17.26}$$

by virtue of the Schwarz inequality

$$\left(\int_C a\, b\, ds \right)^2 \leqslant \int_C a^2\, ds \cdot \int_C b^2\, ds \tag{17.27}$$

applied to (17.24) with $a = \left(\frac{\partial G}{\partial \nu}\right)^{-1/2}$, $b = \left(\frac{\partial G}{\partial \nu}\right)^{1/2}$. Let L_R be the length of $\tilde{C}_R$. Then, we may write (17.26) in the form

$$\frac{d\tilde{V}_R}{dR} \geqslant \frac{L_R{}^2}{2\pi R}. \tag{17.28}$$

By definition of the outer area of $\tilde{B}$, we have

$$\tilde{V}_{R_0} - \tilde{V} = \int_1^{R_0} d\tilde{V}_R \geqslant \int_1^{R_0} \frac{L_R{}^2}{2\pi R} dR. \tag{17.29}$$

Let $U = \inf L_R{}^2$ in the interval $1 \leqslant R \leqslant R_0$. We then arrive at the estimate

$$\tilde{V}_{R_0} - \tilde{V} \geqslant \frac{U}{2\pi} \log R_0. \tag{17.30}$$

We observe next that $\tilde{B}_{R_0}$ contains the body B and hence by the minimum property of $\tilde{B}$ we must have:

$$\begin{aligned} \tilde{\Omega} - \lambda \log \tilde{V} \leqslant \tilde{\Omega}_{R_0} - \lambda \log \tilde{V}_{R_0} \leqslant \tilde{\Omega} + q^2 \frac{R_0{}^2 - 1}{a^2} + \\ + \frac{\Gamma^2}{4\pi^2} \log R_0 - \lambda \log \left(\tilde{V} + \frac{U}{2\pi} \log R_0 \right) \end{aligned} \tag{17.31}$$

by virtue of (17.19) and (17.30). We thus arrive at the following inequality, valid for all values $1 \leqslant R \leqslant R_0$:

$$(17.32) \qquad 0 \leqslant q^2 \frac{R^2 - 1}{a^2} + \frac{\Gamma^2}{4\pi^2} \log R - \lambda \log \left(1 + \frac{U}{2\pi \tilde{V}} \log R. \right).$$

Dividing this inequality by $R - 1$ and letting $R \to 1$; we obtain in the limit

$$(17.33) \quad 0 \leqslant 2 \frac{q^2}{a^2} + \frac{\Gamma^2}{4\pi^2} - \lambda \frac{U}{2\pi \tilde{V}}, \quad \text{i. e.,} \quad U \leqslant \frac{2\pi \tilde{V}}{\lambda} \left(\frac{2 q^2}{a^2} + \frac{\Gamma^2}{4\pi^2} \right).$$

This shows that the lower limit of the lengths L_R of the level curves $\tilde{\mathsf{C}}_R$ is bounded from above uniformly for all R_0. Hence, there exists a sequence of curves $\tilde{\mathsf{C}}_R$ with bounded length which converges to the limit contour $\tilde{\mathsf{C}}$. By a theorem of Carathéodory[1] we can select a subsequence of these curves which converges in the Fréchet sense to a rectifiable curve. Thus, $\tilde{\mathsf{C}}$ itself must be rectifiable.

In order to apply our variational technique we would have to prove that $\tilde{\mathsf{C}}$ is also continuously differentiable. This proof can be given by using methods of interior variation. In order to apply these it is necessary to show first that $\tilde{\mathsf{C}}$ is rectifiable as we have done above; the rest of the proof is then a straightforward application of the calculus of interior variations. We shall not enter into it here since the development of this method would lead us far from our main topic.

In this section we have shown how the variational formulas for the Green's function and the mapping function may be utilized to relate some problems in conformal mapping with the theory of free boundaries in a plane flow. We have given brief indications of how the theory of normal families in the theory of analytic functions can be applied to an existence proof for free boundaries of plane flows. We have considered here only flows with a dipole and circulation at infinity; there is no difficulty in extending this method to other distributions of sources, sinks, and vortices.

It should also be observed that (17.12) implies a monotonic dependence of the term Ω upon the body B. Since Ω is easily evaluated for circular bodies, this remark leads to obvious estimates for the functional Ω and hence, in particular, for the virtual mass and the mapping radius of B. Formulas (17.4) and (14.44) also lead to a variational formula for the moment M exerted by the flow on B.

Pólya (P 5).

---

[1]Carathéodory (C 1), Bolza [9], Garabedian-Lewy-Schiffer (G 3 a), Garabedian-Schiffer (G 5 a), Garabedian-Spencer (G 6).

18. The complex kernel function and its applications: We have given various applications of the variational formula (15.8) for the Green's function and in the last two sections studied extremum problems in fluid dynamics by means of it. We shall now show how purely formal considerations concerning this formula lead to very important functions of the domain D considered.

We observe at first that for $z \in \mathsf{C}$ and $\zeta \in \mathsf{D}$ we have in

$$H_z(\zeta) = \frac{\partial G(z, \zeta)}{\partial \nu_z} \tag{18.1}$$

a harmonic function of ζ which is positive in D since $G(z, \zeta) = 0$ for $z \in \mathsf{C}$ and $G(z, \zeta) > 0$ for $z \in \mathsf{D}$. Further for $\zeta \in \mathsf{C}$ and $z \in \mathsf{D} + \mathsf{C}$, $z \neq \zeta$, we have $G(z, \zeta) = 0$, so we obtain for fixed $\zeta \in \mathsf{C}$ by differentiation with respect to z:

$$\frac{\partial G(z, \zeta)}{\partial \nu_z} = H_z(\zeta) = 0, \qquad \text{for} \qquad \zeta \in \mathsf{C}, \qquad \zeta \neq z. \tag{18.2}$$

Finally, it can easily be seen that $H_z(\zeta)$ becomes infinite if ζ approaches the point z along any path in D which is not tangent to the boundary C. This highly singular behavior of the function $H_z(\zeta)$ on the boundary C of D makes it understandable why the integral

$$\varphi(\zeta) = \oint_{\mathsf{C}} \frac{\partial G(z, \zeta)}{\partial \nu_z} \lambda(z)\, ds_z, \qquad \lambda(z) \text{ continuous on } \mathsf{C}, \tag{18.3}$$

represents a harmonic function in D which for $\zeta \to \zeta_0 \in \mathsf{C}$ has the limiting value $\lambda(\zeta_0)$.

Now let ζ be a point on C, different from z. Since $H_z(\zeta) = 0$ on C and is positive in D, we have clearly

$$\mathfrak{G}(z, \zeta) = \frac{\partial H_z(\zeta)}{\partial \nu_\zeta} = \frac{\partial^2 G(z, \zeta)}{\partial \nu_z \, \partial \nu_\zeta} > 0, \qquad \text{for} \qquad z \neq \zeta, \qquad z \in \mathsf{C}, \qquad \zeta \in \mathsf{C} \tag{18.4}$$

The function $\mathfrak{G}(z, \zeta)$ is defined only on the boundary curve C of D; it is continuous and positive for $z \neq \zeta$, but becomes strongly infinite for $z \to \zeta$.

In order to apply the function $\mathfrak{G}(z, \zeta)$ to boundary value problems for harmonic functions, we must study the singularity of $\mathfrak{G}(z, \zeta)$ for $z = \zeta$ in greater detail. Let us suppose, for sake of simplicity, that the boundary C of the domain considered consists of analytic curves. It can then be shown by the reasoning of (B. II.6) that

$$\text{(18.5)} \qquad \mathfrak{H}_z(\zeta) = \frac{\partial G(z, \zeta)}{\partial \nu_z} - \frac{1}{2\pi} \frac{\partial}{\partial \nu_z}\left(\log \frac{1}{|z-\zeta|}\right), \qquad z \in \mathsf{C}, \qquad \zeta \in \mathsf{D}$$

is a regular harmonic function of ζ in the closed region $\mathsf{D} + \mathsf{C}$. It has for $\zeta \to \mathsf{C}$ the continuous boundary values

$$\text{(18.5')} \qquad \mathfrak{H}_z(\zeta) = -\frac{1}{2\pi} \frac{\partial}{\partial \nu_z}\left(\log \frac{1}{|z-\zeta|}\right), \qquad z \in \mathsf{C}, \qquad \zeta \in \mathsf{C},$$

since $\dfrac{\partial G(z, \zeta)}{\partial \nu_z}$ vanishes for $\zeta \in \mathsf{C}$. It should be remarked that $\mathfrak{H}_z(\zeta)$ also remains finite if ζ runs along C to z; this quantity can be easily expressed in geometric terms and is well known in potential theory [Courant-Hilbert [13], vol. II, p. 269—270]. Furthermore we have

$$\text{(18.5'')} \qquad \frac{\partial \mathfrak{H}_z(\zeta)}{\partial \nu_\zeta} = \mathfrak{G}(z, \zeta) - \frac{1}{2\pi} \frac{\partial^2}{\partial \nu_z\, \partial \nu_\zeta}\left(\log \frac{1}{|z-\zeta|}\right)$$

and since $\mathfrak{G}(z, \zeta)$ is assumed given and $\dfrac{\partial^2}{\partial \nu_z\, \partial \nu_\zeta}\left(\log \dfrac{1}{|z-\zeta|}\right)$ is a simple geometric term, we know also the normal derivative of $\mathfrak{H}_z(\zeta)$ on C. If we know the values on C of a harmonic function ψ and its normal derivative $\partial\psi/\partial\nu$, we may represent it in D by means of the elementary Green's formula

$$\text{(18.6)} \qquad \psi(\zeta) = \frac{1}{2\pi} \oint_{\mathsf{C}} \left(\frac{\partial}{\partial \nu_t}\left(\log \frac{1}{|t-\zeta|}\right) \psi(t) - \log \frac{1}{|t-\zeta|} \frac{\partial \psi(t)}{\partial \nu}\right) ds_t.$$

Thus, we can compute $\mathfrak{H}_z(\zeta)$ in D in an elementary way and, hence, $\dfrac{\partial G(z, \zeta)}{\partial \nu_z}$. But once $\dfrac{\partial G(z, \zeta)}{\partial \nu_z}$ is known in D, we can solve every boundary value problem for D by means of (13.14).

If we carry out the various steps indicated here, we arrive after simple calculations at the following representation of a harmonic function $h(\zeta)$ in terms of its boundary values $h(z)$:

$$h(\zeta) = \frac{1}{2\pi} \int_{\mathsf{C}} \frac{\partial}{\partial \nu_z}\left(\log \frac{1}{|z-\zeta|}\right) h(z)\, ds_z$$

$$\text{(18.6')} \qquad - \frac{1}{4\pi^2} \int_{\mathsf{C}} \int_{\mathsf{C}} \left[\frac{\partial}{\partial \nu_t}\left(\log \frac{1}{|t-\zeta|}\right) \frac{\partial}{\partial \nu_z}\left(\log \frac{1}{|z-t|}\right) + \right.$$

$$\left. + \log \frac{1}{|t-\zeta|} \left(2\pi\, \mathfrak{G}(z, t) - \frac{\partial^2}{\partial \nu_z\, \partial \nu_t}\left(\log \frac{1}{|z-t|}\right)\right)\right] h(z)\, ds_z\, ds_t.$$

Thus we have shown that a knowledge of $\mathfrak{G}(z, \zeta)$ alone enables us to solve the boundary value problem by simple integrations.

The reduction of the Dirichlet problem to the function $\mathfrak{G}(z, \zeta)$ is rather remarkable. This function depends on only two variables, say the arc lengths corresponding to z and ζ on C, while Green's function depends on four variables, namely the coordinates of z and ζ in D. For any numerical treatment of boundary value problems, the function $\mathfrak{G}(z, \zeta)$ seems preferable. Its only serious disadvantage lies in its high order singularity for $z = \zeta$.

The significance of the function $\mathfrak{G}(z, \zeta)$ is clearly exhibited in the variational formula (15.8). Let z and ζ be two points on C and perform a variation of C which leaves small arcs of C near z and ζ unchanged. It can be shown that the equation (15.8) can be differentiated with respect to z and ζ, and we obtain[1]

$$\delta\mathfrak{G}(z, \zeta) = -\oint_{\mathsf{C}} \mathfrak{G}(z, t)\, \mathfrak{G}(t, \zeta)\, \delta\nu_t\, ds_t. \tag{18.7}$$

This is a particularly simple variational formula since it expresses the change of the function $\mathfrak{G}$ in terms of the function itself without derivatives intervening as in (15.8). The elegance of the variational formula (18.7) drew the attention of Hadamard to the significance of the function $\mathfrak{G}(z, \zeta)$ and to its role in potential theory. The main objection to its systematic use was its singular behavior if both argument points coincide.

We shall now introduce a function which is regular in the domain D, is closely related to $\mathfrak{G}(z, \zeta)$ and possesses as simple a variational formula. For this purpose it will be convenient to use a notation introduced by Wirtinger for certain complex differential operators. We define

$$\frac{\partial}{\partial z} = \frac{1}{2}\left(\frac{\partial}{\partial x} - i\,\frac{\partial}{\partial y}\right), \qquad \frac{\partial}{\partial \bar{z}} = \frac{1}{2}\left(\frac{\partial}{\partial x} + i\,\frac{\partial}{\partial y}\right) \tag{18.8}$$

and may now differentiate every function $a(x, y)$ with respect to the complex variables z or $\bar{z}$ provided that $a(x, y)$ possesses first partial derivatives in x and y. It is important to observe that for an analytic complex valued function $f(z) = a(x, y) + i\,b(x, y)$ one has by virtue of the Cauchy-Riemann differential equations:

$$\frac{\partial f}{\partial z} = \frac{1}{2}\left(\frac{\partial a}{\partial x} - i\,\frac{\partial a}{\partial y}\right) + \frac{i}{2}\left(\frac{\partial b}{\partial x} - i\,\frac{\partial b}{\partial y}\right) = \frac{\partial a}{\partial x} + i\,\frac{\partial b}{\partial x} = f'(z) \tag{18.9}$$

[1] P. Lévy [38].

and

$$\frac{\partial f}{\partial \bar{z}} = \frac{1}{2}\left(\frac{\partial a}{\partial x} + i\frac{\partial a}{\partial y}\right) + \frac{i}{2}\left(\frac{\partial b}{\partial x} + i\frac{\partial b}{\partial y}\right) = 0 \tag{18.10}$$

so that our new notation is consistent with the formalism of the theory of analytic functions.

Consider now, for $z \in \mathsf{C}$, the expression

$$\frac{\partial G(z,\zeta)}{\partial z}\frac{dz}{ds} = \frac{1}{2}\left(\frac{\partial G}{\partial x} - i\frac{\partial G}{\partial y}\right)\left(\frac{dx}{ds} + i\frac{dy}{ds}\right) = \frac{1}{2}\left(\frac{\partial G}{\partial x}\frac{dx}{ds} + \frac{\partial G}{\partial y}\frac{dy}{ds}\right) +$$

$$+\frac{i}{2}\left(\frac{\partial G}{\partial x}\frac{dy}{ds} - \frac{\partial G}{\partial y}\frac{dx}{ds}\right). \tag{18.11}$$

The real part of this expression represents $\dfrac{\partial G(z,\zeta)}{\partial s_z}$ and hence vanishes. The vector $\left(-\dfrac{dy}{ds}, \dfrac{dx}{ds}\right)$ has the direction of the interior normal at z with respect to C and consequently we have:

$$\frac{\partial G(z,\zeta)}{\partial z}\cdot\frac{dz}{ds} = -\frac{i}{2}\frac{\partial G(z,\zeta)}{\partial \nu_z} \tag{18.12}$$

where $\dfrac{dz}{ds} = \dfrac{dx}{ds} + i\dfrac{dy}{ds}$ is the complex unit vector in the tangential direction. By means of (18.12) and the corresponding relation

$$\frac{\partial G(z,\zeta)}{\partial \bar{z}}\frac{d\bar{z}}{ds} = \frac{i}{2}\frac{\partial G(z,\zeta)}{\partial \nu_z} \tag{18.13}$$

obtained by taking complex conjugate values in (18.12), we may write (15.8) in the form:

$$\delta G(z,\zeta) = -4\oint_{\mathsf{C}} \frac{\partial G(z,t)}{\partial \bar{t}}\frac{\partial G(t,\zeta)}{\partial t}\,\delta\nu_t\,ds_t. \tag{18.14}$$

Differentiating this relation with respect to z and $\bar{\zeta}$, we obtain

$$\delta\frac{\partial^2 G(z,\zeta)}{\partial z\,\partial\bar{\zeta}} = -4\oint_{\mathsf{C}} \frac{\partial^2 G(z,t)}{\partial z\,\partial\bar{t}}\cdot\frac{\partial^2 G(t,\zeta)}{\partial t\,\partial\bar{\zeta}}\,\delta\nu_t\,ds_t. \tag{18.15}$$

This result can be written in a particularly elegant form if we define

$$K(z,\bar{\zeta}) = -4\frac{\partial^2 G(z,\zeta)}{\partial z\,\partial\bar{\zeta}}. \tag{18.16}$$

With this notation we have

$$\delta K(z, \overline{\zeta}) = \oint_C K(z, \overline{t})\, K(t, \overline{\zeta})\, \delta\nu_t\, ds_t, \tag{18.17}$$

a variational formula as simple as that of $\mathfrak{G}(z, \zeta)$.

Let us now study the function $K(z,\overline{\zeta})$ in some detail. Since $G(z, \zeta)$ is harmonic in both arguments it can easily be shown that K is an analytic function of z and of $\overline{\zeta}$. From the identity $\log|z - \zeta| = (1/2)\log(z - \zeta) + (1/2)\log(\overline{z} - \overline{\zeta})$ it is obvious that this term is destroyed by the operator $\partial^2/\partial z\, \partial\overline{\zeta}$. Since $G(z, \zeta)$ is a combination of $\log|z - \zeta|$ and a regular harmonic function in D, *the function* $K(z,\overline{\zeta})$ *is therefore regular analytic throughout* D *in both arguments,* even if z and ζ coincide. Thus, we have found a certain derivative of the Green's function which is regular analytic in D and which possesses a very simple variational formula (18.17).

Because of the great formal similarity between the variational formulas (18.7) and (18.17) one would suspect a close relation between $\mathfrak{G}(z, \zeta)$ and $K(z,\overline{\zeta})$. This follows indeed easily from (18.12) and (18.13); we differentiate the identity (18.12) with respect to $\overline{\zeta}$ and multiply the result by $\dfrac{d\overline{\zeta}}{ds}$. Using (18.13), we obtain

$$\frac{\partial^2 G(z, \zeta)}{\partial z\, \partial\overline{\zeta}} \frac{dz}{ds} \frac{d\overline{\zeta}}{ds} = \frac{1}{4} \frac{\partial^2 G(z, \zeta)}{\partial\nu_z\, \partial\nu_\zeta} = \frac{1}{4} \mathfrak{G}(z, \zeta), \qquad \text{for} \quad z \in \mathsf{C}, \quad \zeta \in \mathsf{C}. \tag{18.18}$$

Hence, *the function* $K(z,\overline{\zeta})$ *has on* C *the absolute value* $\mathfrak{G}(z, \zeta)$. We see that $K(z,\overline{\zeta})$ will become strongly infinite if z and ζ converge to the same point z_0 on the boundary C of the domain D considered.

The function $K(z,\overline{\zeta})$ has a very remarkable property with respect to all functions $f(z)$ which are analytic in D and continuous in the closed region D + C. In fact, consider the integral

$$I(z) = \iint_D K(z, \overline{\zeta})\, f(\zeta)\, d\tau_\zeta. \tag{18.19}$$

It represents an analytic function of $z \in \mathsf{D}$ and can easily be evaluated by integration by parts. We use the complex form of Green's identity

$$\iint_D a \frac{\partial b}{\partial \bar{\zeta}} d\tau_\zeta = -\frac{i}{2} \oint_C a\, b\, d\zeta - \iint_D b \frac{\partial a}{\partial \bar{\zeta}} d\tau_\zeta \tag{18.20}$$

which holds for all functions $a(x, y)$, $b(x, y)$, continuously differentiable in $\mathsf{D} + \mathsf{C}$. This formula can easily be deduced from the definition (18.8) of the complex differentiation operators and the usual Green's theorem for integration by parts. If we wish to apply (18.20) to the case of the function $K(z, \bar{\zeta})$, we have to take into account the fact that by (18.16)

$$K(z, \bar{\zeta}) = \frac{\partial}{\partial \bar{\zeta}} \left(-4 \frac{\partial G(z, \zeta)}{\partial z} \right) \tag{18.21}$$

and that $\partial G / \partial z$ has a singularity at $\zeta = z$. Thus, we apply (18.20) first to the domain D_ε which is obtained by removing from D the interior of a small circle C_ε with radius ε and center at z. We then obtain:

$$\iint_{\mathsf{D}_\varepsilon} K(z, \bar{\zeta}) f(\zeta)\, d\tau_\zeta = -\frac{i}{2} \oint_{\mathsf{C}+\mathsf{C}_\varepsilon} \left(-4 \frac{\partial G(z, \zeta)}{\partial z} \right) f(\zeta)\, d\zeta. \tag{18.22}$$

since by virtue of (18.10) we have $\partial f / \partial \bar{\zeta} = 0$. Since further $G(z, \zeta) \equiv 0$ in z for $\zeta \in \mathsf{C}$, we also have $(\partial G / \partial z) = 0$ for $\zeta \in \mathsf{C}$. Hence, there remains:

$$\iint_{\mathsf{D}_\varepsilon} K(z, \bar{\zeta}) f(\zeta)\, d\tau_\zeta = 2 i \oint_{\mathsf{C}_\varepsilon} \frac{\partial G(z, \zeta)}{\partial z} f(\zeta)\, d\zeta. \tag{18.23}$$

Using the fact that

$G(z, \zeta) = -(1/4\pi) \log(z - \zeta) - (1/4\pi) \log(\bar{z} - \bar{\zeta}) +$ *a reg. harm. function*,

we may write (18.23) as follows:

$$\iint_{\mathsf{D}_\varepsilon} K(z, \bar{\zeta}) f(\zeta)\, d\tau_\zeta = \frac{1}{2\pi i} \oint_{\mathsf{C}_\varepsilon} \frac{f(\zeta)}{z - \zeta} d\zeta + O(\varepsilon). \tag{18.24}$$

The integration over C_ε is to be extended in the clockwise sense, since C_ε is to be conceived as a boundary curve of D_ε. By Cauchy's theorem, the first right-hand integral is $f(z)$; now letting $\varepsilon \to 0$, we obtain in the limit the identity:

$$\iint_{\mathsf{D}} K(z, \bar{\zeta}) f(\zeta)\, d\tau_\zeta = f(z). \tag{18.25}$$

The function $K(z,\bar{\zeta})$ *has, therefore, the property of reproducing every function* $f(\zeta)$ *which is analytic in* D *and continuous in* D + C *under the above process of integration.* It is called the *reproducing kernel* of this class of analytic functions in D. One can easily derive from the definition of the kernel $K(z,\bar{\zeta})$ by (18.16) that it has the "hermitian" symmetry

$$K(\zeta,\bar{z}) = \overline{K(z,\bar{\zeta})}. \tag{18.26}$$

We shall show that this symmetry and the reproducing property (18.25) determine the kernel $K(z,\bar{\zeta})$ in a unique way. In fact, suppose there were a second kernel $K^*(z,\bar{\zeta})$, analytic in z and $\bar{\zeta}$, also satisfying both equations (18.25) and (18.26). We would have by (18.25) with $K^*(\zeta,\bar{t})$ instead of $f(\zeta)$:

$$\iint_D K(z,\bar{\zeta})\, K^*(\zeta,\bar{t})\, d\tau_\zeta = K^*(z,\bar{t}). \tag{18.27}$$

But we can also write the above integral in the form

$$\iint_D \overline{K^*(t,\bar{\zeta})\, K(\zeta,\bar{z})}\, d\tau_\zeta = \overline{K(t,\bar{z})} = K(z,\bar{t}) \tag{18.28}$$

since $K^*(t,\bar{\zeta})$ will reproduce the analytic function $K(\zeta,\bar{z})$. Comparing (18.27) with (18.28) shows the uniqueness of a reproducing kernel with hermitian symmetry:

$$K^*(z,\bar{t}) = K(z,\bar{t}). \tag{18.29}$$

Putting $f(\zeta) = K(\zeta,\bar{z})$ in (18.25), we obtain the identity

$$\iint_D |K(z,\bar{\zeta})|^2\, d\tau_\zeta = \iint_D K(z,\bar{\zeta})\, K(\zeta,\bar{z})\, d\tau_\zeta = K(z,\bar{z}). \tag{18.30}$$

This shows that the particular derivative $K(z,\bar{z})$ of the Green's function is always positive. The significance of this expression becomes clear if we take the identity (18.25) for an arbitrary permissible function $f(\zeta)$, and apply Schwarz' inequality to it. We obtain by virtue of (18.30)

$$|f(z)|^2 \leqslant K(z,\bar{z}) \iint_D |f(\zeta)|^2\, d\tau_\zeta. \tag{18.31}$$

This is a rather important inequality since it permits us to estimate the value of an analytic function $f(z)$ at each point of the domain D if we only know one characteristic number, its norm $||f||$ defined by

$$\|f\|^2 = \iint_D |f(\zeta)|^2 \, d\tau_\zeta. \tag{18.32}$$

It can be shown[1] that *all functions* $f(\zeta)$ *which are analytic in* D *and have a bounded norm* $\|f\|$ *are reproduced by the kernel* $K(z,\bar{\zeta})$ *according to* (18.25). These functions form a Hilbert space and the identity (18.25) is of central importance in the general theory of this space.

We wish to stress here the importance of the reproducing property (18.25) for the actual construction of the kernel $K(z,\bar{\zeta})$ and of the Green's function $G(z,\zeta)$. It is well known that for a given domain D one can construct a complete orthonormal system of functions $\{f_\nu(\zeta)\}$ analytic in $\mathsf{D}+\mathsf{C}$, i. e., a system with the following properties:

a) The system is orthonormal, i. e., for any two functions $f_\nu(\zeta)$ and $f_\mu(\zeta)$ of the set we have:

$$\iint_D f_\nu(\zeta) \overline{f_\mu(\zeta)} \, d\tau_\zeta = \delta_{\nu\mu}. \tag{18.33}$$

b) The system is complete, i. e., each function $f(\zeta)$ which is analytic in D and continuous in $\mathsf{D}+\mathsf{C}$ can be developed into a Fourier series

$$f(\zeta) = \sum_{\nu=1}^{\infty} a_\nu f_\nu(\zeta), \qquad a_\nu = \iint_D f(\zeta) \overline{f_\nu(\zeta)} \, d\tau_\zeta, \tag{18.34}$$

which converges uniformly in each closed subdomain of D.

In case of a simply-connected finite domain bounded by a simple closed curve the functions $f_\nu(\zeta)$ may be chosen as polynomials of degree ν. There are various ways of constructing complete orthonormal systems for a given domain D and there exist infinitely many different systems for a fixed domain D. Let us select one such system and develop the kernel $K(z,\bar{\zeta})$ considered as an analytic function of z for a fixed $\zeta \in \mathsf{D}$. By (18.34) and (18.25), we find

$$K(z,\bar{\zeta}) = \sum_{\nu=1}^{\infty} f_\nu(z) \overline{f_\nu(\zeta)}. \tag{18.34'}$$

This result gives an elegant representation for the reproducing kernel $K(z,\bar{\zeta})$ in terms of any complete orthonormal system for the domain D. The right-hand side is called the *kernel function* of the orthonormal system $\{f_\nu(\zeta)\}$.

[1] Bergman [6].

We recognize that all complete orthonormal systems of a given domain D have the same kernel function and that this kernel function is closely related to the Green's function of the domain.

Let us illustrate the construction of the kernel function $K(z,\overline{\zeta})$ in terms of a complete orthonormal system $\{f_\nu(z)\}$ in the case in which D is the interior of the unit circle. Here, we may use the system

$$f_\nu(z) = \left(\frac{\nu}{\pi}\right)^{\frac{1}{2}} z^{\nu-1}, \qquad \nu = 1, 2, \ldots \tag{18.35}$$

which is easily seen to be complete and orthonormal in the domain considered. Hence, we find by (18.34′):

$$K(z,\overline{\zeta}) = \frac{1}{\pi}\sum_{\nu=1}^{\infty} \nu (z\overline{\zeta})^{\nu-1} = \frac{1}{\pi(1-z\overline{\zeta})^2}. \tag{18.36}$$

This result could, of course, have been derived immediately from the formula

$$G(z,\zeta) = \frac{1}{2\pi}\log\left|\frac{1-z\overline{\zeta}}{z-\zeta}\right| \tag{18.37}$$

for the Green's function of the unit circle and serves only as an illustration of the method.

Let us give an application of the formula (18.34′) which is of particular interest in hydrodynamical questions. Let us assume that D is a simply-connected domain bounded by a smooth curve C and that it contains the point at infinity. In Section 13 we saw that Green's function $G(z,\zeta)$ can easily be determined if the function (13.16) which maps D upon the exterior of the unit circle so that the points at infinity correspond is known. We shall show how this mapping function $f(z)$ can be obtained by means of a complete orthonormal set $\{f_\nu(z)\}$ in D. We remark, at first, that any function $f_\nu(z)$ with a bounded norm over the infinite domain D must vanish at infinity at least like $1/z^2$, i. e., must have a series development near infinity of the form:

$$f_\nu(z) = \frac{\alpha_\nu}{z^2} + \frac{\beta_\nu}{z^3} + \ldots. \tag{18.38}$$

In terms of the functions $\{f_\nu(z)\}$ the kernel function $K(z,\overline{\zeta})$ may be constructed by means of (18.34). Using the representation (13.18) for the Green's function and definition (18.16) for the kernel, we find after elementary calculations:

(18.39) $$K(z,\bar{\zeta}) = \frac{f'(z)\overline{f'(\zeta)}}{\pi\left(1-f(z)\overline{f(\zeta)}\right)^2}.$$

In view of the series development (13.16) for $f(z)$ near infinity, we find that $K(z,\bar{\zeta})$ vanishes like $1/z^2$ or $1/\bar{\zeta}^2$ if either of the variables approaches infinity. This is, of course, to be expected since $K(z,\bar{\zeta})$ has a finite norm in D with respect to each variable. It is easily seen from (18.39) and (13.16) that

(18.40) $$\lim_{\zeta\to\infty} \bar{\zeta}^2 K(z,\bar{\zeta}) = \frac{1}{\pi a}\frac{f'(z)}{f(z)^2}.$$

On the other hand, from (18.34′) and (18.38) we derive the limit relation

(18.41) $$\lim_{\zeta\to\infty} \bar{\zeta}^2 K(z,\bar{\zeta}) = \sum_{\nu=1}^{\infty} \bar{a}_\nu f_\nu(z).$$

Comparing (18.40) with (18.41) we obtain the equation:

(18.42) $$-\frac{1}{\pi a}\frac{d}{dz}\left(\frac{1}{f(z)}\right) = \sum_{\nu=1}^{\infty} \bar{a}_\nu f_\nu(z).$$

This is a formula for the calculation of the fundamental mapping function $f(z)$ by means of a complete orthonormal set of functions. One may assume that the point $z = 0$ lies outside of D and one obtains a complete orthonormal set by applying the Gram-Schmidt procedure of orthogonalization to the set z^{-m} $(m = 2, 3, \ldots)$. The calculations involved in this procedure use only integrations of powers of z over the domain D and resolutions of systems of linear equations. Formula (18.42) therefore yields an explicit method for the construction of the mapping function $f(z)$ and of the Green's function of the domain D.

An interesting application of (18.42) is obtained if one observes the limit relation

(18.43) $$\lim_{z\to\infty} z^2 \frac{f'(z)}{(f(z))^2} = \frac{1}{a}$$

which can be derived from (13.16). Hence, using (18.42) and (18.38) we obtain:

(18.44) $$\frac{1}{\pi a^2} = \sum_{\nu=1}^{\infty} |a_\nu|^2.$$

We have called $r = 1/a$ the mapping radius of the domain D and have shown its importance in the lift problem and the free boundary problem for plane flows. We have now the elegant representation for r:

$$r^2 = \pi \sum_{\nu=1}^{\infty} |a_\nu|^2 \tag{18.45}$$

in terms of the first coefficients of a complete orthonormal set with respect to D.

Bergman (B 1), (B 2), [3], [4], [5], [6], Bochner (B 30), Courant [12] Appendix, Garabedian-Schiffer (G 4), Nehari (N 1), Schiffer (S 2), (S 3), (S 4), Wirtinger (W 7).

19. Axially symmetric motion of an incompressible fluid: The treatment of two-dimensional fluid flow is much simpler than the general theory of an incompressible, irrotational steady motion. This is due to the smaller number of independent variables in the differential equations and the fact that all physical quantities are independent of the z-coordinate. We may obtain other simplifications of the general theory by assuming that the quantities considered do not depend on some other coordinate. The most important example is the case of axially symmetric motion.

We introduce cylindrical coordinates R, φ, and z by the definitions

$$R^2 = x^2 + y^2, \qquad \varphi = \arctan \frac{y}{x}, \qquad z = z. \tag{19.1}$$

This means that we have distinguished the axis $R = 0$, i. e., $x = y = 0$. We now assume that the motion is the same in every plane through the axis, i. e., that all physical quantities are independent of the angular coordinate which distinguishes the different planes through the axis, and that a fluid particle stays in the same plane during its entire motion. Such a motion occurs, for example, when a solid of revolution moves with constant speed in the direction of its axis in a liquid otherwise at rest. In general, for an axially symmetric flow it will be necessary that the rigid boundaries of the flow region be surfaces of revolution around the distinguished axis of the motion.

In our special case the velocity potential of the flow has the form

$$U(x, y, z) = U(R, z) \tag{19.2}$$

and since U must satisfy Laplace's equation we easily derive the following partial differential equation in R and z:

$$\frac{\partial^2 U}{\partial R^2} + \frac{1}{R}\frac{\partial U}{\partial R} + \frac{\partial^2 U}{\partial z^2} = 0. \tag{19.3}$$

This equation may be put into the form

$$\frac{\partial}{\partial R}\left(R\frac{\partial U}{\partial R}\right)+\frac{\partial}{\partial z}\left(R\frac{\partial U}{\partial z}\right)=0. \tag{19.4}$$

Equation (19.4) may be considered as an integrability condition and leads to the existence of a function $S(R, z)$ such that

$$\frac{\partial S}{\partial R}=-R\frac{\partial U}{\partial z}, \qquad \frac{\partial S}{\partial z}=R\frac{\partial U}{\partial R}. \tag{19.5}$$

This system of first-order partial differential equations is equivalent to the single second-order equation (19.4) for $U(R, z)$ and is analogous to the Cauchy-Riemann system (12.10).

Eliminating U from (19.5) we obtain a second-order partial differential equation for $S(R, z)$:

$$\frac{\partial}{\partial R}\left(\frac{1}{R}\frac{\partial S}{\partial R}\right)+\frac{\partial}{\partial z}\left(\frac{1}{R}\frac{\partial S}{\partial z}\right)=0, \tag{19.6}$$

an equation which is analogous to but different from (19.4).

The velocity field determined by $G(R, z)$ is given by the vector

$$\mathfrak{q}=-\operatorname{grad} U, \qquad u=-\frac{x}{R}\frac{\partial U}{\partial R}, \qquad v=-\frac{y}{R}\frac{\partial U}{\partial R}, \qquad w=-\frac{\partial U}{\partial z}. \tag{19.7}$$

A fluid particle participating in the flow will move along a stream line $x(t)$, $y(t)$, $z(t)$ which satisfies the differential equations:

$$\frac{dx}{dt}=u, \qquad \frac{dy}{dt}=v, \qquad \frac{dz}{dt}=w. \tag{19.8}$$

We see that $\varphi(t)=\arctan\frac{y(t)}{x(t)}$ satisfies the equation:

$$\frac{d\varphi}{dt}=\frac{xv-yu}{R^2}=0, \tag{19.9}$$

i. e., that during the entire motion a particle stays in the same plane $\varphi=$ const. as was to be required for an axially symmetric flow.

We consider next the function $S(t)=S\bigl(R(t), z(t)\bigr)$ and find by virtue of (19.5):

$$\frac{dS}{dt}=\frac{\partial S}{\partial R}\cdot\frac{dR}{dt}+\frac{\partial S}{\partial z}\frac{dz}{dt}=\frac{\partial S}{\partial R}\frac{xu+yv}{R}+\frac{\partial S}{\partial z}w=-\frac{\partial S}{\partial R}\frac{\partial U}{\partial R}-\frac{\partial S}{\partial z}\frac{\partial U}{\partial z}=0. \tag{19.10}$$

Thus, $S(R, z)$ remains constant along each stream line; the stream lines of the axially symmetric flow may be described in closed form by the equation:

$$S(R, z) = \text{const.} \tag{19.11}$$

$S(R, z)$ is called the stream function or the Stokes function of the axially symmetric flow. Its significance may be understood by the following consideration: let us describe the axially symmetric flow in a representative meridian plane R, z; let C_A^B be a curve in this plane running from a point A to another point B. If the arc C_A^B rotates around the axis we will obtain a surface of revolution and we ask for the amount of fluid which passes through this surface per unit time. It is easily seen that this amount is

$$M = 2\pi\rho \int_A^B R\left(\frac{\partial U}{\partial R}\cos(\boldsymbol{\nu}, \mathbf{R}) + \frac{\partial U}{\partial z}\cos(\boldsymbol{\nu}, \mathbf{z})\right) ds \tag{19.12}$$

where $\boldsymbol{\nu}$ is the normal vector to the curve C_A^B in the (R, z)-plane. Now using the differential equations (19.5) and the relations

$$\cos(\boldsymbol{\nu}, \mathbf{z}) = -\cos(\mathbf{s}, \mathbf{R}), \qquad \cos(\boldsymbol{\nu}, \mathbf{R}) = \cos(\mathbf{s}, \mathbf{z}) \tag{19.13}$$

we obtain

$$M = 2\pi\rho \int_A^B \left(\frac{\partial S}{\partial z}\cos(\mathbf{s}, \mathbf{z}) + \frac{\partial S}{\partial R}\cos(\mathbf{s}, \mathbf{R})\right) ds = 2\pi\rho\,(S_B - S_A). \tag{19.14}$$

Thus, the quantity of matter passing per unit of time through any surface of revolution which is bounded by the two circles of revolution through A and B is determined by the difference of the stream function at A and B. This interpretation explains why the stream function is constant along any stream line of the flow.

Let us now consider possible singularities for an axially symmetric flow. The most important ones are the point singularities; for reasons of symmetry an isolated singularity must be located on the axis of the flow, say at $z = \zeta$. In this case, the fundamental singularity (4.1) of the general three-dimensional case

$$U_\zeta(R, z) = \frac{1}{4\pi} \frac{1}{\left(R^2 + (z - \zeta)^2\right)^{1/2}} \tag{19.15}$$

has axial symmetry and is, therefore, the fundamental singularity for the axially symmetric case on the axis. It represents a source of strength one at the point $R = 0$, $z = \zeta$.

By differentiation with respect to ζ, we obtain the velocity potential of a dipole at the point $R = 0$, $z = \zeta$ with axis in the direction of the axis of symmetry. We find:

$$W_\zeta(R, z) = \frac{1}{4\pi} \frac{z - \zeta}{(R^2 + (z - \zeta)^2)^{3/2}}. \tag{19.16}$$

In order to determine the stream function corresponding to a given velocity potential we proceed as follows. We observe that by virtue of (19.7) the symmetry axis is a stream line and that, therefore, S is constant along it. Since $S(R, z)$ has been defined only up to an additive constant, we can now specify it in a unique way by requiring $S = 0$ on the axis of symmetry. Using the first equation of (19.5), we then calculate $S(R, z)$ by the integral:

$$S(R, z) = -\int_0^R R \frac{\partial U(R, z)}{\partial z} dR. \tag{19.17}$$

Applying this formula to the velocity potentials (19.15) and (19.16), we find the following conjugate stream functions:

$$S_\zeta(R, z) = -\frac{1}{4\pi}\left(\frac{z - \zeta}{(R^2 + (z - \zeta)^2)^{1/2}} - 1\right), \tag{19.15'}$$

$$T_\zeta(R, z) = \frac{1}{4\pi} \frac{R^2}{(R^2 + (z - \zeta)^2)^{3/2}}. \tag{19.16'}$$

Another important singularity creating an axially symmetric flow is the dipole at infinity with the velocity potential

$$U(R, z) = c\,z. \tag{19.18}$$

By (19.17) we can determine its conjugate stream function:

$$S(R, z) = -\frac{1}{2} c\,R^2. \tag{19.19}$$

We may, of course, also consider point singularities for the partial differential equation (19.4) which lie at arbitrary points of the (R, z)-plane. But these singularities lead to singular circles in three-dimensional space and do not seem to be of importance for most applications.

Having established the differential equations for axially symmetric flow and given its most important singularities, we come now to the related boundary value problem. We prescribe rigid surfaces of revolution as boundaries for the flow region and represent them by curves C in a meridian plane. Then on each boundary curve C the condition on the velocity potential will be $\frac{\partial U}{\partial \nu} = 0$ while the stream function S must be constant.

Various general methods may be used in order to solve boundary value problems of the above type. We describe, for example, a procedure which was used with success by Kármán in the theory of the motion of an airship. The body of the airship is represented in the meridian plane by a closed curve C, symmetric with respect to the axis $R = 0$. The motion of the air relative to the body is given by a velocity potential which at infinity behaves like cz. The basic idea of the procedure is to place a distribution of sources along the symmetry axis inside the curve C in such a way that under the simultaneous influence of these sources and of the dipole at infinity, the prescribed curve C becomes a stream line. If $\sigma(\zeta)$ denotes the strength density of the sources over the interval $0 \leqslant \zeta \leqslant l$ of the axis of symmetry, we have for the velocity potential

$$U(R, z) = cz + \frac{1}{4\pi}\int_0^l \frac{\sigma(\zeta)\, d\zeta}{(R^2 + (z-\zeta)^2)^{1/2}}. \tag{19.20}$$

We are not quite free in the choice of the source density $\sigma(\zeta)$; if we want a closed surface to exist which encloses finite sources and through which no fluid passes under the flow, we shall clearly have to require that the total source strength be zero, i. e.,

$$\int_0^l \sigma(\zeta)\, d\zeta = 0. \tag{19.21}$$

Using (19.15′) and (19.19), we can easily determine the stream function connected with the velocity potential (19.20). We find:

$$S(R, z) = -\frac{1}{2} c R^2 - \frac{1}{4\pi}\int_0^l \sigma(\zeta)\left(\frac{z-\zeta}{(R^2 + (z-\zeta)^2)^{1/2}} - 1\right) d\zeta. \tag{19.22}$$

By virtue of (19.21) this expression can be simplified to

$$S(R, z) = -\frac{1}{2} c R^2 - \frac{1}{4\pi}\int_0^l \sigma(\zeta)\, \frac{z-\zeta}{(R^2 + (z-\zeta)^2)^{1/2}}\, d\zeta. \tag{19.23}$$

Let $R(z)$, $0 \leqslant z \leqslant l$ be the equation of one half of the boundary curve C; we then have to require that the stream function $S(R, z)$ be zero along C, and this leads to the condition:

$$\frac{1}{2} c R(z)^2 = -\frac{1}{4\pi} \int_0^l \sigma(\zeta) \frac{z-\zeta}{(R(z)^2 + (z-\zeta)^2)^{1/2}} d\zeta, \qquad 0 \leqslant z \leqslant l. \tag{19.24}$$

This is an integral equation of the first kind for the unknown function $\sigma(\zeta)$ and can be treated by the usual methods of the theory of integral equations.

A more systematic way of treating the boundary value problem of axially symmetric flow is by using the Neumann's function connected with the partial differential equation (19.4) or the Green's function of the equation (19.6). Both equations are of the type

$$\operatorname{div}(K \operatorname{grad} T) = 0 \tag{19.25}$$

which was discussed in the first chapter for the three-dimensional case. It should be observed, however, that the axis of symmetry $R = 0$ becomes a singular line for the differential equation (19.6) and this fact leads to considerable complication in the development of a general theory.

v. Kármán (K 1).

20. Associated partial differential equations: In the preceding section, we related the velocity potential U and the stream function S by a pair of first-order partial differential equations. By elimination of either function we obtained second-order partial differential equations for U and S. Although both equations are different, the solution of a boundary value problem for one equation immediately leads to the solution of some boundary value problem for the other one. In this section we shall generalize this relation between two partial differential equations.

Let D be a domain in the (x, y)-plane bounded by a smooth curve C. Let $p(x, y)$ be a continuously differentiable *positive* function in the closed region $\mathsf{D} + \mathsf{C}$. We consider the set of first-order partial differential equations:

$$\frac{\partial \varphi}{\partial x} = p(x, y) \frac{\partial \psi}{\partial y}, \qquad \frac{\partial \varphi}{\partial y} = -p(x, y) \frac{\partial \psi}{\partial x}. \tag{20.1}$$

This system of equations clearly represents a generalization of the Cauchy-Riemann equations and of the relations between velocity potential and stream function in the axially symmetric case. The study of this more general system will clarify various results which we obtained in the particular special theories.

Eliminating either φ or ψ from (20.1), we obtain for the remaining function the second order partial differential equations:

$$\frac{\partial}{\partial x}\left(\frac{1}{p}\frac{\partial \varphi}{\partial x}\right)+\frac{\partial}{\partial y}\left(\frac{1}{p}\frac{\partial \varphi}{\partial y}\right)=0, \tag{20.2}$$

$$\frac{\partial}{\partial x}\left(p\frac{\partial \psi}{\partial x}\right)+\frac{\partial}{\partial y}\left(p\frac{\partial \psi}{\partial y}\right)=0. \tag{20.3}$$

We shall call the differential equations (20.2) and (20.3) *associated* partial differential equations. If we know a solution of one such equation we can obtain a solution for the associated one by simple integrations. Thus, the theories of the solutions of both equations are closely related.

Let us consider the derivative of the function $\varphi(x, y)$ in the direction of a unit vector $\mathbf{e}$. We have by virtue of (20.1):

$$\frac{\partial \varphi}{\partial e}=\frac{\partial \varphi}{\partial x}\cos(\mathbf{e},\mathbf{x})+\frac{\partial \varphi}{\partial y}\cos(\mathbf{e},\mathbf{y})=p(x, y)\left(\frac{\partial \psi}{\partial x}(-\cos(\mathbf{e},\mathbf{y}))+\frac{\partial \psi}{\partial y}\cos(\mathbf{e},\mathbf{x})\right). \tag{20.4}$$

Now, $-\cos(\mathbf{e},\mathbf{y})$, $\cos(\mathbf{e},\mathbf{x})$ are the components of the unit vector $\mathbf{n}$ which is obtained from $\mathbf{e}$ by a rotation of 90^0 in the positive sense. Hence, we have proved:

$$\frac{\partial \varphi}{\partial e}=p(x, y)\frac{\partial \psi}{\partial n}. \tag{20.5}$$

Similarly, we can show:

$$\frac{\partial \psi}{\partial e}=-\frac{1}{p(x, y)}\frac{\partial \varphi}{\partial n}. \tag{20.6}$$

This result leads to an interesting connection between different boundary value problems related to the differential equations (20.2) and (20.3). In fact, suppose it were required to determine a solution $\varphi(x, y)$ of (20.2) which has on the boundary C of D prescribed values $\mu(s)$ for the normal derivative. According to (20.6) its conjugate function $\psi(x, y)$ satisfies on the boundary curve the condition

$$\frac{\partial \psi}{\partial s}=-\frac{1}{p}\mu(s), \qquad \psi=-\int_0^s\frac{1}{p}\mu(s)\,ds. \tag{20.7}$$

Thus, instead of solving the second boundary value problem for the equation (20.2), we may determine a solution of (20.3) with given boundary values (20.7). Having solved this first boundary value problem for the associated differential equation, we arrive at the required function $\varphi(x, y)$ by simple integrations. Similarly, we can show that the first boundary value problem with respect to (20.2) is equivalent to the second boundary value problem for (20.3).

This close connection between the different boundary value problems implies interesting cross-relations between the Green's and Neumann's functions belonging to the associated differential equations. The theory of these fundamental solutions for equations of the type (20.2) or (20.3) has been discussed in Chapter I for the case of three independent variables. The theory for two variables is exactly analogous to the previous one and we shall not repeat the arguments but only apply the results obtained there.

Let $G(P, Q)$ and $N(P, Q)$, $\Gamma(P, Q)$ and $H(P, Q)$ denote the Green's and Neumann's functions for the equations (20.2) and (20.3), respectively. We prescribe a continuous function $\mu(s)$ of the arc length on the boundary curve C of the domain D such that

$$\oint_{\mathsf{C}} \frac{1}{p} \mu(s)\, ds = 0. \tag{20.8}$$

This is a restriction on $\mu(s)$ which is analogous to (I.2.10) in the three-dimensional case. As in that case, we can assert that there exists a solution $\varphi(x, y)$ of (20.2) which has on C the values $\mu(s)$ for its normal derivative. This function may be expressed in terms of the Neumann's function $N(P, Q)$ analogously to (I.4.23):

$$\varphi(Q) = -\oint_{\mathsf{C}} N(P, Q) \frac{1}{p(P)} \mu(s_P)\, ds_P. \tag{20.9}$$

Let $\psi(Q)$ be the conjugate function to $\varphi(Q)$. By virtue of (20.7) we may put:

$$\varphi(Q) = \oint_{\mathsf{C}} N(P, Q) \frac{\partial \psi(P)}{\partial s} ds_P = -\oint_{\mathsf{C}} \psi(P) \frac{\partial N(P, Q)}{\partial s_P} ds_P. \tag{20.10}$$

On the other hand, using Green's formula (I.4.12) with respect to the differential equation (20.3), we may express $\psi(Q)$ by its boundary values on C as follows:

$$\psi(Q) = \oint_{\mathsf{C}} \frac{\partial \Gamma(P, Q)}{\partial \nu_P} \cdot p(P)\, \psi(P)\, ds_P. \tag{20.11}$$

Let us use the complex operators (18.8). We can then condense the two equations (20.1) into the one complex equation:

$$\frac{\partial \varphi}{\partial z} = i\, p\,(x, y)\, \frac{\partial \psi}{\partial z}. \tag{20.12}$$

If $\zeta = \xi + i\,\eta$ is the complex coordinate of the point Q, we obtain from (20.10), (20.11), and (20.12) the identity:

$$0 = \oint_{\mathsf{C}} \psi\,(P) \left(\frac{\partial^2 N\,(P,Q)}{\partial s_P\, \partial \zeta} + i\, p\,(Q)\, \frac{\partial^2 \Gamma\,(P,Q)}{\partial \nu_P\, \partial \zeta}\, p\,(P) \right) ds_P. \tag{20.13}$$

Since the boundary values $\psi\,(P)$ of a solution of (20.3) can be prescribed quite arbitrarily we derive from (20.13) the identity:

$$\frac{\partial^2 N\,(P,Q)}{\partial s_P\, \partial \zeta} + i\, p\,(P)\, p\,(Q)\, \frac{\partial^2 \Gamma\,(P,Q)}{\partial \nu_P\, \partial \zeta} = 0, \qquad P \in \mathsf{C}, \qquad Q \in \mathsf{D}. \tag{20.14}$$

Similarly, we may derive the relation

$$\frac{\partial^2 G\,(P,Q)}{\partial \nu_P\, \partial \zeta} - i\, p\,(P)\, p\,(Q)\, \frac{\partial^2 H\,(P,Q)}{\partial s_P\, \partial \zeta} = 0, \qquad P \in \mathsf{C}, \qquad Q \in \mathsf{D}. \tag{20.15}$$

From (20.12) and (20.14) we learn that the two functions

$$\Phi\,(Q) = \frac{\partial N\,(P,Q)}{\partial s_P} \qquad \text{and} \qquad \Psi\,(Q) = p\,(P)\, \frac{\partial \Gamma\,(P,Q)}{\partial \nu_P} \tag{20.16}$$

are conjugate functions of Q satisfying the system (20.1). Hence, by virtue of (20.5) we find:

$$\frac{\partial \Phi\,(Q)}{\partial s_Q} = p\,(Q)\, \frac{\partial \Psi\,(Q)}{\partial \nu_Q} \qquad \text{for} \qquad Q \in \mathsf{C}, \tag{20.17}$$

i. e.,

$$\frac{\partial^2 N\,(P,Q)}{\partial s_P\, \partial s_Q} = p\,(P)\, p\,(Q)\, \frac{\partial^2 \Gamma\,(P,Q)}{\partial \nu_P\, \partial \nu_Q}, \qquad P \in \mathsf{C}, \quad Q \in \mathsf{C}. \tag{20.18}$$

Similarly, from (20.15) we derive:

$$\frac{\partial^2 G\,(P,Q)}{\partial \nu_P\, \partial \nu_Q} = p\,(P)\, p\,(Q)\, \frac{\partial^2 H\,(P,Q)}{\partial s_P\, \partial s_Q}, \qquad P \in \mathsf{C}, \quad Q \in \mathsf{C}. \tag{20.19}$$

We have thus established relations between the derivatives of the fundamental solutions of associated partial differential equations. This result is of particular interest in the case of Laplace's equation. Laplace's equation corresponds to the case $p \equiv 1$ and is, therefore, self-associated.

We have in this case $G \equiv \Gamma$ and $N \equiv H$ and the two equations (20.18) and (20.19) coincide. There is therefore a very simple relation between the second derivatives of Green's and Neumann's function on the boundary of the domain considered. In Section 18 we were led to the consideration of the function

$$\mathfrak{G}(z, \zeta) = \frac{\partial^2 G(z, \zeta)}{\partial \nu_z \, \partial \nu_\zeta} \tag{20.20}$$

and discussed its importance for the boundary value problem of the Laplace equation. We have now found a new aspect of this important expression.

The principal purpose of the present section was to show the close relation between functions solving associated differential equations and to clarify the significance of these equations in various boundary value problems. All results can be condensed into the relations (20.18) and (20.19) between the fundamental solutions.

21. Two-dimensional compressible fluid flow: In this section we consider the motion of a plane flow which is again assumed to be stationary and irrotational but where the assumption of incompressibility has been dropped. We thus return to the problem considered in Section 2 but with the simplification that the velocity vector $\mathfrak{q}$ has only the two components u and v which depend only upon the coordinates x, y of the plane of the flow. We restrict ourselves to the case in which no exterior forces act upon the fluid; for this case Bernoulli's law takes the form

$$\frac{1}{2}\mathfrak{q}^2 + i(\rho) = \text{const.}, \tag{21.1}$$

and $i(\rho)$ is a given function of ρ, dependent upon the assumptions made about the physical properties of the fluid.

Let us denote the velocity potential of the plane flow by $\varphi(x, y)$; we have

$$\mathfrak{q} = -\operatorname{grad} \varphi, \qquad u = -\frac{\partial \varphi}{\partial x}, \qquad v = -\frac{\partial \varphi}{\partial y}. \tag{21.2}$$

The continuity equation (2.7) now takes the form:

$$\frac{\partial}{\partial x}\left(\rho \frac{\partial \varphi}{\partial x}\right) + \frac{\partial}{\partial y}\left(\rho \frac{\partial \varphi}{\partial y}\right) = 0. \tag{21.3}$$

Interpreting this equation as an integrability condition, we may assert the existence of a function $\psi(x, y)$ such that

(21.4) $$\rho \frac{\partial \varphi}{\partial x} = \frac{\partial \psi}{\partial y}, \qquad \rho \frac{\partial \varphi}{\partial y} = -\frac{\partial \psi}{\partial x}.$$

We again call $\psi(x, y)$ the stream function of the flow considered and in the usual way show that $\psi(x, y)$ remains constant along each stream line.

The system of differential equations (21.4) seems similar to (20.1) but is in fact quite different from it. By virtue of (21.1) ρ is some function of $\mathfrak{q}^2 = \left(\frac{\partial \varphi}{\partial x}\right)^2 + \left(\frac{\partial \varphi}{\partial y}\right)^2$ and introducing this relation in (21.4), we obtain a system of equations which is highly non-linear in $\varphi(x, y)$. If we put (21.3) in explicit form, $\left(\text{using the notation } \varphi_x = \frac{\partial \varphi}{\partial x},\ \varphi_{xx} = \frac{\partial^2 \varphi}{\partial x^2}, \text{ etc.}\right)$ we obtain the equation:

$$\varphi_{xx}\left(1 + \frac{2\rho'(\mathfrak{q}^2)}{\rho}\varphi_x^2\right) + \varphi_{yy}\left(1 + \frac{2\rho'(\mathfrak{q}^2)}{\rho}\varphi_y^2\right) + 4\frac{\rho'(\mathfrak{q}^2)}{\rho}\varphi_{xy}\varphi_x\varphi_y = 0.$$
(21.5)

In order to understand the significance of the term $2\rho'/\rho$, we differentiate equation (21.1) with respect to $\mathfrak{q}^2$ and use the definition (2.2) of the function $i(\rho)$. We find

(21.6) $$\frac{1}{2} + \frac{dp}{d\rho} \cdot \frac{\rho'(\mathfrak{q}^2)}{\rho} = 0, \qquad \text{i. e.,} \qquad \frac{2\rho'}{\rho} = -\left(\frac{dp}{d\rho}\right)^{-1}.$$

Let us set

(21.7) $$c^2 = \frac{dp}{d\rho}.$$

c is the local velocity of sound in the medium and itself depends on ρ and, therefore, upon $\mathfrak{q}^2$. We may now write (21.5) in the form:

(21.8) $$\varphi_{xx}\left(1 - \frac{\varphi_x^2}{c^2}\right) + \varphi_{yy}\left(1 - \frac{\varphi_y^2}{c^2}\right) - 2\varphi_{xy}\frac{\varphi_x\varphi_y}{c^2} = 0.$$

A similar non-linear differential equation may be obtained for the stream function $\psi(x, y)$ by eliminating the velocity potential $\varphi(x, y)$ from the system (21.4).

It is obvious that a non-linearity of a differential equation with respect to the independent variable is much easier to treat than non-linearity with respect to the dependent variable. Therefore one frequently uses the artifice of changing the dependent variables in a complicated differential equation. If some term formed from the dependent variable creates particular difficulties it will be advantageous to choose this term as one independent variable. If we look at the system (21.4) we recognize that the combination

$$q^2 = \varphi_x{}^2 + \varphi_y{}^2 = u^2 + v^2 \tag{21.9}$$

which is the argument of ρ, leads to the non-linearity of the system. We therefore introduce as new variables

$$q = (u^2 + v^2)^{1/2}, \qquad \theta = \arctan \frac{v}{u} \tag{21.10}$$

which are polar coordinates in the so-called velocity plane (u, v). The motion of a fluid particle will be described in the velocity plane by a curve (which may sometimes degenerate into a point) giving the velocity instead of the position as a function of time. Such curves were introduced by Hamilton and are called the *hodograph* of the motion. The plane (u, v) is frequently referred to as the hodograph plane.

The transition from (21.4) to a corresponding system in the hodograph plane is best performed as follows. If $\varphi\,(x, y)$ and $\psi\,(x, y)$ are considered as functions of x and y, their dependence may be expressed in the differential relation

$$d\varphi = \varphi_x\, dx + \varphi_y\, dy, \qquad d\psi = \psi_x\, dx + \psi_y\, dy. \tag{21.11}$$

Assuming that we now consider x and y as the dependent variables and φ and ψ as independent variables, we may solve (21.11) with respect to dx and dy:

$$dx = \frac{\psi_y\, d\varphi - \varphi_y\, d\psi}{\psi_y\, \varphi_x - \varphi_y\, \psi_x}, \qquad dy = \frac{-\psi_x\, d\varphi + \varphi_x\, d\psi}{\psi_y\, \varphi_x - \varphi_y\, \psi_x}. \tag{21.12}$$

We may express all partial derivatives in (21.12) by means of the independent coordinates in the hodograph plane using (21.2) and (21.4). We obtain:

$$dx = -\frac{\left(u\, d\varphi - \dfrac{v}{\rho}\, d\psi\right)}{(u^2 + v^2)}, \qquad dy = -\frac{\left(v\, d\varphi + \dfrac{u}{\rho}\, d\psi\right)}{(u^2 + v^2)}. \tag{21.13}$$

Now, we determine q and θ as independent variables. We consider φ, ψ as functions of q, θ and put $u = q \cos \theta$, $v = q \sin \theta$. We then obtain:

$$dx = -\frac{1}{q}\left(\left(\cos\theta\,\varphi_q - \frac{\sin\theta}{\rho}\psi_q\right)dq + \left(\cos\theta\,\varphi_\theta - \frac{\sin\theta}{\rho}\psi_\theta\right)d\theta\right), \tag{21.14}$$

$$dy = -\frac{1}{q}\left(\left(\sin\theta\,\varphi_q + \frac{\cos\theta}{\rho}\psi_q\right)dq + \left(\sin\theta\,\varphi_\theta + \frac{\cos\theta}{\rho}\psi_\theta\right)d\theta\right). \tag{21.15}$$

Since $x\,(q, \theta)$ and $y\,(q, \theta)$ satisfy identically

$$dx = \frac{\partial x}{\partial q}dq + \frac{\partial x}{\partial \theta}d\theta, \qquad dy = \frac{\partial y}{\partial q}dq + \frac{\partial y}{\partial \theta}d\theta, \tag{21.16}$$

we have by comparing (21.14), (21.15), and (21.16) an explicit representation for all partial derivatives of x and y with respect to q and θ. The conditions of integrability

$$\frac{\partial^2 x}{\partial q\,\partial\theta} = \frac{\partial^2 x}{\partial\theta\,\partial q}, \qquad \frac{\partial^2 y}{\partial q\,\partial\theta} = \frac{\partial^2 y}{\partial\theta\,\partial q} \tag{21.17}$$

lead to differential equations for φ and ψ as functions of q and θ. In this way we obtain the required system of differential equations which arises from (21.4) by the change of variables. We find:

$$\frac{\partial}{\partial\theta}\left(\frac{1}{q}\left(\cos\theta\,\varphi_q - \frac{\sin\theta}{\rho}\psi_q\right)\right) = \frac{\partial}{\partial q}\left(\frac{1}{q}\left(\cos\theta\,\varphi_\theta - \frac{\sin\theta}{\rho}\psi_\theta\right)\right), \tag{21.18}$$

i. e.,

$$-\frac{\sin\theta}{q}\varphi_q - \frac{\cos\theta}{q\,\rho}\psi_q = -\frac{\cos\theta}{q^2}\varphi_\theta + \left(\frac{\sin\theta}{\rho\,q^2} + \frac{\sin\theta}{q\,\rho^2}\rho'\,(q^2)\,2\,q\right)\psi_\theta. \tag{21.19}$$

By virtue of (21.6) and (21.7), we may write this result in the form:

$$-\frac{\sin\theta}{q}\varphi_q + \frac{\cos\theta}{q^2}\varphi_\theta = \frac{\cos\theta}{q\,\rho}\psi_q + \left(\frac{1}{q^2} - \frac{1}{c^2}\right)\frac{\sin\theta}{\rho}\psi_\theta. \tag{21.20}$$

Similarly, we derive from

$$\frac{\partial}{\partial\theta}\left(\frac{1}{q}\left(\sin\theta\,\varphi_q + \frac{\cos\theta}{\rho}\psi_q\right)\right) = \frac{\partial}{\partial q}\left(\frac{1}{q}\left(\sin\theta\,\varphi_\theta + \frac{\cos\theta}{\rho}\psi_\theta\right)\right) \tag{21.21}$$

after easy calculation

$$\frac{\cos\theta}{q}\varphi_q + \frac{\sin\theta}{q^2}\varphi_\theta = \frac{\sin\theta}{\rho\,q}\psi_q - \left(\frac{1}{q^2} - \frac{1}{c^2}\right)\frac{\cos\theta}{\rho}\psi_\theta. \tag{21.22}$$

From (21.20) and (21.22) we derive:

$$\varphi_\theta = \frac{q}{\rho}\psi_q, \qquad \varphi_q = -\left(1 - \frac{q^2}{c^2}\right)\frac{1}{\rho\,q}\psi_\theta. \tag{21.23}$$

This is the desired system of first order partial differential equations for the velocity potential and the stream function in the hodograph plane. Since the coefficients of this system depend only upon the independent variable q, we have obtained a linear system of first order partial differential equations. We have thus proved: *the differential equations of the motion of a plane, steady irrotational compressible fluid flow become linear when referred to the hodograph plane.*

The equations (21.23) are not yet in the normal form (20.1) considered in the last section. They may be brought into this normal form by a change of scale in the hodograph plane. Let $\lambda(q)$ be an arbitrary differentiable function of q and let us use the coordinates λ, θ instead of q, θ in the hodograph plane. The plane whose Cartesian coordinates are λ, θ has been denoted the *pseudo-logarithmic plane.* We have instead of (21.23) the differential equations:

$$\varphi_\theta = \psi_\lambda \frac{q\,\lambda'(q)}{\rho}, \qquad \varphi_\lambda = -\left(1-\frac{q^2}{c^2}\right)\frac{1}{\rho\, q\, \lambda'(q)}\psi_\theta. \tag{21.24}$$

Let us now choose $\lambda(q)$ in such a fashion that the coefficients in both equations become equal except for sign. We have to take

$$\lambda'(q) = \frac{1}{q}\left(1-\frac{q^2}{c^2}\right)^{1/2}, \qquad \lambda = \lambda(q, c) \equiv \lambda(q) \equiv \int \frac{1}{q}\left(1-\frac{q^2}{c^2}\right)^{1/2} dq \tag{21.25}$$

and then obtain the system of first order partial differential equations:

$$\varphi_\theta = \frac{1}{\rho}\left(1-\frac{q^2}{c^2}\right)^{1/2}\psi_\lambda, \qquad \varphi_\lambda = -\frac{1}{\rho}\left(1-\frac{q^2}{c^2}\right)^{1/2}\psi_\theta. \tag{21.26}$$

In these equations we must express the factor

$$l(\lambda) = \frac{1}{\rho}\left(1-\frac{q^2}{c^2}\right)^{1/2} \tag{21.27}$$

as a function of the variable λ of the hodograph plane. *The explicit form of the function $l(\lambda)$ depends on the physical nature of the fluid considered.* Thus, we have brought the basic equations of the fluid dynamics of an irrotational, compressible fluid flow into the normal form:

$$\varphi_\theta = l(\lambda)\,\psi_\lambda, \qquad \varphi_\lambda = -l(\lambda)\,\psi_\theta. \tag{21.28}$$

Obviously, the above transformations are real only in the case that throughout the flow $q^2/c^2 < 1$, i. e., for a subsonic flow.

Bergman (B 11), Kochin-Rose-Kiebel [33], Milne-Thomson [48], Mises-Friedrichs [51] appendix, Sauer [67], Sommerfeld [71].

22. Construction of solutions of the differential equations in the hodograph plane: Since the term $l(\lambda)$ occurring in the differential system (21.28) may be of very complicated form when given explicitly, the first question which arises is to find any solution at all of this system. The second and more difficult question will be to adapt the solutions obtained to the specific boundary value problem posed by the hydrodynamical situation. In this section we shall deal with the first question and discuss two general methods for the construction of particular solutions.

The differential system (21.28) is of the form

$$u_x = l(y)\, v_y, \qquad u_y = -l(y)\, v_x. \tag{22.1}$$

In the case $l(y) \equiv 1$ we would have the Cauchy-Riemann differential equations and could combine $u(x, y)$ and $v(x, y)$ into one single analytic function $f(z) = u + i\,v$ of the complex variable z. New analytic functions can be obtained from $f(z)$ by differentiation or integration with respect to the variable z and if we take the real and imaginary part of each analytic function so obtained, we will obtain a solution pair for the Cauchy-Riemann equations. We shall now show that a similar procedure for the construction of infinitely many pairs of solutions of (22.1) can be established in an analogous way.

To any pair of solutions u, v of (22.1) we associate a function

$$f(z) = u(x, y) + i\,v(x, y) \tag{22.2}$$

of the complex point $z = x + i\,y$. Following Bers-Gelbart we call the function $f(z)$ *l-monogenic* if its real and imaginary parts are connected by the set (22.1) of first order partial differential equations with the coefficient $l(y)$. We call the function

$$f'(z) = u_x + i\,v_x = l(y)\, v_y - \frac{i}{l(y)}\, u_y \tag{22.3}$$

the *l-derivative* of $f(z)$. We state the following theorem:

The l-derivative of an l-monogenic function is l-monogenic. In fact, since the coefficient $l(y)$ of (22.1) depends only upon y we may differentiate the identity (22.1) with respect to x and will find that u_x and v_x satisfy the same set of equations as do u and v.

This simple remark allows us to construct new solutions from one given pair u, v. Our procedure will terminate either if we cannot go on with the differentiation or if we obtain identically vanishing derivatives. Thus, we cannot assert, a priori, that we can construct infinitely many solutions of (22.1) by the process of l-differentiation.

Let us now define the inverse process to l-differentiation which we shall call l-integration. We define the l-integral over a rectifiable curve C between z_0 and z by

$$F(z) = \int_{C}^{(l)} f(z)\, dz = \int_{C} \left(u\, dx - l(y)\, v\, dy\right) + i \int_{C} \left(v\, dx + \frac{u}{l(y)}\, dy\right). \tag{22.4}$$

We observe at first that this l-integral is independent of the curve C connecting the points z_0 and z if the curve C is deformed over a domain in which $f(z)$ is l-monogenic. In fact, the integrability conditions for the two right-hand integrals in (22.4) are identical with the system (22.1). Putting $F(z) = U + i\,V$, we obtain the system of differential equations

$$U_x = l(y)\, V_y, \qquad U_y = -\, l(y)\, V_x. \tag{22.5}$$

Thus, the process of l-integration creates from any l-monogenic function a new l-monogenic function. It can be continued indefinitely and always creates new pairs of solutions for the system (22.1). Moreover, there always exists a trivial solution of (22.1), namely $u(x, y) = a$, $v(x, y) = b$ with constants a and b, which can be used as a starting point for the process of integration. Thus, we may assert that in the case of a system (22.1) we may always obtain an infinity of particular solutions from a given one by simple quadratures.

The concept of a generalized theory of analytic functions was extended by Bers and Gelbart to the more general system of differential equations

$$\sigma_1(x)\, u_x = \tau_1(y)\, v_y, \qquad \sigma_2(x)\, u_y = -\, \tau_2(y)\, v_x. \tag{22.6}$$

They characterize this system of differential equations by its matrix

$$\Sigma = \begin{pmatrix} \sigma_1 & \tau_1 \\ \sigma_2 & \tau_2 \end{pmatrix} \tag{22.7}$$

and define the complex valued function $f(z) = u + i\,v$ as Σ-monogenic if its real and imaginary parts satisfy the system (22.6). Processes of Σ-differentiation and Σ-integration can be defined similarly as in this section and an interesting generalized function theory can be developed.

Let us return now to the particular system (21.28) and eliminate the velocity potential $\varphi(\lambda, \theta)$ from it. We obtain a second order partial differential equation for the stream function

$$l(\lambda)\, \Delta\, \psi + l'(\lambda)\, \psi_\lambda = 0, \qquad l'(\lambda) = \frac{dl}{d\lambda}, \qquad \Delta \equiv \frac{\partial^2}{\partial \lambda^2} + \frac{\partial^2}{\partial \theta^2}, \tag{22.8}$$

and we shall discuss procedures for finding particular solutions of this equation. Using the general method indicated in Section I.8 we may simplify (22.8) by putting

$$\Psi = l^{1/2}\psi \tag{22.9}$$

and obtain the partial differential equation for $\Psi(\lambda, \theta)$:

$$\Delta\Psi = L(\lambda)\Psi, \qquad L(\lambda) = \frac{\Delta(l^{1/2})}{l^{1/2}}. \tag{22.10}$$

A natural procedure for solving (22.10) is suggested by the independence of the coefficient $L(\lambda)$ of the variable θ. We may use the method of separation of variables; we obtain a set of solutions

$$C_n(\lambda, \theta) = a_n(\lambda)\cos n\theta, \qquad S_n(\lambda, \theta) = a_n(\lambda)\sin n\theta, \qquad n = 0, 1, 2, \ldots \tag{22.11}$$

where $a_n(\lambda)$ satisfies the ordinary differential equation of second order

$$\frac{d^2 a_n(\lambda)}{d\lambda^2} = \big(L(\lambda) + n^2\big)a_n(\lambda). \tag{22.12}$$

In the case that the fluid considered satisfies the adiabatic equation of state $p\rho^{-\varkappa} = \text{const.}$, the solutions of (22.12) were determined explicitly by Chaplygin and are expressed by hypergeometric functions. If we deal with an incompressible fluid flow ($c = \infty$), we have $L(\lambda) \equiv 0$ and in this case the functions $a_n(\lambda)$ reduce to $a_n(\lambda) = \text{const.}\, e^{\pm n\lambda}$; the particular set of solutions $C_n(\lambda, \theta)$ and $S_n(\lambda, \theta)$ coincide with the set of harmonic functions (in λ, θ) $e^{n\lambda}\cos n\theta$ and $e^{n\lambda}\sin n\theta$. It can easily be seen (Cf. 21.25) that in the incompressible case the relation between $\tilde{\lambda} \equiv \lambda(q, \infty)$ (Cf. 21.25) and q is simply $q = e^{\tilde{\lambda}}$ and hence $q^n \cos n\theta$, $q^n \sin n\theta$ are the expressions in the hodograph plane for the above set. In this case, the λ, θ-plane is exactly the plane of the logarithm of the variable in the hodograph plane. Let $\mathbf{B}$ be a simply connected bounded domain in the (u, v) plane and let f be harmonic in $\mathbf{B}$. Let $\mathbf{B}^*$ be the image of $\mathbf{B}$ in the $(\tilde{\lambda}, \theta)$ plane. Since f may be approximated uniformly in every closed subdomain of $\mathbf{B}$ by polynomials in u and v, it follows that f may be approximated in every closed subdomain of $\mathbf{B}^*$ by linear combinations of $e^{n\tilde{\lambda}}\cos n\theta$, $e^{n\tilde{\lambda}}\sin n\theta$. Analogously, Chaplygin's solutions (22.11) will form such a basis for the regular solutions of the differential equation (22.10).

We may choose for n also non-integral values in (22.11) and (22.12) and in this way obtain multivalued solutions in the hodograph plane. The branch point for these solutions is characterized by the value $\lambda = -\infty$ which corresponds to $q = 0$ in the hodograph plane as can be seen from the definition (21.25). We see, moreover, that $\lambda = -\infty$ will lead to a singular point even for all those Chaplygin solutions (22.11) which are regular at each finite point of the (λ, θ)-plane. Thus, the method of separation of variables leads to single-valued and multi-valued solutions of (22.10) where the singularities lie only at the point $q = 0$.

Methodologically, Chaplygin's construction of infinitely many solutions of (22.10) is closely related to the theory of l-monogenic functions for finding regular solutions of the system (22.1). It will be observed that both procedures are based upon the special dependence of the coefficients of the differential equations upon the independent variables. Both methods seem particularly appropriate for the construction of solutions which are regular at all finite points of a domain in the (λ, θ)-plane.

In the simplest hydrodynamical problems, however, there arises the necessity for constructing solutions of (22.10) which have singularities and branch points at finite points of the (λ, θ)-plane. Consider, for example, the incompressible fluid flow with the complex potential

$$F(z) = \varphi + i\psi = z + \frac{1}{z}. \tag{22.13}$$

Clearly, $F(z)$ determines a flow due to a dipole at infinity in the direction of the x-axis. The stream function

$$\psi(x, y) = y - \frac{y}{x^2 + y^2} \tag{22.14}$$

vanishes along the x-axis and on the unit circumference $x^2 + y^2 = 1$. $F(z)$ therefore represents an incompressible fluid flow in the direction of the x-axis past the rigid obstacle $|z| = 1$. By (12.7) and (12.15), we have

$$\frac{dF(z)}{dz} = 1 - \frac{1}{z^2} = -(u - iv) = w. \tag{22.15}$$

We may consider w as the complex representative point of the flow in the hodograph plane and express the coordinate z in the flow plane in terms of w:

$$z = (1 - w)^{-1/2}. \tag{22.16}$$

Thus, we find from (22.13) the equation:

$$\varphi + i\psi = (1 - w)^{-1/2} + (1 - w)^{1/2} \tag{22.17}$$

which shows that the stream function of the simple incompressible flow (22.13) has a singularity with branch point character at the point $q = 1$,

$\theta = \pi$ (i. e., $\lambda = 0$, $\theta = \pi$) of the hodograph plane and is a two-valued function in this plane. In the general case of a compressible fluid flow and even in the simplest examples of flow around closed curves, we must expect stream functions which are multivalued and possess algebraic or possibly even logarithmic singularities.

We shall now describe a procedure which will permit the construction of solutions of (22.10) with a great variety of singularities. We set up a formal series

$$\Psi(\lambda, \theta) = \sum_{n=0}^{\infty} G_n(\lambda)\, g_n(\lambda, \theta) \tag{22.18}$$

for the solution of (22.10). We assume that each function g_n is harmonic in λ and θ. We insert this series into the differential equation and make use of the identity (I.2.3); we assume that all formal transformations on the series (22.18) are legitimate and we shall justify them a posteriori by proving uniform convergence of the series in question and the differentiated series. We find:

$$\Delta\Psi - L\Psi = \sum_{n=0}^{\infty} \left(g_n (G_n'' - L\, G_n) + 2 \frac{\partial g_n}{\partial \lambda} G_n' \right). \tag{22.19}$$

Let us now make additional assumptions on the functions $G_n(\lambda)$ and $g_n(\lambda, \theta)$. We shall require

$$G_0 = 1, \quad G'_{n+1} = G_n'' - L\, G_n, \quad G_n(-\infty) = 0, \quad n = 1, 2, \ldots, \tag{22.20}$$

$$2 \frac{\partial g_n}{\partial \lambda} = - g_{n-1}, \quad g_0(\lambda, \theta) \text{ harmonic, but otherwise arbitrary.} \tag{22.21}$$

Inserting these relations into (22.19), we obtain

$$\Delta\Psi - L\Psi = \sum_{n=0}^{\infty} (g_n G'_{n+1} - g_{n-1} G_n') = 0, \tag{22.22}$$

in view of the fact that $G_0' = 0$. Thus, we obtain a formal solution of the differential equation (22.10) which is constructed from a well-defined set of functions $G_n(\lambda)$ $(n = 0, 1, 2, \ldots)$ and a set of harmonic functions $g_n(\lambda, \theta)$ the first of which is entirely arbitrary.

Given a harmonic function $g_0(\lambda, \theta)$ we can easily solve the recursion (22.21) in closed form. Let $\Phi_0(\zeta)$ be analytic in $\zeta = \lambda + i\,\theta$ and let

$g_0(\lambda, \theta) = \operatorname{Re}\Phi_0$. Let correspondingly $g_n(\lambda, \theta) = \operatorname{Re}\Phi_n(\zeta)$ for appropriate analytic functions $\Phi_n(\zeta)$. Condition (22.21) will be fulfilled if the relations

$$\frac{d\Phi_n(\zeta)}{d\zeta} = -\frac{1}{2}\Phi_{n-1}(\zeta), \qquad n = 1, 2, \ldots \tag{22.23}$$

hold. Put

$$\Phi_n(\zeta) = \frac{(-1)^n}{(n-1)!\,2^n}\int_0^\zeta \Phi_0(t)(\zeta - t)^{n-1}\,dt, \qquad n = 1, 2, \ldots. \tag{22.24}$$

It is easy to verify that with this definition the equations (22.23) will be fulfilled. Thus, we have determined the functions $g_n(\lambda, \theta)$ in the form:

$$g_n(\lambda, \theta) = \frac{(-1)^n}{(n-1)!\,2^n}\operatorname{Re}\left(\int_0^\zeta \Phi_0(t)(\zeta - t)^{n-1}\,dt\right), \qquad n = 1, 2, \ldots. \tag{22.25}$$

We have therefore a formal solution for the differential equation (22.10) of the form

$$\Psi(\lambda, \theta) = \operatorname{Re}\left(\Phi_0(\zeta) + \int_0^\zeta \Phi_0(t)\,U(\lambda, \theta; t)\,dt\right) \tag{22.26}$$

with

$$U(\lambda, \theta : t) = \sum_{n=1}^{\infty}\frac{(-1)^n}{(n-1)!\,2^n}G_n(\lambda)(\zeta - t)^{n-1}. \tag{22.27}$$

All our formal considerations will be completely valid in that part of the (λ, θ)-plane where we can prove the uniform convergence of the series (22.27) and of its derivatives for all values of the variable t needed in the integration.

The convergence of the series (22.27) is best studied by the *method of dominants*, i. e., by considering series which have term by term larger absolute values than the series for $U(\lambda, \theta; t)$. The main problem arises from the functions $G_n(\lambda)$ which occur in the U-series and which are defined in an involved fashion by a differential recursion formula. At first we determine simpler functions $Q_n(\lambda)$ which satisfy the inequalities

$$|G_n(\lambda)| \leqslant Q_n(\lambda), \qquad \left|\frac{d^\nu G_n(\lambda)}{d\lambda^\nu}\right| \leqslant \frac{d^\nu Q_n(\lambda)}{d\lambda^\nu}, \qquad \nu = 1, 2, \ldots. \tag{22.28}$$

The Q_n serve, therefore, for estimating the G_n as well as all their derivatives and we shall denote the relation established by (22.28) between G_n and Q_n by the symbol $G_n \ll Q_n$ and call Q_n a dominant for G_n.

In order to construct such functions $Q_n(\lambda)$ we shall make the following assumption about the coefficient $L(\lambda)$ which occurs in (22.10). *We shall assume that* $L(\lambda)$ *is an analytic function of* λ *for* $\lambda < 0$ *which has a dominant of the form* $C(\varepsilon - \lambda)^{-2}$, $C > 0$, $\varepsilon < 0$. In the theory of an adiabatic gas it is usual to choose the point $\lambda = 0$ to correspond to the velocity of sound, i. e., to $q = c$. Since by virtue of (21.25), we have $\frac{d\lambda}{dq} \geqslant 0$ we recognize that negative values of λ correspond to all subsonic velocities and that, in particular, the state of rest corresponds to $\lambda = -\infty$. It can then be shown that for any $\varepsilon < 0$ such a constant C can indeed be determined. Thus, our theory will be applicable in this most important special case.

Let us now make the assumption

$$L(\lambda) \ll C(\varepsilon - \lambda)^{-2}, \qquad C > 0, \qquad \varepsilon < 0 \tag{22.29}$$

and construct a sequence of functions $Q_n(\lambda)$ by the recursion formula:

$$\begin{aligned} Q'_{n+1} &= Q_n'' + C(\varepsilon - \lambda)^{-2} Q_n, \qquad n = 1, 2, \ldots, \\ Q_0 &= 1, \qquad Q_n(-\infty) = 0, \qquad n = 1, 2, \ldots. \end{aligned} \tag{22.30}$$

We may solve this recursion explicitly by setting

$$Q_n(\lambda) = n!\,(\varepsilon - \lambda)^{-n} \mu_n \tag{22.31}$$

and requiring that the coefficients μ_n satisfy the recursion formula

$$\mu_0 = 1, \qquad \mu_{n+1} = \mu_n (n^2 + n + C)(n+1)^{-2} = \mu_n \frac{(n+\alpha)(n+\beta)}{(n+1)^2} \tag{22.32}$$

with

$$\alpha = \frac{1}{2} - \left(\frac{1}{4} - C\right)^{1/2}, \qquad \beta = \frac{1}{2} + \left(\frac{1}{4} - C\right)^{1/2}. \tag{22.33}$$

We see that the $Q_n(\lambda)$ are all positive and have positive derivatives of all orders as long as $\lambda < \varepsilon < 0$. It is easily seen that

$$G_n(\lambda) \ll Q_n(\lambda) \tag{22.34}$$

since the Q_n are constructed from integrals and derivatives of $C(\varepsilon - \lambda)^{-2}$ in exactly the same way as were the G_n from $-L(\lambda)$. But in each term of the new construction only positive elements occur each of which is larger than the absolute value of the corresponding element in the previous construction.

The coefficients μ_n occurring in the dominants $Q_n(\lambda)$ are easily identified as the coefficients of the hypergeometric series

$$H(\alpha, \beta, 1; x) = \sum_{\nu=0}^{\infty} \mu_\nu x^\nu . \tag{22.35}$$

It is well known that this series converges uniformly for $|x| \leqslant a < 1$ as long as neither parameter α or β is zero or a negative integer. As can be seen from (22.33), this last condition is fulfilled.

Consider now the series

$$\begin{aligned} \Omega(\lambda, \theta; t) &= \sum_{n=1}^{\infty} \frac{Q_n(\lambda)}{(n-1)!\, 2^n} |\zeta - t|^{n-1} = \\ &= \sum_{n=1}^{\infty} u_n n \frac{|\zeta - t|^{n-1}}{2^n (\varepsilon - \lambda)^n} = \frac{1}{2} (\varepsilon - \lambda)^{-1} \sum_{n=1}^{\infty} n\, \mu_n \left(\frac{|\zeta - t|}{2(\varepsilon - \lambda)} \right)^{n-1} . \end{aligned} \tag{22.36}$$

Since by virtue of (22.35)

$$\sum_{n=1}^{\infty} n\, \mu_n x^{n-1} = \frac{d H(\alpha, \beta, 1; x)}{dx} \equiv H'(x), \tag{22.37}$$

we finally have

$$\Omega(\lambda, \theta; t) = \frac{1}{2(\varepsilon - \lambda)} H' \left(\frac{|\zeta - t|}{2(\varepsilon - \lambda)} \right). \tag{22.38}$$

Comparing the series (22.27) and (22.36) we recognize that Ω has term by term larger coefficients than U. Hence the series for U will converge uniformly at least in that domain of the (λ, θ)-plane where the series for Ω converges. It is easily seen that all partial derivatives of the U-series will converge in that same domain by virtue of (22.34). Thus, we can guarantee the convergence of the U-series and the fact that (22.26) represents a solution of (22.10) at least as long as in the integral in (22.26) we have

$$\frac{|\zeta - t|}{2(\varepsilon - \lambda)} \leqslant a < 1, \qquad \lambda < \varepsilon < 0. \tag{22.39}$$

Since we start the integration at $t = 0$, we find as first condition on ζ:

$$|\zeta| \leqslant 2a|\lambda| < 2|\lambda|. \tag{22.40}$$

In view of $\zeta = \lambda + i\theta$, we find that the point ζ must satisfy

$$|\theta| < \sqrt{3}\, |\lambda|, \tag{22.41}$$

i. e., must lie in an angle of 120^0 symmetric to the λ-axis in the left half plane. Conversely, it can be seen that if ζ lies in this angular region it can always be connected with the origin by a path along which t fulfills (22.39) for an appropriate value $a < 1$. Thus, we can construct solutions of (22.10) in the angular region $|\theta| < \sqrt{3}\,|\lambda|$ by means of the formula (22.26).

Let us now explain the significance of this method. As long as we stay in the angular region described, *we may associate with every analytic function* $\Phi_0(\zeta)$ *a solution* Ψ *of equation* (22.10). In the case of an incompressible fluid we will have $L(\lambda) = 0$ and $U \equiv 0$; in this case, the operation (22.26) is equivalent to the formation of a solution of Laplace's equation by taking the real part of analytic functions. In the general case, also, the procedure is a mapping of analytic functions into the space of solutions of the differential equation (22.10). The singularities and branch points of the original analytic function $\Phi_0(\zeta)$ will, in general, go over into singularities and branch points of the solution (22.26). Thus, this formula is a convenient tool for creating singularities of prescribed character at given points of the (λ, θ)-plane.

In order to deal with a compressible fluid with a given equation of state, we must first calculate once and for all the coefficients $G_n(\lambda)$ and so determine the generating function U. Once this is done, we may associate with any singularity occurring in the hodograph plane of an incompressible fluid flow a singularity for the compressible case by inserting the corresponding analytic function $\Phi_0(\zeta)$ of the incompressible case into (22.26). It should be remarked that we can operate easily with multivalued functions $\Phi_0(\zeta)$ and develop solutions Ψ of (22.10) which are defined on domains on Riemann surfaces which cover the (λ, θ)-plane several times.

Bergman (B 6), (B 8), (B 9), (B 10), (B 11), (B 13), (B 17), (B 18), (B 31) Bers and Gelbart (B 28), (B 29), v. Mises and Schiffer (M 3).

23. The hodograph method and boundary value problems in the physical plane: The basic problem of fluid dynamics is the determination of the velocity potential or the stream function of a flow in a region of the (x, y)-plane bounded by a rigid curve **C** and possessing sources and sinks of given strength and location. This problem represents a non-linear boundary value problem and leads to great difficulties in the general case.

We may linearize the differential equations of the fluid motion by passing to the hodograph plane. The equations (21.23) have, however, coefficients which behave singularly if the fluid velocity surpasses the velocity of sound c.

Thus, a successful application of our method of linearization will depend on the subsonic character of the flow. In this case, we may also define the new variable $\lambda(q)$ and pass to the (λ, θ)-plane in which the equations become particularly simple. It is now easily shown that isolated point sources create unbounded velocities in their neighborhood; thus, we shall restrict ourselves to the case in which the flow domain in the (x, y)-plane contains the point at infinity and in which the flow originates from a dipole there. Such a flow is possible without arbitrarily large values of the velocity.

In order to obtain an approximate solution for the given problem, we shall first solve the boundary value problem for the same dipole at infinity and the same boundary **C** for the case of an incompressible flow. We have discussed this problem in Section 14 and in Section 18 have described a constructive procedure in terms of orthogonal functions for obtaining the necessary mapping function. In this section we shall assume that we know how to solve the boundary value problem in the incompressible case. Let

(23.1) $$F(z) = \varphi + i\psi = Az + a_0 + \frac{a_1}{z} + \dots$$

be the complex velocity potential developed into a power series of z near the dipole at infinity. By (12.15), we compute the velocity function of the incompressible flow near infinity

(23.2) $$w = F'(z) = u - iv = -A + \frac{a_1}{z^2} + \dots .$$

Since in the case of an incompressible fluid flow $\lambda = \log q$, we have

(23.3) $$\zeta = \lambda + i\theta = \log \overline{w}.$$

Thus, we derive from (23.2) and (23.3):

(23.4) $$\zeta = \log(-\overline{A}) - \left(\frac{\overline{a}_1}{\overline{A}}\right)\frac{1}{\overline{z}^2} + \dots .$$

We calculate

(23.5) $$z = \frac{a}{(\overline{\zeta} - \beta)^{1/2}} + P\left((\overline{\zeta} - \beta)^{1/2}\right)$$

where $P(\tau)$ represents a regular power series in τ converging in a neighborhood of the origin. Thus, in the logarithmic plane we obtain a complex potential

(23.6) $$\overline{F^*(\zeta)} = F\left(z(\overline{\zeta})\right) = \frac{A^*}{(\overline{\zeta} - \beta)^{1/2}} + P^*\left((\overline{\zeta} - \beta)^{1/2}\right).$$

We recognize from (23.4) that the image of the flow domain in the (λ, θ)-plane covers this plane in a non-schlicht manner and has the point $\zeta = \log(-\bar{A})$ as a second order branch point. The stream function $\psi(\lambda, \theta)$ appears as $\operatorname{Re}\left(i F^*(\zeta)\right)$ and vanishes on the boundary $\mathfrak{C}$ of the image of the flow domain $\mathfrak{D}$ in the ζ-plane. In formula (22.26) we possess a linear operation which associates with each analytic function $\Phi_0(\zeta)$ a solution $\Psi(\lambda, \theta)$ of the equation (22.10). We may assume that in the case of not too high flow velocities $\Psi(\lambda, \theta)$ will not differ too much from $\operatorname{Re}\left(\Phi_0(\zeta)\right)$ which is the corresponding solution in the incompressible case. Let us also assume that the hodograph domain corresponding to the incompressible flow lies entirely in the region where the operator (22.26) is applicable. We then associate with $i F^*(\zeta) = \Phi_0(\zeta)$ a solution $\Psi(\lambda, \theta)$ of the equation (22.10) of the compressible case. In this way, we obtain a function which at the point $\log(-\bar{A}) = \zeta_\infty$ has a singularity which corresponds to a dipole of the compressible fluid flow. $\Psi(\lambda, \theta)$ will not be zero on the boundary $\mathfrak{C}$ of the non-schlicht domain $\mathfrak{D}$; we shall have to solve the boundary value problem wherein a solution of (22.10) is determined which is regular in $\mathfrak{D}$ and has on $\mathfrak{C}$ the same boundary values as Ψ. If we subtract this new solution from Ψ, we obtain a solution of (22.10) which has at ζ_∞ a singularity of the desired type and vanishes on $\mathfrak{C}$. In the second part of this book we shall discuss how the boundary value problem for differential equations of the type (22.10) can be treated if a complete set of particular solutions for the equations is available. The methods of the preceding section can be applied for the purpose of obtaining such a complete set.

Having obtained a solution $\Psi(\lambda, \theta)$ of (22.10) with prescribed singularity at ζ_∞ and vanishing on the boundary $\mathfrak{C}$ of the domain $\mathfrak{D}$, we now have to investigate the type of flow which this solution represents in the physical (x, y)-plane. For this purpose, we calculate the functions ψ and φ connected with Ψ by means of (22.9) and (21.4). This yields φ and ψ as known functions of the variables λ and θ, and, hence, by (21.25) as known functions of q and θ. Now, we can map the hodograph plane into the physical plane x, y by means of (21.14) and (21.15). This yields:

$$x = -\int \left(\frac{1}{q} \left(\cos\theta\, \varphi_q - \frac{\sin\theta}{\rho} \psi_q \right) dq + \frac{1}{q} \left(\cos\theta\, \varphi_\theta - \frac{\sin\theta}{\rho} \psi_\theta \right) d\theta \right), \tag{23.7}$$

$$y = -\int \left(\frac{1}{q} \left(\sin\theta\, \varphi_q + \frac{\cos\theta}{\rho} \psi_q \right) dq + \frac{1}{q} \left(\sin\theta\, \varphi_\theta + \frac{\cos\theta}{\rho} \psi_\theta \right) d\theta \right). \tag{23.8}$$

The integrations must be carried out from a fixed point q_0, θ_0 to the point q, θ which corresponds to x, y. The exact nature of the path of integration is unessential since we have formulated the differential equations of hydrodynamics in the hodograph plane as the integrability conditions for these two integrals.

It can easily be seen that the point ζ_∞ in the (λ, θ)-plane corresponds under the map to the point at infinity of the (x, y)-plane and that the flow behaves there as if a dipole were situated at infinity. The boundary $\mathfrak{C}$ of the domain in the (λ, θ)-plane will go into some curve $\mathbf{C}^*$ which will, of course, be different in general from the initial curve $\mathbf{C}$ for which we wanted to solve the boundary value problem. We obtain instead a dipole flow past a boundary $\mathbf{C}^*$ which will not be too different from $\mathbf{C}$ if the velocities involved are not too near the sonic velocity.

We shall now show how we can again use the boundary value theory for differential equations of a type similar to (I.2.1) in order to improve the approximate result which we obtained by means of the hodograph method. Let s $(0 \leqslant s \leqslant L)$ be the length parameter on the curve $\mathbf{C}$ which will be supposed smooth. We shall assume that we can associate with each point $P(s)$ on $\mathbf{C}$ a corresponding point $Q(s)$ on $\mathbf{C}^*$ by proceeding along the normal to $\mathbf{C}$ at $P(s)$ until we meet the curve $\mathbf{C}^*$. Let $\delta\nu(s)$ be the distance $\overline{PQ}$ and consider it positive if Q lies on the interior normal and negative in the contrary case. We also assume that $\max\limits_{0 \leqq s \leqq L} |\delta\nu(s)| = \varepsilon$ is sufficiently small so that we may neglect higher powers of ε in our calculations.

In $\psi(x, y)$ we have constructed the stream function of the compressible fluid flow past the contour $\mathbf{C}^*$; we wish, however, to construct the stream function $\psi_0(x, y)$ belonging to the curve $\mathbf{C}$ given originally. Both functions ψ and ψ_0 satisfy the same partial differential equation

$$\frac{\partial}{\partial x}\left(\frac{1}{\rho}\frac{\partial \psi}{\partial x}\right) + \frac{\partial}{\partial y}\left(\frac{1}{\rho}\frac{\partial \psi}{\partial y}\right) = 0, \tag{23.9}$$

where ρ is a known function of $(\psi_x{}^2 + \psi_y{}^2)$. They both have the same singularity at infinity and their difference function

$$\chi(x, y) = \psi_0(x, y) - \psi(x, y) \tag{23.10}$$

will be regular near infinity. If the curves $\mathbf{C}^*$ and $\mathbf{C}$ are in an ε-neighborhood we may assume that the difference between the corresponding stream functions is also of the order of magnitude ε. On the boundary curve $\mathbf{C}^*$ we have $\psi = 0$ and, since $\psi_0 = 0$ on $\mathbf{C}$, we derive

$$\psi_0 \big(Q(s) \big) = \frac{\partial \psi_0(Q)}{\partial \nu} \delta \nu + o(\varepsilon) \qquad \text{on } \mathbf{C}^*. \tag{23.11}$$

Thus, up to error terms $o(\varepsilon)$, $\chi(x, y)$ has the boundary values on $\mathbf{C}^*$:

$$\chi(Q) = \frac{\partial \psi(Q)}{\partial \nu} \delta \nu. \tag{23.12}$$

We have expressed the boundary values of the desired corrective function $\chi(Q)$ in known terms up to an error of order (ε^2) at most. We next observe that to within the same limits of precision $\chi(Q)$ satisfies a linear differential equation. In order to derive this equation, consider a family of solutions $\psi(x, y, \tau)$ of the non-linear partial differential equation (23.9) which depends on some parameter τ. Let

$$\sigma(x, y; \tau) = \frac{\partial \psi(x, y; \tau)}{\partial \tau}; \tag{23.13}$$

we then derive for $\sigma(x, y; \tau)$ the linear partial differential equation

$$\begin{aligned} &\frac{\partial}{\partial x}\left(\frac{1}{\rho}\frac{\partial \sigma}{\partial x}\right) + \frac{\partial}{\partial y}\left(\frac{1}{\rho}\frac{\partial \sigma}{\partial y}\right) - \frac{\partial}{\partial x}\left(2\frac{\dot{\rho}}{\rho^2}\frac{\partial \psi}{\partial x}\left(\frac{\partial \psi}{\partial x}\frac{\partial \sigma}{\partial x} + \frac{\partial \psi}{\partial y}\frac{\partial \sigma}{\partial y}\right)\right) \\ &- \frac{\partial}{\partial y}\left(2\frac{\dot{\rho}}{\rho^2}\frac{\partial \psi}{\partial y}\left(\frac{\partial \psi}{\partial x}\frac{\partial \sigma}{\partial x} + \frac{\partial \psi}{\partial y}\frac{\partial \sigma}{\partial y}\right)\right) = 0 \end{aligned} \tag{23.14}$$

by differentiating the identity (23.9) with respect to the parameter τ. Here ρ appears as a known function of the variable $r = \left(\frac{\partial \psi}{\partial x}\right)^2 + \left(\frac{\partial \psi}{\partial y}\right)^2$ and $\dot{\rho} = \frac{\partial \rho}{\partial r}$. The equation (23.14) is called *the variational equation* of the non-linear differential equation (23.9). It is the linear differential equation which characterizes infinitesimal changes of solutions of (23.9); it is easily shown that *the difference function* $\chi(x, y)$ *satisfies the equation* (23.14) *up to terms* $o(\varepsilon)$.

Since the stream function $\psi(x, y)$ which belongs to the contour $\mathbf{C}^*$ is known, we have in (23.14) a linear differential equation with known coefficients for the corrective term $\chi(x, y)$. This equation is to be solved with the known boundary values (23.12) prescribed for the solution on $\mathbf{C}^*$. Thus, the solution $\psi_0(x, y)$ for the given contour $\mathbf{C}$ can be determined up to an error $o(\varepsilon)$ if we are able to solve the boundary value problem for the equation (23.14).

In the second part of the book we will develop a rather general method for solving the boundary value problems of linear partial differential equations which possess a positive Dirichlet integral. We shall now show that equation (23.14) is of this type. For this purpose, we introduce the bilinear integral

(23.15)
$$E\{\sigma, \omega\} = \\ = \iint_D \left(\frac{1}{\rho} \operatorname{grad} \sigma \cdot \operatorname{grad} \omega - 2 \frac{\dot{\rho}}{\rho^2} (\operatorname{grad} \psi \cdot \operatorname{grad} \sigma)(\operatorname{grad} \psi \cdot \operatorname{grad} \omega) \right) dx\, dy$$

depending on two twice continuously differentiable functions σ and ω in some given domain D with a smooth boundary curve C. By means of Green's identity, we may write $E\{\sigma, \omega\}$ in the form:

(23.16)
$$E\{\sigma, \omega\} = -\oint_C \omega \left(\frac{1}{\rho} \frac{\partial \sigma}{\partial \nu} - 2 \frac{\dot{\rho}}{\rho^2} (\operatorname{grad} \psi \cdot \operatorname{grad} \sigma) \frac{\partial \psi}{\partial \nu} \right) ds \\ - \iint_D \omega \left(\operatorname{div} \left(\frac{1}{\rho} \operatorname{grad} \sigma \right) - \operatorname{div} \left(2 \frac{\dot{\rho}}{\rho^2} (\operatorname{grad} \psi \cdot \operatorname{grad} \sigma) \operatorname{grad} \psi \right) \right) dx\, dy.$$

It is easily seen that the coefficient of ω in the area integral is precisely the left-hand side of (23.14). If, therefore, $\sigma(x, y)$ is a solution of (23.14) and if $\omega(x, y)$ vanishes on the boundary C of D, we shall have:

(23.17)
$$E\{\sigma, \omega\} = 0.$$

Consider now the quadratic integral

(23.18)
$$E\{\sigma\} = E\{\sigma, \sigma\} = \iint_D \left(\frac{1}{\rho} (\operatorname{grad} \sigma)^2 - 2 \frac{\dot{\rho}}{\rho^2} (\operatorname{grad} \psi \cdot \operatorname{grad} \sigma)^2 \right) dx\, dy.$$

We have the obvious identity

(23.19)
$$E\{\sigma + \omega\} = E\{\sigma\} + 2\, E\{\sigma, \omega\} + E\{\omega\}.$$

We shall show, at first, that $E\{\sigma\}$ is positive-definite for all non-constant functions $\sigma(x, y)$. For this purpose, we must calculate the value of $\dot{\rho}$. In Section 21 we have expressed the density ρ as a function of q^2 and showed in (21.6) that

(23.20)
$$\frac{d\rho(q^2)}{d(q^2)} = \rho'(q^2) = -\frac{\rho}{2c^2}$$

where c is the local velocity of sound. We now have $r = \psi_x{}^2 + \psi_y{}^2 = \rho^2 q^2$ by virtue of (21.2) and (21.4). Hence, we have:

(23.21)
$$1 = 2\rho q^2 \frac{d\rho}{dr} + \rho^2 \frac{dq^2}{dr} = 2\rho q^2 \dot{\rho} + \rho^2 \frac{dq^2}{dr}.$$

On the other hand:

$$\dot{\rho} = \frac{d\rho}{dr} = \rho'(q^2)\frac{dq^2}{dr} = -\frac{\rho}{2c^2}\frac{dq^2}{dr}. \tag{23.22}$$

Eliminating dq^2/dr from (23.21) and (23.22), we obtain

$$\dot{\rho} = -\frac{1}{2\rho c^2}\left(1 - \frac{q^2}{c^2}\right)^{-1}. \tag{23.23}$$

This shows that for subsonic motion $\dot{\rho} < 0$, and the definiteness of $E\{\sigma\}$ follows.

Now let $\sigma(x, y)$ be a solution of (23.14) and $O(x, y)$ be an arbitrary continuously differentiable function in $\mathsf{D} + \mathsf{C}$ with the same boundary values on C as $\sigma(x, y)$. The difference function $\omega = O - \sigma$ will vanish on C and, hence, by (23.17) and (23.19), we will have

$$E\{O\} = E\{\sigma\} + E\{\omega\} \geqslant E\{\sigma\}. \tag{23.24}$$

Thus, we have proved: the solution $\sigma(x, y)$ of (23.14) minimizes the integral

$$E\{\sigma\} = \iint_{\mathsf{D}} \left(\frac{1}{\rho}(\operatorname{grad}\sigma)^2 + \frac{1}{\rho^3 c^2}\left(1 - \frac{q^2}{c^2}\right)^{-1}(\operatorname{grad}\psi \cdot \operatorname{grad}\sigma)^2\right) dx\, dy \tag{23.25}$$

among all continuously differentiable functions with the same boundary values.

We see that the differential expression on the left-hand side of (23.14), i. e.,

$$\operatorname{div}\left(\frac{1}{\rho}\operatorname{grad}\sigma\right) + \operatorname{div}\left(\frac{1}{\rho^3 c^2}\left(1 - \frac{q^2}{c^2}\right)^{-1}(\operatorname{grad}\psi \cdot \operatorname{grad}\sigma)\operatorname{grad}\psi\right) = \Lambda(\sigma) \tag{23.26}$$

is the functional derivative of the quadratic functional $E\{\sigma\}$ just as in Chapter I.6 we showed that the differential expression $\operatorname{div}(\varkappa \operatorname{grad} u)$ is the functional derivative of the quadratic functional $D\{u\}$, defined in (I.6.2). We may, therefore, apply to (23.14) the method of the Dirichlet integral which will be discussed extensively in the second part of this book.

Sauer [67], Bergman (B 8), (B 17), Mises and Schiffer (M 3).

24. Singularities in the hodograph plane and their application: We have been discussing compressible fluid flows due to a dipole at infinity. There exists a more general type of flow which also satisfies the requirement that the maximum velocity be finite and the theory of subsonic flow is applicable to it. This flow has a combined dipole and vortex at infinity. We have already studied flows of this type in the incompressible case in Section 14 and have shown that its complex potential near infinity has the series development:

$$F(z) = A\,z + \frac{i\,\Gamma}{2\pi}\log z + a_0 + \frac{a_1}{z} + \cdots \tag{24.1}$$

where Γ denotes the circulation associated with the vortex at infinity. Let us study the form of the singularity which corresponds in the hodograph plane to this type of flow. Near infinity the velocity function has the form

$$w = \overline{f(z)} = -A - \frac{i\,\Gamma}{2\pi z} + \frac{a_1}{z^2} + \cdots \tag{24.2}$$

By virtue of (23.3), we then derive

$$\zeta = \log(-\overline{A}) - \frac{i\,\Gamma}{2\pi\,\overline{A}}\cdot\frac{1}{\overline{z}} + \cdots \tag{24.3}$$

for the relation between the ζ-plane and the z-plane. Thus, the complex potential will have the following form in the ζ-plane near the point $\zeta_\infty = \log(-\overline{A})$:

$$F\left(z(\overline{\zeta})\right) = \frac{i\,\Gamma}{2\,\pi}\frac{1}{\overline{\zeta}-\overline{\zeta}_\infty} - \frac{i\,\Gamma}{2\,\pi}\log(\overline{\zeta}-\overline{\zeta}_\infty) + a_0 + a_1(\overline{\zeta}-\overline{\zeta}_\infty) + \cdots \tag{24.4}$$

We recognize that in the case of an incompressible fluid the singular point corresponds to a singular point in the ζ-plane located at the finite point ζ_∞ and of the same character as the singular point in the physical plane. The point ζ_∞ is not a branch point singularity if a non-vanishing circulation exists.

It is natural to try to obtain analogous singularities for the case of a compressible fluid flow. One remarks at first that one cannot take the function $\Phi_0(\zeta) = \dfrac{1}{\zeta-\zeta_\infty}$ and apply the operation (22.26) to it; for, in this case, the integration will introduce logarithmic terms with branch point at ζ_∞ and will create a multi-valued stream function of rather complicated type over the domain in question. This function will be a solution of the correct differential equation, but will not lead to a physically significant flow pattern. In order to create a compressible fluid flow with a singularity at a point ζ_∞ which is not a branch point of the (λ, θ)-domain we proceed as follows. Let $\mathfrak{D}$ be the domain for which the stream function is to be determined; this domain may lie schlicht over the (λ, θ)-plane or it may cover part of it in a non-schlicht fashion. Suppose that we can map $\mathfrak{D}$ conformally upon a schlicht domain $\mathfrak{B}$ in the V-plane by an analytic function

$$\zeta = R(V), \qquad V = \alpha + i\beta. \tag{24.5}$$

The function $\Psi(\lambda, \theta)$ becomes a function of the coordinates (α, β) in the V-plane and it is easily seen that

$$\Delta_V \Psi = \Delta_\zeta \Psi \cdot \left|\frac{d\zeta}{dv}\right|^2, \qquad \Delta_V \equiv \frac{\partial^2}{\partial \alpha^2} + \frac{\partial^2}{\partial \beta^2}, \qquad \Delta_\zeta \equiv \frac{\partial^2}{\partial \lambda^2} + \frac{\partial^2}{\partial \theta^2}. \tag{24.6}$$

Thus, the differential equation (22.10) goes over into

$$\Delta_V \Psi = L \cdot |R'(V)|^2 \Psi \tag{24.7}$$

for a function Ψ of the variables α, β in a schlicht domain over the V-plane. By this reasoning we have shown that *the boundary value problem for a non-schlicht domain* $\mathfrak{D}$ *and a differential equation* (22.10) *may be reduced to a boundary value problem for a schlicht domain and a differential equation of the same type.* We shall deal extensively with differential equations $\Delta \Psi = P(\alpha, \beta) \Psi$ over a schlicht domain in Part B and prove, in particular, the existence of fundamental singularities at arbitrarily prescribed points of the domain. We shall now use these fundamental singularities in the domain $\mathfrak{D}$ over the (λ, θ)-plane in order to construct flow patterns analogous to those with the complex potential (24.4) in the incompressible case.

We consider the partial differential equations for the stream function and the velocity potential which arise from (21.28) by elimination of either φ or ψ:

$$\frac{\partial}{\partial \lambda}\left(l(\lambda)\, \psi_\lambda\right) + \frac{\partial}{\partial \theta}\left(l(\lambda)\, \psi_\theta\right) = 0, \tag{24.8}$$

$$\frac{\partial}{\partial \lambda}\left(\frac{1}{l(\lambda)} \varphi_\lambda\right) + \frac{\partial}{\partial \theta}\left(\frac{1}{l(\lambda)} \varphi_\theta\right) = 0. \tag{24.9}$$

Let $P \equiv (\lambda, \theta)$ and $Q \equiv (\lambda_\infty, \theta_\infty)$ be two points in the domain $\mathfrak{D}$ and let us assume that Q is not a branch point of $\mathfrak{D}$ over the (λ, θ)-plane. We define the two fundamental singularities for the differential equations (24.8) and (24.9) in analogy to (I.3.16):

$$S(P, Q) = A(P, Q) \log |\zeta - \zeta_\infty| + B(P, Q) \tag{24.10}$$

$$T(P, Q) = C(P, Q) \log |\zeta - \zeta_\infty| + D(P, Q). \tag{24.11}$$

$S(P, Q)$ is a twice continuously differentiable function of $P \in \mathfrak{D}$ except for $P = Q$ and a solution of (24.8). A and B are twice continuously differentiable throughout $\mathfrak{D}$ and we require

$$l(Q)\, A(Q, Q) = -\frac{1}{2\pi}. \tag{24.12}$$

Similarly, $T(P, Q)$ has the same continuity properties, is a solution of (24.9), and we normalize by requiring:

$$\frac{1}{l(Q)}\, C(Q, Q) = -\frac{1}{2\pi}. \tag{24.13}$$

$S(P, Q)$ is the stream function of a flow which has a singularity at Q. In order to understand its character let us return to the differential equations (21.4) which connect the stream function and velocity potential in the physical plane. Let γ be a closed curve which may enclose singularities of the flow. We have

$$\oint_\gamma \rho \frac{\partial \varphi}{\partial \nu}\, ds = -\oint_\gamma d\psi \tag{24.14}$$

and

$$\oint_\gamma d\varphi = -\oint_\gamma (u\, dx + v\, dy) = \oint_\gamma \frac{1}{\rho} \frac{\partial \psi}{\partial \nu}\, ds. \tag{24.15}$$

The first integral represents the quantity of matter which passes through the curve γ per unit time while the second integral describes the circulation of the flow along the curve.

We now recognize that the flow with the stream function $S(P, Q)$ does not have a source at the point Q since the inflow through a little curve around Q is given by $\oint d\psi$ and ψ is a single-valued function. We have thus a vortex at Q, and in order to determine its strength we must calculate the corresponding velocity potential φ and determine its period around Q. It is easily seen that near Q the velocity potential belonging to $S(P, Q)$ has the form:

$$\varphi_S(P, Q) = -\frac{1}{2\pi} \operatorname{Im}\left(\log(\zeta - \zeta_\infty)\right) + \text{single-valued function.} \tag{24.16}$$

It has, therefore, the period -1 around the singular point Q and hence $S(P, Q)$ represents a vortex singularity with strength -1.

Similarly, $T(P,Q)$ is the velocity potential of a flow which has no circulation around the point Q. Its corresponding stream function has near Q the form

$$\psi_T(P,Q) = \frac{1}{2\pi}\,\mathrm{Im}\,\bigl(\log(\zeta - \zeta_\infty)\bigr) + \text{single-valued function}, \tag{24.17}$$

Hence, in view of (24.14) the flow has at Q a sink of strength one.

We can derive further singularities for the velocity potential and the stream function by the usual method of differentiation with respect to the parameter point. We derive from $S(P,Q)$ the two new stream functions:

$$\Xi(P,Q) = \frac{\partial S(P,Q)}{\partial \lambda_\infty} = A(P,Q)\frac{\lambda_\infty - \lambda}{|\zeta - \zeta_\infty|^2} + \frac{\partial A}{\partial \lambda_\infty}\log|\zeta - \zeta_\infty| + \frac{\partial B}{\partial \lambda_\infty}, \tag{24.18}$$

and

$$Z(P,Q) = \frac{\partial S(P,Q)}{\partial \theta_\infty} = A(P,Q)\frac{\theta_\infty - \theta}{|\zeta - \zeta_\infty|^2} + \frac{\partial A}{\partial \theta_\infty}\log|\zeta - \zeta_\infty| + \frac{\partial B}{\partial \theta_\infty}. \tag{24.19}$$

We can also derive new velocity potentials by differentiating the function $T(P,Q)$ with respect to the coordinates of Q. But this does not lead to new flow patterns since it is easily seen that the corresponding stream functions will behave like (24.18) and (24.19) near Q.

We may now consider a flow which in the domain $\mathfrak{D}$ of the (λ, θ)-plane has the stream function

$$\psi(P) = a_1 S(P,Q) + a_2 \psi_T(P,Q) + a_3 \Xi(P,Q) + a_4 Z(P,Q) + s(P) \tag{24.20}$$

where $s(P)$ is a solution of (24.8) which is regular throughout $\mathfrak{D}$ and has been added to the four preceding terms in order to ensure that $\psi(P) = 0$ on the boundary $\mathfrak{C}$ of the domain $\mathfrak{D}$ considered. $s(P)$ will, of course, depend on Q and the a_i. The flow thus obtained is the natural generalization of the incompressible fluid flow with the complex potential (24.4). In the incompressible case, the total source strength of the flow must be zero and hence only a dipole and a vortex can be placed at the point of infinity in the (x, y)-plane. In the case of a compressible fluid, we may add a source of arbitrary strength at infinity. The flow will then be described by four parameters, namely, the strength and the direction of the dipole, the strength of the source and the circulation of the vortex. In the stream function (24.20), however, we have six parameters, namely the four coefficients a_i and the two coordinates of the point Q in the (λ, θ)-plane. We must, therefore, expect two conditions between all these parameters.

These conditions are, indeed, provided by the requirement that the boundary $\mathfrak{C}$ of the domain $\mathfrak{D}$ be mapped into a closed curve in the physical plane by means of the formulas (23.7) and (23.8). The integrals which occur in these formulas do not change if we vary the paths of integration without moving their end points, provided that we do not deform the path over a point at which the integrands become singular. We may, therefore, assert that the integrals vanish if taken over a closed curve in the $\mathfrak{D}$-domain which does not include singular points of the flow. The integrals extended over the boundary $\mathfrak{C}$ of $\mathfrak{D}$, however, need not vanish since $\mathfrak{D}$ contains the singular point Q. Thus, to the same point $P \in \mathfrak{C}$ there will, in general, belong different points (x, y) if P runs repeatedly over $\mathfrak{C}$; only under special choice of the coefficients a_i will we be sure that $\mathfrak{C}$ is mapped onto a closed curve of the (x, y)-plane. In order to calculate the integrals (23.7) and (23.8) over the closed curve $\mathfrak{C}$, we may shrink the path of integration without changing the values of the integrals until instead of $\mathfrak{C}$ we obtain a circle of radius ε around the singular point Q. We may write (23.7) and (23.8) in the form

$$(24.21) \qquad x = -\int \left(\frac{\cos\theta}{q} d\varphi - \frac{\sin\theta}{q\rho} d\psi \right), \qquad y = -\int \left(\frac{\sin\theta}{q} d\varphi + \frac{\cos\theta}{q\rho} d\psi \right).$$

The requirement that the integrals (24.21) vanish if extended over the closed boundary curve $\mathfrak{C}$, can be expressed by the conditions

$$(24.22) \qquad \oint_{\gamma_\varepsilon} \left(\frac{\cos\theta}{q} d\varphi - \frac{\sin\theta}{q\rho} d\psi \right) = 0$$

and

$$(24.23) \qquad \oint_{\gamma_\varepsilon} \left(\frac{\sin\theta}{q} d\varphi + \frac{\cos\theta}{q\rho} d\psi \right) = 0,$$

where γ_ε denotes the circumference $|\lambda - \lambda_\infty|^2 + |\theta - \theta_\infty|^2 = \varepsilon^2$. These integrals can easily be evaluated by developing all functions involved in powers of $(\lambda - \lambda_\infty)$ and $(\theta - \theta_\infty)$ and by letting $\varepsilon \to 0$. We shall not enter here into the computational details. It is clear that the procedure leads to two linear homogeneous equations for the coefficients a_i in the representation (24.20).

Special consideration is necessary in the case in which the domain $\mathfrak{D}$ is unbounded. This will happen if there are stagnation points in the flow, i. e., points for which $q = 0$ and consequently $\lambda = -\infty$. Here the point at infinity is best investigated by returning to the hodograph plane itself where the critical point $q=0$ will be at the origin. It can be shown that the same linear relations for the a_i must be fulfilled and that the integration around the origin in the hodograph plane does not lead to additional terms.

Let us now consider a generalization of the Blasius formulas which were derived in Section 14 for an incompressible fluid flow. By means of these formulas we were able to express the force and the moment of the fluid pressures on the rigid obstacle C. Using the formalism of function theory we were able to express the forces and the moment in terms of certain coefficients of the development for the complex potential near the singular point of the flow. We shall show that similar results can also be obtained in the case of a compressible fluid flow.

We start with Bernoulli's law (21.1); we differentiate this identity with respect to x and y and, using the definition (2.2) for $i(\rho)$ we obtain

(24.24) $$\rho\, u\, u_x + \rho\, v\, v_x + p_x = 0, \qquad \rho\, u\, u_y + \rho\, v\, v_y + p_y = 0.$$

We combine the continuity equation

(24.25) $$(\rho\, u)_x + (\rho\, v)_y = 0$$

with both equations (24.24) and make use of the irrotational character of the flow

(24.26) $$v_x = u_y.$$

We then obtain

(24.27) $$\frac{\partial}{\partial x}(\rho\, u^2 + p) + \frac{\partial}{\partial y}(\rho\, u\, v) = 0, \qquad \frac{\partial}{\partial x}(\rho\, u\, v) + \frac{\partial}{\partial y}(\rho\, v^2 + p) = 0.$$

These two equations may be interpreted as integrability conditions and show that the integrals

(24.28) $$\oint_{\gamma}\big(\rho\, u\, v\, dx - (\rho\, u^2 + p)\big)\, dy, \qquad \oint_{\gamma}\big((\rho\, v^2 + p)\, dx - \rho\, u\, v\, dy\big)$$

do not change if the curve of integration is deformed in such a way that the endpoints do not move and γ always remains in the regularity domain of the flow. Let us observe that, by virtue of (21.4), we have

(24.29) $$\rho\, v\, dx - \rho\, u\, dy = -d\psi$$

and let us denote the normal vector $\left(-\dfrac{dy}{ds}, \dfrac{dx}{ds}\right)$ of the curve γ by $\boldsymbol{\nu}$. We may then combine both integrals (24.28) into one vector integral and obtain

$$\mathbf{J} = -\int_{\gamma} \mathbf{q}\, d\psi + \int_{\gamma} p\, \boldsymbol{\nu}\, ds. \tag{24.30}$$

This integral depends only on the endpoints of the curve of integration γ as long as all curves γ compared enclose a regularity domain of the flow.

If we choose for γ the closed boundary curve C of the flow, the first integral in (24.30) will vanish since C is a stream line and consequently satisfies $\psi = \text{const.}$ Thus, $\mathbf{J}$ will represent the vector of the total force exerted by the flow upon C. This integral may be evaluated by deforming the path of integration C into any convenient curve surrounding the singularity. We may also carry out the evaluation of the integral $\mathbf{J}$ on a small circle in the (λ, θ)-plane if the nature of the singularity is given to us in this plane. This procedure will be applicable, in particular, if the flow is described by a stream function (24.20) for some known domain $\mathfrak{D}$ in the (λ, θ)-plane.

Finally, from (24.27) we derive the equation

$$\frac{\partial}{\partial x}\big(y(\rho u^2 + p) - x\rho u v\big) + \frac{\partial}{\partial y}\big(y\rho u v - x(\rho v^2 + p)\big) = 0. \tag{24.31}$$

This shows that the integral

$$M = \oint_{\gamma} \big[\big(y\rho u v - x(\rho v^2 + p)\big)dx - \big(y(\rho u^2 + p) - x\rho u v\big)dy\big] \tag{24.32}$$

depends only upon the endpoints of the curve γ in the above sense. Using (24.29) we may simplify the integral to

$$M = \oint_{\gamma} (xv - yu)\, d\psi - \oint_{\gamma} p\,(x\,dx + y\,dy). \tag{24.33}$$

If we again choose for γ the boundary curve C, the first integral will vanish because of $\psi = \text{const.}$, and the second will describe the moment of all pressure forces on C with respect to an axis perpendicular to the (x, y)-plane. We may again evaluate the moment integral by calculating it over a path near the singularities of the flow and can usually perform these calculations with greater convenience in the (λ, θ)-plane.

In the last two sections we have shown that most results of the theory of an incompressible fluid flow can be extended to the case of compressible fluids. The best analogy between both theories exists in the hodograph and (λ, θ)-planes since the differential equations encountered there are linear.

Gelbart (G 7), Lin (L 19), Mises-Friedrichs [51].

CHAPTER III

ELECTRO- AND MAGNETOSTATICS

1. The general equations of the electrostatic field: We consider a finite domain D in (x, y, z)-space and describe an electrostatic field in D by the vector field $\mathbf{E}(P) = (E_x, E_y, E_z)$ of the electric field strength. Whatever the physical nature of the medium filling D may be, we may always assert that the principle of conservation of energy will hold in this field. Hence, the work done in forcing a charged particle along a path γ in D from a point P_0 to another point P must be independent of the path and will only depend upon the endpoints of γ. Holding the initial point P_0 fixed, we obtain in

$$\Phi(P) = -\int_{P_0}^{P} (E_x\,dx + E_y\,dy + E_z\,dz) = \int_{P_0}^{P} \mathbf{E}\cdot d\mathbf{s} \tag{1.1}$$

a function of the endpoint P of the integration. $\Phi(P)$ is called the potential of the electrostatic field and is more convenient for describing such a field than the three component functions of $\mathbf{E}$. Furthermore, from (1.1) we derive the relation

$$\mathbf{E} = -\operatorname{grad}\Phi \tag{1.2}$$

for the field strength in terms of the potential Φ.

In order to find the law by which a given charge density distribution $\rho(P)$ in D creates the electrostatic field described by $\Phi(P)$, we must know the nature of the medium in which the phenomena take place. This is described by a function $\varkappa(P)$, the dielectric coefficient of the medium at the point P. If we assume that $\varkappa$ is a differentiable function, the linear relation between the electrostatic field $\mathbf{E}$ and the local charge density $\rho(P)$ is given by the partial differential equation

$$\operatorname{div}(\varkappa\mathbf{E}) = 4\pi\rho. \tag{1.3}$$

Introducing the electrostatic potential $\Phi(P)$ by means of (1.2), we then arrive at the Laplace-Poisson equation connecting $\Phi(P)$ and $\rho(P)$:

$$\operatorname{div}(\varkappa\operatorname{grad}\Phi) = -4\pi\rho. \tag{1.4}$$

This equation enables us to determine the charge density $\rho(P)$ if the electrostatic field has been measured and Φ has been determined. There arises the important converse problem: to determine the electrostatic field from a given charge density $\rho(P)$ and appropriate boundary conditions on the boundary S of D.

For this purpose, we consider the corresponding homogeneous partial differential equation

$$\operatorname{div}(\varkappa \operatorname{grad} \Phi) = 0 \tag{1.5}$$

which played a central role in the theory of steady heat flow, considered in Chapter I. Let $S(P, Q)$ be a fundamental singularity of (1.5) which fulfills the requirement (I.3.15), or what is equivalent, (I.3.16—17). By means of Green's identity (I.4.4) we have for any two functions $u(P)$ and $v(P)$ which are twice continuously differentiable in the closed region $\mathsf{D} + \mathsf{S}$:

$$\iiint_{\mathsf{D}} \bigl(u \operatorname{div}(\varkappa \operatorname{grad} v) - v \operatorname{div}(\varkappa \operatorname{grad} u)\bigr) d\tau = - \iint_{\mathsf{S}} \varkappa \left(u \frac{\partial v}{\partial \nu} - v \frac{\partial u}{\partial \nu}\right) d\sigma. \tag{1.6}$$

Let us apply this general result to the functions $u = \Phi(P)$ and $v = S(P, Q)$ in the domain D_ε which is bounded by the surface S and a sphere with small radius ε around the point Q. Finally letting $\varepsilon \to 0$, we obtain by virtue of (I.3.15)

$$\Phi(Q) = \iint_{\mathsf{S}} \varkappa(P) \left(\Phi(P) \frac{\partial S(P,Q)}{\partial \nu_P} - S(P,Q) \frac{\partial \Phi}{\partial \nu_P}\right) d\sigma_P + \\ + 4\pi \iiint_{\mathsf{D}} S(P,Q) \rho(P) \, d\tau_P. \tag{1.7}$$

This formula shows that we can determine the electrostatic potential at each point $Q \in \mathsf{D}$ if we know the charge density $\rho(P)$ all over D and know Φ and its normal derivative $\dfrac{\partial \Phi}{\partial \nu}$ on the boundary S of D.

We can even determine the electrostatic potential $\Phi(P)$ in D if we know the charge density $\rho(P)$ in D and the values of $\Phi(P)$ on S. In fact, we observe that the function

$$\varphi(Q) = \Phi(Q) - 4\pi \iiint_{\mathsf{D}} S(P,Q) \rho(P) \, d\tau_P \tag{1.8}$$

is a solution of the linear homogeneous differential equation (1.5) and we already saw in Chapter I that such a solution is uniquely determined by its values on the boundary S of D. We may solve the problem in explicit form if the Green's function $G(P, Q)$ of the equation (1.5) with respect to the domain D is known. In (I.4) we defined $G(P, Q)$ as that particular fundamental singularity which vanishes on S; hence, (1.7) takes the particularly simple form:

$$\Phi(Q) = \iint_S \varkappa(P)\Phi(P)\frac{\partial G(P,Q)}{\partial \nu_P}\, d\sigma_P + 4\pi \iiint_D \rho(P)\, G(P,Q)\, d\tau_P. \tag{1.9}$$

Thus far, we have assumed the finiteness of the domain D in order to insure the convergence of all integrals encountered. We may easily extend all definitions and statements to infinite domains D if we define an appropriate concept of regularity for a function $\Phi(P)$ at infinity. Following the example of the theory of harmonic functions [see (II.4)] we define $\Phi(P)$ to be regular at infinity if it becomes a regular function at the origin by the transformation by reciprocal radii (II.4.7), (II.4.9). Thus, we shall call $\Phi(P)$ continuously differentiable at infinity if it behaves there like $1/r$ and if its gradient vanishes like $1/r^2$. Under these conditions all transformations of this section remain valid even for a domain D which contains the point at infinity.

Frank-Mises [14] vol. 2, Jeans [24], Ollendorff [57].

2. Conductor potentials and induction coefficients: Formula (1.9) is particularly useful in problems of the following type which occur very frequently in electrostatics. One supposes that the domain D considered is bounded by one or more conducting surfaces S_i which form the entire boundary

$$S = \sum_{i=1}^{n} S_i \tag{2.1}$$

of D. A conducting surface by its very definition possesses a constant value of the electrostatic potential for all its points. Let Φ_i be the constant values of the potential $\Phi(Q)$ on the conducting surfaces S_i; then (1.9) may be written in the form:

$$\Phi(Q) = \sum_{i=1}^{n} \Phi_i \Omega_i(Q) + 4\pi \iiint_D \rho(P)\, G(P,Q)\, d\tau_P \tag{2.2}$$

where

$$\Omega_i(Q) = \iint\limits_{S_i} \varkappa(P) \frac{\partial G(P,Q)}{\partial \nu_P} d\sigma_P \tag{2.3}$$

is a particular solution of (1.5) which can be computed once and for all if the domain D is given. It is easy to interpret $\Omega_i(Q)$ in electrostatic terms: $\Omega_i(Q)$ is an electrostatic potential whose corresponding charge density $\rho(P)$ vanishes throughout D and which has the boundary value one on S_i and zero on all the other conductors. It represents the so-called conductor potential of the surface S_i with respect to the entire domain D and is obtained by grounding all conductors S_j $(j \neq i)$ and bringing S_i to the potential 1. We see that these conductor potentials can easily be calculated if the Green's function of the domain D is known.

Let s be a closed surface in D which encloses a subdomain $\mathsf{d} \subset \mathsf{D}$. The total charge in d is given by the integrals:

$$e = \iiint\limits_{\mathsf{d}} \rho \, d\tau = -\frac{1}{4\pi} \iiint\limits_{\mathsf{d}} \operatorname{div}(\varkappa \operatorname{grad} \Phi) \, d\tau = \frac{1}{4\pi} \iint\limits_{\mathsf{s}} \varkappa \frac{\partial \Phi}{\partial \nu} d\sigma. \tag{2.4}$$

Thus, we may calculate the total charge inside any closed surface s if we know only the gradient of the corresponding potential on the surface. It is this fact which makes the concept of lines of force and their flux through surfaces s so useful for the intuitive treatment of electrostatic problems. We shall use (2.4) in order to calculate the electrostatic charge on the surface of a conductor S_i if the potential Φ in D is known. Since the space Δ_i enclosed by S_i is screened electrostatically from D, we may assume that Φ has the constant value Φ_i all over Δ_i; this will not affect the field in D but will allow us to continue Φ continuously into Δ_i. By virtue of (1.4) this extended field will not lead to new charges in Δ_i. On the other hand, if P_0 is a point on the boundary component S_i of D we shall be able to calculate the charge density near P_0 by considering a closed surface s in $\mathsf{D} + \Delta_i$ surrounding the boundary point P_0 in question.

We proceed as follows. We select a neighborhood σ around P_0 on S_i. At each point P we erect the normal $\boldsymbol{\nu}$ to S_i and continue it in both directions by an amount ε. All points lying on these normal segments form a cylindrical box d with surface s. By (2.4), we recognize that the charge in d has the value:

$$e_\varepsilon(\sigma) = -\frac{1}{4\pi} \iint\limits_{\sigma} \varkappa(P) \frac{\partial \Phi(P)}{\partial \nu} d\sigma + O(\varepsilon). \tag{2.5}$$

In fact, in the integration over the surface **s** we have only to consider that part which lies in **D** since on the other part $\operatorname{grad} \Phi = 0$. Since $\operatorname{grad} \Phi$ is bounded in **D** the contribution of the vertical walls of the cylinder **d** to the surface integral are of order of magnitude $O(\varepsilon)$ and in the integration over the base of the cylinder in **D** we may replace each point on the base by its corresponding point in σ without committing an error larger than $O(\varepsilon)$. Letting $\varepsilon \to 0$, we recognize that the surface element σ carries an electrostatic charge with surface density

$$\mu(P) = -\frac{1}{4\pi} \varkappa(P) \frac{\partial \Phi(P)}{\partial \nu}. \tag{2.6}$$

Since the point P_0 was quite arbitrary this result holds for every boundary point on a conducting surface.

Let us compute, for example, the different charges e_{ik} which are located on the conductors S_k if the particular conductor S_i is kept at unit potential while all other conductors are grounded. The corresponding electrostatic field is described by the potential $\Omega_i(Q)$ and, hence, at each point of the boundary we have:

$$\mu(Q) = -\frac{1}{4\pi} \varkappa(Q) \frac{\partial \Omega_i(Q)}{\partial \nu_Q}. \tag{2.7}$$

Thus, the charge e_{ik} has the value (by virtue of (2.3)):

$$e_{ik} = -\frac{1}{4\pi} \iint\limits_{\mathsf{S}_i} \iint\limits_{\mathsf{S}_k} \varkappa(P)\varkappa(Q) \frac{\partial^2 G(P,Q)}{\partial \nu_P\, \partial \nu_Q} d\sigma_P\, d\sigma_Q. \tag{2.8}$$

This integral is a proper integral for $i \neq k$ since in this case P and Q will not come together under the integration. In order to avoid any possible difficulties for the case $i = k$, we make the observation that the value of the integrals (2.8) will not change if extended over any surfaces S_i', S_k' which are obtained from S_i and S_k by slight deformation into **D**. In fact, the differential equation (1.5) may be considered as the condition that the integral

$$\iint\limits_{\mathsf{s}} \varkappa \frac{\partial \Phi}{\partial \nu} d\sigma = i(\mathsf{s}) \tag{2.9}$$

does not change if the closed surface **s** is deformed continuously over a region in which (1.5) is satisfied.

We see from (2.8) that the equality $e_{ik} = e_{ki}$ holds. The e_{ik} form a symmetric matrix. The coefficients e_{ik} were introduced by Maxwell and are called the *induction coefficients of the conductor system* S. If the conductors S_j have the potentials Φ_j the electrostatic field in D is described by the potential function

$$\Phi(P) = \sum_{j=1}^{n} \Phi_j \Omega_j(P) \tag{2.10}$$

if we assume that no charges occur in D. Since the conductor potential Ω_j induces on S_k the charge e_{jk} and since the charges superimpose themselves linearly, the function $\Phi(P)$ will create the charges

$$e_k = \sum_{j=1}^{n} e_{jk} \Phi_j \qquad \text{on the conductor } S_k. \tag{2.11}$$

It is obvious that we shall not be able to invert the equations (2.11) in the general case. For the charges e_k are significant physical quantities while the potentials Φ_j are essentially defined only up to an additive constant. It is necessary to normalize the Φ-potential in order to make the $e \longleftrightarrow \Phi$-relation a well-determined one. This can be done in two ways; if the domain considered contains the point at infinity, our regularity conditions will require $\Phi = 0$ at infinity and we may normalize the potential by distinguishing this point. In every other case, we may distinguish some particular conductor, say S_1, and require that Φ vanish there. In the next section we shall show that with this normalization the relations (2.11) can be inverted in a unique way. Hence, Maxwell's induction coefficients allow us to solve the following problem: to determine the charges e_j which must be brought upon each S_j in order that the conductor S_j obtains the value Φ_j for its potential function.

Jeans [24], Maxwell [46].

3. The energy of the electrostatic field: If an electrostatic field **E** has been established in D and we wish to introduce an additional charge e at the point $P \in D$ we must do work against the field. If we disregard the change of field which the charge e will create by its own electrostatic effect (i. e., if we assume e sufficiently small) the work will be given by the formula $W = e\Phi(P)$. If we wish to calculate the work necessary to assemble the charges in D and on its conducting boundary S which create the field **E** we cannot disregard, of course, the influence of the charges introduced. But we may proceed as follows; we assume that at each point P in D and on S a proportion λ of the charge density has been assembled. The work necessary to bring an additional fraction $\triangle \lambda$ of these charges to each point will then be

$$\triangle W = \iiint_{\mathsf{D}} (\triangle \lambda \cdot \rho) \cdot (\lambda \Phi)\, d\tau + \iint_{\mathsf{S}} (\triangle \lambda \cdot \mu) \cdot (\lambda \Phi)\, d\sigma; \tag{3.1}$$

for, since the field depends linearly upon the charges the λ-fold charge densities will create a λ-fold electrostatic potential. We obtain from (3.1) the exact formula:

$$\frac{dW(\lambda)}{d\lambda} = \lambda \left(\iiint_{\mathsf{D}} \rho \Phi\, d\tau + \iint_{\mathsf{S}} \mu \Phi\, d\sigma \right) \tag{3.2}$$

whence, by integration from $\lambda = 0$ to $\lambda = 1$ we obtain the whole potential energy which has been stored by assembling the charges:

$$W = \frac{1}{2} \iiint_{\mathsf{D}} \rho \Phi\, d\sigma + \frac{1}{2} \iint_{\mathsf{S}} \mu \Phi\, d\sigma. \tag{3.3}$$

We may apply the differential relations (1.4) and (2.6) in order to express the energy of the electrostatic field in terms of the potential Φ itself:

$$W = -\frac{1}{8\pi} \iiint_{\mathsf{D}} \Phi \operatorname{div} (\varkappa \operatorname{grad} \Phi)\, d\tau - \frac{1}{8\pi} \iint_{\mathsf{S}} \varkappa \Phi \frac{\partial \Phi}{\partial \nu}\, d\sigma. \tag{3.4}$$

Using Green's identity, we may write (3.4) in the particularly elegant form:

$$W = \frac{1}{8\pi} \iiint_{\mathsf{D}} \varkappa (\operatorname{grad} \Phi)^2\, d\tau = \frac{1}{8\pi} \iiint_{\mathsf{D}} \varkappa\, \mathbf{E}^2\, d\tau. \tag{3.5}$$

It was this beautiful representation for the energy of the electrostatic field which led physicists to consider the field rather than the charges as the seat of the energy connected with the state of electrization.

We have already discussed in (I.6) the intrinsic relation between the differential equation

$$\operatorname{div} (\varkappa \operatorname{grad} \Phi) = 0 \tag{3.6}$$

and the Dirichlet integral (3.5). We have shown there that the solution Φ of (3.6) solves the following minimum problem: among all continuously differentiable functions $\Phi(P)$ in D with given values on the boundary S

of D, the solution of (3.6) with the prescribed boundary values leads to the minimum for the integral

$$\text{D}\{\Phi\} = \iiint\limits_{\mathsf{D}} \varkappa \, (\operatorname{grad} \Phi)^2 \, d\tau. \tag{3.7}$$

Thus, the whole electrostatic theory can be condensed into the single statement that the energy of an electrostatic field is given by

$$W = \frac{1}{8\pi} \iiint\limits_{\mathsf{D}} \varkappa \, \mathbf{E}^2 \, d\tau. \tag{3.8}$$

The principle of conservation of energy then necessarily leads to the existence of a potential function $\Phi(P)$ and the requirement that the energy of the field be minimal leads to the differential equation (3.6).

In the above result we prescribe the boundary values of the function Φ and derive its differential equation as a minimum condition for the Dirichlet integral (3.7). In *Thomson's principle* we consider conversely vector fields $\mathfrak{q}(P)$ which satisfy the differential equation

$$\operatorname{div} (\varkappa \, \mathfrak{q}) = 0 \tag{3.9}$$

under the normalizing conditions

$$\frac{1}{4\pi} \iint\limits_{\mathsf{S}_j} \varkappa \, \mathfrak{q} \cdot \boldsymbol{\nu} \, d\sigma = e_j \qquad j = 1, 2, \ldots n \tag{3.10}$$

with respect to the boundary components S_j. If we ask for that vector field which minimizes the energy integral

$$W(\mathfrak{q}) = \frac{1}{4\pi} \iiint\limits_{\mathsf{D}} \varkappa \, \mathfrak{q}^2 \, d\tau, \tag{3.11}$$

we obtain the electrostatic field $\mathbf{E} = -\operatorname{grad} \Phi$ which belongs to the potential Φ corresponding to the charges e_j placed on the conductors S_j.

In fact, let $\mathfrak{q}(P)$ be any permissible vector field. We may write

$$W(\mathfrak{q}) = \frac{1}{4\pi} \iiint\limits_{\mathsf{D}} \varkappa \, (\operatorname{grad} \Phi)^2 \, d\tau - \frac{1}{2\pi} \iiint\limits_{\mathsf{D}} \varkappa \operatorname{grad} \Phi \cdot (\operatorname{grad} \Phi + \mathfrak{q}) \, d\tau +$$

$$+ \frac{1}{4\pi} \iiint\limits_{\mathsf{D}} \varkappa \, (\operatorname{grad} \Phi + \mathfrak{q})^2 \, d\tau. \tag{3.12}$$

Since Φ satisfies the differential equation (3.6) and $\mathfrak{q}$ satisfies (3.9), we have

$$\iiint_{\mathsf{D}} \varkappa \operatorname{grad} \Phi \cdot (\operatorname{grad} \Phi + \mathfrak{q})\, d\tau = -\sum_{j=1}^{n} \iint_{\mathsf{S}_j} \varkappa \Phi \left(\frac{\partial \Phi}{\partial \nu} + \mathfrak{q} \cdot \mathbf{v} \right) d\sigma. \tag{3.13}$$

Now, Φ has constant values Φ_j on the conductors S_j and, by (3.10), we have

$$-\frac{1}{4\pi} \iint_{\mathsf{S}_j} \varkappa \frac{\partial \Phi}{\partial \nu}\, d\sigma = e_j = \frac{1}{4\pi} \iint_{\mathsf{S}_j} \varkappa\, \mathfrak{q} \cdot \mathbf{v}\, d\sigma. \tag{3.14}$$

Thus, the entire expression (3.13) vanishes and there remains from (3.12)

$$W(\mathfrak{q}) = \frac{1}{4\pi} \iiint_{\mathsf{D}} \varkappa (\operatorname{grad} \Phi)^2\, d\tau + \frac{1}{4\pi} \iiint_{\mathsf{D}} \varkappa (\operatorname{grad} \Phi + \mathfrak{q})^2\, d\tau \geqslant$$

$$\geqslant \frac{1}{4\pi} \iiint_{\mathsf{D}} \varkappa (\operatorname{grad} \Phi)^2\, d\tau. \tag{3.15}$$

Equality can hold only for $\mathfrak{q} = -\operatorname{grad} \Phi$ and thus the statement of Thomson's principle is proved. Dirichlet's principle compares scalar functions with given boundary values; Thomson's principle compares solenoidal vector fields but with much less restrictive conditions on the boundaries. Both methods lead to upper bounds for the electrostatic energy. Thomson's principle is the analogue of the inequality (II.3.14) for the kinetic energy of a fluid flow.

The energy of an electrostatic field in a domain D bounded by n conductors S_i can be easily expressed in terms of the constant values Φ_i of the potential on the S_i and the induction coefficients e_{ik}. In fact, we have by Green's theorem:

$$W = \frac{1}{8\pi} \iiint_{\mathsf{D}} \varkappa (\operatorname{grad} \Phi)^2\, d\tau = -\frac{1}{8\pi} \sum_{j=1}^{n} \iint_{\mathsf{S}_j} \varkappa \Phi \frac{\partial \Phi}{\partial \nu}\, d\sigma =$$

$$= -\frac{1}{8\pi} \sum_{j=1}^{n} \Phi_j \iint_{\mathsf{S}_j} \varkappa \frac{\partial \Phi}{\partial \nu}\, d\sigma \tag{3.16}$$

since the potential Φ satisfies equation (3.6) if the entire field is due to charges upon the conductors S_i. By virtue of (2.6), we have

$$-\frac{1}{4\pi} \iint_{\mathsf{S}_j} \varkappa \frac{\partial \Phi}{\partial \nu}\, d\sigma = e_j \tag{3.17}$$

where e_j is the total charge on the jth conductor. Since the field is entirely described by the constant values Φ_j of the potential on S_j, we may express the e_j by (2.11) and in this way finally obtain the identity:

$$W = \frac{1}{8\pi}\iiint\limits_{\mathsf{D}} \varkappa\,(\operatorname{grad}\Phi)^2\, d\tau = \frac{1}{2}\sum_{i,j} e_{ij}\,\Phi_i\,\Phi_j. \tag{3.18}$$

We recognize that the matrix of the induction coefficients e_{ij} leads to a non-negative quadratic form. The form on the right-hand side of (3.18) can vanish only if $\operatorname{grad}\Phi \equiv 0$ in D, i. e., if Φ is constant in the domain. If D is an infinite domain, we use the first type of normalization indicated at the end of the last section and suppose that $\Phi = 0$ at infinity. In this way, the physical potential Φ will satisfy the mathematical regularity condition at infinity to which we were led at the end of Chap. I. The only possible value for the constant is then the value zero and we find that the quadratic form $\sum\limits_{i,j=1}^{n} e_{ij}\,\Phi_i\,\Phi_j$ is positive-definite since it can vanish only if all variables Φ_i are zero. Consequently, the determinant $|e_{ij}|$ is different from zero and the system of linear equations (2.11) can be solved with respect to the Φ_j.

Consider now the case in which D is finite. Here every constant A is a permissible harmonic function. If Φ has on all S_j the same value A, it must coincide with the harmonic function $\Phi = A$. Hence, we conclude from (2.10):

$$\sum_{j=1}^{n} \Omega_j(P) = 1. \tag{3.19}$$

By virtue of (2.6) the charge density on all bounding conductors will vanish in the case of a constant potential. Thus, we deduce from (2.11) the relations

$$\sum_{j=1}^{n} e_{jk} = 0 \qquad \text{for} \qquad k = 1, 2, \ldots, n. \tag{3.20}$$

The sum of each column in the induction matrix therefore vanishes in the case of a finite domain. From (2.11) we infer that

$$\sum_{k=1}^{n} e_k = 0 \tag{3.21}$$

since the matrix e_{jk} is symmetric and also the sum of each matrix row has to vanish. Consequently, we are not free to prescribe the charge on the conductor system S_j arbitrarily but must observe the law (3.21) that the total charge be zero.

The quadratic form $\sum_{i,j=1}^{n} e_{ij}\Phi_i\Phi_j$ will vanish only if all Φ_i have the same value a; the vanishing of this form if all $\Phi_i = a$ can also be inferred from (3.20). Let us now use the second type of normalization for the potential which we indicated in the last section and assume, for example, $\Phi_1 = 0$. The quadratic form $\sum_{i,j=2}^{n} e_{ij}\Phi_i\Phi_j$ now can vanish only if all Φ_i have the same value as Φ_1, i. e., if they are all zero. Thus, this reduced quadratic form is positive-definite and the matrix e_{ij} $(i, j = 2, \ldots, n)$ has, consequently, a non-vanishing determinant.

We are thus able to solve the linear system of equations (2.11) for the case of a finite domain D also, if only the necessary condition (3.21) is fulfilled. In fact, we may assume $\Phi_1 = 0$ and solve the system (2.11) for $k = 2, \ldots, n$. The values Φ_j thus obtained will also automatically satisfy the first equation (2.11) by virtue of the relations (3.20) and (3.21). Thus, the inversion of the relations between the charges and the potentials on the conductors S_j can be performed in every case.

4. The magnetostatic field: The theory of the magnetostatic field has a great similarity to that of the electrostatic field. The field is described by a vector field $\mathbf{H}(P)$ with the component functions H_x, H_y, H_z which expresses the local field strength at the point P. The work done by moving a magnetic pole of strength one along a curve γ is given by the integral

$$A = \int_{\gamma} \mathbf{H} \cdot ds = \int_{\gamma} (H_x\,dx + H_y\,dy + H_z\,dz). \tag{4.1}$$

Since a magnetic field can be created by electric currents which are due to certain sources of energy, we cannot apply the principle of conservation of energy as immediately as in the electrostatic case. It may, in fact, be possible to gain work by the motion of a magnetic pole over a closed curve γ on account of energy provided by the sources of the electric current. According to Ampere's law, we have for any closed curve

$$A = \oint_{\gamma} \mathbf{H} \cdot ds = 4\pi J, \tag{4.2}$$

where J is the sum of all currents on conductors enclosed by the path γ. In regions of the magnetic field where no conductors are situated, we have

$$\oint_{\gamma} \mathbf{H} \cdot ds = 0 \tag{4.3}$$

for closed curves γ in this region and, hence, we may introduce a potential Φ for the magnetostatic forces such that

$$\mathbf{H} = -\operatorname{grad} \Phi. \tag{4.4}$$

We introduce a local function $\mu(P)$, the magnetic permeability, as the analogue of the dielectric coefficient $\varkappa(P)$ in the electrostatic case and postulate in correspondence to (1.4) that the divergence of the vector field $\mu(P)\mathbf{H}$ represents the density of magnetic sources. However, we have to supplement this mathematical requirement by the statement of physical experience that no non-vanishing magnetic sources occur in nature so that we obtain the simple law:

$$\operatorname{div}[\mu \operatorname{grad} \Phi] = 0 \tag{4.5}$$

for the potential of the magnetic field. This is again the differential equation (1.5) or the equation (I.2.1) but with a different physical interpretation.

Let us suppose that a magnetic field $\mathbf{H}_0$ has been created by a given distribution of permanent magnets and stationary currents in empty space, i. e., with permeability $\mu_0 \equiv 1$. Let us now fill the space with a medium of known magnetic permeability $\mu(P)$ and ask for the new magnetic field which the same sources will induce. We describe the new magnetostatic field by

$$\mathbf{H}(P) = \mathbf{H}_0(P) + \mathbf{K}(P) \tag{4.6}$$

where $\mathbf{K}(P)$ is the additional field caused by the magnetic properties of the medium. For each closed curve γ in space we obviously have:

$$\oint_{\gamma} \mathbf{H} \cdot ds = \oint_{\gamma} \mathbf{H}_0 \cdot ds \tag{4.7}$$

since the currents enclosed by each curve γ have not changed by the change of the medium. Hence, we may conclude that for each closed curve γ:

$$\oint_{\gamma} \mathbf{K} \cdot ds = 0. \tag{4.8}$$

This means that the vector field **K** can be derived from a potential ψ in the form:

$$\mathbf{K} = -\operatorname{grad}\psi. \tag{4.9}$$

Let us next use the fact that no magnetic sources can occur, i. e.,

$$\operatorname{div}(\mu\,\mathbf{H}) = \operatorname{div}(\mu\,\mathbf{H}_0) + \operatorname{div}(\mu\,\mathbf{K}) = 0. \tag{4.10}$$

Using the simple vector identity

$$\operatorname{div}(\mu\,\mathbf{H}_0) = \mu\operatorname{div}\mathbf{H}_0 + \mathbf{H}_0\cdot\operatorname{grad}\mu \tag{4.11}$$

and the fact $\operatorname{div}\mathbf{H}_0 = 0$, we derive from (4.9) and (4.10) the differential equation:

$$\operatorname{div}(\mu\operatorname{grad}\psi) = \mathbf{H}_0\cdot\operatorname{grad}\mu. \tag{4.12}$$

This is an inhomogeneous differential equation for the determination of the corrective potential ψ and is analogous to the differential equation (1.4) in electrostatics. It can be solved by using the fundamental singularity connected with the corresponding homogeneous differential equation:

$$\operatorname{div}(\mu\operatorname{grad}\psi) = 0. \tag{4.13}$$

A very important class of permeability functions $\mu(P)$ is that of piecewise constant functions. This class of permeability functions is encountered if we work with various bodies in space, each of which has a different but constant permeability. In this case, the function $\mu(P)$ ceases to be differentiable on the boundaries of the different bodies and the equation $\operatorname{div}(\mu\,\mathbf{H}) = 0$ must be modified. We assume that the boundary surfaces between two adjacent media are smooth; we take a piece of a boundary surface σ and over it construct a cylindrical box d of height 2ε as described in Section 2. Let s denote its surface; we then replace the requirement $\operatorname{div}(\mu\,\mathbf{H}) = 0$ by the statement

$$\iint_{\mathsf{s}} \mu\,\mathbf{H}\cdot\boldsymbol{\nu}\,d\sigma = 0 \tag{4.14}$$

which also expresses the fact that the sum of all magnetic sources in d is zero. Let μ_1 and H_{ν_1} denote the permeability and normal component of **H** in the first medium and μ_2, H_{ν_2} the corresponding quantities of the second medium; let $\boldsymbol{\nu}_i$ be the normal directed from the boundary into the medium considered. Then, (4.14) leads to the result

$$\iint_{\sigma} (\mu_1 H_{\nu_1} + \mu_2 H_{\nu_2})\,d\sigma = O(\varepsilon). \tag{4.15}$$

Letting $\varepsilon \to 0$ and using the arbitrariness of the surface element σ, we derive from (4.15) the saltus condition for **H**:

$$\mu_1 H_{\nu_1} + \mu_2 H_{\nu_2} = 0 \tag{4.16}$$

which expresses the non-appearance of magnetic sources on the discontinuity surfaces.

Let us apply the results obtained in order to determine the magnetic field in the metal core of a transformer. We suppose that the core is of the usual toroidal form and we divide its surface into two parts: the surface A where the metal is in contact with air and the surface B around which the wiring is located and in which the current runs. If μ_i is the permeability of the iron and μ_a the permeability of the air, we derive from Ampere's law (4.2) the following discontinuity conditions for the magnetic field:

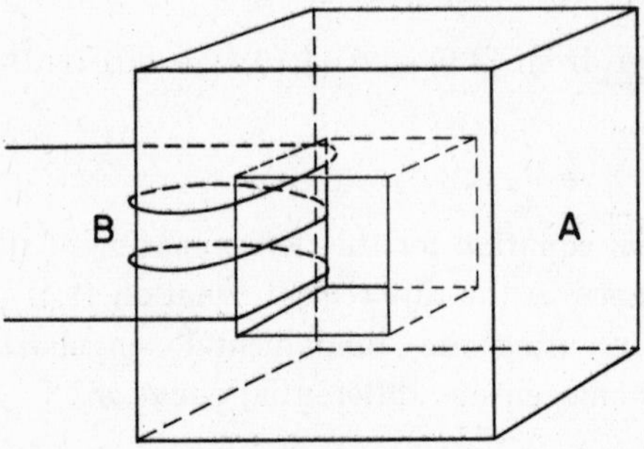

Figure 9

a) The normal components of **H** satisfy everywhere on the boundary of the iron core

$$\mu_i H_{\nu_i} + \mu_a H_{\nu_a} = 0 \tag{4.17}$$

since magnetic sources can occur nowhere.

b) The tangential components of **H** on A pass through continuously and the same holds on B for the tangential component of **H** in the direction of the current.

c) Let H_t be the tangential component of **H** on B perpendicular to the direction of the current in the surrounding wires and let l be the linear current density in the wiring. We then have the discontinuity condition:

$$H_{t_i} - H_{t_a} = 4\pi l. \tag{4.18}$$

Inside the iron and outside in the air **H** possesses a magnetic potential Φ which satisfies Laplace's equation

$$\Delta \Phi = 0. \tag{4.19}$$

The potential $\Phi(P)$ of the magnetostatic field will be determined uniquely in the whole space if in addition to the above conditions we prescribe the character of Φ at infinity. As a regular harmonic function, Φ will possess a series development at infinity of the form

$$(4.20) \qquad \Phi(P) = \frac{a}{r} + \frac{b_1 x + b_2 y + b_3 z}{r^3} + \dots, \qquad r = (x^2 + y^2 + z^2)^{1/2}.$$

Since each sphere S_R must include a zero total amount of magnetic sources, the flux of the magnetic field through the sphere must vanish, i. e.,

$$(4.21) \qquad \iint_{S_R} \frac{\partial \Phi}{\partial \nu} d\sigma = 0,$$

and this leads easily to the result

$$(4.22) \qquad a = 0.$$

Thus, we must require that the magnetostatic potential becomes zero at infinity at least of the order of $(1/r^2)$. It can be shown that all requirements enumerated determine the magnetic field **H** in a unique way.

In order to carry out the actual determination of **H** we may proceed in two steps. At first we may disregard the permeability of the iron and determine the magnetic field $\mathbf{H}_0(P)$ which would have been created by the current in the wiring without the presence of the iron core. We may find $\mathbf{H}_0$ by theoretical or experimental methods. Next, we try to represent the actual magnetic field **H** in the form

$$(4.23) \qquad \mathbf{H} = \mathbf{H}_0 + \mathbf{K}$$

and to determine the corrective field **K**. It is easily seen that **K** has continuous tangential components at the boundary of the iron core since the discontinuity (4.18) of H_t is by Ampere's law easily shown to be the same as that of H_{0t}. Thus, from (4.9) we may derive **K** from a potential ψ which is harmonic inside and outside the iron core and has continuous tangential derivatives on the surface of the core. The normal components of grad ψ satisfy by (4.17) and (4.23) the requirement:

$$(4.24) \qquad \mu_i \frac{\partial \psi}{\partial \nu_i} + \mu_a \frac{\partial \psi}{\partial \nu_a} = (\mu_i - \mu_a)\, \mathbf{H}_0 \cdot \boldsymbol{\nu}_i,$$

since the normal component of $\mathbf{H}_0$ is, of course, continuous on the surface. We have to find a harmonic function ψ in the whole space which vanishes at least as strongly as $(1/r^2)$ at infinity and has the saltus condition (4.24) on the given surface **S** of the iron core.

We may try to express the potential ψ in the following form:

$$(4.25) \qquad \psi(P) = \iint_S \omega(Q) \frac{1}{r(P,Q)} d\sigma_Q, \qquad r(P,Q) = \overline{PQ}.$$

It is well known from elementary potential theory that such an integral represents a harmonic function inside and outside of the surface S. It is continuous if P passes through S and the tangential derivatives of ψ on S are continuous through the surface. But the normal derivatives of ψ are discontinuous and satisfy the jump conditions:

$$(4.26)\qquad \begin{aligned} \frac{\partial \psi}{\partial \nu_i} &= -2\pi\omega(P) + \iint_S \omega(Q)\frac{\partial}{\partial \nu_P}\left(\frac{1}{r(P,Q)}\right) d\sigma_Q, \\ \frac{\partial \psi}{\partial \nu_a} &= -2\pi\omega(P) - \iint_S \omega(Q)\frac{\partial}{\partial \nu_P}\left(\frac{1}{r(P,Q)}\right) d\sigma_Q, \end{aligned}$$

where $\dfrac{\partial}{\partial \nu_P}$ denotes the normal derivative at the point $P \in \mathsf{S}$ in the direction of the normal $\boldsymbol{\nu}_i$.

Inserting the formulas (4.26) into (4.24), we obtain the requirement for $\omega(P)$:

$$(4.27)\qquad \begin{aligned} -2\pi\omega(P)(\mu_i + \mu_a) + (\mu_i - \mu_a)\iint_S \omega(Q)\frac{\partial}{\partial \nu_P}\left(\frac{1}{r(P,Q)}\right) d\sigma_Q &= \\ = F(P)(\mu_i - \mu_a)& \end{aligned}$$

where $F(P) = \mathbf{H}_0 \cdot \boldsymbol{\nu}_i$ is a known function of the point $P \in \mathsf{S}$. We thus obtain the integral equation for $\omega(P)$:

$$(4.28)\qquad \omega(P) - \frac{1}{2\pi}\frac{\mu_i - \mu_a}{\mu_i + \mu_a}\iint_S \omega(Q) K(P,Q)\, d\sigma_Q = -\frac{1}{2\pi} F(P)\frac{\mu_i - \mu_a}{\mu_i + \mu_a}$$

with the kernel

$$(4.29)\qquad K(P,Q) = \frac{\partial}{\partial \nu_P}\left(\frac{1}{r(P,Q)}\right).$$

It is also known from potential theory that the following equation holds:

$$(4.30)\qquad \iint_S \frac{\partial}{\partial \nu_P}\left(\frac{1}{r(P,Q)}\right) d\sigma_P = \begin{cases} 4\pi \text{ for } Q \text{ inside } \mathsf{S} \\ 2\pi \text{ for } Q \text{ on } \mathsf{S} \\ 0 \text{ for } Q \text{ outside } \mathsf{S} \end{cases}$$

since the left-hand integral represents the flux through S of a radial field due to a unit source at Q. Hence, we have for $Q \in \mathsf{S}$:

$$(4.31)\qquad \iint_S K(P,Q)\, d\sigma_P = 2\pi.$$

We apply this result by integrating the equation (4.28) over all points $P \in S$. Interchanging the orders of integration we obtain

$$\frac{2\mu_a}{\mu_i + \mu_a} \iint_S \omega(Q)\, d\sigma_Q = -\frac{1}{2\pi} \left(\frac{\mu_i - \mu_a}{\mu_i + \mu_a}\right) \iint_S F(P)\, d\sigma_P. \tag{4.32}$$

Because of the absence of sources in the magnetostatic field $\mathbf{H}_0$, we have

$$\iint_S \mathbf{H}_0 \cdot \boldsymbol{\nu}_i\, d\sigma = \iint_S F(P)\, d\sigma_P = 0. \tag{4.33}$$

Hence, we conclude from (4.32):

$$\iint_S \omega(Q)\, d\sigma_Q = 0 \tag{4.34}$$

as a first condition for the unknown function $\omega(Q)$. By means of this result we easily recognize that the function $\psi(P)$ defined by (4.25) vanishes at infinity at least of the order of $(1/r^2)$. The requirement on the behavior of the corrective potential $\psi(P)$ at infinity is thus automatically fulfilled by our set-up.

Let us write equation (4.28) in the standard form

$$\omega(P) = f(P) + \frac{\lambda}{2\pi} \iint_S \omega(Q)\, K(P,Q)\, d\sigma_Q, \tag{4.35}$$

$$f = -\frac{1}{2\pi} \frac{\mu_i - \mu_a}{\mu_i + \mu_a} F, \qquad \lambda = \frac{\mu_i - \mu_a}{\mu_i + \mu_a}.$$

For sufficiently small values of λ, we may solve this equation by successive approximation. We put $\omega_0(P) = f(P)$ and recursively

$$\omega_n(P) = f(P) + \frac{\lambda}{2\pi} \iint_S K(P,Q)\, \omega_{n-1}(Q)\, d\sigma_Q. \tag{4.36}$$

The result may be expressed explicitly if we define the iterated kernels

$$K^{(n)}(P,Q) = \iint_S K(P,T)\, K^{(n-1)}(T,Q)\, d\sigma_T, \qquad K^{(1)} = K. \tag{4.37}$$

We then easily find by induction:

$$\omega_n(P) = f(P) + \frac{\lambda}{2\pi} \iint_S K^{(1)}(P,Q) f(Q)\, d\sigma_Q + \ldots + \tag{4.38}$$
$$+ \left(\frac{\lambda}{2\pi}\right)^{n-1} \iint_S K^{(n-1)}(P,Q) f(Q)\, d\sigma_Q.$$

If this procedure converges, it gives the solution of the integral equation (4.35) in the form of the Neumann series:

$$\omega(P) = f(P) + \sum_{\nu=1}^{\infty} \left(\frac{\lambda}{2\pi}\right)^{\nu} \iint_S K^{(\nu)}(P,Q) f(Q)\, d\sigma_Q. \tag{4.39}$$

It can be shown in the general theory of integral equations that the Neumann series, and consequently the approximation procedure, converges as long as λ remains smaller in absolute value than the least possible absolute value of an eigenvalue of the homogeneous integral equation

$$\omega(P) = \frac{\lambda}{2\pi} \iint_S \omega(Q) K(P,Q)\, d\sigma_Q. \tag{4.40}$$

We shall now prove that for the particular type (4.29) of the kernel $K(P,Q)$ no eigenvalue exists which is smaller in absolute value than 1. We are not sure a priori that equation (4.40) has only real eigenvalues and thus we have to admit the possibility that a complex eigenvalue λ_0 exists with a corresponding complex-valued eigenfunction $\omega_0(P)$. But from the fact that $K(P,Q)$ is real it is clear that the conjugate complex function $\overline{\omega_0(P)}$ will then also be an eigenfunction of (4.40) with the eigenvalue $\bar{\lambda}_0$. Let us now define the complex-valued harmonic function

$$\psi(P) = \iint_S \omega_0(Q) \frac{1}{r(P,Q)}\, d\sigma_Q \tag{4.41}$$

by means of the eigenfunction $\omega_0(Q)$. $\psi(P)$ is regular harmonic inside and outside of S and is even continuous through this surface. By virtue of (4.26) and the integral equation (4.40), we obtain the following values for its normal derivatives on the boundary surface S:

$$\frac{\partial \psi(P)}{\partial \nu_i} = 2\pi \left(\frac{1}{\lambda_0} - 1\right) \omega_0(P), \qquad \frac{\partial \psi(P)}{\partial \nu_a} = -2\pi \left(\frac{1}{\lambda_0} + 1\right) \omega_0(P). \tag{4.42}$$

Let us next integrate the equation (4.40) with respect to P over S. Using (4.31), we obtain

$$(4.43) \qquad (1-\lambda_0)\iint_{\mathsf{S}} \omega_0(Q)\, d\sigma_Q = 0$$

which shows that for $\lambda_0 \neq 1$ the integral of ω_0 over S vanishes. Let us assume from now on that $\lambda_0 \neq 1$; then we conclude from (4.41) that $\psi(P)$ vanishes at infinity at least like $(1/r^2)$. We may apply Green's identity to the harmonic functions $\psi(P)$ and $\overline{\psi(P)}$ with respect to the interior J and the exterior E of S and obtain:

$$(4.44) \qquad \begin{aligned} \iiint_{\mathsf{J}} |\mathrm{grad}\,\psi|^2\, d\tau &= \iiint_{\mathsf{J}} (\mathrm{grad}\,\psi \cdot \mathrm{grad}\,\overline{\psi})\, d\tau = \\ &= -2\pi\left(\frac{1}{\lambda_0}-1\right)\iint_{\mathsf{S}} \omega_0(P)\,\overline{\psi(P)}\, d\sigma, \end{aligned}$$

$$(4.45) \qquad \begin{aligned} \iiint_{\mathsf{E}} |\mathrm{grad}\,\psi|^2\, d\tau &= \iiint_{\mathsf{E}} (\mathrm{grad}\,\psi \cdot \mathrm{grad}\,\overline{\psi})\, d\tau = \\ &= 2\pi\left(\frac{1}{\lambda_0}+1\right)\iint_{\mathsf{S}} \omega_0(P)\,\overline{\psi(P)}\, d\sigma. \end{aligned}$$

Both left-hand integrals are real and non-negative. It is impossible that both should vanish since in this case ψ would be constant in E and J; thus, by (4.42), we would have $\omega_0(P) = 0$. But $\omega_0(P)$ was assumed, of course, to be a non-trivial eigenfunction corresponding to the eigenvalue λ_0. We can thus assert

$$(4.46) \qquad \iint_{\mathsf{S}} \omega_0\,\overline{\psi}\, d\sigma \neq 0.$$

Eliminating this integral from (4.44) and (4.45), we learn at once that λ_0 is real; consequently, ω_0 and ψ can be assumed to be real, too. Since, furthermore, both integrals (4.44) and (4.45) are non-negative, we obtain by multiplying these two equations:

$$(4.47) \qquad 1-\frac{1}{\lambda_0{}^2} \geqslant 0, \qquad |\lambda_0| \geqslant 1.$$

The result just obtained guarantees the convergence of the Neumann's series in our particular problem (4.28), (4.35) as long as $|\lambda| < 1$. Since μ_i

and μ_a are by their very nature positive quantities, the coefficient λ defined in (4.35) will always satisfy this requirement. Thus, *we have proved the existence of a solution ψ satisfying the conditions of the transformer problem.*

While the theoretical part of the transformer problem has been answered satisfactorily by the above considerations there remains one practical difficulty in our treatment. The permeability constant of iron being enormously large compared to the permeability of air, the factor $\lambda = \frac{\mu_i - \mu_a}{\mu_i + \mu_a}$ is very near to one. We shall show that $\lambda = 1$ is indeed an eigenvalue of the homogeneous integral equation (4.40); hence, the convergence of the Neumann's series (4.39) might be extremely bad. We shall indicate a procedure for investigating the convergence of this series and give a useful artifice which can be applied in many analogous cases.

Let us consider the homogeneous integral equation

$$\omega(P) = \frac{\lambda}{2\pi} \iint_S \omega(Q) K(Q, P)\, d\sigma_Q \tag{4.48}$$

which has the transposed kernel $K(Q, P)$ instead of the kernel $K(P, Q)$ in (4.40). By virtue of (4.31), we are able to give immediately an eigenvalue and an eigenfunction of this problem. In fact, select $\lambda = 1$ and choose for $\omega(P)$ any constant value; then the equation (4.48) will be fulfilled. We have thus shown that $\lambda_0 = 1$ is an eigenvalue for the transposed kernel $K(Q, P)$; by the general theory of integral equations it is then also an eigenvalue for the integral equation (4.40) in which we are interested.

Let us now study the eigenfunction $\omega_0(P)$ belonging to the eigenvalue $\lambda_0 = 1$ of the equation (4.40). By (4.41) we define a corresponding function $\psi(P)$ which is regular harmonic in the exterior E and the interior J of S. $\psi(P)$ need not vanish at infinity more quickly than $(1/r)$ since we cannot now assert that $\iint_S \omega_0\, d\sigma = 0$. But we can still apply Green's theorem with respect to J and obtain (4.44). Since $\lambda_0 = 1$, we derive the result $\psi =$ const. in J. We know furthermore that $\psi(P)$ changes continuously through S. Hence, $\psi(P)$ is a harmonic function in E which has on S a constant boundary value. $\psi(P)$ is not a constant since it is regular harmonic even at infinity. This function is closely related to the conductor potential $V(P)$ of S which is defined as follows: a) $V(P)$ is regular harmonic in the exterior E of S. b) $V(P)$ has the constant boundary value one on S. The conductor potential $V(P)$ is uniquely defined by these two requirements.

For suppose that there were two harmonic functions $V(P)$ and $V^*(P)$ satisfying both requirements. Then $V^*(P) - V(P)$ would also be regular harmonic in **E** and vanish everywhere on **S**. By the maximum principle, we have then $V^*(P) \equiv V(P)$.

Since $\omega_0(P)$ is defined only up to a multiplicative constant, the same is true for $\psi(P)$ and we may determine $\psi(P)$ by requiring the boundary value 1 on **S**. Thus, we can assert:

$$\psi(P) = V(P), \qquad P \in \mathsf{E}. \tag{4.49}$$

By virtue of (4.42), we can then express the eigenfunction $\omega_0(P)$:

$$\omega_0(P) = -\frac{1}{4\pi}\frac{\partial V(P)}{\partial \nu_P}. \tag{4.50}$$

We have thus expressed the eigenfunction $\omega_0(P)$ belonging to $\lambda_0 = 1$ in terms of the conductor potential. Conversely, it is not difficult to verify that the function (4.50) is, indeed, a solution of the homogeneous integral equation (4.40).

Let us show next that the value $\lambda_0 = -1$ is not an eigenvalue of (4.40). If there were an eigenfunction $\omega_0(P)$ belonging to the eigenvalue $\lambda = -1$, we might again define for it the harmonic function $\psi(P)$ by means of (4.41). $\psi(P)$ would vanish at infinity at least like $(1/r^2)$ and formulas (4.44) and (4.45) could be applied. We would deduce from $\lambda_0 = -1$ and (4.45) that $\psi \equiv 0$ in **E**. Since ψ is continuous through **S**, it will represent a regular harmonic function in **J** with the boundary values zero on **S**. But then the maximum principle would imply $\psi \equiv 0$ in **J**, and from (4.42) we would finally arrive at $\omega_0(P) = 0$. This contradicts the original assumption that a non-trivial eigenfunction $\omega_0(P)$ exists for the eigenvalue $\lambda_0 = -1$. Thus, we have shown: *The integral equation* (4.40) *has the eigenvalue* $\lambda_0 = +1$ *and all other eigenvalues are real and larger in absolute value than one.* Consider now the new kernel $K_1(P, Q)$, defined by

$$K_1(P,Q) = K(P,Q) - 2\pi\beta\frac{\partial V(P)}{\partial \nu_P}, \qquad \beta = \left(\iint_{\mathsf{S}} \frac{\partial V}{\partial \nu}\, d\sigma\right)^{-1}. \tag{4.51}$$

Since $\partial V / \partial \nu_P$ is an eigenfunction of (4.40) with the eigenvalue one, we derive from (4.31) and (4.51) the two equations:

$$\iint_{\mathsf{S}} K_1(P,Q)\frac{\partial V(Q)}{\partial \nu_Q}\, d\sigma_Q = 0, \tag{4.52}$$

(4.53) $$\iint_S K_1(P,Q)\, d\sigma_P = 0.$$

The first equation may be interpreted as saying that $\partial V/\partial \nu$ is also an eigenfunction of the new kernel $K_1(P,Q)$ but belonging to the eigenvalue $\lambda_0 = \infty$. From the second equation, we infer that every eigenfunction $v(P)$ of the homogeneous integral equation

(4.54) $$v(P) = \frac{\lambda}{2\pi} \iint_S v(Q)\, K_1(P,Q)\, d\sigma_Q$$

satisfies the condition

(4.55) $$\iint_S v\, d\sigma = 0.$$

But then, we have by (4.51):

(4.56) $$v(P) = \frac{\lambda}{2\pi} \iint_S v(Q)\, K_1(P,Q)\, d\sigma_Q = \frac{\lambda}{2\pi} \iint_S v(Q)\, K(P,Q)\, d\sigma_Q.$$

Thus, every eigenfunction of the new integral equation (4.54) is also an eigenfunction of the integral equation (4.40) with the same eigenvalue. Conversely, every eigenfunction $\omega_0(P)$ of (4.40) which does not belong to $\lambda = 1$ satisfies (4.43) and consequently also (4.54). We thus have shown: *The kernel $K_1(P,Q)$ has exactly the same eigenfunctions and eigenvalues as the kernel $K(P,Q)$ except for the eigenvalue $\lambda_0 = 1$ and the corresponding eigenfunction $\partial V/\partial \nu$.*

We may now define the iterations of the K_1-kernel as follows:

$$K_1^{(n)}(P,Q) = \iint_S K_1(P,T)\, K_1^{(n-1)}(T,Q)\, d\sigma_T, \qquad K_1^{(1)}(P,Q) = K_1(P,Q)$$

(4.57)

and construct the following kernel:

(4.58) $$K_1^{(-1)}(P,Q;\lambda) = \sum_{\nu=1}^{\infty} \left(\frac{\lambda}{2\pi}\right)^{\nu} K_1^{(\nu)}(P,Q).$$

This kernel series converges for all values λ which are in absolute value less than the smallest absolute value of an eigenvalue of $K_1(P,Q)$. Thus, the series (4.58) will surely converge for $|\lambda| \leqslant 1$ and by means of it we may now solve the integral equation (4.35) in the form

$$(4.59) \qquad \omega(P) = f(P) + \iint_S K_1^{(-1)}(P, Q; \lambda) f(Q) \, d\sigma_Q.$$

Since $K_1(P, Q)$ is easily constructed from $K(P, Q)$ and the conductor potential $V(P)$, we are able to construct the kernel $K_1^{(-1)}$ by means of a geometrically convergent series once the conductor potential $V(P)$ is known. We are then able to solve every integral equation (4.35) for arbitrarily given $f(P)$ by simple integration. The conductor potential $V(P)$ will be discussed in Section 5 and will be constructed in terms of the Green's function. Aside from its own interest as a potential-theoretic function, it has importance in numerical questions, as we have seen, for it enables us to construct the rapidly convergent kernel $K_1^{(-1)}$ which is frequently needed in potential theory and electrostatics and magnetostatics.

If for a given surface S various integral equations (4.35) with different terms $f(P)$ have to be treated, then the construction of the kernel $K_1^{(-1)}$ would be advantageous, while if we want to treat one particular integral equation (4.35), the recursion (4.36) seems preferable. We are now able to show, a posteriori, its convergence even when λ is equal to one. In fact, since $\iint_S f \, d\sigma = 0$ is guaranteed by the type of problem considered, we have

$$(4.60) \qquad f^{(1)}(P) = \iint_S K_1(P, Q) f(Q) \, d\sigma_Q = \iint_S K(P, Q) f(Q) \, d\sigma_Q.$$

By virtue of (4.53), we have $\iint_S f_1(P) \, d\sigma = 0$ and hence:

$$(4.61) \qquad f^{(2)}(P) = \iint_S K_1(P, Q) f^{(1)}(Q) \, d\sigma_Q = \iint_S K_1^{(2)}(P, Q) f(Q) \, d\sigma_Q =$$

$$= \iint_S K(P, Q) f^{(1)}(Q) \, d\sigma_Q = \iint_S K^{(2)}(P, Q) f(Q) \, d\sigma_Q.$$

Continuing this reasoning by induction we find generally:

$$(4.62) \qquad f^{(n)}(P) = \iint_S K_1^{(n)}(P, Q) f(Q) \, d\sigma_Q = \iint_S K^{(n)}(P, Q) f(Q) \, d\sigma_Q.$$

Thus, the series (4.39) will converge for all λ values needed since the series (4.58) converges.

In many considerations, it is impossible to consider the permeability μ_i in the iron core of a transformer as a constant. In fact, the permeability depends to a certain extent upon the field strength $|\mathbf{H}|$. If we insert the known function $\mu(|\mathbf{H}|^2)$ into the differential equation (4.5), we obtain the non-linear differential equation:

$$\operatorname{div}\Big(\mu\big((\operatorname{grad}\Phi)^2\big)\operatorname{grad}\Phi\Big) = 0 \tag{4.63}$$

for the potential of the magnetic field. This equation has to be treated with the boundary and discontinuity conditions mentioned before.

One convenient way of dealing with such a non-linear problem is the following method of successive approximation. One at first disregards the variability of μ_i with $\mathbf{H}$ and solves the magnetostatic problem for constant value of μ_i. One calculates the field $\mathbf{H}_0$ which is obtained in this way and then considers the function $\mu_1(P) = \mu(|\mathbf{H}_0|^2)$ as a better approximation for μ_i. One has thus the linear differential equation:

$$\operatorname{div}\big(\mu_1(P)\operatorname{grad}\Phi\big) = 0 \tag{4.64}$$

which can be treated by the linear methods discussed in this book. One derives a new magnetic field $\mathbf{H}_1$ belonging to a potential Φ which satisfies (4.64). One may improve this result again by using $\mu_2(P) = \mu(|\mathbf{H}_1|^2)$ as a better approximation for the permeability distribution in the transformer core and repeat the whole procedure. This method is very satisfactory since the variability of μ with the field strength is not too great. It is, therefore, possible to stop the approximation after very few steps. But even in the first step one has to deal with a differential equation of the type (4.64) which is more difficult than the simple Laplace equation.

Courant-Hilbert [13] vol. 1, Frank-Mises [14] vol. 2, Jeans [24], Maxwell [46].

5. The conductor potential; spherical harmonics: We return to the electrostatic problem and simplify matters considerably by assuming the dielectric factor $\varkappa$ to be a constant, say one, in the domain D considered. The electrostatic potential $\Phi(P)$ will then satisfy the simple Laplace-Poisson equation

$$\Delta\Phi = -4\pi\rho \tag{5.1}$$

at points of the domain D where electrostatic charges occur, and Laplace's equation

$$\Delta\Phi = 0 \tag{5.2}$$

in the charge-free part of D. We assume D bounded by a system S of conducting surfaces S_j and know, therefore, that on each surface S_j the potential Φ will have a constant value Φ_j.

The simplest electrostatic problem for a set of conductors S_j bounding a domain D is the following. We bring all the conductors S_j to zero potential by grounding; we then bring a point charge, say of strength one, to a point $Q \in \mathsf{D}$ and ask for the potential created in D by the point charge and by the surface charge distribution on S which is induced by the point charge. This potential $\Phi(P;Q)$ is characterized by the three properties:

a) Except for $P = Q$, $\Phi(P;Q)$ is a harmonic function of $P \in \mathsf{D}$.

b) If we subtract the potential $\big(r(P,Q)\big)^{-1}$ of the unit charge at Q from $\Phi(P;Q)$ we obtain the potential of the induced charges on S, and this function is harmonic at Q. Thus: $\Phi(P;Q) - \big(r(P,Q)\big)^{-1}$ is regular harmonic at Q.

c) The potential $\Phi(P;Q)$ has the boundary value zero on S since all conductors S_j are grounded.

These three properties suffice to determine $\Phi(P;Q)$ in a unique way. Let $G(P,Q)$ be the Green's function of D for Laplace's equation. The function $\Phi(P;Q) - 4\pi G(P,Q)$ is harmonic everywhere in D and vanishes on the boundary S of D. Hence, by virtue of the maximum principle, we have:

$$\Phi(P;Q) = 4\pi G(P,Q). \tag{5.3}$$

The potential created by a point charge at Q in the presence of a grounded conductor system is essentially the Green's function of that system with parameter point at Q. This interpretation is of historical interest since it led mathematicians rather early to postulate the existence of a Green's function on intuitive grounds.

There is no great formal difference in the study of the Green's function for a constant dielectric factor or for a variable $\varkappa(P)$ as considered in Sections 1—3. The main advantage of the assumption $\varkappa = 1$ consists in the fact that the simple fundamental solution $S(P,Q) = \dfrac{1}{4\pi r(P,Q)}$ is available. Since we have an intuitive understanding of this elementary function, various statements can be made about the Green's function which cannot be made in the same form in the general case. As an illustration, consider the inequality

$$0 \leqslant G(P,Q) \leqslant \frac{1}{4\pi r(P,Q)}. \tag{5.4}$$

This result is an immediate consequence of the maximum principle and the fact that $(r(P, Q))^{-1}$ is always non-negative.

Another advantage in considering the case of a constant dielectric factor comes from the fact that we are dealing with harmonic functions which have well-known series developments in terms of spherical harmonics. We arrive at the theory of spherical harmonics if we ask for ordinary polynomials in x, y, z which satisfy Laplace's equation (5.2). Since a polynomial $\pi_n(x, y, z)$ which is homogeneous of degree n in its variables is changed by the application of the Laplace operator Δ to a polynomial which is homogeneous of degree $n - 2$, it is natural to decompose every polynomial $\pi(x, y, z)$ into the form

$$\pi(x, y, z) = \sum_{i=0}^{n} \pi_i(x, y, z), \tag{5.5}$$

$$\pi_i(x, y, z) = \text{homogeneous polynomial of } i^{\text{th}} \text{ degree.}$$

If we require $\pi(x, y, z)$ to satisfy Laplace's equation, we clearly have to demand that each polynomial $\pi_i(x, y, z)$ satisfies this equation separately. Let us next introduce polar coordinates r, ϑ, φ by the definition

$$x = r\cos\varphi\sin\vartheta, \qquad y = r\sin\varphi\sin\vartheta, \qquad z = r\cos\vartheta. \tag{5.6}$$

Because of the homogeneity of $\pi_l(x, y, z)$, we may write

$$\pi_l(x, y, z) = r^l S_l(\vartheta, \varphi) \tag{5.7}$$

where $S_l(\vartheta, \varphi)$ is a trigonometrical polynomial of its variables. The interesting fact about $S_l(\vartheta, \varphi)$ is that it gives rise not only to one, but to two harmonic functions. In fact, let us perform a transformation by reciprocal radii (II.4.7) in the (x, y, z)-space. In polar coordinates, we can express it in the simple form

$$x' = \frac{1}{r}\cos\varphi\sin\vartheta, \qquad y' = \frac{1}{r}\sin\varphi\sin\vartheta, \qquad z' = \frac{1}{r}\cos\vartheta. \tag{5.8}$$

By Kelvin's theorem [see (II.4)], the new function

$$\pi_l^*(x, y, z) = \frac{1}{r}\pi_l(x', y', z') \tag{5.9}$$

will also be harmonic. But in view of the homogeneity of π_l, we can write

$$\pi_l^*(x, y, z) = \frac{1}{r^{l+1}} S_l(\vartheta, \varphi) = \frac{1}{r^{2l+1}}\pi_l(x, y, z). \tag{5.10}$$

The functions $S_l(\vartheta, \varphi)$ play an important role in the theory of harmonic functions. Since they depend upon the variables ϑ and φ only and are periodic in these two variables, they are best represented as single-valued functions of the points on the unit sphere. This explains their name, spherical harmonics.

One of the most important properties of the spherical harmonics is an immediate consequence of Green's identity. In fact, applying this integral identity to two homogeneous harmonic polynomials π_l and π_k with respect to the interior of the unit sphere, Σ_1, we obtain

$$\iint_{\Sigma_1} \left(\pi_l \frac{\partial \pi_k}{\partial \nu} - \pi_k \cdot \frac{\partial \pi_l}{\partial \nu} \right) d\sigma = 0. \tag{5.11}$$

We observe that on a sphere differentiation in the direction of the interior normal is, but for the sign, identical with radial differentiation. Hence, in view of (5.7):

$$\iint_{\Sigma_1} \left(r^l S_l(\vartheta, \varphi) \cdot k r^{k-1} S_k(\vartheta, \varphi) - r^k S_k(\vartheta, \varphi) \cdot l r^{l-1} S_l(\vartheta, \varphi) \right) d\sigma = 0, \tag{5.12}$$

i. e.,

$$\iint_{\Sigma_1} S_l(\vartheta, \varphi) S_k(\vartheta, \varphi)\, d\sigma = 0 \qquad \text{for} \qquad k \neq l. \tag{5.13}$$

Thus, we have proved: *Spherical harmonics of different degrees are orthogonal to each other under integration over the unit sphere.*

Since by a well-known formula of calculus

$$\Delta \Phi = \frac{1}{r^2} \frac{\partial}{\partial r} \left(r^2 \frac{\partial \Phi}{\partial r} \right) + \frac{1}{r^2 \sin \vartheta} \frac{\partial}{\partial \vartheta} \left(\sin \vartheta \frac{\partial \Phi}{\partial \vartheta} \right) + \frac{1}{r^2 \sin^2 \vartheta} \frac{\partial^2 \Phi}{\partial \varphi^2} \tag{5.14}$$

and since $\pi_l(x, y, z)$ is harmonic, we derive from (5.7) the differential equation for $S_l(\vartheta, \varphi)$:

$$\Lambda(S_l) \equiv \frac{1}{\sin \vartheta} \frac{\partial}{\partial \vartheta} \left(\sin \vartheta \frac{\partial S_l}{\partial \vartheta} \right) + \frac{1}{\sin^2 \vartheta} \frac{\partial^2 S_l}{\partial \varphi^2} = -l(l+1) S_l. \tag{5.15}$$

Let us now make the decomposition

$$\begin{aligned} S_l(\vartheta, \varphi) = a_l^{(0)}(\vartheta) + a_l^{(1)}(\vartheta) \cos \varphi + b_l^{(1)}(\vartheta) \sin \varphi + \ldots \\ \ldots + a_l^{(l)}(\vartheta) \cos l\varphi + b_l^{(l)}(\vartheta) \sin l\varphi; \end{aligned} \tag{5.16}$$

clearly such a representation is possible since $S_l(\vartheta, \varphi)$ contains trigonometric terms in φ of order l at most. We make the observation that the operator Λ applied to each term $a_l^{(m)}(\vartheta)\cos m\varphi$ or $b_l^{(m)}(\vartheta)\sin m\varphi$ changes the ϑ-dependent factor but leaves the φ-dependent factor unchanged:

$$\Lambda\big(a_l^{(m)}(\vartheta)\cos m\varphi\big) = A_l^{(m)}(\vartheta)\cos m\varphi, \qquad (5.17)$$
$$\Lambda\big(b_l^{(m)}(\vartheta)\sin m\varphi\big) = B_l^{(m)}(\vartheta)\sin m\varphi.$$

Thus, in order that equation (5.15) be satisfied, each term

$$S_l^{(m)}(\vartheta, \varphi) = a_l^{(m)}(\vartheta)\cos m\varphi, \qquad m = 0, 1, 2, \ldots, \qquad (5.18)$$
$$S_l^{(-m)}(\vartheta, \varphi) = b_l^{(m)}(\vartheta)\sin m\varphi, \qquad m = 1, 2, \ldots,$$

must separately satisfy the equation

$$\Lambda\big(S_l^{(m)}(\vartheta, \varphi)\big) + l(l+1)\, S_l^{(m)}(\vartheta, \varphi) = 0, \qquad m = -l, \ldots, l. \qquad (5.19)$$

Thus, each spherical harmonic $S_l(\vartheta, \varphi)$ can be broken up into $2l+1$ elementary spherical harmonics $S_l^{(m)}(\vartheta, \varphi)$. It can easily be shown that to each pair of indices l, m there exists exactly one non-vanishing spherical harmonic $S_l^{(m)}(\vartheta, \varphi)$ determined up to a multiplicative constant. Since

$$\iint_{\Sigma_1} S_k^{(m)}(\vartheta, \varphi)\, S_l^{(n)}(\vartheta, \varphi)\, d\sigma = \int_{\vartheta=0}^{\pi}\int_{\varphi=0}^{2\pi} S_k^{(m)} S_l^{(n)} \sin\vartheta\, d\vartheta\, d\varphi, \qquad (5.20)$$

we deduce from the orthogonality of the trigonometric functions $\cos m\varphi$, $\sin m\varphi$

$$\iint_{\Sigma_1} S_k^{(m)}(\vartheta, \varphi)\, S_l^{(n)}(\vartheta, \varphi)\, d\sigma = 0, \quad \text{if} \quad k \neq l, \quad \text{or} \quad m \neq n. \qquad (5.21)$$

We now determine the $S_l^{(n)}(\vartheta, \varphi)$ in a completely unique way by imposing the usual normalization condition

$$\iint_{\Sigma_1} \big(S_l^{(n)}(\vartheta, \varphi)\big)^2\, d\sigma = \frac{4\pi}{2l+1}. \qquad (5.22)$$

Under this normalization, the functions $S_l(\vartheta, \varphi)$ are uniquely determined up to their sign. Thus, we have proved: *every spherical harmonic $S_l(\vartheta, \varphi)$ can be uniquely decomposed into a sum of spherical harmonics $S_l^{(m)}(\vartheta, \varphi)$ which are orthogonal to each other over the unit sphere.*

We consider now an infinite domain D bounded by a closed smooth surface S. Let $G(P, Q)$ be the Green's function of D and let Q be a fixed finite point in D. Then Green's function will be regular harmonic near infinity, i. e., outside a sufficiently large sphere. It is well known from elementary potential theory that every function $\Phi(P)$ which is harmonic near infinity can be developed in a series of spherical harmonics of the form:

$$\Phi(P) = \sum_{l=0}^{\infty} \frac{S_l(\vartheta, \varphi)}{r^{l+1}} = \sum_{l=0}^{\infty} \frac{\pi_l(x, y, z)}{r^{2l+1}}. \tag{5.23}$$

In the case of the Green's function $G(P, Q)$ the spherical harmonics will, of course, depend upon the source point Q. But using the fixed spherical harmonics $S_l^{(m)}$, we may exhibit this dependence in the form:

$$G(P, Q) = \sum_{l=0}^{\infty} \frac{1}{r^{l+1}} \left(\sum_{m=-l}^{l} c_l^{(m)}(Q)\, S_l^{(m)}(\vartheta, \varphi) \right). \tag{5.24}$$

where only the coefficients $c_l^{(m)}(Q)$ must be determined.

We may find each coefficient $c_l^{(m)}(Q)$ easily by means of the orthonormality formulas (5.21) and (5.22). In fact, let Σ_R be a sphere around the origin with a very large radius R. We define the homogeneous polynomial of lth degree

$$\pi_l^{(m)}(x, y, z) = r^l\, S_l^{(m)}(\vartheta, \varphi) \tag{5.25}$$

and consider the integral

$$\frac{1}{R} \iint_{\Sigma_R} G(P, Q)\, \pi_l^{(m)}(P)\, d\sigma_P = J_l^{(m)}(Q). \tag{5.26}$$

By virtue of (5.25), (5.21), and (5.22), we have:

$$J_l^{(m)}(Q) = \frac{4\pi}{2l+1}\, c_l^{(m)}(Q). \tag{5.27}$$

In order to obtain an elegant interpretation for the coefficients $c_l^{(m)}(Q)$ it is, however, more expedient to use the following equation:

$$\iint_{\Sigma_R} \left(\frac{\partial G(P, Q)}{\partial r} \cdot \pi_l^{(m)}(P) - G(P, Q)\, \frac{\partial \pi_l^{(m)}(P)}{\partial r} \right) d\sigma_P = -4\pi\, c_l^{(m)}(Q), \tag{5.28}$$

which again follows from the orthonormality relations and the series development (5.24). The advantage of this last formula lies, of course, in the fact that we may now change the surface of integration; if we replace $\dfrac{\partial}{\partial r}$ by $\dfrac{\partial}{\partial \nu}$ and take care that the surface of integration still encloses the source point Q and the boundary S, the value of the integral will not be affected. Even if we deform the surface of integration over the point Q, we can still find the value of the integral by means of Green's theorem. In particular, let us extend the integration over the boundary surface S itself where the Green's function vanishes: by easy calculations, we find:

$$\iint_{\mathsf{S}} \pi_l^{(m)}(P) \frac{\partial G(P,Q)}{\partial \nu_P} d\sigma_P = \pi_l^{(m)}(Q) - 4\pi c_l^{(m)}(Q). \tag{5.29}$$

This identity now reveals the nature of the coefficients $c_l^{(m)}(Q)$. We observe that the left-hand side of (5.29) is a regular harmonic function throughout D. $\pi_l^{(m)}(Q)$ is regular harmonic at all finite points of D, but becomes strongly infinite at infinity for $l > 0$ and is, as a non-vanishing constant, singular at infinity even for $l = 0$. Thus $4\pi c_l^{(m)}$ is regular harmonic in D except for the point at infinity where it behaves like $\pi_l^{(m)}(Q)$. The left-hand side of (5.29) has, furthermore, the same boundary values on S as the function $\pi_l^{(m)}(Q)$, since, in general, the function

$$\Phi(Q) = \iint_{\mathsf{S}} \mu(P) \frac{\partial G(P,Q)}{\partial \nu_P} d\sigma_P \tag{5.30}$$

will be harmonic in D and have the boundary values $\mu(Q)$ on S. Thus, we have found the important result: *the function* $4\pi c_l^{(m)}(Q)$ *is harmonic in* D *except for the point at infinity where it behaves like* $\pi_l^{(m)}(Q)$, *and vanishes on the boundary* S *of* D. Thus, the function $4\pi c_l^{(m)}(Q)$ may be interpreted as the potential created if a grounded conductor is brought into an electrostatic field with the potential $\pi_l^{(m)}(Q)$, due to infinitely remote charges. It can be shown that the potential due to any "multipole" at infinity can be represented as a linear combination of terms $\pi_l^{(m)}(Q)$ with constant coefficients. Thus, the most general multipole field which is regular at each finite point outside a given conductor S can be expressed in terms of the coefficients of the development of the corresponding Green's function near infinity.

The role of the $c_l^{(m)}(Q)$ becomes still more intuitive when we proceed to particular cases of the general result. Since every polynomial of degree less than two is harmonic, we derive from (5.6), (5.18), and the normalization conditions (5.22):

$$S_0^{(0)}(\vartheta,\varphi) = 1, \quad \pi_1^{(1)}(P) = x, \quad \pi_1^{(0)}(P) = z, \quad \pi_1^{(-1)}(P) = y. \tag{5.31}$$

Thus, the first few functions $c_l^{(m)}(Q)$ can be easily interpreted.

The function $4\pi c_0^{(0)}(Q)$ is harmonic in D except for the point at infinity where it has the limit one; it vanishes on the boundary S of D as do all functions $c_l^{(m)}(Q)$; thus, the function

$$V(P) = 1 - 4\pi c_0^{(0)}(P) \tag{5.32}$$

is regular harmonic in D and has on S the boundary value one. $V(P)$ is the conductor potential of the surface S. It has been expressed by means of the first coefficient of the Green's function $G(P, Q)$ at infinity.

The physical meaning of the conductor potential is obvious. Suppose we place the charge e on the conducting surface S; this charge will distribute itself over the surface S with an appropriate surface density $\mu(P)$ such that the value of the electrostatic potential $\Phi(P)$ induced will be a constant Φ_0 on S. In the exterior D of S, $\Phi(P)$ will be a harmonic function since we now assume that $\varkappa = 1$ in D. Then the uniqueness theorem for harmonic functions leads to the identity

$$\Phi(P) = \Phi_0 V(P). \tag{5.33}$$

By virtue of (2.6), we find for the surface density of the charge on S:

$$\mu(P) = -\frac{1}{4\pi}\frac{\partial \Phi(P)}{\partial \nu} = -\frac{\Phi_0}{4\pi}\frac{\partial V(P)}{\partial \nu}. \tag{5.34}$$

The relation between the charge e which we place on the conductor S and the potential Φ_0 created is given by the formula:

$$e = \iint_{\mathsf{S}} \mu \, d\sigma = \left(-\frac{1}{4\pi}\iint_{\mathsf{S}} \frac{\partial V}{\partial \nu}\, d\sigma\right)\Phi_0. \tag{5.35}$$

The proportionality factor between potential and charge on a conductor is called its electrostatic capacity C. Thus, we have proved:

$$C = -\frac{1}{4\pi}\iint_{\mathsf{S}} \frac{\partial V}{\partial \nu}\, d\sigma, \tag{5.36}$$

and we have expressed the capacity in terms of the conductor potential.

There are two other representations for the capacity C of a conductor which are frequently used. We observe that since $V(P)$ is regular harmonic in D and has the boundary value one on S, it may be expressed by means of its boundary values and the Green's function as follows:

$$V(P) = \iint_{\mathsf{S}} \frac{\partial G(P, Q)}{\partial \nu_Q}\, d\sigma_Q. \tag{5.37}$$

Now let S* be a smooth surface in D surrounding S; we have by Green's theorem:

$$-\frac{1}{4\pi}\iint_{S}\frac{\partial V}{\partial \nu}d\sigma = \frac{1}{4\pi}\iint_{S^*}\frac{\partial V}{\partial \nu}d\sigma = -\frac{1}{4\pi}\iint_{S^*}\iint_{S}\frac{\partial^2 G(P,Q)}{\partial \nu_P\,\partial \nu_Q}d\sigma_P\,d\sigma_Q. \tag{5.38}$$

Thus, by virtue of (5.36) we obtain:

$$C = -\frac{1}{4\pi}\iint_{S^*}\iint_{S}\frac{\partial^2 G(P,Q)}{\partial \nu_P\,\partial \nu_Q}d\sigma_P\,d\sigma_Q, \tag{5.39}$$

an explicit representation of the capacity in terms of the Green's function. This result is, of course, closely related to the formula (2.8) in the general case.

Let us next develop the conductor potential $V(P)$ into a series of type (5.23) near infinity. We have

$$V(P) = \frac{a}{r} + v(P) \tag{5.40}$$

where $v(P)$ is harmonic in D and vanishes near infinity at least as strongly as $1/r^2$. Let Σ_R again be the surface of a sufficiently large sphere of radius R around the origin. By Green's theorem, we have:

$$-\frac{1}{4\pi}\iint_{S}\frac{\partial V}{\partial \nu}d\sigma = -\frac{1}{4\pi}\iint_{\Sigma_R}\left(-\frac{a}{R^2}+\frac{\partial v}{\partial r}\right)d\sigma. \tag{5.41}$$

Since $\partial v/\partial r$ converges to zero as $R \to \infty$ at least like $1/R^3$ and since the surface area of Σ_R is only $4\pi R^2$, we conclude from (5.41) by letting $R \to \infty$:

$$-\frac{1}{4\pi}\iint_{S}\frac{\partial V}{\partial \nu}d\sigma = a. \tag{5.42}$$

Thus, comparing (5.36) and (5.42), we obtain:

$$V(P) = \frac{C}{r} + O\left(\frac{1}{r^2}\right), \tag{5.43}$$

i. e., the electrostatic capacity of a conductor can be defined as the first coefficient in the series development of its conductor potential near infinity.

We discussed already in Section 4 the use of the conductor potential in certain integral equations connected with the potential theory of a surface S. There is another important aspect of the function $V(P)$ which is often needed. Let us observe, at first, that Green's function $G(P, Q)$ is for a finite source point Q regular harmonic at infinity. We have, therefore, the relation

$$\lim_{P \to \infty} G(P, Q) = 0, \tag{5.44}$$

i. e.,

$$G(\infty, Q) = 0. \tag{5.44'}$$

Since Green's function is symmetric with respect to both argument points, we are led to the conclusion:

$$G(P, \infty) = 0, \qquad P \in \mathsf{D}. \tag{5.45}$$

Thus, the Green's function with the source point at infinity is regular harmonic everywhere, even at its source point. On the other hand, the potential $1 - V(P)$ is harmonic in D except for the point at infinity and has the boundary value zero on S; in many respects it plays the role of the Green's function with the source point at infinity.

As an application of the conductor potential, let us consider the class of all harmonic functions $\Phi(P)$ which are continuously differentiable in the closed region $\mathsf{D} + \mathsf{S}$. Each such $\Phi(P)$ possesses at infinity a series development in spherical harmonics of the form

$$\Phi(P) = \frac{a}{r} + \varphi(P) \tag{5.46}$$

where $\varphi(P)$ contains all the terms which vanish at infinity at least as quickly as $1/r^2$. The first coefficient a in the series development of $\Phi(P)$ can also be expressed in the form

$$a = -\frac{1}{4\pi} \iint_{\mathsf{S}} \frac{\partial \Phi}{\partial \nu} \, d\sigma. \tag{5.47}$$

This can be derived from Green's theorem in the same way as (5.42) was derived from (5.40). If we interpret $\Phi(P)$ as an electrostatic potential, a will be the total amount of charge which must be placed on or within the closed surface S in order to create the field in D. Hence, a is called the charge coefficient of $\Phi(P)$. We can now derive by Green's theorem:

$$-\iint_{\mathsf{S}} \frac{\partial V}{\partial \nu} \Phi \, d\sigma = 4\pi a. \tag{5.48}$$

We may replace the surface integral in this formula by the Dirichlet product between the two function $V(P)$ and $\Phi(P)$ over D and obtain:

$$\text{(5.49)} \qquad \mathrm{D}\{V,\Phi\} = \iiint\limits_{\mathsf{D}} \operatorname{grad} V \cdot \operatorname{grad} \Phi \, d\tau = 4\pi a.$$

The advantage of this formula is the fact that we are now able to apply the formalism of the Dirichlet integral which was discussed in (I.6). For example, Schwarz' inequality (I.6.8) applied to (5.49) leads to

$$\text{(5.50)} \qquad (4\pi a)^2 \leqslant \mathrm{D}\{V\} \cdot \mathrm{D}\{\Phi\}.$$

But using (5.49) for $\Phi = V$, and in view of (5.43), we obtain

$$\text{(5.51)} \qquad \mathrm{D}\{V\} = 4\pi C$$

and hence:

$$\text{(5.52)} \qquad 4\pi C^{-1} \leqslant \frac{1}{a^2} \mathrm{D}\{\Phi\}.$$

This inequality is valid for all harmonic functions $\Phi(P)$ considered and can become an equality only if $\Phi(P)$ is a multiple of the conductor potential. In (5.52) we have a convenient formula for obtaining a lower limit for the capacity of a given conductor S in terms of an arbitrary harmonic function $\Phi(P)$.

Since the electrostatic energy of a field with potential $\Phi(P)$ is given by (3.5) as

$$\text{(5.53)} \qquad W = \frac{1}{8\pi} \mathrm{D}\{\Phi\}$$

we can interpret (5.52) as follows: *among all electrostatic fields in* D *due to a total charge* a *located in the complement of* D, *we obtain the minimum energy*

$$\text{(5.54)} \qquad W_{min} = \frac{1}{2} \frac{a^2}{C}$$

when the charge is in equilibrium in the conducting boundary S *of* D.

Jeans [24], Kellogg [30], Sternberg-Smith [77]; Schiffer-Szegö (S 6).

6. Polarization of a conducting surface: In this section we shall consider the physical significance of the functions $4\pi c_1^{(m)}(Q)$ which were defined in Section 5. For the sake of convenience, however, we shall now denote the space coordinates by x_i ($i = 1, 2, 3$) and denote that function $4\pi c_1^{(m)}(Q)$ which behaves like x_i near infinity (cf. (5.31)) by $\Psi_i(P)$. Thus, each $\Psi_i(P)$

vanishes on the boundary S of D and is regular harmonic in D except for the point at infinity where it has the form

$$\Psi_i(P) = x_i - \psi_i(P) \tag{6.1}$$

where $\psi_i(P)$ is regular harmonic at infinity.

The physical meaning of the potentials $\Psi_i(P)$ is easily explained. We consider the uniform field $\mathbf{E}_0 = -\mathbf{e}_i$ ($\mathbf{e}_i$ = unit vector in the ith direction) with the corresponding electrostatic potential x_i. Such a field is realized very closely in the interior of a plate condenser. We now bring a grounded conductor S into this uniform field: the field $\mathbf{E}_0$ will polarize the conductor and create a surface charge on it which in turn will affect the electrostatic field $\mathbf{E}_0$. The outcome of this interaction is an electrostatic field with the potential $\Psi_i(P)$. We therefore call the functions $\Psi_i(P)$ the polarization potentials of the conductor S. In the last section we showed that these polarization potentials may be obtained as coefficients in the development of the Green's function of S near infinity.

If $\mathbf{e} = (\alpha_1, \alpha_2, \alpha_3)$ is an arbitrary unit vector and $\mathbf{E}_0 = -\lambda\,\mathbf{e}$ is a uniform electrostatic field in the direction $-\mathbf{e}$ and with strength λ, it will belong to the potential $\lambda(\alpha_1 x_1 + \alpha_2 x_2 + \alpha_3 x_3)$. If the grounded conductor S is acted on by this field, it will obviously react and create a field in its exterior with the potential $\lambda \sum_{i=1}^{3} \alpha_i \Psi_i(P)$. Thus we are able to express the polarization field in an arbitrary direction by linear superposition of the fields with respect to the coordinate axes.

We can interpret the regular harmonic potentials $-\psi_i(P)$ as the potentials of the reaction field which is created by the polarized charges on S. We assume for $\psi_i(P)$ the following development in spherical harmonics near infinity:

$$\psi_i(P) = \frac{A_i}{r} + \frac{1}{r^3} \sum_{k=1}^{3} e_{ik}\, x_k + O\left(\frac{1}{r^3}\right). \tag{6.2}$$

The charges A_i were acquired by the originally uncharged conductor from the infinite charge reservoir to which it is connected by the grounding. If we had brought an isolated conductor S into the homogeneous uniform field in the i-direction, no such charges would have been possible. Since also in this case the total potential $\tilde{\Psi}_i(P)$ would have to behave at infinity like x_i and be constant on S, we would clearly have

$$\tilde{\Psi}_i(P) = \Psi_i(P) + \frac{A_i}{C} V(P). \tag{6.3}$$

In fact, the potentials $\tilde{\Psi}_i(P)$ have the required asymptotic behavior, are constant on S and, because of (5.43) and (6.1), the charge on S connected with $\tilde{\Psi}_i(P)$ is zero. Correspondingly, to the $\psi_i(P)$ we define the reaction potentials of the isolated conductor

$$\tilde{\psi}_i(P) = \psi_i(P) - \frac{A_i}{C} V(P) = \frac{1}{r^3} \sum_{k=1}^{3} \tilde{e}_{ik} x_k + O\left(\frac{1}{r^3}\right). \tag{6.4}$$

From (6.2) and (6.4) we can now calculate the electrostatic energy of the reaction field created on a grounded or an isolated conductor. We consider the general case of a potential $\psi = \lambda \sum_{i=1}^{3} a_i \psi_i$ or $\tilde{\psi} = \lambda \sum_{i=1}^{3} a_i \tilde{\psi}_i$. By (3.5)

$$W = \frac{1}{8\pi} \iiint_D (\operatorname{grad} \psi)^2 \, d\tau \quad \text{and} \quad \tilde{W} = \frac{1}{8\pi} \iiint_D (\operatorname{grad} \tilde{\psi})^2 \, d\tau. \tag{6.5}$$

Using the usual Dirichlet formalism, we find:

$$W = \frac{\lambda^2}{8\pi} \sum_{i,k=1}^{3} a_i a_k \, D\{\psi_i, \psi_k\}, \qquad \tilde{W} = \frac{\lambda^2}{8\pi} \sum_{i,k=1}^{3} a_i a_k \, D\{\tilde{\psi}_i, \tilde{\psi}_k\}. \tag{6.6}$$

By virtue of (6.4), we have:

$$D\{\psi_i, \psi_k\} = D\{\tilde{\psi}_i, \tilde{\psi}_k\} + \frac{A_i}{C} D\{\tilde{\psi}_k, V\} + \frac{A_k}{C} D\{\tilde{\psi}_i, V\} + \frac{A_i A_k}{C^2} D\{V\}. \tag{6.7}$$

Now, $\tilde{\psi}_i$ has been constructed so as to be charge-free and by virtue of (5.49) we therefore have

$$D\{\tilde{\psi}_i, V\} = 0, \qquad \text{for} \qquad i = 1, 2, 3. \tag{6.8}$$

Furthermore, using (5.51), we derive from (6.7):

$$D\{\psi_i, \psi_k\} = D\{\tilde{\psi}_i, \tilde{\psi}_k\} + \frac{4\pi}{C} A_i A_k. \tag{6.9}$$

Thus, we derive from (6.6) and (6.9) the following relation between the energies of polarization of a grounded and an isolated conductor:

$$W = \tilde{W} + \frac{\lambda^2}{2C} \left(\sum_{i=1}^{3} a_i A_i \right)^2. \tag{6.10}$$

We have already considered the potentials $\psi_i\,(P)$ in Section II.8, and in (II.8.36) have proved that

$$\mathrm{D}\,\{\psi_i, \psi_k\} = 4\pi\, e_{ki} - V\,\delta_{ik} \tag{6.11}$$

where V is the volume enclosed by surface **S**. Thus, the electrostatic energy of the reaction potential considered for the grounded conductor is by (6.6) and (6.11):

$$W = \frac{1}{2}\lambda^2 \sum_{i,k=1}^{3} e_{ik}\,\alpha_i\,\alpha_k - \frac{\lambda^2}{8\pi} V. \tag{6.12}$$

The matrix $((e_{ik}))$ which is symmetric (by (6.11)) is the coefficient scheme of the quadratic vector function W. Hence, the e_{ik} form a tensor, the so-called polarization tensor. This tensor enables us to calculate the energy of the reaction field created on the grounded conductor **S** by a uniform dipole field of arbitrary strength and direction. In analogy to the representation of virtual mass given in (II.8.43) we define the polarization in the direction $\mathfrak{e}$ by the formula

$$W_P = 4\pi \sum_{i,k=1}^{3} e_{ik}\,\alpha_i\,\alpha_k - V. \tag{6.13}$$

Analogously, the polarization of an isolated conductor will be defined by

$$\tilde{W}_P = 4\pi \sum_{i,k=1}^{3} \tilde{e}_{ik}\,\alpha_i\,\alpha_k - V. \tag{6.13'}$$

By means of (6.10) we can immediately calculate the energy $\tilde{W}$ of the reaction field in the case of an isolated conductor. However, we can also introduce a formalism involving the coefficients $\tilde{e}_{ik}$ which is completely analogous to that for the e_{ik} and which permits a direct calculation of $\tilde{W}$. In fact, we easily calculate

$$\mathrm{D}\,\{\tilde{\psi}_i, \tilde{\psi}_k\} = -\iint_{\mathbf{S}} \tilde{\psi}_i \frac{\partial \tilde{\psi}_k}{\partial \nu}\, d\sigma = -\iint_{\mathbf{S}} \left(x_i - \frac{A_i}{C}\right) \frac{\partial \tilde{\psi}_k}{\partial \nu}\, d\sigma \tag{6.14}$$

since $\tilde{\psi}_i$ has on **S** the boundary value $x_i - A_i/C$. Since $\tilde{\psi}_k$ is charge-free, we have

$$\iint_{\mathbf{S}} \frac{\partial \tilde{\psi}_k}{\partial \nu}\, d\sigma = 0, \tag{6.15}$$

i. e.,

(6.16)
$$D\{\tilde{\psi}_i, \tilde{\psi}_k\} = -\iint_S x_i \frac{\partial \tilde{\psi}_k}{\partial \nu} d\sigma.$$

Using the series development (6.4) for $\tilde{\psi}_k(P)$ at infinity, we obtain by the same reasoning as was used in Section II.8

$$D\{\tilde{\psi}_i, \tilde{\psi}_k\} = 4\pi \tilde{e}_{ki} - \iint_S \tilde{\psi}_k \frac{\partial x_i}{\partial \nu} d\sigma = 4\pi \tilde{e}_{ki} - \iint_S \left(x_k - \frac{A_k}{C}\right) \frac{\partial x_i}{\partial \nu} d\sigma.$$
(6.17)

Since x_i is harmonic in the interior of S, we clearly have

(6.18)
$$\iint_S \frac{\partial x_i}{\partial \nu} d\sigma = 0.$$

Thus, we easily obtain from (6.17) the result:

(6.19)
$$D\{\tilde{\psi}_i, \tilde{\psi}_k\} = 4\pi \tilde{e}_{ki} - V\delta_{ik}$$

which is an exact analogue of (6.11).

The preceding considerations show that the polarization $\tilde{W}_P$ of an isolated conductor is connected with the electrostatic energy of the reaction field in exactly the same way as the polarization W_P of a grounded conductor is connected with the energy of its reaction field.

We may also consider the Dirichlet products between the functions $\tilde{\psi}_i(P)$ and the functions $\varphi_i(P)$ which play a role in the theory of the flow past the surface S due to a dipole at infinity and which were defined in (II.6.10). These functions are harmonic in the exterior D of S except at infinity and on the boundary satisfy the condition

(6.20)
$$\frac{\partial \varphi_i}{\partial \nu} = -\frac{\partial x_i}{\partial \nu}.$$

Hence, we find:

(6.21)
$$D\{\tilde{\psi}_k, \varphi_i\} = -\iint_S \tilde{\psi}_k \frac{\partial \varphi_i}{\partial \nu} d\sigma = \iint_S \left(x_k - \frac{A_k}{C}\right) \frac{\partial x_i}{\partial \nu} d\sigma.$$

By virtue of (6.18) and the formula

(6.22)
$$\iint_S x_k \frac{\partial x_i}{\partial \nu} d\sigma = V\delta_{ik}$$

we obtain:

(6.23)
$$D\{\tilde{\psi}_k, \varphi_i\} = V\delta_{ik}.$$

Comparing this result with (II.8.38) we recognize that the $\tilde{\psi}_k$ have the same Dirichlet products with the velocity potentials φ_i as had the ψ_k. Thus, the formal considerations at the end of section (II.8) also hold for these potentials and, in particular, we may derive the inequality:

$$V^2 \leqslant \tilde{W}_P W \tag{6.24}$$

between the electrostatic polarization $\tilde{W}_P$ and the hydrodynamical virtual mass W. This result is an improvement of inequality (II.8.42) since by (6.10) we have $\tilde{W}_P \leqslant W_P$.

We could develop similar theories for the reaction potentials of a conductor in the presence of higher multipole singularities at infinity. For this purpose we would need the additional functions $c_l^{(m)}(P)$ which occur in the series development of the Green's function near infinity. We shall not enter here into this theory; it is sufficiently clear from the preceding how the Green's function permits a unified treatment of the various harmonic functions which occur in the potential theory of a given conductor S. While in hydrodynamical problems the fundamental functions are specified by requirements with respect to their normal derivatives, in electrostatics the boundary values of the functions play the central role; therefore, Neumann's function plays the decisive part in fluid dynamics while Green's function has the central role in potential theory.

Schiffer-Szegö (S 6).

7. Forces and moments in a conductor system: Let us consider a system of n smooth closed surfaces S_i which together form the boundary S of an infinite domain D. We assume that S_i are conductors and give the charge e_i to the ith conductor. We shall obtain an electrostatic field $\mathbf{E}$ in D with a potential $\Phi(P)$ which has constant boundary values Φ_i on each conductor S_i. The relation between the charges e_i and the potentials Φ_i has already been established in the case of an arbitrary dielectric factor $\varkappa$. In Section 2 we found:

$$e_k = \sum_{j=1}^{n} e_{jk} \Phi_j, \tag{7.1}$$

where the coefficients

$$e_{ik} = -\frac{1}{4\pi} \iint\limits_{\mathsf{S}_i^*} \iint\limits_{\mathsf{S}_k^*} \frac{\partial^2 G(P, Q)}{\partial \nu_P \, \partial \nu_Q} \, d\sigma_P \, d\sigma_Q \tag{7.2}$$

are the induction coefficients of the conductor system S. The integration surfaces S_i^* are arbitrary smooth surfaces in D, each of which encloses only the corresponding conductor S_i.

The charge distributions on the conductors exert forces and moments upon each other and restraints are needed in order to prevent the conductor system from moving under their influence. In this section we shall establish formulas for the force and moment which the field exerts upon each one of the conducting surfaces S_i. For this purpose we select one fixed conductor, say S_1, submit it to a given motion and compute the work performed. Using the elements of mechanics we shall be able to calculate from this result the forces and moments acting upon the body considered.

Let O be the centroid of the conductor S_1; we choose it as the origin of our coordinate system and describe every point on S_1 by the radius vector $\mathbf{r}$ from O. Let $\mathbf{a}$ and $\mathbf{b}$ be two fixed vectors; we consider the displacement

$$\mathbf{d} = \varepsilon\,(\mathbf{a} + \mathbf{b} \times \mathbf{r}) \qquad \varepsilon > 0,\ \text{small}, \tag{7.3}$$

of all the points of S_1. This is in the first approximation a rigid motion of the surface S_1 in which the conductor is translated by an amount $\varepsilon\,\mathbf{a}$ and rotated around the axis $\mathbf{b}$ through an angle $\varepsilon\,|\mathbf{b}|$.

If ε is sufficiently small we may consider this displacement as simply a variation of the boundary surfaces S of the domain D. In Section II.15 we derived a variational formula for the Green's function of a plane domain D with respect to a change of the boundary. We have already indicated that our reasoning could be extended to a greater number of dimensions; in fact, exactly the same argument which was applied there leads to the formula

$$\delta G(P,Q) = -\iint_{S} \frac{\partial G(P,T)}{\partial \nu_T}\,\frac{\partial G(T,Q)}{\partial \nu_T}\,\delta\nu_T\, d\sigma_T \tag{7.4}$$

which describes the change of the Green's function of the domain D if every point T on the surface S is shifted by a small amount $\delta\nu_T$ in the direction of the interior normal $\boldsymbol{\nu}$ at T with respect to D.

It is now easy to calculate from (7.2) and (7.4) the variation of the induction coefficients e_{ik} under the same change of boundary. We find:

$$\delta e_{ik} = -\frac{1}{4\pi}\iint_{S}\iint_{S_i^*}\iint_{S_k^*} \frac{\partial^2 G(P,T)}{\partial \nu_P\,\partial \nu_T}\,\frac{\partial^2 G(T,Q)}{\partial \nu_T\,\partial \nu_Q}\,\delta\nu_T\, d\sigma_T\, d\sigma_P\, d\sigma_Q. \tag{7.5}$$

In order to simplify this result we again introduce the functions

$$(7.6) \qquad \Omega_i(Q) = \iint_{S_i} \frac{\partial G(P,Q)}{\partial \nu_P} d\sigma_P$$

which were already considered in Section 2 for the more general case of a variable $\varkappa$. $\Omega_i(P)$ is that harmonic function in D which vanishes on all conductors S_j, except for S_i where it has the value one. It is called the conductor potential of S_i with respect to the whole system S. By Green's theorem the integration in (7.6) need not be extended over the conducting surface itself, but can be taken over any surface S_i^* which encloses the surface S_i only and separates it from the point Q considered. If we keep S_i^* fixed and let the point Q cross the surface so that S_i^* encloses simultaneously the surface S_i and the point Q, we shall have to correct formula (7.6) by taking into account the discontinuity of the integral:

$$(7.7) \qquad \Omega_i(Q) = 1 + \iint_{S_i^*} \frac{\partial G(P,Q)}{\partial \nu_P} d\sigma_P.$$

For a fixed surface S_i^* this formula will hold if Q approaches the boundary S_i. Thus, in particular:

$$(7.8) \qquad \frac{\partial \Omega_i(Q)}{\partial \nu_Q} = \iint_{S_i^*} \frac{\partial^2 G(P,Q)}{\partial \nu_P \, \partial \nu_Q} d\sigma_P \quad \text{for} \quad Q \in S_i.$$

Hence, we may transform (7.5) into the elegant variational formula:

$$(7.9) \qquad \delta e_{ik} = -\frac{1}{4\pi} \iint_{S} \frac{\partial \Omega_i}{\partial \nu} \frac{\partial \Omega_k}{\partial \nu} \delta \nu \, d\sigma.$$

In the case of the particular deformation (7.3) we have

$$(7.10) \qquad \delta \nu = \varepsilon \, [\mathbf{a} \cdot \boldsymbol{\nu} + (\mathbf{b} \times \mathbf{r}) \cdot \boldsymbol{\nu}] \quad \text{on } S_1, \quad \delta \nu = 0 \quad \text{on } S_i, \quad i > 1.$$

(Note that here and in the following, terms of order ε^2 are neglected.) Using the well-known formula of vector algebra:

$$(7.11) \qquad (\mathbf{b} \times \mathbf{r}) \cdot \boldsymbol{\nu} = \mathbf{b} \cdot (\mathbf{r} \times \boldsymbol{\nu}),$$

we derive from (7.9) and (7.10):

$$(7.12) \qquad \delta e_{ik} = -\frac{\varepsilon}{4\pi} \iint_{S_1} \frac{\partial \Omega_i}{\partial \nu} \frac{\partial \Omega_k}{\partial \nu} \big(\mathbf{a} \cdot \boldsymbol{\nu} + \mathbf{b} \cdot (\mathbf{r} \times \boldsymbol{\nu})\big) \, d\sigma.$$

Since the charge e_k on the kth conductor cannot change under the variation of the conductor system, we can calculate the change of the potentials of each conductor from (7.1):

$$0 = \sum_{j=1}^{n} \delta e_{jk} \Phi_j + \sum_{j=1}^{n} e_{jk} \, \delta\Phi_j. \tag{7.13}$$

In Section 3 we have shown that in the case of an infinite domain **D** the symmetric matrix $((e_{jk}))$ can be inverted. Let $((\varepsilon_{jk}))$ denote the matrix inverse to $((e_{jk}))$; it will also be symmetric and will satisfy:

$$\sum_{k=1}^{n} e_{jk} \, \varepsilon_{kl} = \delta_{jl}. \tag{7.14}$$

Thus, we can solve (7.13) for $\delta\Phi_j$ and find:

$$\delta\Phi_l = -\sum_{j,\,k=1}^{n} \delta e_{jk} \, \varepsilon_{kl} \, \Phi_j. \tag{7.15}$$

The energy of a system of charged conductors was determined in (3.18). It may be expressed in the form:

$$W = \frac{1}{2} \sum_{l=1}^{n} e_l \Phi_l. \tag{7.16}$$

Since the charges do not change under the variation of the conductor system, we find for the change of energy connected with the deformation:

$$\delta W = \frac{1}{2} \sum_{l=1}^{n} e_l \, \delta\Phi_l = -\frac{1}{2} \sum_{j,\,k,\,l=1}^{n} \delta e_{jk} \, \varepsilon_{kl} \, e_l \, \Phi_j. \tag{7.17}$$

But by inverting (7.1), and in view of the symmetry of the matrix $((e_{jk}))$, we derive

$$\sum_{l=1}^{n} \varepsilon_{kl} \, e_l = \Phi_k. \tag{7.18}$$

Thus, finally:

$$\delta W = -\frac{1}{2} \sum_{j,\,k=1}^{n} \delta e_{jk} \, \Phi_j \Phi_k. \tag{7.19}$$

This result is interesting for the following reason; if we had kept every conductor $\mathbf{S}_i$ at a fixed potential Φ_i by connecting it with the pole of a battery with prescribed potential, we would have had for the same deformation the change of energy:

$$\delta W = \frac{1}{2} \sum_{j,k=1}^{n} \delta e_{jk} \Phi_j \Phi_k, \tag{7.20}$$

i. e., the same numerical value but with reverse sign. In this case, the energy reservoir of the batteries is, of course, responsible for the change in the deformation work.

By using (7.12), we can bring (7.19) into the form:

$$\delta W = \frac{\varepsilon}{8\pi} \iint_{\mathbf{S}_1} \left(\sum_{i=1}^{n} \Phi_i \frac{\partial \Omega_i}{\partial \nu} \right)^2 (\mathbf{a} \cdot \boldsymbol{\nu} + \mathbf{b} \cdot (\mathbf{r} \times \boldsymbol{\nu}))\, d\sigma. \tag{7.21}$$

We introduce the vectors:

$$\mathbf{F}_1 = -\frac{1}{8\pi} \iint_{\mathbf{S}_1} \left(\sum_{i=1}^{n} \Phi_i \frac{\partial \Omega_i}{\partial \nu} \right)^2 \boldsymbol{\nu}\, d\sigma, \tag{7.22}$$

$$\mathbf{M}_1 = -\frac{1}{8\pi} \iint_{\mathbf{S}_1} \left(\sum_{i=1}^{n} \Phi_i \frac{\partial \Omega_i}{\partial \nu} \right)^2 (\mathbf{r} \times \boldsymbol{\nu})\, d\sigma. \tag{7.23}$$

Then, we can express the work done by an infinitesimal translation of $\mathbf{S}_1$: $\delta \mathbf{a} = \varepsilon\, |\mathbf{a}|$ in the direction of the vector $\mathbf{a}$, and an infinitesimal rotation $\delta \alpha = \varepsilon |\mathbf{b}|$ around the axis $\mathbf{b}$ in the form:

$$\delta W = -\varepsilon\, \mathbf{a} \cdot \mathbf{F}_1 - \varepsilon\, \mathbf{b} \cdot \mathbf{M}_1. \tag{7.24}$$

This result shows that $\mathbf{F}_1$ is the vector of all forces acting on the body and $\mathbf{M}_1$ the moment of these forces.

The variational formula for the Green's function has enabled us to calculate the forces acting in a system of charged conductors. It is quite instructive to derive the action-reaction principle of mechanics of closed systems from formulas (7.22) and (7.23). According to this principle, we must have

$$\sum_{i=1}^{n} \mathbf{F}_i = 0, \qquad \sum_{i=1}^{n} \mathbf{M}_i = 0. \tag{7.25}$$

Clearly, the left-hand sums in (7.25) are again given by the formulas (7.22) and (7.23), but the integration is now extended over the entire boundary S. This means that in the deformation of S each point of S is translated by the same amount and subjected to the same rigid rotation. But Green's function does not change under an Euclidean motion and the e_{ik} also remain unchanged if the whole system is moved by the same rigid motion. Hence, $\delta W = 0$ in this case which proves the laws (7.25).

The same forces and moments, but with opposite sign, will act upon each conductor of the system S if we keep the potentials Φ_i and not the charges e_i fixed. We might have derived the formulas (7.22) and (7.23) in a more direct way by calculating charge density and field strength at each boundary point and by summing over all interacting forces and moments. However, in the case of prescribed potentials Φ_i, the energy considerations which led to our variational treatment above seems to be much more convenient and natural.

Hadamard [18].

8. Orthogonal harmonic functions: In this section, we shall systematize the formalism of the Dirichlet product

(8.1)
$$\mathrm{D}\{\varphi, \psi\} = \iiint_{\mathsf{D}} (\operatorname{grad}\varphi \cdot \operatorname{grad}\psi)\, d\tau$$

in order to obtain explicit constructions for the fundamental solutions of Laplace's equation with respect to a given domain D. We shall assume that D is bounded by a finite number of smooth closed surfaces S_i which together form its boundary S.

It is convenient to define the class Σ_h of all functions $\varphi(P)$ which are harmonic in D and continuously differentiable in the closed region D + S. If φ and ψ both belong to Σ_h, we may apply Green's identity in order to write the Dirichlet integral (8.1) in either of the forms:

(8.2)
$$\mathrm{D}\{\varphi, \psi\} = -\iint_{\mathsf{S}} \varphi \frac{\partial \psi}{\partial \nu}\, d\sigma = -\iint_{\mathsf{S}} \psi \frac{\partial \varphi}{\partial \nu}\, d\sigma.$$

No fundamental solution of the Laplace equation belongs to Σ_h since each such function becomes infinite at its source point in D. We can, however, construct functions of class Σ_h by considering differences between such fundamental solutions where the infinities destroy each other. Consider, for example, the function

(8.3)
$$K(P, Q) = N(P, Q) - G(P, Q).$$

This difference between the Neumann's and the Green's function of the domain D has already been defined in (II.8.21) in the case of an infinite domain. In this particular case we proved it to be positive throughout D. In the case of a finite domain D this property of the function $K(P, Q)$ does not hold, but there are many other interesting properties of $K(P, Q)$ which should draw our attention to it. It is a regular harmonic function for $P \in$ D since the infinities of the Neumann's and the Green's function at the source point Q have cancelled. In fact, by virtue of the smoothness of the boundary S of D, the function $K(P, Q)$ belongs to the class Σ_h. It is symmetric in both its argument points since the functions $N(P, Q)$ and $G(P, Q)$ are symmetric. *If $K(P, Q)$ is known to us for some domain* D *we can solve both the first and the second boundary value problem with respect to the domain* D.

In fact, the first boundary value problem has the general solution:

$$\varphi(Q) = \iint_S \frac{\partial G(P,Q)}{\partial \nu_P} \varphi(P)\, d\sigma_P \tag{8.4}$$

which expresses the function $\varphi(Q) \in \Sigma_h$ in terms of its boundary values on S. But by virtue of (8.3), we have

$$\frac{\partial K(P,Q)}{\partial \nu_P} = \frac{\partial N(P,Q)}{\partial \nu_P} - \frac{\partial G(P,Q)}{\partial \nu_P}. \tag{8.5}$$

By the very definition of the Neumann's function given in Sections II.5 and II.6, its normal derivative is well known on S. If D is a finite domain, we have by (II.5.2):

$$\frac{\partial N(P,Q)}{\partial \nu_P} = A^{-1}, \qquad A = \text{surface area of S}, \tag{8.6}$$

and if D contains the point at infinity, we have the even simpler property

$$\frac{\partial N(P,Q)}{\partial \nu_P} = 0. \tag{8.7}$$

Thus, (8.4) may be written in the form

$$\varphi(Q) = -\iint_S \frac{\partial K(P,Q)}{\partial \nu_P} \varphi(P)\, d\sigma_P + \frac{1}{A}\iint_S \varphi(P)\, d\sigma \tag{8.8}$$

if D is finite and

$$\varphi(Q) = -\iint_S \frac{\partial K(P,Q)}{\partial \nu_P} \varphi(P)\, d\sigma_P \tag{8.9}$$

if D contains the point at infinity. In both cases, we have solved the first boundary value problem in terms of the function $K(P, Q)$.

Since $K(P, Q)$ belongs to the class Σ_h, we can express (8.8) and (8.9) by means of Dirichlet integrals using (8.2). We obtain

$$\varphi(Q) = \mathrm{D}\{K(P, Q), \varphi(P)\} + \frac{1}{A}\iint_{S} \varphi(P)\, d\sigma \tag{8.10}$$

for a finite domain D and

$$\varphi(Q) = \mathrm{D}\{K(P, Q), \varphi(P)\} \tag{8.11}$$

for an infinite domain D. We are now able to solve the second boundary value problem in terms of the function $K(P, Q)$; in fact, we have again by (8.2):

$$\varphi(Q) = -\iint_{S} K(P, Q)\frac{\partial \varphi}{\partial \nu_P}\, d\sigma_P + \frac{1}{A}\iint_{S} \varphi(P)\, d\sigma \tag{8.12}$$

and

$$\varphi(Q) = -\iint_{S} K(P, Q)\frac{\partial \varphi}{\partial \nu_P}\, d\sigma_P \tag{8.13}$$

in the cases of a finite or an infinite domain D, respectively. In each case, $\varphi(Q)$ has been represented by means of its normal derivatives on S, in the first case up to an additive constant.

Thus, while we need the Neumann's function $N(P, Q)$ to solve the boundary value problems of the second kind and the Green's function $G(P, Q)$ for the boundary value problems of the first kind, it is sufficient to have the regular harmonic function $K(P, Q)$ in order to solve both problems simultaneously. This fact shows the significance of this difference function; we shall call it the *kernel function of the Laplace equation for the domain* D *considered.*

We may remove the distinction between finite and infinite domains by the following consideration. In the case of a finite domain D, every constant is a regular harmonic function of the class Σ_h. Every non-constant function $\varphi(P) \in \Sigma_h$ can be transformed into another element φ^* of Σ_h by subtraction of an appropriate constant such that

$$\iint_{S} \varphi^*\, d\sigma = 0 \tag{8.14}$$

but still $\varphi^* (P)$ is not identically zero in D. Since this transformation is of a most elementary nature, we may, without loss of generality, change our definition of the class Σ_h for the case of a finite domain D by adding to the previous requirements the condition that each $\varphi \in \Sigma_h$ must satisfy the equation

$$\iint_S \varphi \, d\sigma = 0. \tag{8.15}$$

Having imposed this restriction upon the class Σ_h in the case of a finite domain D, we now have the same formula:

$$\begin{aligned} \varphi (Q) = \mathrm{D} \{K (P, Q), \varphi (P)\} &= -\iint_S \frac{\partial K (P, Q)}{\partial \nu_P} \varphi (P) \, d\sigma_P = \\ &= -\iint_S K (P, Q) \frac{\partial \varphi (P)}{\partial \nu} \, d\sigma_P \end{aligned} \tag{8.16}$$

in the case of a finite or an infinite domain D.

Let us turn now to the first equation (8.16). If we consider the Dirichlet operation as a product between two vectors in function space and introduce a complete orthonormal system, then $K (P, Q)$ may be considered a matrix in this linear space because of its two arguments and it acts as unit matrix in its multiplication since it reproduces every element of Σ_h. The kernel $K (P, Q)$ has, therefore, also been called *the reproducing kernel of the class* Σ_h.

The kernel $K (P, Q)$ yields estimates for the elements of Σ_h in terms of their Dirichlet integrals. In fact, applying Schwarz' inequality to the first equation in (8.16), we obtain

$$(\varphi (Q))^2 \leqslant \mathrm{D}_P \{K (P, Q)\} \cdot \mathrm{D} \{\varphi\}. \tag{8.17}$$

Now, if instead of $\varphi (P)$, we use the function $K (P, Q)$ itself, then (8.16) becomes

$$\mathrm{D}_P \{K (P, Q)\} = K (Q, Q) \tag{8.18}$$

so that finally:

$$|\varphi (Q)|^2 \leqslant \mathrm{D} \{\varphi\} \cdot K (Q, Q). \tag{8.19}$$

This result shows that the absolute value of a harmonic function $\varphi (Q)$ can be estimated in terms of its Dirichlet norm by means of the kernel function. The estimate is the best possible since for the particular choice $\varphi (P) = K (P, Q)$ we have equality in (8.19). We can now also understand why it was convenient to restrict the class Σ_h by (8.15) in the case of a finite domain **D**. In fact, the Dirichlet norm $D\{\varphi\}$ does not change if an arbitrary constant is added to the harmonic function φ; thus, in order to establish an inequality of the type (8.19) it was necessary to exclude the arbitrary addition of constants by some normalizing condition of the type (8.15).

We shall now construct the kernel function $K(P, Q)$ in terms of a complete orthonormal system $(\varphi_i(P))$ in Σ_h. We shall call a system of functions $\varphi_i(P) \in \Sigma_h$ orthonormal if it satisfies the equations:

$$D\{\varphi_i, \varphi_k\} = \delta_{ik}. \tag{8.20}$$

We shall call the system complete in Σ_h if every element φ of Σ_h can be developed in a Fourier series of the φ_i in the form:

$$\varphi(P) = \sum_{i=1}^{\infty} a_i \varphi_i(P), \qquad a_i = D\{\varphi, \varphi_i\} \tag{8.21}$$

such that this series converges uniformly to $\varphi(P)$ in each closed subdomain of **D**. It can be shown that there exists a complete orthonormal set in Σ_h for every domain **D** of the type considered here.

Let us, in particular, develop the kernel function $K(P, Q)$ in terms of an orthonormal system. We may apply (8.21) but the coefficients a_i will now depend upon the parameter point Q. By virtue of the reproducing property of the kernel we can easily calculate all the a_i and obtain:

$$a_i(Q) = \varphi_i(Q), \tag{8.22}$$

i. e.,

$$K(P, Q) = \sum_{i=1}^{\infty} \varphi_i(P)\, \varphi_i(Q). \tag{8.23}$$

Thus, the kernel function $K(P, Q)$ has been represented in a particularly simple form in terms of a complete orthonormal system $(\varphi_i(P))$ in Σ_h. It should be observed that there are infinitely many possible choices for complete orthonormal systems in Σ_h; but the representation of $K(P, Q)$ in terms of such a system has always the same invariant form (8.23).

Formula (8.23) provides a useful tool for the actual construction of the kernel function and consequently for the solution of the boundary value problems of the first and second kind. In the case of Laplace's equation infinitely many particular solutions are known; we have all the spherical harmonics at our disposal and can, by transformation by reciprocal radii, construct from them further infinite sequences of harmonic functions which are regular in the whole space except for one arbitrarily prescribed point. If **D** is bounded by n closed surfaces $\mathbf{S}_i$ let us choose n points O_i each lying in that complement Δ_i of **D** which is enclosed by the particular surface $\mathbf{S}_i$. To each O_i we choose the transformed set of spherical harmonics which are regular in the whole space, except for O_i. It can easily be shown that if we orthonormalize all these functions for all values of $i = 1, 2, \ldots, n$, we obtain a complete orthonormal set in Σ_h. Thus, the construction of $K(P, Q)$ is reduced to the orthonormalization of a known system of functions; this implies the calculation of Dirichlet integrals with known integrands and the calculation of large determinants which occur because of the orthogonalization. The numerical work may be rather long, but in principle we have reduced the determination of the kernel function to elementary processes and can actually construct it to any desired degree of precision.

In many cases one can obtain interesting inequalities and estimates by the calculation of a finite number of orthonormal functions. Let us illustrate this by a particular application. We consider the infinite exterior of a closed smooth conductor **S** and construct its kernel function. We may use an orthonormal system the first element of which is a multiple of the conductor potential $V(P)$ considered in Section 5. Since we have by (5.51)

$$\text{D}\{V\} = 4\pi C \tag{8.24}$$

where C is the electrostatic capacity of the conductor **S**, we obtain from $V(P)$ by normalization

$$\varphi_1(P) = \frac{V(P)}{(4\pi C)^{1/2}}. \tag{8.25}$$

Let

$$\varphi_\nu(P) = \frac{a_\nu}{r} + \ldots \tag{8.26}$$

be the development of the elements of the orthonormal system in spherical harmonics near infinity. By the orthogonality with respect to $\varphi_1(P)$ and by virtue of (5.49) we have

$$\text{D}\{\varphi_\nu, \varphi_1\} = 4\pi a_\nu = 0, \qquad \nu > 1. \tag{8.27}$$

We recognize that all the $\varphi_\nu(P)$ are charge-free for $\nu > 1$ and vanish at infinity at least as rapidly as $1/r^2$.

We then find:

$$K(P, Q) = \frac{V(P)\,V(Q)}{4\pi C} + \sum_{\nu=2}^{\infty} \varphi_\nu(P)\,\varphi_\nu(Q), \tag{8.28}$$

and, in particular:

$$K(Q,Q) = \frac{(V(Q))^2}{4\pi C} + \sum_{\nu=2}^{\infty} (\varphi_\nu(Q))^2. \tag{8.29}$$

Multiply this equation by ρ^2, ($\rho^2 \equiv \xi^2 + \eta^2 + \zeta^2$, $Q = (\xi, \eta, \zeta)$), and let $\rho \to \infty$.

Since

$$V(Q) = \frac{C}{\rho} + \dots \tag{8.30}$$

and $\lim_{\rho \to \infty} \rho^2 \varphi_\nu(Q)^2 = 0$ we find:

$$\lim_{\rho \to \infty} \rho^2 K(Q,Q) = \frac{1}{4\pi} C. \tag{8.31}$$

Now let $\psi_1(P), \dots, \psi_l(P)$ be any set of orthonormal functions of the class Σ_h. Since this set can be completed to a complete orthonormal set by addition of further orthonormal functions $\psi_{l+1}(P), \dots,$ we deduce from (8.23)

$$K(Q,Q) \geqslant \sum_{i=1}^{l} \psi_i(Q)^2. \tag{8.32}$$

Introducing this inequality in (8.31), we derive

$$\frac{1}{4\pi} C \geqslant \lim_{\rho \to \infty} \left(\rho^2 \sum_{i=1}^{l} \psi_i(Q)^2\right). \tag{8.33}$$

Thus, the electrostatic capacity of a conductor can be estimated from below if only a finite number of orthonormal functions are known. Each additional function $\psi_{l+1}(Q)$ leads to an improvement of the estimate. The theory of the kernel function and of orthonormal systems thus leads to a systematic approximation procedure for the capacity C. We may also put (8.33) in the following form: let

$$\psi_i(P) = \frac{a_i}{r} + \dots \qquad i = 1, 2, \dots, l, \tag{8.34}$$

be the developments of l orthonormal functions of Σ_h near infinity. Then:

$$\frac{1}{4\pi} C \geqslant \sum_{i=1}^{l} a_i^2. \tag{8.35}$$

Similar applications of finite orthonormal sets are possible in various problems of potential theory and in each case the theory of the kernel function gives useful estimates of important theoretical quantities.

Let us consider finally the Dirichlet product between the kernel function $K(P, Q)$ and the fundamental singularity

$$S(P, R) = \frac{1}{4\pi r(P, R)}. \tag{8.36}$$

The integral encountered will be an improper one because of the infinity of $S(P, R)$ at the point $R \in \mathsf{D}$. But it is easily seen that the integral converges if it is defined as the limit of a sequence of integrals over the domain D from which spheres around R with radii tending to zero have been deleted. Using (8.2), we can show:

$$D\{K(P,Q), S(P, R)\} = -\iint_{\mathsf{S}} S(P, R) \frac{\partial K(P,Q)}{\partial \nu_P} d\sigma_P. \tag{8.37}$$

By virtue of (8.3) this yields

$$D\{K(P,Q), S(P, R)\} = -\frac{1}{A}\iint_{\mathsf{S}} S(P, R)\, d\sigma_P + \iint_{\mathsf{S}} S(P, R) \frac{\partial G(P,Q)}{\partial \nu_P} d\sigma_P \tag{8.38}$$

in the case of a finite domain D, and

$$D\{K(P,Q), S(P, R)\} = \iint_{\mathsf{S}} S(P, R) \frac{\partial G(P,Q)}{\partial \nu_P} d\sigma_P \tag{8.39}$$

if D is infinite. The function

$$s(Q, R) = \iint_{\mathsf{S}} S(P, R) \frac{\partial G(P,Q)}{\partial \nu_P} d\sigma_P \tag{8.40}$$

is regular harmonic for $R \in \mathsf{D}$ and $Q \in \mathsf{D}$ and has for $Q \in \mathsf{S}$ the boundary value $S(Q, R)$. Hence, we can write the Green's function of D in the form

$$G(Q, R) = S(Q, R) - s(Q, R) \tag{8.41}$$

since the right-hand side of (8.41) has the proper singularity for $Q = R$ and vanishes on the boundary S of D. Thus, we have proved:

$$G(Q, R) = S(Q, R) - D\{K(P,Q), S(P, R)\} - \frac{1}{A}\iint_{\mathsf{S}} S(P, R)\, d\sigma_P \tag{8.42}$$

in the case of finite D and

$$G(Q, R) = S(Q, R) - D\{K(P, Q), S(P, R)\} \tag{8.43}$$

for an infinite D. In each case, Green's function has been expressed in a simple form by means of the function $K(P, Q)$. By virtue of (8.3), we can, of course, also represent the Neumann's function in terms of the kernel function.

It is not possible to give analogously simple formulas for the construction of the kernel function $K(P, Q)$ if either the Green's or the Neumann's function is given. It thus appears that the kernel function is more fundamental than either one of these important functions. We shall deal with the theory of the kernel function in a systematic way in Part B. For the sake of simplicity, we shall consider there only the case of two-dimensional domains and also make other simplifying assumptions, so that the case of the harmonic kernel function considered now cannot be considered as a special case of the general theory developed in the second part. However, the general outlook and most methods developed there can also be applied to our present case.

Bergman [6], (B 1), Schiffer-Szegö (S 6).

Chapter IV

ELASTICITY

1. Strain tensor fields: By an elastic body we shall mean a continuum which may be deformed by the application of forces on its boundary surfaces or at its interior points, and which returns to its initial form after the forces are released.

We label each particle of the body by its original coordinates x_i in the undeformed body. The displacement of each such particle will be described by a vector field $\mathbf{u}(x_i) \equiv (u_1, u_2, u_3)$, the displacement vector field.

Let $x_i^{(0)}$ be a point of the continuum and let $u_i^{(0)}$ be its displacement vector. Under the deformation the neighboring points will move by the amount

$$u_i = u_i^{(0)} + \sum_{k=1}^{3} \frac{\partial u_i}{\partial x_k} dx_k + \dots, \qquad x_i = x_i^{(0)} + dx_i, \tag{1.1}$$

and consequently we have the relative displacement with respect to $x_i^{(0)}$

$$u_i - u_i^{(0)} = \sum_{k=1}^{3} \frac{\partial u_i}{\partial x_k} dx_k + \ldots \tag{1.1a}$$

Neglecting higher order terms in (1.1a), we see that the neighborhood of the point $x_i^{(0)}$ will be subjected to an affine transformation with the matrix $\left(\left(\delta_{ik} + \frac{\partial u_i}{\partial x_k}\right)\right)$.

In order to analyze this linear transformation we introduce the notation

$$e_{ik} = \frac{1}{2}\left(\frac{\partial u_i}{\partial x_k} + \frac{\partial u_k}{\partial x_i}\right), \qquad \omega_{ik} = \frac{1}{2}\left(\frac{\partial u_i}{\partial x_k} - \frac{\partial u_k}{\partial x_i}\right). \tag{1.2}$$

We have the decomposition

$$\frac{\partial u_i}{\partial x_k} = e_{ik} + \omega_{ik}, \tag{1.3}$$

or, in matrix form:

$$M = \left(\left(\frac{\partial u_i}{\partial x_k}\right)\right) = T + \Omega = ((e_{ik})) + ((\omega_{ik})). \tag{1.4}$$

We may write the transformation formula (1.1a) in the form:

$$\delta\mathbf{u} = T\,d\mathbf{x} + \Omega\,d\mathbf{x}, \qquad \mathbf{x} = \begin{pmatrix} x_1 \\ x_2 \\ x_3 \end{pmatrix}, \tag{1.5}$$

and consider the deformation of the neighborhood as characterized by two linear transformations, one with the symmetric matrix T and the other with the antisymmetric matrix Ω.

In the linearized theory of elasticity we assume that the terms $\frac{\partial u_i}{\partial x_k}$ are small, that is, that the displacement vector changes slowly through the continuum. Hence, δu_i is to be considered small as compared to dx_i, and

$$dx_i^* = dx_i + \delta u_i, \tag{1.6}$$

the relative position of the point $(x_i^{(0)} + dx_i)$ after the deformation, may be considered as a vector $d\mathbf{x}^* = (dx_1^*, dx_2^*, dx_3^*)$ of length

$$|d\mathbf{x}^*| = (|d\mathbf{x}|^2 + 2\,(d\mathbf{x}, \delta\mathbf{u}))^{1/2} = |d\mathbf{x}| + \frac{(d\mathbf{x}, \delta\mathbf{u})}{|d\mathbf{x}|}. \tag{1.7}$$

The contribution of the antisymmetric component $\Omega\,d\mathbf{x}$ of $\delta\mathbf{u}$ in the above formula is zero. Hence all lengths and consequently scalar products are not affected by a transformation $d\mathbf{x} + \Omega\, d\mathbf{x}$, which represents, therefore, an infinitesimal rigid rotation leaving distances and angles unchanged.

The actual deformation is, therefore, described by the matrix T. By its very construction, T is a symmetric tensor and is known as the *strain* or *deformation tensor*. T will vary from point to point of the body and form a tensor field on the body.

The natural representation of a symmetric tensor is the quadric

$$\Phi(P) = \sum_{i,k=1}^{3} e_{ik}\, \xi_i\, \xi_k = \text{const.}, \qquad \xi_i = x_i - x_i^{(0)} \tag{1.8}$$

called in our particular case the *strain quadric*. At each point in the neighborhood of $x_i^{(0)}$ with the relative coordinate ξ_i the distortion vector with components

$$\delta\xi_i = \sum_{k=1}^{3} e_{ik}\, \xi_k \tag{1.9}$$

has the direction of the normal to the strain quadric through this point. Under this distortion the radius vector to any point on a fixed quadric $\Phi = \text{const.}$ undergoes a relative increase of length which is inversely proportional to the square of its length.

The principal dilatations l_ν $(\nu = 1, 2, 3)$ are defined as the roots of the cubic equation

$$\det |e_{ik} - l\, \delta_{ik}| = 0. \tag{1.10}$$

The direction cosines $\alpha_k^{(\nu)}$ of the corresponding axes of dilatation satisfy the equations

$$\sum_{k=1}^{3} (e_{ik} - l_\nu\, \delta_{ik})\, \alpha_k^{(\nu)} = 0, \qquad (i = 1, 2, 3). \tag{1.11}$$

Conversely, if the principal dilatations l_ν of the corresponding axes of dilatation with the direction cosines $\alpha_k^{(\nu)}$ are given, then the components of the strain tensor are given by

$$e_{ik} = \sum_{\nu=1}^{3} l_\nu\, \alpha_i^{(\nu)}\, \alpha_k^{(\nu)}. \tag{1.12}$$

This result may be shown by a formal calculation using the orthogonality of the dilatation axes.

Love [43], Planck [61], Sokolnikoff [70], Sommerfeld [72].

2. Stress tensor fields: Let us consider a body which is in a static deformed state owing to the action of external forces independent of time. These forces can be divided into two classes: (1) Forces (like gravity) which act on all parts of the body. We denote them as *mass forces* and shall set them proportional to the element of mass of the body. Let $d\tau = dx_1\, dx_2\, dx_3$ denote the volume element and $\varkappa$ the corresponding density of mass. Then we shall express the force acting on the element by $\mathbf{X}\,\varkappa\, d\tau$, $\mathbf{X} = (X_1, X_2, X_3)$, that is, $\mathbf{X}$ is the force density per unit mass; (2) Forces which act on the surface of the body. For any portion σ of the surface of the body the quotient of the resultant force that acts on it and of the area of σ is called the stress vector on σ. As the portion σ shrinks to a point P, the limit of the stress vector is called the *stress at P*. We shall assume that at every point where the boundary surface of the body has a normal, this limit exists and that the stress has a well defined direction $\mathbf{d}$. The surface force acting on a surface element $d\sigma$ is $\mathbf{F}\, d\sigma$, $\mathbf{F} = (F_1, F_2, F_3)$. The direction $\mathbf{d}$ of the surface force may form an arbitrary angle with the (interior) normal $\boldsymbol{\nu}$ to the surface element $d\sigma$. If the directions $\mathbf{d}$ and $\boldsymbol{\nu}$ are opposite, the surface force acts in the sense of an expansion (like a tension on a stretched wire). If the directions are perpendicular to each other, the surface force acts in the sense of a shear (e. g., in the case of torsion or friction).

Surface forces can also be considered in the interior of the deformed body. If P is an interior point, consider an area element $d\sigma$ through P with normal $\boldsymbol{\nu}$. The stress created in the body by the deformation leads to surface forces on both sides of the area element. These forces are opposite in direction and equal in magnitude. Let $\mathbf{F}_\nu\, d\sigma$ denote the force acting on that side of the element $d\sigma$ with normal $\boldsymbol{\nu}$ which is adjacent to the volume element into which $\boldsymbol{\nu}$ is pointing. We can express all force densities $\mathbf{F}_\nu$ at a given point P in terms of the three force densities $\mathbf{F}_i$ belonging to elements through P with normals in the directions x_i. Let $\mathbf{F}_i = (F_{i1}, F_{i2}, F_{i3})$; then it can be shown by a classical argument that if $\mathbf{F}_\nu = (F_{\nu,1}, F_{\nu,2}, F_{\nu,3})$, then

$$F_{\nu,i} = \sum_{k=1}^{3} F_{ik} \cos(\boldsymbol{\nu}, \mathbf{x}_k) = \mathbf{F}_i \cdot \boldsymbol{\nu}. \tag{2.1}$$

From the geometric significance of this relation, we deduce that the matrix

$$F = ((F_{ik})) \tag{2.2}$$

is a tensor which transforms the normal vector $\boldsymbol{\nu}$ into the stress vector $\mathbf{F}_\nu$. F is called the *stress tensor* at the point P. The stress tensor forms a tensor field over the deformed body. Let V designate a subdomain of B

with surface S having interior normal $\boldsymbol{\nu}$. The total force acting on V is composed of the mass forces in the interior and the surface forces on S. Because of the equilibrium state, this total force must vanish, that is,

$$\iiint_V X_i \varkappa \, d\tau + \iint_S F_{\nu, i} \, d\sigma = 0 \qquad (i = 1, 2, 3). \tag{2.3}$$

Using (2.1) we obtain

$$\iiint_V X_i \varkappa \, d\tau + \iint_S \sum_{k=1}^{3} F_{ik} \cos(\boldsymbol{\nu}, \mathbf{x}_k) \, d\sigma = 0 \qquad (i = 1, 2, 3), \tag{2.4}$$

and, by Green's identity

$$\iiint_V \left(X_i \varkappa - \sum_{k=1}^{3} \frac{\partial F_{ik}}{\partial x_k} \right) d\tau = 0 \qquad (i = 1, 2, 3). \tag{2.5}$$

Because of the arbitrariness of the domain V we find the equilibrium condition

$$\sum_{k=1}^{3} \frac{\partial F_{ik}}{\partial x_k} = X_i \varkappa \qquad (i = 1, 2, 3) \tag{2.6}$$

which can also be written in vector form

$$\varkappa \mathbf{X} = \operatorname{div} F. \tag{2.7}$$

Similarly we may consider the moment equilibrium on the arbitrary domain V. We clearly have

$$\iiint_V (x_i X_k - x_k X_i) \varkappa \, d\tau + \iint_S (x_i F_{\nu, k} - x_k F_{\nu, i}) \, d\sigma = 0, \tag{2.8}$$
$$(i, k = 1, 2, 3).$$

Again using (2.1) and Green's identity, we obtain

$$\iiint_V \left((x_i X_k - x_k X_i) \varkappa - \sum_{j=1}^{3} \frac{\partial}{\partial x_j} (x_i F_{kj} - x_k F_{ij}) \right) d\tau = 0 \tag{2.9}$$

whence

$$(x_i X_k - x_k X_i) \varkappa = \sum_{j=1}^{3} \frac{\partial}{\partial x_j} (x_i F_{kj} - x_k F_{ij}). \tag{2.10}$$

Carrying out the indicated differentiation and using (2.6), there is obtained the symmetry of the stress tensor, i. e.,

$$F_{ik} = F_{ki}. \tag{2.11}$$

In a certain class of elastostatic problems, the exterior forces are considered to be given, i. e., at each interior point of the body we know the mass force density **X** and at each point of the boundary the surface force density **F**. The equilibrium conditions (2.6) represent a first order system of partial differential equations for the components F_{ik} of the stress tensor, while the conditions

$$F_i = \sum_{k=1}^{3} F_{ik} \cos(\boldsymbol{\nu}, \mathbf{x}_k) \qquad (i = 1, 2, 3) \tag{2.12}$$

valid on the surface of the body yield the necessary boundary conditions for this system.

3. Stress-strain relations: In the preceding section we derived equations for the stress tensor field created by given exterior forces. In the present section we shall establish the relations between the fields of strain and stress tensors. We base our theory on the energy concept.

Consider a volume element $d\tau$ in the deformed body. The distortion of the material has stored in it an amount of energy $U\,d\tau$ and the energy density U depends upon the deformation tensor $T = (e_{ik})$. We normalize the energy in such a way that the undistorted state, $T = 0$, corresponds to zero energy. It is physically obvious that the energy of any other state of deformation is positive; hence, the undistorted state corresponds to a minimum of energy. It is easily verified that the components e_{ik} of T can be prescribed arbitrarily at any fixed point of the body. Hence, the minimum condition for the undeformed state is

$$\left.\frac{\partial U}{\partial e_{ik}}\right|_{e_{ik}=0} = 0. \tag{3.1}$$

If we develop U in a power series in the e_{ik}, there will occur only quadratic and higher order terms. It has been pointed out in Section 1 that the deformation terms e_{ik} are to be considered as "infinitesimals", i. e., that only the lowest order terms involving them should be considered. Correspondingly the energy density U must be chosen as a quadratic function of the e_{ik}, and has therefore the form

$$(3.2) \qquad U = \sum_{i,k,l,m=1}^{3} a_{iklm}\, e_{ik}\, e_{lm}$$

where we may assume that $a_{iklm} = a_{lmik}$. The quantity U is also known as the elastic potential of the body.

In order to derive the relation between energy and force, we superimpose on the deformed body an additional slight deformation with the vector field $\triangle u_i$. The work done against the stress forces increases the energy E of the deformed body by an amount

$$(3.3) \qquad \triangle E = \iiint_B \left(\sum_{i=1}^{3} \varkappa X_i \triangle u_i \right) d\tau + \iint_S \sum_{i=1}^{3} F_i \triangle u_i \, d\sigma.$$

Using (2.6), we then obtain

$$(3.4) \qquad \triangle E = \iiint_B \left(\sum_{i,k=1}^{3} \frac{\partial F_{ik}}{\partial x_k} \triangle u_i \right) d\tau + \iint_S \sum_{i=1}^{3} F_i \triangle u_i \, d\sigma =$$

$$= - \iiint_B \sum_{i,k=1}^{3} F_{ik} \cdot \frac{1}{2} \left(\frac{\partial \Delta u_i}{\partial x_k} + \frac{\partial \Delta u_k}{\partial x_i} \right) d\tau$$

$$- \iint_S \sum_{i,k=1}^{3} F_{ik} \triangle u_i \cos(\boldsymbol{\nu}, \mathbf{x}_k) \, d\sigma + \iint_S \sum_{i=1}^{3} F_i \triangle u_i \, d\sigma$$

by virtue of Green's identity and the symmetry of the stress tensor. Thus we have from (1.2) and (2.12)

$$(3.5) \qquad \triangle E = - \iiint_B \left(\sum_{i,k=1}^{3} F_{ik} \triangle e_{ik} \right) d\tau.$$

On the other hand, the change Δe_{ik} of the strain tensor leads to a change of energy density

$$(3.6) \qquad \triangle U = \sum_{i,k=1}^{3} \frac{\partial U}{\partial e_{ik}} \triangle e_{ik}.$$

Comparing (3.5) and (3.6) and considering the freedom in the choice of $\triangle e_{ik}$ we obtain

$$F_{ik} = -\frac{\partial U}{\partial e_{ik}}. \tag{3.7}$$

From (3.2) we obtain

$$F_{ik} = -2\sum_{l,m=1}^{3} a_{iklm}\, e_{lm}, \tag{3.8}$$

i. e., a linear relationship between the strain and the stress tensor which is a generalization of Hooke's Law of the one-dimensional case.

If we count all the symmetries of the coefficient system a_{iklm} we find that there exist twenty-one independent material constants which determine the elastic behavior of the body. This number can be reduced considerably by assuming symmetry properties in the elastic behavior of the material. The most important case is that of an isotropic medium in which the elastic properties are completely independent of the direction. In this case all physical quantities must be invariant with respect to rotations of the coordinate system.

At every point of an isotropic body, the elastic potential is a quadratic function of the e_{ik} where the coefficients a_{iklm} are now independent of the choice of the coordinate system. We may therefore assume that the deformation tensor is already on principal axes and that the elastic potential is a quadratic function of the principal dilatations l_ν ($\nu = 1, 2, 3$). It must, moreover, be a symmetric function of the l_ν since we can interchange the axes by an appropriate rotation. By a well known theorem on symmetric functions, U can be expressed as a linear combination of $\sum_{\nu=1}^{3} l_\nu^2$ and $\left(\sum_{\nu=1}^{3} l_\nu\right)^2$:

$$U = \frac{\lambda}{2}\left(\sum_{\nu=1}^{3} l_\nu\right)^2 + \mu \sum_{\nu=1}^{3} l_\nu^2 \tag{3.9}$$

where λ and μ are material constants. We see at first that $\sum_{\nu=1}^{3} l_\nu$ can vanish for an appropriate choice of the deformation tensor. The energy density, on the other hand, must be positive for a non-identically vanishing deformation tensor. Hence, we have $\mu > 0$. By the Schwarz inequality we have

(3.10)
$$\left(\sum_{\nu=1}^{3} l_\nu\right)^2 \leqslant 3 \sum_{\nu=1}^{3} l_\nu^2$$

and consequently

(3.11)
$$0 < U \leqslant \left(\frac{3\lambda}{2} + \mu\right) \sum_{\nu=1}^{3} l_\nu^2.$$

Thus,

(3.12)
$$\frac{3\lambda}{2} + \mu > 0.$$

In various formulas of elasticity theory, the material constant

(3.13)
$$\alpha = 1 + \frac{\lambda}{\mu}.$$

is used. The above inequality is equivalent to

(3.14)
$$\alpha > \frac{1}{3}.$$

λ and μ are called the Lamé constants of the isotropic body. $\sigma = \frac{1}{2}(1 - \alpha^{-1}) = \frac{1}{2}\frac{\lambda}{\mu + \lambda}$ is denoted as the Poisson ratio.

The expressions $\sum_{\nu=1}^{3} l_\nu$ and $\sum_{\nu=1}^{3} l_\nu^2$ can easily be expressed in terms of the components of T. The quantity $\sum_{\nu=1}^{3} l_\nu$ is the trace of T while $\sum_{\nu=1}^{3} l_\nu^2$ is closely related to the second invariant of T. We easily calculate

(3.15)
$$U = \frac{\lambda}{2}\left(\sum_{i=1}^{3} e_{ii}\right)^2 + \mu \sum_{i,k=1}^{3} e_{ik}^2.$$

Let us write

(3.16)
$$\gamma = \sum_{i=1}^{3} e_{ii};$$

then using (3.15) and (3.7) we obtain the stress-strain relation for the isotropic body

(3.17)
$$F_{ik} = -\lambda\gamma\,\delta_{ik} - 2\mu e_{ik}.$$

Now we are able to derive the differential equation system for the components of the displacement vector for a given field of exterior forces. Inserting (3.17) into (2.6) we obtain

$$-\lambda\frac{\partial\gamma}{\partial x_i}-2\mu\sum_{k=1}^{3}\frac{\partial e_{ik}}{\partial x_k}=X_i\,\varkappa. \tag{3.18}$$

Using (1.2) and (3.16) we may write

$$(\lambda+\mu)\,\text{grad div}\,\mathbf{u}+\mu\Delta\,\mathbf{u}=-\mathbf{X}\,\varkappa. \tag{3.19}$$

Finally using (3.13) we obtain the elliptic partial differential system

$$\Delta\,\mathbf{u}+a\,\text{grad div}\,\mathbf{u}=-\frac{\varkappa}{\mu}\,\mathbf{X}. \tag{3.20}$$

These differential equations determine the deformation of the elastic body if the exterior forces are known and if the proper boundary conditions are considered. In the next section we shall discuss the most important boundary conditions in elastostatic problems and discuss methods for the solution of the corresponding problems.

4. The energy integral and boundary value problems: In the preceding section we derived the partial differential equation system for the displacement vector field of an elastic isotropic body. We obtained a system of three linear differential equations of elliptic type with constant coefficients. The system is inhomogeneous if exterior mass forces are present. In the case where no exterior mass forces are acting and the deformation of the body is created by surface forces only we obtain a homogeneous system of equations which can be treated in a way which is closely analogous to all other homogeneous differential equations in this book.

We shall again obtain an understanding of the different types of boundary value problems by considering an energy integral. For the sake of simplicity we shall assume that the body B is finite and is bounded by a smooth surface S. If a state of deformation with the displacement vector $\mathbf{u}$ exists, the energy stored in the body is given by

$$E=\iiint_{\mathsf{B}} U\,d\tau=\frac{\mu}{2}\iiint_{\mathsf{B}}\left(2\sum_{i,k=1}^{3}e_{ik}^{\,2}+(a-1)\left(\sum_{i=1}^{3}e_{ii}\right)^2\right)d\tau. \tag{4.1}$$

Using the definition (1.2), this can also be written in the form

$$E = \frac{\mu}{2} \iiint_B \left(\sum_{i,k=1}^{3} \frac{\partial u_i}{\partial x_k} \left(\frac{\partial u_i}{\partial x_k} + \frac{\partial u_k}{\partial x_i} \right) + (\alpha - 1)(\operatorname{div} \mathbf{u})^2 \right) d\tau. \tag{4.2}$$

As in Chapter I, we now introduce the corresponding bilinear Dirichlet integral

$$\mathrm{e}\{\mathbf{u}, \mathbf{v}\} = \iiint_B \left[\sum_{i,k=1}^{3} \frac{\partial u_i}{\partial x_k} \left(\frac{\partial v_i}{\partial x_k} + \frac{\partial v_k}{\partial x_i} \right) + (\alpha - 1) \operatorname{div} \mathbf{u} \operatorname{div} \mathbf{v} \right] d\tau; \tag{4.3}$$

we clearly have

$$\mathrm{e}\{\mathbf{u}, \mathbf{v}\} = \mathrm{e}\{\mathbf{v}, \mathbf{u}\}, \quad \mathrm{e}\{\mathbf{u}, \mathbf{u}\} \geqslant 0. \tag{4.4}$$

The latter is a consequence of the inequality $\alpha > 1/3$ valid for the material constant.

The close relation between the Dirichlet integral (4.3) and the partial differential equation (3.20) is exhibited by the following identity which is an immediate consequence of Green's formula.

$$\mathrm{e}\{\mathbf{u}, \mathbf{v}\} = -\iint_S (\mathbf{u} \cdot \mathfrak{T}(\mathbf{v}))\, d\sigma - \iiint_B \mathbf{u} \cdot [\triangle \mathbf{v} + \alpha \operatorname{grad} \operatorname{div} \mathbf{v}]\, d\tau \tag{4.5}$$

where $\mathfrak{T}$ denotes a vector depending linearly upon its argument vector $\mathbf{v}$ and has the components

$$\mathfrak{T}_i(\mathbf{v}) = \sum_{k=1}^{3} \cos(\boldsymbol{\nu}, \mathbf{x}_k) \left(\frac{\partial v_i}{\partial x_k} + \frac{\partial v_k}{\partial x_i} \right) + (\alpha - 1) \cos(\boldsymbol{\nu}, \mathbf{x}_i) \operatorname{div} \mathbf{v}. \tag{4.6}$$

The vector function $\mathfrak{T}(\mathbf{v})$ has a simple and important physical interpretation. According to (2.12) and (3.17), we have the following relation between the boundary stress F_i and the displacement vector $\mathbf{u}$:

$$F_i = -\mu \mathfrak{T}_i(\mathbf{u}). \tag{4.7}$$

Thus, up to a constant material factor the linear vector function $\mathfrak{T}_i(\mathbf{u})$ represents the boundary stress in terms of the displacement vector. Using (3.20) and (4.7), we may write identity (4.5) in the form:

$$\mathrm{e}\{\mathbf{u}, \mathbf{v}\} = \frac{1}{\mu} \iint_S \mathbf{u} \cdot \mathbf{F}\, d\sigma + \frac{1}{\mu} \iiint_B \mathbf{u} \cdot \mathbf{X} \varkappa\, d\tau, \tag{4.5 a}$$

where **F** and **X** are the systems of boundary and mass force densities connected with the displacement vector field **v**.

We use the definite character of the energy integral e $\{\mathbf{u}, \mathbf{u}\}$ in order to establish certain uniqueness theorems related to the differential equation system

$$\triangle \mathbf{u} + a \operatorname{grad} \operatorname{div} \mathbf{u} = 0. \tag{4.8}$$

If a vector field **u** *satisfies the differential equation* (4.8) *in the domain* B *and vanishes on its boundary* S, *then we have* $\mathbf{u} \equiv 0$ *in* B. To prove this theorem, we apply the identity (4.5) with $\mathbf{v} \equiv \mathbf{u}$. Because of (4.8) and the vanishing of **u** on S, we find

$$\mathrm{e}\,\{\mathbf{u}, \mathbf{u}\} = 0, \tag{4.9}$$

that is, by (4.1)

$$e_{ik} = \frac{1}{2}\left(\frac{\partial u_i}{\partial x_k} + \frac{\partial u_k}{\partial x_i}\right) = 0, \qquad i, k = 1, 2, 3. \tag{4.10}$$

At no point of B does the displacement vector field **u** create a real distortion. It represents a rigid motion of the body and **u** has necessarily the form

$$\mathbf{u} = \mathbf{a} + \mathbf{b} \times \mathbf{r}, \qquad \mathbf{r} \equiv (x_1, x_2, x_3). \tag{4.11}$$

Conversely, one verifies immediately that every vector field **u** of the form (4.11) satisfies the six differential equations (4.10). We thus see that Euclidean motions and only these create a displacement vector field with vanishing energy integral e $\{\mathbf{u}, \mathbf{u}\}$.

The vanishing of **u** on S implies $\mathbf{u} \equiv 0$, for each component of **u** is a harmonic function in B.

Let **u** *be a vector field satisfying the differential equation* (4.8) *in* B. *Suppose that there exists a linear relation*

$$\mathfrak{T}(\mathbf{u}(P)) - \Pi(P)\,\mathbf{u}(P) \equiv 0, \qquad P \in \mathsf{S} \tag{4.12}$$

with a positive-definite symmetric matrix function $\Pi(P)$ *defined on* S. *Then, we have* $\mathbf{u} \equiv 0$ *in* B. To show this, we again apply the identity (4.5) with $\mathbf{v} = \mathbf{u}$ and obtain

$$\mathrm{e}\,\{\mathbf{u}, \mathbf{u}\} = -\iint_{\mathsf{S}} \mathbf{u} \cdot (\Pi(P)\,\mathbf{u})\, d\sigma \leqslant 0. \tag{4.13}$$

Thus, we have simultaneously the equations

$$\mathrm{e}\,\{\mathbf{u}, \mathbf{u}\} = 0, \qquad \mathbf{u} \cdot (\Pi(P)\,\mathbf{u}) = 0 \qquad \text{on } \mathsf{S}. \tag{4.14}$$

The same reasoning as before leads to $\mathbf{u} \equiv 0$.

Let $\mathfrak{u}$ *be a vector field satisfying the differential equation* (4.8) *in* B *and the condition* $\mathfrak{T}(\mathfrak{u}) \equiv 0$ *on* S. *Then, we have* $\mathfrak{u} = \mathfrak{a} + \mathfrak{b} \times \mathfrak{r}$ *in* B *with* $\mathfrak{a}$ *and* $\mathfrak{b}$ *arbitrary*. From (4.5) we conclude again that $e\{\mathfrak{u}, \mathfrak{u}\} = 0$ and that consequently

$$\mathfrak{u} = \mathfrak{a} + \mathfrak{b} \times \mathfrak{r}.$$

On the other hand, we may write (4.6) in the form

$$(4.6\text{ a}) \qquad \mathfrak{T}_i(\mathfrak{u}) = 2 \sum_{k=1}^{3} \cos(\boldsymbol{\nu}, \mathbf{x}_k)\, e_{ik} + (\alpha - 1) \cos(\boldsymbol{\nu}, \mathbf{x}_i) \sum_{k=1}^{3} e_{kk}.$$

This form shows that $\mathfrak{T}(\mathfrak{u}) = 0$ if $\mathfrak{u}$ is the displacement vector due to a Euclidean motion. Thus, every vector field (4.11) will satisfy the assumptions of our theorem and the assertion is proved.

The above three theorems may be considered as the uniqueness theorems related to the following three boundary value problems.

Problem A: An elastic body B *is deformed by the action of surface stresses and the displacement vector of each boundary point is prescribed. To determine the displacement vector field in* B. *In other words, we have to determine a solution* $\mathfrak{u}$ *of the differential equation* (4.8) *with prescribed boundary values*

$$(4.15) \qquad \mathfrak{u}(P) = \mathfrak{b}(P), \qquad P \in S.$$

This is the first boundary value problem of elastostatics. As we have seen above, the solution is unique if its exists.

Problem B: An elastic body B *is kept in a state of deformation by stresses acting on its surface. A linear combination of displacements and stresses on the boundary is prescribed. To determine the displacement vector field in* B. *That is, we seek a solution* $\mathfrak{u}$ *of* (4.8) *for which*

$$(4.16) \qquad \mathfrak{T}\big(\mathfrak{u}(P)\big) - \Pi(P)\, \mathfrak{u}(P) = \mathfrak{b}(P)$$

is prescribed on S. In order to be sure that a unique solution of this problem exists we have to assume that $\Pi(P)$ is a symmetric positive-definite matrix. In this case, our previous result will guarantee the uniqueness of the solution.

Boundary value problems of this type arise if a body B is clamped elastically and subjected to surface stresses $\mathfrak{b}(P)$. The displacement of the boundary will create elastic reaction stresses which are linear vector functions of the displacement.

Problem C: An elastic body is deformed by stresses on its surface S. *These stresses are prescribed at every point of* S. *To determine the displacement vector field in* B. *That is, we seek a solution* $\mathfrak{u}$ *of* (4.8) *for which*

$$(4.17) \qquad \mathfrak{T}\big(\mathbf{u}(P)\big) = \mathbf{b}(P), \qquad P \in \mathsf{S}$$

is prescribed. We know from the last uniqueness theorem above that the displacement vector field **u** is uniquely determined up to a Euclidean motion.

We remark that problem B is the most general one and that A and C can be considered as limiting cases for very large or very small values of the matrix $\Pi(P)$. However, the fact that problem B possesses a uniquely determined solution while problem C does not shows that one must be very cautious in such limit considerations.

Tedone (T 2).

5. Betti's formula and the fundamental singularity: From the symmetry of the Dirichlet integral e $\{\mathbf{u}, \mathbf{v}\}$ and the identity (4.5), we derive Betti's formula:

$$(5.1) \qquad \iiint_{\mathsf{B}} (\mathbf{u} \cdot [\triangle \mathbf{v} + \alpha \operatorname{grad} \operatorname{div} \mathbf{v}] - \mathbf{v}\,[\triangle \mathbf{u} + \alpha \operatorname{grad} \operatorname{div} \mathbf{u}]\, d\tau =$$

$$= - \iint_{\mathsf{S}} \big(\mathbf{u} \cdot \mathfrak{T}(\mathbf{v}) - \mathbf{v} \cdot \mathfrak{T}(\mathbf{u})\big)\, d\sigma,$$

which holds for every pair of vector fields **u** and **v** which are twice continuously differentiable in the closed region $\mathsf{B} + \mathsf{S}$. In the theory of the differential equation (4.8) this formula plays the same role as does Green's formula in the theory of harmonic functions.

In this latter theory, we could express a harmonic function by means of its boundary values and the boundary values of its normal derivative by applying Green's identity to the harmonic function considered and to a harmonic function which becomes infinite at a prescribed point. It is possible to introduce an analogous discontinuous solution of (4.8) in the Betti formula (5.1).

In fact, we shall show that we can find two constants A and B such that for fixed $k = 1, 2$, or 3:

$$(5.2) \qquad u_i = A \frac{\partial^2 r}{\partial x_i\, \partial x_k} + B \frac{1}{r}\, \delta_{ik}, \qquad i = 1, 2, 3,$$

$r = \big((x_1 - y_1)^2 + (x_2 - y_2)^2 + (x_3 - y_3)^2\big)^{1/2}$, is a solution of (4.8). For this purpose, we remark that

$$(5.3) \qquad \Delta r = \frac{2}{r}$$

and hence:

$$\Delta \mathbf{u} = 2A \operatorname{grad}\left(\frac{\partial}{\partial x_k}\left(\frac{1}{r}\right)\right) \tag{5.4}$$

and

$$\operatorname{div} \mathbf{u} = (2A + B)\frac{\partial}{\partial x_k}\left(\frac{1}{r}\right). \tag{5.5}$$

Thus,

$$\Delta \mathbf{u} + \alpha \operatorname{grad} \operatorname{div} \mathbf{u} = \big(2A + \alpha(2A + B)\big) \operatorname{grad}\left(\frac{\partial}{\partial x_k}\left(\frac{1}{r}\right)\right) \tag{5.6}$$

will vanish identically if we choose

$$-2A\left(1 + \frac{1}{\alpha}\right) = B. \tag{5.7}$$

Since we can construct such a solution vector $\mathbf{u}$ for all three possible values of k, we are led to the following symmetric tensor.

$$L_{ik} = A\frac{\partial^2 r}{\partial x_i\, \partial x_k} + B\frac{1}{r}\,\delta_{ik} \tag{5.8}$$

which depends on the two argument points $P \equiv \{x_i\}$, $Q \equiv \{y_i\}$ and whose columns, and hence rows are solution vectors of the differential equation (4.8).

This tensor field $L(P, Q)$ was introduced by Somigliana and in the theory of (4.8) plays the role of a fundamental singularity. $L(P, Q)$ becomes infinite like $1/r$ if $P \to Q$.

In order to apply Betti's identity to the fundamental tensor L, we introduce the following notation. If T is a tensor (T_{ik}) the linear operator $\mathfrak{T}$ acting on the vectors T_{ik}, for fixed i, will lead to three vectors which form the rows of a new tensor which will be denoted by $\mathfrak{T}(T)$.

Consider the body B with boundary S from which a little sphere of radius ε has been removed around the point Q. We denote the remaining body by B_ε; its boundary consists of S and the surface S_ε of the sphere. In view of (4.5), and since the rows of the L tensor are solutions of the differential equation (4.8), we have

$$e_{\mathsf{B}_\varepsilon}\{\mathbf{w}(P), \mathbf{L}_j(P, Q)\} = -\iint_{\mathsf{S}+\mathsf{S}_\varepsilon} \mathbf{w}(P)\cdot \mathfrak{T}(\mathbf{L}_j(P, Q))\, d\sigma_P \qquad (j = 1, 2, 3). \tag{5.9}$$

Here $e_{\mathsf{B}_\varepsilon}$ is the energy integral extended over the body B_ε and $\mathbf{L}_j(P, Q)$ denotes the vector formed by the j-th row of L. We shall frequently shorten this notation by writing

(5.9 a) $$e_{B_\varepsilon}\{\mathbf{w}(P), \mathbf{L}(P,Q)\} = -\iint\limits_{S+S_\varepsilon} \mathbf{w}(P)\cdot\mathfrak{T}(\mathbf{L}(P,Q))\,d\sigma_P.$$

Our aim is to show that in the limit $\varepsilon \to 0$ we have

(5.10) $$e\{\mathbf{w}(P), \mathbf{L}(P,Q)\} = 4\pi\,\mathbf{w}(Q) - \iint\limits_{S} \mathbf{w}(P)\cdot\mathfrak{T}\big(\mathbf{L}(P,Q)\big)\,d\sigma_P$$

for a proper choice of the constant A which appears in the definition (5.8).

For this purpose it is sufficient to show that

(5.11) $$\lim_{\varepsilon\to 0}\iint\limits_{S_\varepsilon} \mathbf{w}(P)\cdot\mathfrak{T}(\mathbf{L}(P,Q))\,d\sigma_P = -4\pi\,\mathbf{w}(Q).$$

We first observe that by (4.6), (5.2), and (5.5) we have:

(5.12) $$\mathfrak{T}_i(\mathbf{L}_j(P,Q)) = 2A\frac{\partial}{\partial\nu}\left(\frac{\partial^2 r}{\partial x_i\,\partial x_j}\right) + B\frac{\partial}{\partial\nu}\left(\frac{1}{r}\right)\delta_{ij} + B\cos(\boldsymbol{\nu},\mathbf{x}_j)\frac{\partial}{\partial x_i}\left(\frac{1}{r}\right) + (\alpha-1)(2A+B)\cos(\boldsymbol{\nu},\mathbf{x}_i)\frac{\partial}{\partial x_j}\left(\frac{1}{r}\right).$$

We remark that in the case of the sphere, the normal derivative coincides with differentiation with respect to r. In addition, we use the elementary fact that

(5.13) $$\iint\limits_{S_\varepsilon}\frac{(x_i-y_i)(x_j-y_j)}{r^4}\,d\sigma = \frac{4\pi}{3}\delta_{ij}.$$

By means of this formula, we may calculate term by term in the limit formula (5.11) where $\mathfrak{T}_j$ has the form (5.12). A straightforward calculation shows

(5.14) $$\lim_{\varepsilon\to 0}\iint\limits_{S_\varepsilon}\mathbf{w}(P)\cdot\mathfrak{T}\big(\mathbf{L}(P,Q)\big)\,d\sigma_P = -\frac{16\pi A}{3}\mathbf{w}(Q) - 4\pi B\,\mathbf{w}(Q) - \frac{4\pi}{3}B\,\mathbf{w}(Q) - \frac{4\pi}{3}(\alpha-1)(2A+B)\,\mathbf{w}(Q).$$

Thus, using (5.7) we easily see that (5.11) will be fulfilled if we choose

(5.15) $$A = -\frac{1}{2}\frac{\alpha}{\alpha+1}, \qquad B = 1.$$

We therefore normalize the fundamental tensor in the form

$$L_{ik} = \left(-\frac{1}{2}\frac{a}{a+1}\right)\frac{\partial^2 r}{\partial x_i\,\partial x_k} + \frac{1}{r}\,\delta_{ik}. \tag{5.8 a}$$

Identity (5.10) holds for every vector field $\mathbf{w}(P)$ which is continuously differentiable in the closed region $\mathsf{B}+\mathsf{S}$. We have used only the fact that each row of the L tensor is a solution of the differential equation (4.8). If, on the other hand, $\mathbf{w}(P)$ itself is a solution of this differential equation, we may apply (4.5) by integrating with respect to the other factor and obtain

$$\mathrm{e}\,\{\mathbf{w}(P), L(P,Q)\} = -\iint_{\mathsf{S}} \mathfrak{T}(\mathbf{w}(P)) \cdot L(P,Q)\, d\sigma_P. \tag{5.16}$$

Subtracting (5.16) from (5.10) we obtain the second Betti identity

$$\mathbf{w}(Q) = \frac{1}{4\pi}\iint_{\mathsf{S}} \Big(\mathbf{w}(P)\cdot \mathfrak{T}(L(P,Q)) - \mathfrak{T}(\mathbf{w}(P))\cdot L(P,Q)\Big)\, d\sigma_P \tag{5.17}$$

which expresses every solution of (4.8) in terms of its boundary values and its derivatives on the boundary.

6. Fundamental solutions: In general we shall call a tensor field $M(P,Q)$ a *fundamental tensor field* with respect to (4.8) if

$$H(P,Q) = M(P,Q) - L(P,Q) \tag{6.1}$$

is a tensor field which is continuously differentiable in the closed region $\mathsf{B}+\mathsf{S}$ and if each row is a solution vector of (4.8). The importance of a fundamental tensor field lies in the fact that the identities (5.10), (5.16), and (5.17) hold for it as for the special fundamental field $L(P,Q)$. Certain distinguished fundamental tensor fields will now be introduced which will enable us to solve the various boundary value problems discussed in Section 4. We shall call these particular fundamental tensor fields the fundamental solutions.

(a) Green's tensor field. The Green's tensor field is a fundamental tensor field $G(P,Q) = (g_{ik}(P,Q))$ with the boundary condition

$$G(P,Q) = 0 \quad \text{for} \quad P \in \mathsf{S}, \quad Q \in \mathsf{B}. \tag{6.2}$$

The existence of this fundamental solution can be proved for bodies B with sufficiently smooth boundary but we shall not give this proof here.

Applying (5.17), which holds for every fundamental tensor field, to the Green's tensor and using the boundary condition (6.2), we obtain

$$(6.3) \qquad \mathbf{w}(Q) = \frac{1}{4\pi} \iint_S \mathbf{w}(P) \cdot \mathfrak{T}\big(G(P,Q)\big)\, d\sigma_P.$$

This formula permits us to solve the boundary value problem (A) *for* (4.8), i. e. to determine a solution $\mathbf{w}$ in terms of its boundary values.

It is easily seen that the Green's tensor $G(P,Q)$ is symmetric in its argument points. To show this we need only apply Betti's second identity to the tensor fields $G(P,Q)$ and $G(P,R)$ and observe the vanishing of these tensor fields on the boundary.

b) Robin's tensor field. The Robin's tensor field is a fundamental tensor field $R(P,Q) = (r_{ik}(P,Q))$ with the boundary condition

$$(6.4) \qquad \mathfrak{T}\big(R(P,Q)\big) - \Pi(P)\, R(P,Q) = 0; \qquad P \in \mathsf{S}, \qquad Q \in \mathsf{B}$$

where $\Pi(P)$ is a positive definite symmetric matrix which is a continuously differentiable function of P on S. The differentiations implied by $\mathfrak{T}$ refer in (6.4) to the variable P.

If we apply Betti's second identity (5.17) with an arbitrary solution $\mathbf{w}(P)$ of (4.8) and the Robin's tensor field, we find, using (6.4),

$$(6.5) \qquad \mathbf{w}(Q) = \frac{1}{4\pi} \iint_S \Big(\mathbf{w}(P)\, \Pi(P) - \mathfrak{T}\big(\mathbf{w}(P)\big)\Big) R(P,Q)\, d\sigma_P.$$

This formula permits us to express a solution field of (4.8) *in terms of the combination* $\mathbf{b}(P) = \mathfrak{T}(\mathbf{w}(P)) - \Pi(P)\,\mathbf{w}(P)$ *on the boundary* and to solve the boundary value problem B discussed in Section 4. It can be shown that Robin's tensor is symmetric in its argument points.

c) Neumann's tensor field. Neumann's tensor field is a fundamental tensor field $N(P,Q) = (n_{ik}(P,Q))$ for which the following boundary condition holds:

$$(6.6) \qquad \mathfrak{T}(\mathbf{N}_j(P,Q)) = \mathbf{a}_j(Q) + \mathbf{b}_j(Q) \times \mathbf{r}; \qquad P \in \mathsf{S}, \qquad Q \in \mathsf{B}, \qquad \mathbf{r} = (x_1, x_2, x_3)$$

where $\mathbf{N}_j$ denotes the j-th row of the Neumann's tensor.

In order to understand the meaning of the boundary condition (6.6), it should be remembered that vector fields $\mathbf{u} = \mathbf{a} + \mathbf{b} \times \mathbf{r}$ are the trivial solutions of the differential equation (4.8) and have, moreover, a vanishing energy integral $e\{\mathbf{u}, \mathbf{u}\}$. Thus, our requirement (6.6) is that the linear vector function $\mathfrak{T}\big(N(P,Q)\big)$ be 0 modulo such trivial solutions.

Neumann's function itself is not determined uniquely by the boundary condition (6.6), in fact, if we add to any permissible Neumann's tensor field a tensor field whose rows are each of the form $\mathbf{a}_j(Q) + \mathbf{b}_j(Q) \times \mathbf{r}$, we do not affect the value of $\mathfrak{T}(N)$. We make use of this arbitrariness in order to impose the following two additional conditions on the Neumann's tensor field:

$$\text{(6.7)} \quad \iint_S N(P,Q)\, d\sigma_P = 0; \qquad \iint_S \mathbf{N}_j(P,Q) \times \mathbf{r}\, d\sigma_P = 0, \qquad (j = 1, 2, 3).$$

Under this normalization, it can be shown in the usual way that the Neumann tensor is symmetric.

If $\mathbf{w}(P)$ is an arbitrary solution of (4.8), Betti's identity (5.17) and the boundary behavior (6.6) of the Neumann tensor lead to the equation

$$\text{(6.8)} \quad w_j(Q) = -\frac{1}{4\pi} \iint_S \mathfrak{T}(\mathbf{w}(P)) \cdot \mathbf{N}_j(P,Q)\, d\sigma_P + \frac{\mathbf{a}_j(Q)}{4\pi} \cdot \iint_S \mathbf{w}(P)\, d\sigma_P - \frac{\mathbf{b}_j(Q)}{4\pi} \cdot \iint_S \mathbf{w}(P) \times \mathbf{r}\, d\sigma_P.$$

Let us remark that a vector field $\mathbf{w}(Q)$ which satisfies (4.8) and for which $\mathfrak{T}(\mathbf{w})$ is prescribed on the boundary is only determined up to an additional rigid motion $\mathbf{u} = \mathbf{a} + \mathbf{b} \times \mathbf{r}$. We may, therefore, always assume that the vector field $\mathbf{w}(P)$ is normalized by the conditions

$$\text{(6.9)} \quad \iint_S \mathbf{w}(P)\, d\sigma_P = 0; \qquad \iint_S \mathbf{w}(P) \times \mathbf{r}\, d\sigma_P = 0.$$

For vector fields with this normalization, the identity (6.8) simplifies to

$$\text{(6.8 a)} \quad \mathbf{w}(Q) = -\frac{1}{4\pi} \iint_S \mathfrak{T}(\mathbf{w}(P)) \cdot N(P,Q)\, d\sigma_P.$$

This formula gives the solution of the boundary value problem (C), i. e., to express a solution of (4.8) in terms of its $\mathfrak{T}$ vector on S.

We can create regular tensor fields by the subtraction of two fundamental tensor fields and we shall derive various properties of these difference tensors. Let us define the symmetric tensor

$$\text{(6.10)} \quad K(P,Q) = \frac{1}{4\pi}\left(N(P,Q) - G(P,Q)\right).$$

Each row and column of this tensor is a solution field of (4.8). If $\mathbf{w}(P)$ is another solution of (4.8) with normalization (6.9), we have by (4.5)

$$\text{(6.11)} \qquad \mathrm{e}\,\{\mathbf{w}(P), K(P,Q)\} = -\frac{1}{4\pi}\iint_{S} \mathfrak{T}(\mathbf{w}(P)) \cdot K(P,Q)\, d\sigma_P.$$

Because of the vanishing of G on S and because of (6.8a), we have

$$\text{(6.12)} \qquad \mathrm{e}\,\{\mathbf{w}(P), K(P,Q)\} = \mathbf{w}(Q).$$

That is, *the regular tensor field* K *has the property of reproducing every normalized solution of* (4.8) *under the Dirichlet product* (4.3).

Consider next the regular tensor field

$$\text{(6.13)} \qquad T(P,Q) = \frac{1}{4\pi}\big(R(P,Q) - G(P,Q)\big).$$

Applying (4.5), with respect to a solution field $\mathbf{w}(P)$ (not necessarily normalized) and $T(P,Q)$ we find

$$\text{(6.14)} \qquad \mathrm{e}\,\{\mathbf{w}(P), T(P,Q)\} = -\frac{1}{4\pi}\iint_{S} T(P,Q)\, \mathfrak{T}(\mathbf{w}(P))\, d\sigma_P = -\frac{1}{4\pi}\iint_{S} R(P,Q)\, \mathfrak{T}(\mathbf{w}(P))\, d\sigma_P.$$

By virtue of (6.5) we can write this result as follows:

$$\text{(6.15)} \qquad \mathrm{e}\,\{\mathbf{w}(P), T(P,Q)\} + \frac{1}{4\pi}\iint_{S} \mathbf{w}(P) \cdot (\Pi(P)\, R(P,Q))\, d\sigma_P = \mathbf{w}(Q).$$

This result suggests the introduction of a new metric in the linear space of all vector fields which are continuously differentiable in the closed region $B + S$. We define the bilinear functional

$$\text{(6.16)} \qquad \mathrm{d}\,\{\mathbf{u}, \mathbf{v}\} = \frac{1}{4\pi}\iint_{S} \mathbf{u}(P) \cdot (\Pi(P)\, \mathbf{v}(P))\, d\sigma_P$$

which is positive definite and symmetric. Let

$$\text{(6.17)} \qquad \mathrm{e}_{\Pi}\,\{\mathbf{u}, \mathbf{v}\} = \mathrm{e}\,\{\mathbf{u}, \mathbf{v}\} + \mathrm{d}\,\{\mathbf{u}, \mathbf{v}\}.$$

Formula (6.15) can then be interpreted as

$$\text{(6.15 a)} \qquad \mathrm{e}_{\Pi}\,\{\mathbf{w}(P), T(P,Q)\} = \mathbf{w}(Q).$$

For each given positive definite and symmetric tensor field $\Pi(P)$, we can thus define a metric $e_\Pi\{\mathbf{u}, \mathbf{v}\}$ in the space of the solutions of (4.8) which are continuously differentiable in $\mathsf{B} + \mathsf{S}$. The closure of this linear space forms a Hilbert space H_Π in which $T(P, Q)$ is the reproducing kernel.

For many applications of the theory of Hilbert spaces it is convenient to express the Dirichlet integral $e\{\mathbf{u}, \mathbf{v}\}$ as an integral over the interior of B without referring to the boundary S which occurs in the definition of $d\{\mathbf{u}, \mathbf{v}\}$. For this purpose we introduce three tensor fields $\Pi_j(P)$ ($j = 1, 2, 3$) which are continuously differentiable in the region $\mathsf{B} + \mathsf{S}$ and on S satisfy the equation

$$\sum_{j=1}^{3} \Pi_j(P) \cos(\boldsymbol{\nu}, \mathbf{x}_j) = -\Pi(P). \tag{6.18}$$

Then, we have by Green's theorem

$$d\{\mathbf{u}, \mathbf{v}\} = \frac{1}{4\pi} \iiint_{\mathsf{B}} \sum_{j=1}^{3} \frac{\partial}{\partial x_j} (\mathbf{u} \cdot \Pi_j \mathbf{v})\, d\tau \tag{6.19}$$

and have expressed d in terms of a volume integral.

If we wish to deal in a similar way with the $\boldsymbol{K}$ tensor field, we must consider the linear space of all solutions of (4.8) which are continuously differentiable in $\mathsf{B} + \mathsf{S}$ and satisfy the normalization (6.9). In this space, we use the metric $e\{\mathbf{u}, \mathbf{v}\}$ and obtain as the closure of this metric space the Hilbert space H_0. $K(P, Q)$ is the reproducing kernel tensor of H_0.

Fredholm (F 4), Tedone (T 2).

7. Construction of the fundamental solutions in terms of orthonormal solution fields: Let us consider the Hilbert space H_Π of solutions of (4.8). It is always possible to find a complete orthonormal system of vectors $\mathbf{w}^{(i)}(P)$ in H_Π such that every element $\mathbf{w}(P)$ of H_Π can be represented in the form

$$\mathbf{w}(P) = \sum_{i=1}^{\infty} \lambda_i \mathbf{w}^{(i)}(P) \tag{7.1}$$

where

$$\lambda_i = e_\Pi\{\mathbf{w}, \mathbf{w}^{(i)}\}. \tag{7.2}$$

From the identity

$$\mathbf{w}(Q) = e_\Pi\{\mathbf{w}(P), T(P, Q)\} \tag{7.3}$$

we obtain by the Schwarz inequality which obviously holds for the e_{Π} metric,

$$|\mathbf{w}(Q)|^2 \leqslant e_{\Pi}\{\mathbf{w}(P), \mathbf{w}(P)\} \sum_{j=1}^{3} e_{\Pi}\{\mathbf{T}_j(P,Q), \mathbf{T}_j(P,Q)\}, \tag{7.4}$$

where $\mathbf{T}_j$ is the j-th row of the tensor $\boldsymbol{T}$. Thus, we have a uniform estimate for the absolute value of each vector $\mathbf{w}(P)$ at all points of a closed subdomain of **B** in terms of its norm $e_{\Pi}\{\mathbf{w}, \mathbf{w}\}$. We make the following application of this result. If a sequence of elements $\mathbf{w}^{(\nu)}(P)$ converges in H_{Π} to a limit $\mathbf{w}(P)$, the $\mathbf{w}^{(\nu)}(P)$ will converge uniformly (pointwise) in each closed subdomain of **B**. In other words (7.4) implies that pointwise convergence follows from convergence in norm. In particular, we see that the series development (7.1) converges uniformly in each closed subdomain of **B**.

Let us develop each row of the kernel tensor $\boldsymbol{T}(P,Q)$ in a series (7.1). By virtue of (7.2) and the reproducing property of the $\boldsymbol{T}$ kernel we clearly have

$$\boldsymbol{T} \equiv (T_{ik}(P,Q)) = \left(\sum_{\nu=1}^{\infty} w_i^{(\nu)}(P)\, w_k^{(\nu)}(Q) \right). \tag{7.5}$$

Thus, we are able to construct the kernel $\boldsymbol{T}$ if a complete orthonormal set of solution vectors is known. In Part B we shall discuss general methods for obtaining complete sets of solutions in the case of a special partial differential equation and those considerations can be easily generalized so as to apply to the present case.

In an analogous way the kernel tensor $\boldsymbol{K}(P,Q)$ can be constructed from a complete orthonormal system in H_0. In this case the kernel will also have the normalization (6.9).

We observe that the boundary values of the kernels $\boldsymbol{T}(P,Q)$ and $\boldsymbol{K}(P,Q)$ are the tensor fields $\boldsymbol{R}(P,Q)$ and $\boldsymbol{N}(P,Q)$, respectively. Thus, if we are able to sum the kernel tensors on the boundary **S**, we shall have the values of the tensor fields which are necessary for the representations (6.5) and (6.8a) of the boundary value problems (B) and (C). For the solution of the first boundary value problem we make the following remark. Let us prescribe an arbitrary vector field $\mathbf{v}(P)$ which is continuously differentiable in $\mathbf{B}+\mathbf{S}$ and has on **S** the normalization (6.9). It is always possible to find a solution field of (4.8) which has the same boundary values as the vector field $\mathbf{v}(P)$. In fact, let

$$\mathbf{w}(Q) = e\{\mathbf{v}(P), \boldsymbol{K}(P,Q)\}. \tag{7.6}$$

This obviously represents a solution of (4.8). By (4.5) we have

$$\mathbf{w}(Q) = -\iint_{S} \mathbf{v}(P) \cdot \mathfrak{T}\big(K(P,Q)\big)\, d\sigma_P \tag{7.7}$$

and using (6.10) and (6.6) we find

$$w_j(Q) = -\frac{1}{4\pi}\iint_{S} \mathbf{v}(P) \cdot \big(\mathbf{a}_j(Q) + \mathbf{b}_j(Q) \times \mathbf{r}\big)\, d\sigma_P + \tag{7.8}$$

$$+ \frac{1}{4\pi}\iint_{S} \mathbf{v}(P) \cdot \mathfrak{T}\big(\mathbf{G}_j(P,Q)\big)\, d\sigma_P.$$

Because of the normalization (6.9) we may write

$$\mathbf{w}(Q) = \frac{1}{4\pi}\iint_{S} \mathbf{v}(P) \cdot \mathfrak{T}\big(\mathbf{G}(P,Q)\big)\, d\sigma_P \tag{7.8 a}$$

and from (6.3) we see that the right-hand side is a solution of (4.8) possessing the boundary values $\mathbf{v}(P)$. Thus we have proved that *Dirichlet multiplication with the kernel tensor* $\boldsymbol{K}(P, Q)$ *transforms an arbitrary vector field* $\mathbf{v}(P)$ *into a solution with the same boundary values.*

For the sake of completeness we shall show how the fundamental solutions can themselves be obtained from the kernel tensors by means of simple Dirichlet integrals. We start from the fact that

$$\mathrm{e}_{II}\{\mathbf{w}(P), \boldsymbol{G}(P,Q)\} = 0 \tag{7.9}$$

for every solution $\mathbf{w}(P)$ of (4.8) which has continuous derivatives in $\mathsf{B} + \mathsf{S}$. This is an immediate consequence of (5.16), (6.16), and (6.17). Next consider the identity

$$\mathrm{e}_{II}\{\boldsymbol{T}(P,Q), \boldsymbol{G}(P,O) - \boldsymbol{L}(P,O)\} = \boldsymbol{G}(Q,O) - \boldsymbol{L}(Q,O); \tag{7.10}$$

on the other hand, we have from (7.9)

$$\mathrm{e}_{II}\{\boldsymbol{T}(P,Q), \boldsymbol{G}(P,O)\} = 0. \tag{7.9 a}$$

Thus, finally

$$\boldsymbol{G}(Q,O) = \boldsymbol{L}(Q,O) - \mathrm{e}_{II}\{\boldsymbol{T}(P,Q), \boldsymbol{L}(P,O)\}. \tag{7.11}$$

Since all terms on the right-hand side are known once the reproducing kernel T has been calculated, we have expressed the Green's tensor field in terms of known quantities. From (6.13) we also derive the identity

$$R(Q,O) = 4\pi T(Q,O) + L(Q,O) - e_{\Pi}\{T(P,Q), L(P,O)\}. \tag{7.12}$$

Working in the same fashion in H_0 instead of in H_{Π} we obtain a corresponding formula for $N(P,Q)$.

Bergman (B 3).

8. Particular solutions: In order to solve the boundary value problems considered, by means of orthonormal vectors, we must be able to construct a sufficiently large set of particular solutions of the differential equation

$$\Delta \mathbf{u} + a \operatorname{grad} \operatorname{div} \mathbf{u} = 0. \tag{8.1}$$

Let us denote

$$\gamma = \operatorname{div} \mathbf{u}. \tag{8.2}$$

We then obtain from (8.1) by taking the divergence and observing that Δ commutes with the other differential operators occurring,

$$\Delta \gamma = 0. \tag{8.3}$$

Taking the Laplacian of (8.1) we derive, in view of (8.3),

$$\Delta \Delta \mathbf{u} = 0. \tag{8.4}$$

Thus, every component of a solution field of (8.1) is a biharmonic function.

In order to derive solutions of (8.1) we shall first give a general method for constructing solutions of the biharmonic equation (8.4). Let $\varphi(P)$ and $\psi(P)$ be two arbitrary harmonic functions and $r^2 = \sum_{i=1}^{3} x_i^2$, then

$$f(P) = r^2 \varphi(P) + \psi(P) \tag{8.5}$$

will be a solution of the biharmonic equation. In fact,

$$\Delta f(P) = 6\varphi(P) + 4 \sum_{i=1}^{3} x_i \frac{\partial \varphi(P)}{\partial x_i}. \tag{8.6}$$

It is well known that the expression

$$\sum_{i=1}^{3} x_i \frac{\partial \varphi}{\partial x_i} = r \frac{\partial \varphi}{\partial r} \tag{8.7}$$

is a harmonic function if φ is harmonic; this can be verified by direct differentiation. Thus, it is clear that

$$\Delta \Delta f(P) = 0. \tag{8.8}$$

We shall now show that every biharmonic function can be expressed in the form (8.5). Given a biharmonic $f(P)$, consider its Laplacian

$$\Delta f(P) = D(P), \tag{8.9}$$

which is, by definition, a harmonic function. If we set up $f(P)$ in the form (8.5) we obtain from (8.6) the differential equation

$$6\varphi + 4r\frac{\partial \varphi}{\partial r} = D, \tag{8.10}$$

which has the particular integral

$$\varphi(P) = \frac{r^{-3/2}}{4} \int_0^r r^{1/2} D\, dr \tag{8.11}$$

where the integration is to be taken along a fixed radius vector.

We must show that the solution φ thus obtained is a harmonic function. Taking this for granted for the moment, we observe that $f(P) - r^2 \varphi(P) = \psi(P)$ is a harmonic function, and the representation (8.5) is proved.

In order to prove the harmonicity of φ we use the following lemma. Let $D(P)$ be a harmonic function. Then the function

$$\Phi(P) = r^{-k} \int_0^r r^{k-1} D\, dr, \qquad k > 0 \tag{8.12}$$

will also be harmonic. The harmonicity of φ follows from this lemma by selecting $k = 3/2$.

To prove the lemma, it is sufficient to restrict ourselves to homogeneous harmonic polynomials, i. e., to harmonic functions which can be written in the form

$$H(P) = r^n h(\alpha, \beta) \tag{8.13}$$

where r, α, β are the spherical coordinates. In fact, every harmonic function may be developed into spherical harmonics which are precisely of this form. We now observe the identity

$$r^{-k} \int_0^r r^{k-1} H\, dr = \frac{H}{n+k} \tag{8.14}$$

which proves the result.

We have obtained the general representation (8.5) of biharmonic functions in terms of harmonic functions. Our next aim is a representation formula for the solutions of the differential equation (8.1). We have the additional requirement that its divergence must also be a harmonic function. We shall show that we can obtain an infinite set of solutions of (8.1) of the form

$$\mathbf{u}(P) = r^2 \operatorname{grad} \varphi(P) + \mathbf{h}(P) \tag{8.15}$$

where $\varphi(P)$ is a harmonic function and $\mathbf{h}(P)$ is a vector with harmonic components. It is already clear from the above that each component of $\mathbf{u}$ is biharmonic. Let us now compute

$$\operatorname{div} \mathbf{u} = \operatorname{div} \mathbf{h} + 2r \frac{\partial \varphi}{\partial r} \tag{8.16}$$

and

$$\Delta \mathbf{u} = 6 \operatorname{grad} \varphi + 4 \left(\sum_{j=1}^{3} x_j \operatorname{grad} \frac{\partial \varphi}{\partial x_j} \right) = 2 \operatorname{grad} \varphi + 4 \operatorname{grad} \left(r \frac{\partial \varphi}{\partial r} \right). \tag{8.17}$$

Thus, (8.1) takes the form

$$2 \operatorname{grad} \varphi + 4 \operatorname{grad} \left(r \frac{\partial \varphi}{\partial r} \right) + \alpha \operatorname{grad} \operatorname{div} \mathbf{h} + 2\alpha \operatorname{grad} \left(r \frac{\partial \varphi}{\partial r} \right) = 0. \tag{8.18}$$

We integrate this equation and obtain

$$2\varphi + (4 + 2\alpha) \left(r \frac{\partial \varphi}{\partial r} \right) = -\alpha \operatorname{div} \mathbf{h} + \text{const.} = D(P). \tag{8.19}$$

We observe that $D(P)$ is a harmonic function. We can now express φ in terms of D by the formula

$$\varphi = \frac{r^{-\frac{1}{2+\alpha}}}{4 + 2\alpha} \int_0^r r^{\frac{1}{2+\alpha} - 1} D \, dr. \tag{8.20}$$

In view of (8.12), φ will be a harmonic function $\left(k = \dfrac{1}{2 + \alpha} \right)$.

It is now possible to construct an infinite set of solutions of (8.1). Starting with an arbitrary vector $\mathbf{h}$ with harmonic components, we derive by (8.19) and (8.20) the harmonic function φ. The vector field (8.15) will then be a solution of (8.1). Conversely, it can be shown that every solution of (8.1) can be represented in the form (8.15).

We have thus reduced the theory of the solutions of (8.1) to the theory of harmonic functions and can construct every solution in terms of harmonic functions. This enables us to obtain a complete set of solutions for the differential equation considered. We shall not enter here into the details of this procedure.

Formulas giving general solutions of (8.1) were first obtained by Maxwell, Morera, and Boussinesq. These formulas are, however, comparatively complicated. Much later, Galerkin gave a solution in the form

$$\mathbf{u} = \Delta \mathbf{\Phi} - \frac{1}{2(1-\sigma)} \operatorname{grad} \operatorname{div} \mathbf{\Phi} \tag{8.21}$$

where $\mathbf{\Phi}$ is an arbitrary biharmonic vector. Papkovitch and Neuber gave a solution in the form

$$\mathbf{u} = \mathbf{U} + \frac{1}{4(1-\sigma)} \operatorname{grad} (\mathbf{U} \cdot \mathbf{r} - \varphi) \tag{8.22}$$

where $\mathbf{U}$ is an arbitrary harmonic vector, and φ is an arbitrary harmonic function.

Almansi (A 1), Galerkin (G 1), (G 2), Love [43], Neuber (N 2), Papkovitch (P 1), Shapiro (S 9).

9. The theory of thin plates: The developments of Sections 1—8 for the three-dimensional theory of elasticity gave us a complete answer to various boundary value problems occurring there in terms of fundamental tensor fields. However, the formulas in which these tensor fields occur are rather involved, and it is therefore of interest to consider those special cases where the problem has been reduced to a boundary value problem for a scalar function. In Sections 9, 10, and 11 we shall consider two problems in which the equations of elastic equilibrium are reduced to a single fourth order partial differential equation. In the present and following sections, we consider the theory of the bending of thin plates, while in Section 11 we consider elastic equilibrium under the action of plane stresses. We shall see that both cases are reducible to the solution of the biharmonic equation, but under different boundary conditions. In order to illustrate several different methods for treating the biharmonic equation, we shall employ real variables in the first case, while in the second case, we shall use the theory of complex analytic functions.

By a thin plate we shall mean a cylinder whose height is very small compared to its cross section D. We shall assume that D is finite and is bounded by a smooth curve C. The height of the plate will be denoted by h, the upper, lower, and middle surfaces lying in the planes $x_3 = h/2, -h/2, 0,$

respectively. The plate is assumed to be deformed by exterior forces $q(x_1, x_2)$ acting parallel to the x_3-axis and of forces acting on the lateral surface of the plate. We assume that each point of the middle plane is deformed in the direction of the x_3 axis, and that these deflections are small compared to the thickness of the plate. In addition, we shall make the following assumptions as to the behavior of the plate under the deformation. (a) Every straight line segment perpendicular to the middle plane before deformation goes into a straight line segment of equal length perpendicular to the deformed middle plane. (b) The component F_{33} of the stress tensor vanishes, while the squares of the components F_{13} and F_{23} can be neglected.

We shall designate the deflection of the middle plane in the direction of the x_3 axis by $w(x_1, x_2) = u_3(x_1, x_2, 0)$. Using our assumption (a), it follows that in this simplified theory we have

$$u_k = -\frac{\partial w}{\partial x_k} x_3, \qquad (k = 1, 2). \tag{9.1}$$

Thus, from (1.2), it follows that the components e_{ik} $(k = 1, 2)$ of the strain tensor are given by

$$e_{ik} = -x_3 \frac{\partial^2 w}{\partial x_i \, \partial x_k}, \qquad (i, k = 1, 2). \tag{9.2}$$

From assumption (b), and using (3.16) and (3.17) with $i = k = 3$, we find immediately

$$e_{33} = \frac{\lambda}{\lambda + 2\mu} x_3 \Delta w; \qquad \Delta \equiv \frac{\partial^2}{\partial x_1^2} + \frac{\partial^2}{\partial x_2^2}; \tag{9.3}$$

on the other hand, using (3.17) with $i, k = 1, 2$ we obtain

$$F_{kk} = 4\mu \left(\frac{\lambda + \mu}{\lambda + 2\mu}\right) x_3 \left(\frac{\partial^2 w}{\partial x_k^2} + \sigma \frac{\partial^2 w}{\partial x^2_{3-k}}\right), \qquad (k = 1, 2), \tag{9.4 a}$$

$$F_{12} = 2\mu x_3 \frac{\partial^2 w}{\partial x_1 \, \partial x_2}. \tag{9.4 b}$$

It is useful in many applications to note that the stresses F_{ik}, $(i, k = 1, 2)$ are of opposite sign at corresponding points on the upper and lower surfaces of the plate.

We next introduce a matrix $((M_{ik}))$, $(i, k = 1, 2)$, necessary for calculating the moments of the stresses F_{ik} with respect to axes lying in the plane $x_3 = 0$:

(9.5) $$M_{ik} = \int_{-h/2}^{h/2} x_3 F_{ik}\, dx_3.$$

We have explicitly,

(9.6 a) $$M_{kk} = D\left(\frac{\partial^2 w}{\partial x_k^2} + \sigma \frac{\partial^2 w}{\partial x^2_{3-k}}\right), \qquad (k = 1,2),$$

(9.6 b) $$M_{12} = D\,(1-\sigma)\,\frac{\partial^2 w}{\partial x_1\, \partial x_2}$$

where the constant D is given by

(9.7) $$D = \frac{h^3 \mu}{3}\left(\frac{\lambda+\mu}{\lambda+2\mu}\right).$$

The shearing stresses P_k perpendicular to the middle plane are given by

(9.8) $$P_k = \int_{-h/2}^{h/2} F_{k3}\, dx_3.$$

The equilibrium condition for forces perpendicular to the middle plane can be shown in a way analogous to that of Section 2 to be

(9.9) $$\frac{\partial P_1}{\partial x_1} + \frac{\partial P_2}{\partial x_2} + q = 0.$$

On the other hand, the equilibrium conditions for the moments taken about the x_1 and x_2 axes are, respectively,

(9.10) $$P_k = -\sum_{j=1}^{2} \frac{\partial M_{jk}}{\partial x_j} = -D\,\frac{\partial \Delta w}{\partial x_k}, \qquad (k = 1, 2).$$

Thus, finally, substituting in (9.9) we obtain

(9.11) $$\Delta \Delta w = \frac{q}{D}.$$

The deflection w is thus seen to satisfy the biharmonic equation (9.11).

For the energy stored in the plate by the deformation, we have by (3.15), (3.16), (3.17), (9.2) and hypothesis (b),

(9.12) $$U = \frac{6\,D\,x_3^{\,2}}{h^3}\left((\Delta w)^2 - 2\,(1-\sigma)\left(\frac{\partial^2 w}{\partial x_1^{\,2}}\,\frac{\partial^2 w}{\partial x_2^{\,2}} - \left(\frac{\partial^2 w}{\partial x_1\, \partial x_2}\right)^2\right)\right) =$$

$$= \frac{6\,D\,x_3^{\,2}}{h^3}\left(\left(\frac{\partial^2 w}{\partial x_1^{\,2}}\right)^2 + \left(\frac{\partial^2 w}{\partial x_2^{\,2}}\right)^2 + 2\sigma\left(\frac{\partial^2 w}{\partial x_1^{\,2}}\right)\left(\frac{\partial^2 w}{\partial x_2^{\,2}}\right) + 2\,(1-\sigma)\left(\frac{\partial^2 w}{\partial x_1\, \partial x_2}\right)^2\right)$$

so that the total energy E is given by

$$(9.13) \qquad E = \iint_{D} dx_1\, dx_2 \int_{-h/2}^{h/2} U\, dx_3 = \frac{D}{2}\, \mathrm{p}\, \{w, w\}$$

where

$$(9.14) \qquad \mathrm{p}\, \{u, v\} =$$

$$= \iint_{D} \left(\Delta u \Delta v - (1-\sigma) \left(\frac{\partial^2 u}{\partial x_1{}^2} \frac{\partial^2 v}{\partial x_2{}^2} + \frac{\partial^2 u}{\partial x_2{}^2} \frac{\partial^2 v}{\partial x_1{}^2} - 2 \frac{\partial^2 u}{\partial x_1\, \partial x_2} \frac{\partial^2 v}{\partial x_1\, \partial x_2} \right) \right) dx_1\, dx_2.$$

For the bilinear form $\mathrm{p}\, \{u, v\}$, we obviously have

$$(9.15) \qquad \mathrm{p}\, \{u, v\} = \mathrm{p}\, \{v, u\},$$

while for $-1 \leqslant \sigma \leqslant 1$ we have from (9.12),

$$(9.16) \qquad \mathrm{p}\, \{u, u\} \geqslant 0.$$

Equality can hold in (9.16) only if $\sigma = 1$ and u is harmonic, or if $-1 \leqslant \sigma < 1$ and u has the form $u = a_0 + a_1 x_1 + a_2 x_2$. We might note that in the theory of elasticity $\sigma < 1/2$, but we shall not make this restriction in our study of the biharmonic equation. The relation between the bilinear integral (9.14) and the biharmonic equation

$$(9.17) \qquad \Delta \Delta u = 0$$

is exhibited by the following identity which is valid for all functions u and v which are four times continuously differentiable in D and three times on C:

$$(9.18) \qquad \mathrm{p}\, \{u, v\} = \iint_{D} (\Delta \Delta u)\, v\, dx_1\, dx_2 - \int_{C} \left(M\, (u)\, \frac{\partial v}{\partial n} - V\, (u)\, v \right) ds,$$

where

$$(9.19) \qquad M\, (u) = \sigma \Delta u + (1-\sigma) \sum_{j,k=1}^{2} \cos\, (\mathbf{n}, \mathbf{x}_j)\, \cos\, (\mathbf{n}, \mathbf{x}_k)\, \frac{\partial^2 u}{\partial x_j\, \partial x_k}$$

and

$$(9.20) \qquad V\, (u) = \frac{\partial \Delta u}{\partial n} + (1-\sigma) \frac{\partial}{\partial s} \left(\sum_{j,k=1}^{2} (-1)^k \cos\, (\mathbf{n}, \mathbf{x}_j)\, \cos\, (\mathbf{n}, \mathbf{x}_{3-k})\, \frac{\partial^2 u}{\partial x_j\, \partial x_k} \right)$$

and where $\mathbf{n}$ is the inner normal along C. The functional $M\, (u)$ has a physical interpretation as the bending moment around an axis which is tangent to the boundary curve C. The functional $V(u)$ can be shown equal to

$$V = X_3 - \frac{\partial M}{\partial s} \tag{9.21}$$

where X_3 is the magnitude of the force on the edge of the plate acting in the x_3-direction while M is the moment around an axis which is normal to C.

Bergman (B 3), Frank-Mises [14] vol. 2, Ch. 8, Muskhelishvili [54], Nadai [55], Timoshenko [81].

10. Fundamental solutions of the biharmonic equation: In the present section we shall show how to solve various boundary value problems for the homogeneous biharmonic equation (9.17). One can proceed in the usual manner to obtain solutions of these boundary value problems for the inhomogeneous equation of elasticity (9.11). We distinguish four boundary value problems for the biharmonic equation (9.17). Let $f_i(P)$, $(i = 1, 2)$, be two arbitrarily given functions defined for $P \in \mathrm{C}$. We may require a solution u of (9.17) which on C satisfies any one of the following four pairs of conditions

$$u(P) = f_1(P), \qquad \frac{\partial u(P)}{\partial n} = f_2(P) \tag{10.1 a}$$

$$u(P) = f_1(P), \qquad M(u(P)) = f_2(P) \tag{10.1 b}$$

$$M(u(P)) = f_1(P), \qquad V(u(P)) = f_2(P) \tag{10.1 c}$$

$$\frac{\partial u(P)}{\partial n} = f_1(P), \qquad V(u(P)) = f_2(P). \tag{10.1 d}$$

It should be observed that the boundary value problem (10.1a) is completely independent of σ. Solutions of (9.11) satisfying conditions (10.1a), (10.1b) and (10.1c) with $f_i \equiv 0$ are particularly important in applications inasmuch as they correspond respectively to the built-in edge, the simply-supported edge, and the free edge.

In the event that a solution to the problems (10.1a) — (10.1d) exists, the positive definite character of the energy integral $\mathrm{p}\{u, u\}$ may be employed in order to prove uniqueness theorems. In fact, we show as follows that the solution is determined uniquely in (10.1a) and (10.1b), up to an arbitrary linear function in (10.1c), and up to an arbitrary constant in (10.1d). *If a solution u of the differential equation* (9.17) *satisfies the boundary conditions* $u = 0$, $\dfrac{\partial u}{\partial n} = 0$ *on* C, *then* $u \equiv 0$ *throughout* D. To prove this theorem, apply identity (9.18) with $v = u$. This yields p $\{u, u\} = 0$. Thus, u must be a harmonic function. But it is required to vanish on C and hence $u \equiv 0$ in D.

Let u be a solution of (9.17), *which on the boundary* C *satisfies* $u = 0$, $M(u) = 0$. *Then* $u \equiv 0$ *throughout* D. Application of (9.18) yields p $\{u, u\} = 0$. Thus again, u must be harmonic, and vanishing on C, must be $\equiv 0$.

Let u be a solution of (9.17) *which on* C *satisfies* $M(u) = 0$, $V(u) = 0$. *Then, if* $-1 \leqslant \sigma < 1$, *u must be a linear function while if* $\sigma = 1$, *u is an arbitrary harmonic function.* For in either case p $\{u, u\} = 0$. If $-1 \leqslant \sigma < 1$, u must be linear, and conversely, if u is any linear function, then $M(u) = 0$ and $V(u) = 0$. If $\sigma = 1$, u may be harmonic, and again if u is any harmonic function $M(u) = 0$ and $V(u) = 0$.

Let u be a solution of (9.17) *which on* C *satisfies* $\dfrac{\partial u}{\partial n} = 0$, $V(u) = 0$. *Then u = constant.* For since u must be harmonic, $\dfrac{\partial u}{\partial n} = 0$ implies u = constant. But for an arbitrary constant the condition $V(u) = 0$ will be satisfied on C.

From the symmetry of the integral p $\{u, v\}$, we may obtain from (9.18) the Rayleigh-Green identity

$$\int\!\!\int_{D} ((\Delta\Delta u)\, v - u\,\Delta\Delta v)\, dx_1\, dx_2 = \tag{10.2}$$

$$= \int_{C} \left(M(u) \frac{\partial v}{\partial n} - V(u)\, v - M(v) \frac{\partial u}{\partial n} + V(v)\, u \right) ds$$

which holds for all functions u and v which are four times continuousl- differentiable in D and three times on C. We next introduce a fundament... singularity for the differential equation (9.17). Let

$$S(P, Q) = r^2 \log r, \quad r^2 = (x_1 - y_1)^2 + (x_2 - y_2)^2, \quad P = (x_1, x_2), \quad Q = (y_1, y_2). \tag{10.3}$$

Considered as a function of each of its argument points, S is regular except for $P = Q$. Moreover, as can be established by direct differentiation

$$\Delta S = 4(\log r + 1); \qquad \Delta\Delta S = 0, \qquad P \neq Q. \tag{10.4}$$

The identity (10.2) and the fundamental singularity S enable us to represent a solution u of (9.17) in terms of the boundary data u, $\frac{\partial u}{\partial n}$, $V(u)$, and $M(u)$. We shall show that for all biharmonic functions u for which (10.2) is applicable we have

$$(10.5)\qquad u(Q) = \frac{1}{8\pi}\int_{\mathsf{C}}\Big(-M_P\big(u(P)\big)\frac{\partial S(P,Q)}{\partial n_P} + V_P\big(u(P)\big)S(P,Q) + + M_P\big((S(P,Q)\big)\frac{\partial u(P)}{\partial n_P} - V_P\big(S(P,Q)\big)u(P)\Big)ds_P.$$

We delete a small circle of radius r and center at Q from the domain D, designating the circumference by C_r. From (9.17) and (10.2) with $v = S$, we obtain

$$(10.6)\qquad \int_{\mathsf{C}+\mathsf{C}_r}\Big(-M(u)\frac{\partial S}{\partial n} + V(u)S + M(S)\frac{\partial u}{\partial n} - V(S)u\Big)ds = 0.$$

It may now be verified from (10.3) that $\frac{\partial^2 S}{\partial x_i\,\partial x_j} = 2(x_i - y_i)(x_j - y_j)/r^2$ if $i \neq j$ and hence it follows by (9.19) and (9.20) that

$$(10.7)\qquad \lim_{r\to 0}\int_{\mathsf{C}_r} V(S)\,u\,ds = 8\pi u(Q)$$

while the limits of the integrals around C_r of the other terms of (10.6) are each zero.

In general, we shall call a solution $G(P,Q)$ a *fundamental solution* of the biharmonic equation in D if $G(P,Q) + S(P,Q)$ is a regular solution of (9.17) in D when considered either as a function of P or Q. It is clear that the formula (10.5) holds when $S(P,Q)$ is replaced by any fundamental solution.

It may be shown that if D possesses a sufficiently smooth boundary, there exists a fundamental solution $G(P,Q)$ which satisfies the following boundary conditions

$$(10.8)\qquad G(P,Q) = 0;\qquad \frac{\partial G(P,Q)}{\partial n_P} = 0;\qquad P\in\mathsf{C},\qquad Q\in\mathsf{D}.$$

The function G may be proven symmetric in the usual way. Substituting (10.8) in (10.5), we find, as a representation of the first boundary value problem above,

$$(10.9)\qquad u(Q) = \frac{1}{8\pi}\int_C \left(M_P\left(G(P,Q)\right)\frac{\partial u(P)}{\partial n} - V_P\left(G(P,Q)\right)u(P)\right) ds_P.$$

For the unit circle, it is easily shown that the Green's function is given by

$$(10.10)\qquad G(z_1, z_2) = |z_1 - z_2|^2 \log\left|\frac{\bar{z}_1 z_2 - 1}{z_1 - z_2}\right| - \frac{1}{2}(|z_1|^2 - 1)(|z_2|^2 - 1).$$

We consider next only the case $-1 \leqslant \sigma < 1$. We shall assume that there exists a fundamental solution $N(P, Q)$ which behaves like the Neumann's function in the harmonic case. We shall require that

$$(10.11)\qquad M_P(N(P,Q)) = 0, \qquad V_P\left(N(P,Q)\right) = a_0(Q) + a_1(Q)\,x_1 + a_2(Q)\,x_2;$$
$$P \in \mathsf{C}, \qquad Q \in \mathsf{D}.$$

The functions $a_i(Q)$ cannot be chosen arbitrarily, but must be determined as follows. If in (10.5), we select $S = N$, $u = 1, x_1, x_2$ then, using (10.11) we obtain

$$-8\pi y_i = \int_C V_P\left(N(P,Q)\right) x_i\, ds_P = \sum_{k=0}^{2} a_k(Q) \int_C x_i x_k\, ds, \qquad (i = 0, 1, 2),$$

(10.12)

where we have written $x_0 = y_0 \equiv 1$. In view of the fact that the functions x_i $(i = 0, 1, 2)$ are independent, it follows that the determinant

$$\left|\int_C x_i x_k\, ds\right| \neq 0$$

so that the system (10.12) may be solved for $a_i(Q)$ $(i = 0, 1, 2)$. If a fundamental solution $N(P, Q)$ exists with the properties (10.11) it will be determined only up to a linear function. It will be convenient to assume that N has been normalized by the conditions

$$(10.13)\qquad \int_C x_i N(P,Q)\, ds_P = 0, \qquad (i = 0, 1, 2).$$

This normalization guarantees the symmetry of $N(P, Q)$ with respect to its argument points. Utilizing (10.5) and (10.11) we obtain the representation

$$(10.14)\qquad u(Q) = \frac{1}{8\pi}\int_C \left(M_P\left(u(P)\right)\frac{\partial N(P,Q)}{\partial n_P} + V_P\left(u(P)\right)N(P,Q)\right) ds_P +$$
$$+ \frac{1}{8\pi}\sum_{i=0}^{2} a_i(Q)\int_C x_i\, u(P)\, ds_P.$$

If, therefore, we consider a normalized class Γ of solutions u such that

(10.15) $$\int_C x_i u(P)\, ds_P = 0, \qquad (i = 0, 1, 2),$$

then solutions of the class Γ possess a representation of the form

(10.17) $$u(Q) = \frac{1}{8\pi} \int_C \left(M_P(u) \frac{\partial [N(P,Q) - G(P,Q)]}{\partial n_P} + V_P(u) [N(P,Q) - G(P,Q)] \right) ds_P.$$

Let us therefore introduce a kernel $K(P, Q)$ by

(10.18) $$K(P,Q) = \frac{1}{8\pi} \big(N(P,Q) - G(P,Q)\big).$$

The kernel $K(P, Q)$ is a regular solution in D in each argument point, is symmetric, and inasmuch as G obviously satisfies conditions (10.15), is in Γ. We may also write (10.17) in the form

$$u(Q) = \int_C \left(-M(u) \frac{\partial K(P,Q)}{\partial n_P} + V(u) K(P, Q) \right) ds_P, \qquad u \equiv u(P) \in \Gamma,$$

(10.19)

thus yielding a representation of the third boundary value problem. In view of (9.18), equation (10.19) may be written as

(10.20) $$u(Q) = \mathrm{p}\,\{u(P), K(P,Q)\}, \qquad u \in \Gamma,$$

so that in the p-metric, the kernel K possesses a reproducing property for all $u \in \Gamma$. Its symmetry and membership in Γ mean, moreover, that it is uniquely characterized by (10.20). In view of (10.2), we may also write

$$u(Q) = \int_C \left(V_P\big(K(P,Q)\big) u(P) - M_P\big(K(P,Q)\big) \frac{\partial u(P)}{\partial n} \right) ds_P, \qquad u \in \Gamma,$$

(10.21)

which expresses the solution of the first boundary value problem for all $u \in \Gamma$.

The closure of the linear space Γ forms a Hilbert space Γ^2 for which the reproducing kernel is $K(P, Q)$. For every element $u \in \Gamma^2$, we have the inequality

(10.22) $$|u(P)|^2 \leqslant ||u||\, K(P, P).$$

From the general theory (see also B.II.2), it can be shown that there exists a complete orthonormal basis $\{u_n(P)\}$ for Γ^2 such that every $u \in \Gamma^2$ may be represented in the form

$$(10.23) \qquad u(P) = \sum_{n=0}^{\infty} a_n u_n(P), \qquad a_n = \mathrm{p}\{u, u_n\}.$$

From the convergence in norm of (10.23), and from inequality (10.22), it follows that the series (10.23) converges uniformly and absolutely in every closed subset of D. In particular, the function

$$(10.24) \qquad K_1(P,Q) = \sum_{n=0}^{\infty} u_n(P)\, u_n(Q), \qquad P, Q \in \mathsf{D}$$

converges uniformly and absolutely in every closed subset of D and possesses the reproducing property (10.20) for the space Γ^2. We may therefore identify (10.24) with (10.18).

For the case of a finite simply-connected domain bounded by sufficiently smooth curves, a complete system of solutions for Γ^2 may be obtained as follows. By an argument which is similar to that of (8.5), it may be shown that every biharmonic function u in D may be written in the form

$$(10.25) \qquad u(P) = r^2 \varphi(P) + \psi(P), \qquad r = \overline{OP},$$

where φ and ψ are conveniently chosen functions which are harmonic in D. Conversely, it is easily shown that every u of form (10.25) is biharmonic. We now introduce the set of harmonic functions

$$(10.26) \qquad \varphi_{2n}(P) = \mathrm{Re}\,(z^n), \qquad \varphi_{2n+1}(P) = \mathrm{Im}\,(z^n), \qquad z = x_1 + i\,x_2;$$
$$P = (x_1, x_2) \qquad (n = 0, 1, \ldots)$$

and we then form the set of biharmonic functions

$$(10.27) \qquad u_\nu(P) = r^2 \varphi_n(P) + \varphi_m(P) \qquad (m, n = 0, 1, 2, \ldots,)$$

where the index ν refers to some ordering of the pairs (m, n). The solution u_ν will not, in general, belong to Γ, but upon the addition of an appropriate linear function, the normalizing conditions (10.15) can be met. The completeness of the system (10.27) in Γ^2 may now be shown from the fact that any harmonic function in D can be approximated uniformly in any closed subset of D by a linear combination of the functions φ_n.

A direct computation shows that the inner product p $\{u, v\}$ has, in polar coordinates, the form

$$(10.28) \qquad \mathrm{p}\{u, v\} = \iint_D \Bigg[\Delta u \, \Delta v - (1-\sigma) \bigg[\frac{1}{r} \left(\frac{\partial u}{\partial r} \frac{\partial^2 v}{\partial r^2} + \frac{\partial^2 u}{\partial r^2} \frac{\partial v}{\partial r} \right) + \\ + \frac{1}{r^2} \left(\frac{\partial^2 u}{\partial \theta^2} \frac{\partial^2 v}{\partial r^2} - 2 \frac{\partial^2 u}{\partial r \, \partial \theta} \frac{\partial^2 v}{\partial r \, \partial \theta} + \frac{\partial^2 u}{\partial r^2} \frac{\partial^2 v}{\partial \theta^2} \right) + \\ + \frac{2}{r^3} \left(\frac{\partial u}{\partial \theta} \frac{\partial^2 v}{\partial \theta \, \partial r} + \frac{\partial^2 u}{\partial \theta \, \partial r} \frac{\partial v}{\partial \theta} \right) - \frac{2}{r^4} \frac{\partial u}{\partial \theta} \frac{\partial v}{\partial \theta} \bigg] \Bigg] r \, dr \, d\theta.$$

For the case of the unit circle, a complete orthonormal system in Γ may be obtained by appropriate selection of the constants $\alpha_n, \beta_n, \gamma_n, \delta_n$ in the functions $\alpha_2 r^2 + \beta_2$; $(\alpha_n r^{n+2} + \beta_n r^n) \cos n\theta$, $(\gamma_n r^{n+2} + \delta_n r^n) \sin n\theta$, $n \geqslant 1$. By the use of this complete orthonormal set, the kernel K may be constructed for the unit circle. In this particular case, convergence of (10.24) may be directly established for $P \in \mathrm{C}$, $Q \in \mathrm{D}$ so that (10.19) gives the solution to the third boundary value problem.

We turn now briefly to the case $\sigma = 1$. The first boundary value problem, as remarked, is unaltered, while the problems (10.1b) — (10.1d) may be written in the simplified form:

$$(10.29') \qquad u(P) = f_1(P), \qquad \Delta u(P) = f_2(P); \qquad P \in \mathrm{C}$$

$$(10.29'') \qquad \Delta u(P) = f_1(P), \qquad \frac{\partial \Delta u(P)}{\partial n} = f_2(P); \qquad P \in \mathrm{C}$$

$$(10.29''') \qquad \frac{\partial u(P)}{\partial n} = f_1(P), \qquad \frac{\partial \Delta u(P)}{\partial n} = f_2(P); \qquad P \in \mathrm{C}.$$

We shall show that (10.29') — (10.29''') may be reduced to a boundary value problem for harmonic functions. We consider (10.29') first. The function

$$(10.30) \qquad h(Q) = \Delta u(Q)$$

is, in view of (9.17), harmonic. If we therefore designate by $G^*(P, Q)$ the Green's function of D for Laplace's equation and introduce

$$(10.31) \qquad h(Q) = \int_{\mathrm{C}} \frac{\partial G^*(P, Q)}{\partial n_P} f_2(P) \, ds_P,$$

then $h(Q)$ is harmonic in D and assumes the boundary values $f_2(P)$. Let

$$u_1(Q) = \frac{1}{2\pi} \iint_D h(P) \log r \, dx_1 \, dx_2; \qquad r = \overline{PQ}. \tag{10.32}$$

Then by the Laplace-Poisson equation, we have

$$\Delta u_1(Q) = h(Q). \tag{10.33}$$

Again, determine that function $h_1(P)$ which is harmonic in D and on C assumes the boundary values $f_1(P) - u_1(P)$, and set

$$u(P) = u_1(P) + h_1(P). \tag{10.34}$$

It is now clear that $u(P)$ is that biharmonic function which satisfies the boundary conditions (10.29′).

The case (10.29″) cannot, in general, be solved. For by (10.30), it appears that we must find a harmonic function with given values and values of its normal derivative on the boundary. This problem is overdetermined.

The case (10.29‴) can be treated in a manner similar to (10.29′) by introducing $N^*(P, Q)$, the Neumann's function of D, for Laplace's equation.

It is sometimes of importance to consider complex solutions of the biharmonic equation. In view of the identity $\Delta = 4 \frac{\partial^2}{\partial z \, \partial \bar{z}}$ (cf. II.18.8), it can be shown (see (11.36) — (11.40)) that every solution of the biharmonic equation in D may be represented in the form

$$\varphi(x_1, x_2) = \operatorname{Re}\left(\bar{z} f(z) + g(z)\right), \qquad z = x_1 + i x_2 \tag{10.35}$$

where $f(z)$ and $g(z)$ are analytic functions in D. For the class E^2 of functions of the form

$$F(z, \bar{z}) = \bar{z} f(z) + g(z) \tag{10.36}$$

whose modulus is square integrable over D, we may find a closed and orthonormal system $\{F_n\}$ $n = 1, 2, \ldots$ with respect to the inner product

$$\mathrm{P}\{F_1, F_2\} \equiv \iint_D F_1 \overline{F_2} \, dx_1 \, dx_2. \tag{10.37}$$

Let us define a complex kernel function for the class E^2 by means of

$$K_4(z, \bar{z}; \zeta, \bar{\zeta}) = \sum_{n=0}^{\infty} F_n(z, \bar{z}) \overline{F_n(\zeta, \bar{\zeta})}; \qquad \zeta = y_1 + i y_2. \tag{10.38}$$

It may be shown that the series (10.38) converges absolutely and uniformly in any closed set in D. The kernel K_4 possesses the properties

(10.39) $$K_4(z, \bar{z}; \zeta, \bar{\zeta}) = \overline{K_4(\zeta, \bar{\zeta}; z, \bar{z})}$$

(10.40) $$F(z, \bar{z}) = \mathrm{P}\{F(\zeta, \bar{\zeta}), \overline{K_4(z, \bar{z}; \zeta, \bar{\zeta})}\}.$$

Furthermore, K_4 may be identified with a certain derivative of the Green's function characterized by (10.8). When written in complex notation, the Green's function possesses the characteristic form

(10.41) $$G(P, Q) = |z - \zeta|^2 \log \frac{1}{|z - \zeta|} + H(P, Q)$$

$$\equiv -\frac{1}{2}(z - \zeta)(\bar{z} - \bar{\zeta}) \log (z - \zeta)(\bar{z} - \bar{\zeta}) + H(P, Q)$$

where H is a regular biharmonic function in D. We now define the function

(10.42) $$M(P, Q) = \frac{\partial^4 G}{\partial z^2 \, \partial \bar{\zeta}^2}.$$

It is clear from (10.41) that this process of differentiation destroys the singularity of G, so that M is regular throughout D. Moreover, $M(P, Q) = \overline{M(Q, P)}$. For a given function $F(Q) = F(\zeta, \bar{\zeta}) = \bar{\zeta} f(\zeta) + g(\zeta)$ let us evaluate the integral

(10.43) $$I(P) = \iint_{\mathrm{D}} M(P, Q) F(Q) \, dy_1 \, dy_2.$$

We denote by D_ε the domain D after deleting the small circle $|z - \zeta| < \varepsilon$. Upon integration by parts we obtain,

(10.44) $$\iint_{\mathrm{D}_\varepsilon} \frac{\partial^4 G}{\partial z^2 \, \partial \bar{\zeta}^2} F \, dy_1 \, dy_2 = \frac{1}{2i} \int_C \frac{\partial^3 G}{\partial z^2 \, \partial \bar{\zeta}} F \, d\zeta - \frac{1}{2i} \int_{|z - \zeta| = \varepsilon} \frac{\partial^3 G}{\partial z^2 \, \partial \bar{\zeta}} F \, d\zeta$$

$$- \iint_{\mathrm{D}_\varepsilon} \frac{\partial^3 G}{\partial z^2 \, \partial \bar{\zeta}} f \, dy_1 \, dy_2.$$

By (10.41) we have the development

(10.45) $$\frac{\partial^3 G}{\partial z^2 \, \partial \bar{\zeta}} = \frac{1}{2(z - \zeta)} + \frac{\partial^3 H}{\partial z^2 \, \partial \bar{\zeta}}$$

and by (10.8),

$$\frac{\partial^3 G}{\partial z^2 \, \partial \bar{\zeta}} = 0 \qquad \text{for} \qquad Q \in \mathsf{C}. \tag{10.46}$$

Hence by letting $\varepsilon \to 0$ we have from (10.44),

$$I(P) = -\frac{\pi}{2} F(z, \bar{z}) - \iint_{\mathsf{D}} \frac{\partial^3 G}{\partial z^2 \, \partial \bar{\zeta}} f \, dy_1 \, dy_2. \tag{10.47}$$

We integrate once more by parts and obtain

$$\iint_{\mathsf{D}} \frac{\partial^3 G}{\partial z^2 \, \partial \bar{\zeta}} f \, dy_1 \, dy_2 = \frac{1}{2i} \int_{\mathsf{C}} \frac{\partial^2 G}{\partial z^2} f \, d\zeta - \iint_{\mathsf{D}} \frac{\partial^2 G}{\partial z^2} \frac{\partial f(\zeta)}{\partial \bar{\zeta}} \, dy_1 \, dy_2. \tag{10.48}$$

The first integral vanishes by (10.8) while the second vanishes since the Cauchy-Riemann equations imply $\dfrac{\partial f(\zeta)}{\partial \bar{\zeta}} = 0$. Thus,

$$F(z, \bar{z}) = -\frac{2}{\pi} \iint_{\mathsf{D}} \frac{\partial^4 G}{\partial z^2 \, \partial \bar{\zeta}^2} F(\zeta, \bar{\zeta}) \, dy_1 \, dy_2. \tag{10.49}$$

Comparing this with (10.40), we obtain the identity

$$K_4(z, \bar{z}; \zeta, \bar{\zeta}) = -\frac{2}{\pi} \frac{\partial^4 G(z, \bar{z}; \zeta, \bar{\zeta})}{\partial z^2 \, \partial \bar{\zeta}^2}. \tag{10.50}$$

We can also show how the functions $F_n(z, \bar{z})$ which were originally introduced as complete and orthonormal in the space E^2 lead to functions which are orthonormal with respect to the metric $\mathrm{p}\{u, v; -1\}$. We use this notation to designate the inner product (9.14) with $\sigma = -1$. It can be shown by a formal differentiation that if $\varphi(z, \bar{z})$ and $\psi(z, \bar{z})$ are both of the form (10.36), then we have

$$\mathrm{p}\{\varphi, \bar{\psi}; -1\} = 8 \iint_{\mathsf{D}} \frac{\partial^2 \varphi}{\partial z^2} \overline{\left(\frac{\partial^2 \psi}{\partial z^2} \right)} \, dx_1 \, dx_2. \tag{10.51}$$

If we now determine functions $H_n(z, \bar{z}) = h_{2n}(x_1, x_2) + i \, h_{2n+1}(x_1, x_2)$ by the conditions

$$\frac{\partial^2 H_n}{\partial z^2} = F_n; \qquad \frac{\partial^2 H_n}{\partial \bar{z}^2} = 0 \qquad (n = 0, 1, \ldots,), \tag{10.52}$$

then the functions H_n, $n = 1, 2, \ldots,$ are again of the form (10.36), so that we have

$$\text{(10.53)} \qquad \mathrm{p}\,\{H_n, \overline{H}_m; -1\} = 8 \iint_D F_n \overline{F_m}\, dx_1\, dx_2 = 8\, \delta_{mn}.$$

For the kernel K_4 we have the relation

$$\text{(10.54)} \qquad K_4(z, \overline{z}; \zeta, \overline{\zeta}) =$$

$$= 2 \frac{\partial^4}{\partial z^2\, \partial \overline{\zeta}^2} \left[\sum_{n=0}^{\infty} \left(h_{2n}(x_1, x_2)\, h_{2n}(y_1, y_2) + h_{2n+1}(x_1, x_2)\, h_{2n+1}(y_1, y_2) \right) \right].$$

Bergman (B 3), Bergman-Schiffer (B 23), Frank-Mises [14] vol. 1, Ch. 19, Friedrichs (F 6), Hadamard (H 1), Kantorovitch-Kriloff [28], Lauricella (L 1), Michell (M 1), Muskhelishvili [54], E. Reissner (R 1), Schiffer (S 2), Schröder (S 8), Zaremba (Z 1).

11. Plane strain: In the present section, we shall consider the case of plane strain. In this case, we assume that

$$\text{(11.1)} \qquad u_3 = 0, \qquad \frac{\partial u_k}{\partial x_3} = 0 \qquad (k = 1, 2).$$

Under these assumptions, the strain tensor T is reduced to $T = ((e_{ik}))$ $(i, k = 1, 2)$. By (3.17) we have

$$\text{(11.2)} \quad F_{kk} = -\lambda\gamma - 2\mu \frac{\partial u_k}{\partial x_k}, \quad (k = 1, 2, 3), \qquad F_{12} = -\mu \left(\frac{\partial u_1}{\partial x_2} + \frac{\partial u_2}{\partial x_1} \right),$$

$$F_{13} = F_{23} = 0.$$

$$\text{(11.2')} \qquad F_{33} = \sigma (F_{11} + F_{22}).$$

By (2.6), since we assume that no mass forces are present, we have

$$\text{(11.3)} \qquad \sum_{k=1}^{2} \frac{\partial F_{ik}}{\partial x_k} = 0 \qquad (i = 1, 2).$$

In view of (11.3), there exists a function $W(x_1, x_2)$ such that

$$\text{(11.4)} \qquad F_{ik} = (-1)^{i+k} \frac{\partial^2 W}{\partial x_{3-i}\, \partial x_{3-k}}.$$

The function W is generally designated as the Airy stress function. From (11.3) we can derive

$$2\frac{\partial^2 F_{12}}{\partial x_1\,\partial x_2} = -\sum_{k=1}^{2}\frac{\partial^2 F_{kk}}{\partial x_k^2}. \tag{11.5}$$

From (11.2) we obtain

$$e_{kk} = -\frac{1}{E}\left(F_{kk} - \sigma\sum_{i\neq k}^{3} F_{ii}\right), \quad (k=1,2), \qquad e_{12} = -\frac{(1+\sigma)}{E}F_{12}, \tag{11.6}$$

$$e_{k3} = 0, \qquad (k = 1, 2, 3)$$

where $E = \dfrac{\mu\,(3\,\lambda + 2\,\mu)}{\lambda + \mu}$ is the modulus of elasicity of the material in tension and compression. By differentiating (1.2) we have

$$\frac{\partial^2 e_{11}}{\partial x_2^2} + \frac{\partial^2 e_{22}}{\partial x_1^2} = 2\frac{\partial^2 e_{12}}{\partial x_1\,\partial x_2}, \tag{11.7}$$

so that by (11.6), (11.5) and (11.2′)

$$\sum_{k=1}^{2}\frac{\partial^2 F_{kk}}{\partial x_{3-k}^2} + \frac{\partial^2 F_{kk}}{\partial x_k^2} = \Delta\sum_{k=1}^{2} F_{kk} = 0. \tag{11.8}$$

Using (11.4), we obtain

$$\Delta\,\Delta\,W = 0. \tag{11.9}$$

Thus we see that the Airy stress function W must satisfy the biharmonic equation.

The energy of deformation $\tilde{V}$ for a plate of unit thickness may be computed by (3.15). We find

$$\tilde{V} = \iint_D \left(\frac{\lambda}{2}(e_{11} + e_{22})^2 + \mu\,(e_{11}^2 + e_{22}^2 + 2\,e_{12}^2)\right) dx_1\,dx_2 \tag{11.10}$$

and through (11.2), (11.6), and (11.4) this may be written in either of the two alternate forms

$$\tilde{V} = -\frac{1}{2}\iint_D (e_{11}F_{11} + e_{22}F_{22} + 2\,e_{12}F_{12})\,dx_1\,dx_2 \tag{11.11}$$

$$(11.12)\qquad \tilde{V} = \frac{1-\sigma^2}{2E}\iint_D \left(\left(\frac{\partial^2 W}{\partial x_1^2}\right)^2 + \left(\frac{\partial^2 W}{\partial x_2^2}\right)^2 - \frac{2\sigma}{1-\sigma}\frac{\partial^2 W}{\partial x_1^2}\frac{\partial^2 W}{\partial x_2^2} + \right.$$

$$\left. + \frac{2}{1-\sigma}\left(\frac{\partial^2 W}{\partial x_1 \partial x_2}\right)^2\right) dx_1\, dx_2.$$

It will therefore be convenient to introduce the bilinear form

$$(11.13)\qquad \mathrm{p}^*\{u, v\} = \iint_D \left(\frac{\partial^2 u}{\partial x_1^2}\frac{\partial^2 v}{\partial x_1^2} + \frac{\partial^2 u}{\partial x_2^2}\frac{\partial^2 v}{\partial x_2^2}\right.$$

$$\left. - \frac{\sigma}{1-\sigma}\left(\frac{\partial^2 u}{\partial x_1^2}\frac{\partial^2 v}{\partial x_2^2} + \frac{\partial^2 u}{\partial x_2^2}\frac{\partial^2 v}{\partial x_1^2}\right) + \frac{2}{1-\sigma}\frac{\partial^2 u}{\partial x_1 \partial x_2}\frac{\partial^2 v}{\partial x_1 \partial x_2}\right) dx_1\, dx_2.$$

It is clear that $\mathrm{p}^*\{u, v\} = \mathrm{p}^*\{v, u\}$ while for $-1 \leqslant \sigma < \frac{1}{2}$, $\mathrm{p}^*\{u, u\} \geqslant 0$, equality holding only if u is a linear function. (In what follows we shall restrict ourselves to the case $-1 \leqslant \sigma < 1/2$). The energy $\tilde{V}$ may also be expressed as a line integral around C in the following way. From (11.11) and (1.2) we may write

$$(11.14)\qquad \tilde{V} = -\frac{1}{2}\iint_D \left(\frac{\partial u_1}{\partial x_1}F_{11} + \frac{\partial u_2}{\partial x_2}F_{22} + \left(\frac{\partial u_2}{\partial x_1} + \frac{\partial u_1}{\partial x_2}\right)F_{12}\right) dx_1\, dx_2$$

so that by integration by parts we find

$$(11.15)\qquad \tilde{V} = \frac{1}{2}\int_C \left(\sum_{i=1}^{2} u_i \sum_{k=1}^{2} F_{ik}\cos(\mathbf{n}, \mathbf{x}_k)\right) ds +$$

$$+ \frac{1}{2}\iint_D \left(\sum_{i=1}^{2} u_i \sum_{k=1}^{2} \frac{\partial F_{ik}}{\partial x_k}\right) dx_1\, dx_2.$$

In view of (2.12) and (11.3) we have

$$\tilde{V} = \frac{1}{2}\int_C (u_1 F_1 + u_2 F_2)\, ds = \frac{1}{2}\int_C \mathbf{u}\cdot\mathbf{F}\, ds, \quad \mathbf{u} = (u_1, u_2), \quad \mathbf{F} = (F_1, F_2).$$

(11.16)

More generally, we shall have

$$(11.17)\qquad \mathrm{p}^*\{W^{(1)}, W^{(2)}\} = \frac{E}{(1-\sigma^2)}\int_C \mathbf{u}^{(1)}\cdot\mathbf{F}^{(2)}\, ds$$

where the strain vector $\mathbf{u}^{(1)}$ and the stress $\mathbf{F}^{(2)}$ correspond to the stress functions $W^{(1)}$ and $W^{(2)}$, respectively. From (2.12) and (11.4) we derive

$$F_k = (-1)^k \frac{\partial}{\partial s}\left(\frac{\partial W}{\partial x_{3-k}}\right) \qquad (k = 1, 2) \tag{11.18}$$

so that

$$\frac{\partial W}{\partial x_k} = (-1)^{k+1} \int_{s_0}^{s} F_{3-k}\, ds + C_k \quad (k = 1, 2). \tag{11.19}$$

We may now formulate the following two boundary value problems: (1) to find a solution W of (11.9) with prescribed displacement vector $\mathbf{u}$ on **C**. (2) to find a solution W of (11.9) with prescribed force vector $\mathbf{F}$ on **C**. In the event that solutions to these boundary value problems exist, then W is determined up to a linear function; for, $\mathbf{u} = 0$ or $\mathbf{F} = 0$ on **C** implies the vanishing of the energy integral (11.16), and hence W must be linear.

We consider the class $\tilde{\Gamma}$ of solutions W of the biharmonic equation which are normalized in the following sense:

$$W(0,0) = 0, \qquad \left.\frac{\partial W}{\partial x_i}\right|_{0,0} = 0 \qquad (i = 1, 2). \tag{11.20}$$

The closure of the linear space $\tilde{\Gamma}$ in the sense of the p* metric forms a Hilbert space $\tilde{\Gamma}^2$. In $\tilde{\Gamma}^2$ we may find a complete and orthonormal system of solutions $\{W_n(x_1, x_2)\}$ such that every solution W of $\tilde{\Gamma}^2$ possesses a representation of the form

$$W(x_1, x_2) = \sum_{n=0}^{\infty} \mathrm{p}^* \{W, W_n\}\, W_n(x_1, x_2). \tag{11.21}$$

The space $\tilde{\Gamma}^2$ possesses a reproducing kernel $K^*(x_1, x_2; y_1, y_2)$ given by

$$K^*(x_1, x_2; y_1, y_2) = \sum_{n=0}^{\infty} W_n(x_1, x_2)\, W_n(y_1, y_2) \tag{11.22}$$

and possessing the characteristic properties

$$K^*(x_1, x_2; y_1, y_2) = K^*(y_1, y_2; x_1, x_2), \tag{11.23}$$

$$W(x_1, x_2) = \mathrm{p}^* \{K^*(x_1, x_2; y_1, y_2), W(y_1, y_2)\} \tag{11.24}$$

for all $W \in \tilde{\Gamma}^2$. The series (11.21) and (11.22) converge absolutely and uniformly in every closed set interior to **D**. Through (11.17) we find the alternate representations

$$W(x_1, x_2) = \frac{E}{1-\sigma^2} \sum_{n=0}^{\infty} \left(\int_C \mathbf{u}^{(n)} \cdot \mathbf{F} \, ds \right) W_n(x_1, x_2) \tag{11.25}$$

$$W(x_1, x_2) = \frac{E}{1-\sigma^2} \sum_{n=0}^{\infty} \left(\int_C \mathbf{u} \cdot \mathbf{F}^{(n)} \, ds \right) W_n(x_1, x_2)$$

which give the normalized solutions of the first and second boundary value problems, respectively.

We shall now show briefly how the convergence of (11.22) may be established. In most cases where kernel functions have been introduced (II.18, III.8, IV.6) and in Part B (II.1), they are defined in terms of the Neumann's and the Green's functions. Their various properties as well as their representation were derived by utilizing the properties of these latter functions. It is also possible to base a definition of the kernel functions on orthonormal expansions of the type (11.22), and to develop their theory from this point of view. The proof of the convergence of (11.22) which we are about to give may be adapted to the various kernels considered in this book. It yields the convergence of (11.22) only for values of the arguments which are interior to the domain. However, the regularity of the kernel function when one argument point is in the interior and the second argument point is on the boundary is frequently required for the solution of boundary value problems, and to establish this fact we must have recourse to its representation by Green's and Neumann's functions.

Let $W(x_1, x_2)$ *be a solution of the biharmonic equation of class* $\tilde{\Gamma}^2$, *and suppose that*

$$\left. \frac{\partial^2 W}{\partial x_1^{\,2}} \right|_{\substack{x_1 = x_1^* \\ x_2 = x_2^*}} = 1, \qquad (x_1^*, x_2^*) \in \mathsf{D}; \tag{11.26}$$

then for fixed σ, $-1 < \sigma < 1/2$ *there exists a positive constant* d *such that*

$$\mathrm{p}^* \{W, W\} \geqslant d > 0 \tag{11.27}$$

independently of W. We shall show this as follows. From (11.13) we have that for some positive constant α.

$$\mathrm{p}^* \{W\} \geqslant \alpha \iint_{\mathsf{D}} \left(\frac{\partial^2 W}{\partial x_1^{\,2}} \right)^2 dx_1 \, dx_2. \tag{11.28}$$

It is no restriction of generality to assume that (x_1^*, x_2^*) is the origin. If now C_r designates a circle of radius r and center at the origin, we shall have

$$\text{(11.29)} \qquad p^* \{W\} \geqslant \alpha \iint\limits_{C_r} \left(\frac{\partial^2 W}{\partial x_1^2} \right)^2 dx_1 \, dx_2.$$

Inasmuch as we may now write

$$\text{(11.30)} \qquad \frac{\partial^2 W}{\partial x_1^2} = 1 + c\, r^2 + \ldots$$

where the remainder consists of terms of the form $r^n \cos n\varphi$, $r^{n+2} \cos n\varphi$, $r^n \sin n\varphi$, $r^{n+2} \sin n\varphi$, $n \geqslant 1$, which are orthogonal over C_r with each other and with $(1 + c\, r^2)$, it is clear that the statement (11.27) is now established.

Let now $\{W_n\}$ be an orthonormal family in $\tilde{\Gamma}^2$. For each integer n, let us determine that function $W(x_1, x_2)$ of $\tilde{\Gamma}^2$ which possesses the form

$$\text{(11.31)} \qquad W(x_1, x_2) = \sum_{\nu=0}^{n} a_\nu W_\nu(x_1, x_2),$$

satisfies the condition

$$\text{(11.32)} \qquad \left. \frac{\partial^2 W}{\partial x_1^2} \right|_{\substack{x_1 = x_1^* \\ x_2 = x_2^*}} = 1,$$

and is such that $p^* \{W, W\} = \text{minimum}$. To this end, let us write

$$\text{(11.33)} \qquad a_\nu = \frac{\dfrac{\partial^2 W_\nu(x_1^*, x_2^*)}{\partial x_1^2}}{\displaystyle\sum_{\mu=0}^{n} \left(\frac{\partial^2 W_\mu(x_1^*, x_2^*)}{\partial x_1^2} \right)^2} + \alpha_\nu$$

where the α_ν are a new set of unknowns. It is easily seen that (11.32) becomes

$$\text{(11.34)} \qquad \sum_{\nu=0}^{n} \alpha_\nu \frac{\partial^2 W_\nu(x_1^*, x_2^*)}{\partial x_1^2} = 0.$$

Now we have

$$\text{(11.35)} \qquad p^* \{W, W\} = \sum_{\mu,\nu=0}^{n} a_\mu a_\nu \, p^* \{W_\mu, W_\nu\} = \sum_{\mu,\nu=0}^{n} a_\mu a_\nu \delta_{\mu\nu} =$$

$$= \sum_{\nu=0}^{n} (a_\nu)^2 = \left(\sum_{\nu=0}^{n} \left(\frac{\partial^2 W_\nu(x_1^*, x_2^*)}{\partial x_1^2} \right)^2 \right)^{-1} + \sum_{\nu=0}^{n} \alpha_\nu^2.$$

The last equality follows from (11.34). Thus, the minimum value is $\left(\sum_{\nu=0}^{n}\left(\frac{\partial^2 W_\nu(x_1^*, x_2^*)}{\partial x_1^2}\right)^2\right)^{-1}$ and comes from the selection $a_\nu \equiv 0$. By our previous result, $\left(\sum_{\nu=0}^{n}\left(\frac{\partial^2 W_\nu(x_1^*, x_2^*)}{\partial x_1^2}\right)^2\right)^{-1} \geqslant d$ for all n, and hence $\sum_{\nu=0}^{\infty}\left(\frac{\partial^2 W_\nu(x_1^*, x_2^*)}{\partial x_1^2}\right)^2 < \infty$. By the use of the Schwarz inequality, we may show the uniform convergence of $\sum_{\nu=0}^{\infty}\frac{\partial^2 W_\nu(x_1, x_2)}{\partial x_1^2}\frac{\partial^2 W_\nu(y_1, y_2)}{\partial y_1^2}$. By similar arguments we may show the uniform convergence of $\sum_{\nu=0}^{\infty}\frac{\partial^2 W_\nu}{\partial x_1\,\partial x_2}\frac{\partial^2 W_\nu}{\partial y_1\,\partial y_2}$ and of $\sum_{\nu=0}^{\infty}\frac{\partial^2 W_\nu}{\partial x_2^2}\frac{\partial^2 W_\nu}{\partial y_2^2}$. The convergence of (11.22) now follows after a two-fold integration on each argument point.

It is of considerable interest to show how the boundary value problems (1) and (2) may be expressed as boundary value problems for analytic functions of a complex variable. The function ΔW is harmonic in D, so that we may set

$$\Delta W = 4\,\mathrm{Re}\,(\varphi'(z))\,; \qquad z = x_1 + i\,x_2, \tag{11.36}$$

for an appropriate analytic function $\varphi(z) = p(x_1, x_2) + i\,q(x_1, x_2)$. In view of the fact that $\Delta \equiv 4\frac{\partial^2}{\partial z\,\partial \bar{z}}$, (cf. II.18.8), a computation shows immediately that

$$\frac{\partial^2}{\partial z\,\partial \bar{z}}\Big(W - \mathrm{Re}\big(\bar{z}\,\varphi(z)\big)\Big) = 0 \tag{11.37}$$

so that

$$p_1(x_1, x_2) = W - \mathrm{Re}\big(\bar{z}\,\varphi(z)\big) = W - p\,x_1 - q\,x_2 \tag{11.38}$$

is a harmonic function. We may therefore let

$$p_1(x_1, x_2) = \mathrm{Re}\,(\chi(z)) \tag{11.39}$$

for an appropriate analytic function $\chi(z)$. We therefore have

$$W = \mathrm{Re}\,[\bar{z}\,\varphi(z) + \chi(z)]. \tag{11.40}$$

It should be observed that through (11.36) $\varphi(z)$ is determined only up to a quantity of the form $i\alpha z + \beta$ where α is real and β is a complex constant. We have now

$$(11.41) \qquad 2\frac{\partial W}{\partial \bar{z}} = \frac{\partial W}{\partial x_1} + i\frac{\partial W}{\partial x_2} = \varphi(z) + z\overline{\varphi'(z)} + \overline{\chi'(z)}.$$

Combining this with (11.19), we have

$$(11.42) \qquad \varphi(z) + z\overline{\varphi'(z)} + \overline{\chi'(z)} = \int_{s_0}^{s} (F_2 - iF_1)\,ds + \text{const.}$$

The solution of the second boundary value problem is accordingly reduced to the determination of two analytic functions φ and χ which on the boundary C satisfy the relation (11.42).

We turn now to the analytic formulation of the first boundary value problem. It may be shown by a direct differentiation using (11.2) and (11.3), that the quantities $(\lambda + 2\mu)\gamma$ and $2\mu\omega \equiv \mu\left(\frac{\partial u_2}{\partial x_1} - \frac{\partial u_1}{\partial x_2}\right)$ satisfy the Cauchy-Riemann equations. Furthermore, from (11.2) it follows that

$$(11.43) \qquad 4\,\mathrm{Re}(\varphi') = \Delta W = -2(\lambda + \mu)\gamma$$

and therefore

$$(11.44) \qquad 2\mu\omega = -\frac{2(\lambda + 2\mu)}{\lambda + \mu}\,\mathrm{Im}(\varphi').$$

Now from (11.2) and (11.4) we have

$$(11.45) \quad 2\mu\frac{\partial u_1}{\partial x_1} = \frac{\partial^2 W}{\partial x_1^2} - \frac{\lambda + 2\mu}{2(\lambda + \mu)}\Delta W = \frac{\partial^2 W}{\partial x_1^2} - \frac{2(\lambda + 2\mu)}{\lambda + \mu}\frac{\partial(\mathrm{Re}(\varphi))}{\partial x_1},$$

the last equality coming from (11.36). From (11.2), (11.4), and (11.44), we find

$$(11.46) \quad 2\mu\frac{\partial u_1}{\partial x_2} = \frac{\partial^2 W}{\partial x_2\,\partial x_1} - 2\mu\omega = \frac{\partial^2 W}{\partial x_2\,\partial x_1} - \frac{2(\lambda + 2\mu)}{\lambda + \mu}\frac{\partial(\mathrm{Re}(\varphi))}{\partial x_2}.$$

After multiplying (11.46) by i and subtracting from (11.45) we find

$$(11.47) \qquad 2\mu\frac{\partial u_1}{\partial z} = \frac{\partial}{\partial z}\left(\frac{\partial W}{\partial x_1} - \frac{2(\lambda + 2\mu)}{\lambda + \mu}\,\mathrm{Re}(\varphi)\right)$$

so that

$$(11.48) \qquad 2\mu u_1 = \frac{\partial W}{\partial x_1} - \frac{2(\lambda + 2\mu)}{\lambda + \mu}\,\mathrm{Re}(\varphi).$$

In a similar way, we may derive

$$2\mu u_2 = \frac{\partial W}{\partial x_2} - \frac{2(\lambda + 2\mu)}{\lambda + \mu} \operatorname{Im}(\varphi). \tag{11.49}$$

Multiplying (11.49) by i and adding to (11.48), we find

$$2\mu (u_1 + i u_2) = 2\frac{\partial W}{\partial \bar{z}} - \frac{2(\lambda + 2\mu)}{\lambda + \mu} \varphi \tag{11.50}$$

and finally, from (11.41),

$$-2\mu (u_1 + i u_2) = \frac{\lambda + 3\mu}{\lambda + \mu} \varphi(z) - z\overline{\varphi'(z)} - \overline{\chi'(z)}. \tag{11.51}$$

When the functions φ and χ have been determined, the forces F_{ik} may be determined from

$$F_{11} + F_{22} = \Delta W = 4 \operatorname{Re}(\varphi'(z)) \tag{11.52}$$

$$F_{22} - F_{11} + 2iF_{12} = 2(\bar{z}\varphi''(z) + \chi''(z)). \tag{11.53}$$

As regards the derivation of (11.53), we have from (11.2),

$$F_{22} - F_{11} + 2iF_{12} = 4\mu \frac{\partial(u_1 - i u_2)}{\partial z} = 4\frac{\partial}{\partial z}\left(\frac{\partial W}{\partial z} - \frac{(\lambda + 2\mu)}{\lambda + \mu}\overline{\varphi}\right), \tag{11.54}$$

the last equality coming from (11.48) and (11.49). Application of (11.40) now yields (11.53).

Summarizing, we see that we have reduced both boundary value problems to the determination of two analytic functions $\varphi(z)$ and $\chi(z)$ which are regular in D and on the boundary C satisfy the condition

$$k\varphi(z) - z\overline{\varphi'(z)} - \overline{\chi'(z)} = g(z). \tag{11.55}$$

Here k is a constant, while $g(z)$ is a given single-valued and continuous complex function defined on C. In the first boundary value problem we must choose

$$k = \frac{\lambda + 3\mu}{\lambda + \mu}, \qquad g(z) = -2(\mu(u_1(z) + i u_2(z)), \tag{11.56}$$

while in the second boundary value problem we have

$$k = -1, \qquad g(z) = \int_{s_0}^{s} (-F_2 + iF_1)\, ds + \text{const}. \tag{11.57}$$

We shall now show how these problems may be reduced to an integral equation of Fredholm type. For the sake of simplicity we shall assume that D is finite, simply connected, and possesses an analytic boundary. Let $z = w(t)$ map the circle $|t| < 1$ conformally onto D. Then our problem is reduced to the determination of two analytic functions

$$\Phi(t) = \varphi(w(t)), \qquad \Psi(t) = \chi'(w(t)) \tag{11.58}$$

which are regular in the unit circle and on its boundary satisfy

$$k\Phi(t) - \frac{w(t)}{\overline{w'(t)}}\overline{\Phi'(t)} - \overline{\Psi(t)} = G(t) \tag{11.59}$$

where $G(t) = g(w(t))$. Inasmuch as the mapping function will be regular on the boundary, $G(t)$ will be continuous on $|t| = 1$.

At the outset let us make two preliminary observations. Let $F(t) = u(t) + i\,v(t)$ be a function which is regular in $|t| < 1$ and continuous on the boundary b. In view of the fact that $\operatorname{Re}\left(\frac{\tau+t}{\tau-t}\right)$ is the Poisson kernel (cf. II.13), we have

$$\frac{1}{2\pi}\int_{b} u(\tau)\frac{\tau+t}{\tau-t}ds_\tau = F(t) - i\,v(0), \tag{11.60}$$

$$\frac{1}{2\pi}\int_{b} v(\tau)\frac{\tau+t}{\tau-t}ds_\tau = -iF(t) + i\,u(0), \tag{11.61}$$

$$\frac{1}{2\pi}\int_{b} \overline{F(\tau)}\frac{\tau+t}{\tau-t}ds_\tau = \overline{F(0)}. \tag{11.62}$$

Secondly, let $g(\tau)$ and $h(\tau)$ be two continuous functions defined on b. Then the identity $g(\tau) = h(\tau)$ is equivalent to the two identities

$$\int_{b} (g(\tau) - h(\tau))\frac{\tau+t}{\tau-t}ds_\tau \equiv 0, \qquad \int_{b} [\overline{g(\tau)} - \overline{h(\tau)}]\frac{\tau+t}{\tau-t}ds_\tau \equiv 0. \tag{11.63}$$

For, adding these two integrals, we have $\int_{b} \operatorname{Re}(g(\tau) - h(\tau))\frac{\tau+t}{\tau-t}ds_\tau \equiv 0.$

Now the real part of this integral is a harmonic function which on b coincides with $\operatorname{Re}(g(\tau) - h(\tau))$. Hence, $\operatorname{Re}(g(\tau) - h(\tau)) \equiv 0$. Similarly, $\operatorname{Im}(g(\tau) - h(\tau)) = 0$ so that $g(\tau) = h(\tau)$.

By the above remark, the identity (11.59) is equivalent to the two identities

$$(11.64)\quad \frac{1}{2\pi}\int_{\mathbf{b}}\left(k\Phi(\tau)-\frac{w(\tau)}{w'(\tau)}\overline{\Phi'(\tau)}-\overline{\Psi(\tau)}\right)\frac{\tau+t}{\tau-t}ds_\tau=\frac{1}{2\pi}\int_{\mathbf{b}}G(\tau)\frac{\tau+t}{\tau-t}ds_\tau$$

$$(11.65)\quad \frac{1}{2\pi}\int_{\mathbf{b}}\left(\overline{k\Phi(\tau)}-\overline{\frac{w(\tau)}{w'(\tau)}}\Phi'(\tau)-\Psi(\tau)\right)\frac{\tau+t}{\tau-t}ds_\tau=\frac{1}{2\pi}\int_{\mathbf{b}}\overline{G(\tau)}\frac{\tau+t}{\tau-t}ds_\tau.$$

In view of (11.60) — (11.62), (11.64) and (11.65) reduce to

$$(11.66)\quad k\Phi(t)-\frac{1}{4\pi}\int_{\mathbf{b}}\frac{w(\tau)}{w'(\tau)}\overline{\Phi'(\tau)}\frac{\tau+t}{\tau-t}ds_\tau=\frac{1}{4\pi}\int_{\mathbf{b}}G(\tau)\frac{\tau+t}{\tau-t}ds_\tau+$$

$$+\frac{1}{2}(k\Phi(0)+\overline{\Psi(0)}),$$

$$(11.67)\quad \Psi(t)+\frac{1}{4\pi}\int_{\mathbf{b}}\overline{\frac{w(\tau)}{w'(\tau)}}\Phi'(\tau)\frac{\tau+t}{\tau-t}ds_\tau=-\frac{1}{4\pi}\int_{\mathbf{b}}\overline{G(\tau)}\frac{\tau+t}{\tau-t}ds_\tau+$$

$$+\frac{1}{2}(\overline{k\Phi(0)}+\Psi(0)).$$

Because of the arbitrariness in the definition of $\Phi(t)$, we may require that $k\Phi(0)+\overline{\Psi(0)}=(0)$. By observing that on the circle **b** we have $ds_\tau=\dfrac{d\tau}{i\tau}$, we may rewrite(11.66) in the form

$$(11.68)\quad k\Phi(t)-\frac{1}{2\pi i}\int_{\mathbf{b}}\frac{w(\tau)}{w'(\tau)}\frac{\overline{\Phi'(\tau)}}{\tau-t}d\tau+a_0=A(t)+a_1$$

where

$$a_0=\frac{1}{4\pi}\int_{\mathbf{b}}\frac{w(\tau)}{w'(\tau)}\overline{\Phi'(\tau)}\,ds_\tau,\qquad a_1=-\frac{1}{4\pi}\int_{\mathbf{b}}G(\tau)\,ds_\tau,$$

$$A(t)=\frac{1}{2\pi i}\int_{\mathbf{b}}G(\tau)\frac{d\tau}{\tau-t}.$$

By adding and subtracting $w(t)$ we obtain

$$(11.69)\quad k\Phi(t)-\frac{1}{2\pi i}\int_{\mathbf{b}}\frac{w(\tau)-w(t)}{w'(\tau)(\tau-t)}\overline{\Phi'(\tau)}\,d\tau-\frac{w(t)}{2\pi i}\int_{\mathbf{b}}\frac{\overline{\Phi'(\tau)}}{w'(\tau)}\frac{d\tau}{\tau-t}+a_0=$$

$$=A(t)+a_1.$$

Now, $\dfrac{\Phi'(t)}{w'(t)}$ is regular in $|t| < 1$ and continuous on **b** so that by (11.62) we have

$$\frac{1}{4\pi}\int_{\mathbf{b}} \overline{\frac{\Phi'(\tau)}{w'(\tau)}}\,\frac{\tau+t}{\tau-t}\,ds_\tau + \frac{1}{4\pi}\int_{\mathbf{b}} \overline{\frac{\Phi'(\tau)}{w'(\tau)}}\,ds_\tau = \tag{11.70}$$

$$= \frac{1}{2\pi i}\int_{\mathbf{b}} \frac{\overline{\Phi'(\tau)}\,d\tau}{\overline{w'(\tau)}\,(\tau - t)} = \frac{1}{2}\,\overline{\frac{\Phi'(0)}{w'(0)}}$$

and (11.69) takes the form

$$k\Phi(t) - \frac{1}{2\pi i}\int_{\mathbf{b}} \frac{w(\tau) - w(t)}{\overline{w'(\tau)}\,(\tau - t)}\,\overline{\Phi'(\tau)}\,d\tau - \frac{w(t)\,\overline{\Phi'(0)}}{2\,\overline{w'(0)}} + a_0 = A(t) + a_1. \tag{11.71}$$

If we now differentiate (11.71) with respect to t, and set

$$l = \frac{1}{k}\left(\overline{\frac{\Phi'(0)}{w'(0)}}\right) \tag{11.72}$$

$$\vartheta(t) = \Phi'(t) - l\,w'(t), \tag{11.73}$$

then we obtain

$$\vartheta(t) - \frac{1}{2\pi i k}\int_{\mathbf{b}} \frac{\partial}{\partial t}\left(\frac{w(t) - w(\tau)}{\overline{w'(\tau)}\,(\tau - t)}\right)\overline{\vartheta(\tau)}\,d\tau = \frac{A'(t)}{k}. \tag{11.74}$$

Since $w(t)$ is regular on the boundary, $\dfrac{w(t) - w(\tau)}{t - \tau}$ is also regular for $t = \tau$. We may therefore consider (11.74) for values of t on **b**. When the real and imaginary parts of (11.74) are taken, there will be obtained a system of two integral equations of Fredholm type. Once $\Phi'(t)$ has been determined from (11.74), Ψ may be determined directly through (11.67).

Mikhlin [47], Muskhelishvili [54], Sherman (S 10).

PART B

Kernel Function Methods in the Theory of Boundary Value Problems

CHAPTER I

PROPERTIES OF SOLUTIONS

1. Introduction: In this part we shall study the theory of partial differential equations of elliptic type

$$(1.1)^* \qquad \Delta u = q(x, y)\, u(x, y), \qquad \Delta = \frac{\partial^2}{\partial x^2} + \frac{\partial^2}{\partial y^2}, \qquad q > 0,$$

or more generally, those which can be considered as the Euler-Lagrange equations of a positivedefinite energy integral

$$(1.2) \qquad \mathrm{E}\{u\} = \iint_{\mathsf{D}} [u_x^2 + u_y^2 + 2\,a\,u\,u_x + 2\,b\,u\,u_y + c\,u^2]\, dx\, dy$$

where D is a region of the x, y-plane. The important role of this type of partial differential equation in theoretical physics has been expounded in detail in Part A. In general mathematical treatments one is satisfied with an existence proof for solutions of (1.1) corresponding to given boundary conditions and this itself is quite a task. The practical question of the numerical representation of such solutions and of their detailed behavior is almost entirely neglected. It is the aim of this part not only to prove the fact that the boundary value problems can be solved but also to develop a formal theory of the solutions of (1.1), leading to identities and series developments for the fundamental functions of Green, Neumann and Robin connected with the equation and a given domain D.

We intend to show in this part that the general treatment of (1.1) can be best accomplished by concentrating on the theory of these fundamental functions. If, for a given domain D and a fixed equation (1.1) these

* A list of the symbols and notations used in Part B will be found on p. 404.

expressions have been computed, all essential boundary value problems for D with respect to (1.1) can be solved; furthermore, these fundamental functions possess so many interesting properties that a clear insight into the qualitative and quantitative behavior of all solutions of (1.1) can be easily derived from them.

2. Notation and definitions: In order to avoid troublesome technicalities which might hide the essential features of our methods, we shall assume that the domain D in which (1.1) is to be studied is finite and bounded by n closed analytic curves C_ν, ($\nu = 1, 2, \ldots n; n \geqslant 1$); we denote by $C = \sum_{\nu=1}^{n} C_\nu$ the boundary of D. Most results of our theory will apply immediately in the case of a piecewise analytic or even piecewise smooth boundary. Exceptions will arise in the statements concerning the regularity of the l-kernel on the boundary and in the variational theory where a uniquely defined normal is presupposed. However, even in this part of the theory a large number of results can be saved by additional arguments using approximation theory. Let $q(x, y)$ be a continuously differentiable *positive* function in D + C. In this case, we may consider (1.1) as the Euler-Lagrange equation of the Dirichlet or energy integral

$$\text{(2.1)} \qquad E\{u\} = \iint_D [u_x^2 + u_y^2 + q u^2]\, dx\, dy.$$

We shall develop our theory in this particular case and the reader will have no difficulty in extending our reasoning to the more general energy term (1.2).

We consider all functions $v(x, y)$ which are twice continuously differentiable in D + C. We may interpret each $v(x, y)$ as a vector in an infinite-dimensional space with a metric based on the scalar product

$$\text{(2.2)} \qquad E\{v, w\} = \iint_D [v_x w_x + v_y w_y + q v w]\, dx\, dy.$$

Then the functions $v(x, y)$ (for which obviously $E\{v\} < \infty$) form a linear space Ω; the length of each vector v is given by $(E\{v\})^{1/2}$ and the angle between v and w is expressed by

$$\text{(2.3)} \qquad \cos \alpha = \frac{E\{v, w\}}{(E\{v\}\, E\{w\})^{1/2}}.$$

This geometric interpretation is possible because of the following two inequalities which arise from the quadratic and positive-definite character of $\mathrm{E}\{u\}$:

(2.4) $$(\mathrm{E}\{v, w\})^2 \leqslant \mathrm{E}\{v\}\,\mathrm{E}\{w\},$$ the Schwarz inequality,

(2.5) $$(\mathrm{E}\{v+w\})^{1/2} \leqslant (\mathrm{E}\{v\})^{1/2} + (\mathrm{E}\{w\})^{1/2},$$ the triangle (Minkowski) inequality.

Two functions v and w in Ω are called *orthogonal* if $\mathrm{E}\{v, w\} = 0$ and v is called *normal* if $\mathrm{E}\{v\} = 1$.

For each pair of functions v and w in Ω we have Green's identity[1]:

(2.6) $$\mathrm{E}\{v, w\} = -\int_{C} v \frac{\partial w}{\partial \nu}\, ds - \iint_{D} v\,[\Delta w - q w]\, dx\, dy$$

where $\frac{\partial}{\partial \nu}$ denotes differentiation in the direction of the *interior* normal on C and s is the length parameter on this boundary.

We now introduce two subspaces of Ω: (a) The linear space Ω^0 of all functions $v \in \Omega$ which vanish on C. (b) The linear space Σ of all functions $u \in \Omega$ which satisfy the differential equation (1.1). In view of (2.6) we conclude that

(2.7) $$\mathrm{E}\{u, v\} = 0 \quad \text{if} \quad u \in \Sigma, \quad v \in \Omega^0.$$

We call the spaces Σ and Ω^0 orthogonal to each other since every vector in Σ is orthogonal to every vector in Ω^0. Let $w \in \Omega$ be an arbitrary vector. From the existence theorem for the first boundary value problem with respect to D and the partial differential equation (1.1) we know that there exists a function $u \in \Sigma$ with the same values as w on C; hence $w - u = v \in \Omega^0$. Thus, we have proved:

(2.8) $$\Omega = \Sigma + \Omega^0$$

i. e., we can decompose the linear space Ω into two orthogonal subspaces Σ and Ω^0. The only common element of both spaces is the zero function, since it must have the norm zero. We shall frequently denote points (x, y) or (ξ, η) by capital letters P or Q and write $v(P)$ instead of $v(x, y)$. If we have functions $K(P, Q)$ depending on several variable points the symbol

[1] Actually this formula can be derived under the weaker assumptions that v is continuously differentiable in D and continuous in D + C, and w is twice continuously differentiable in D and continuously differentiable in D + C. Cf. Courant-Hilbert [13], vol. 2, p. 231.

E $\{K(T, P), K(T, Q)\}$ is always to be understood as referring to operations *with respect to the common point T* while P and Q are treated as parameters. In cases of doubt, we shall denote the domain of integration for the E-multiplication by a subscript, i. e., $E_D\{v, w\}$. We will also use the notation

$$\text{(2.2}'\text{)} \qquad E\{v, w\} = \iint_D [\text{grad}\, v \cdot \text{grad}\, w + q\, v\, w]\, dx\, dy.$$

Courant [12], Courant-Hilbert [13], vol. 2, Fréchet [15], Gunther [17], Julia [26], v. Neumann [56], Stone [78].

3. Properties of the solutions of (1.1): The differential equation (1.1) is one of the simplest extensions of Laplace's equation and hence it is to be expected that its solutions will have several properties in common with harmonic functions. One of the most useful features of the above solutions is expressed by the following theorem: *Let $u(P)$ be a solution of* (1.1) *which has non-negative boundary values on* C. *Then $u(P) \geqslant 0$ in* D.

In order to prove this result, let us study the minimum value of $u(P)$ in D + C. If $u(P)$ had negative values in D, the minimum value $u(P_0)$ taken on at some $P_0 \in D$ would clearly be negative. Hence, at the minimum point P_0 we would have the usual minimum conditions:

$$\text{(3.1)} \qquad u_x = u_y = 0 \quad \text{and} \quad u_{xx} \geqslant 0, \quad u_{yy} \geqslant 0.$$

In view of the differential equation (1.1), however, this leads to

$$\text{(3.2)} \qquad \Delta u = q\, u \geqslant 0, \quad \text{i. e.} \quad u(P_0) \geqslant 0.$$

This contradicts the assumption $u(P_0) < 0$ and proves the theorem.

Each solution $u(P)$ with non-negative boundary values is, moreover, a subharmonic function in view of its non-negativeness in D and the differential equation satisfied. Thus, we may assert that it attains its maximum on the boundary C of D. Similar statements can obviously be made with respect to solutions $u(P)$ of (1.1) which have non-positive boundary values on C.

Let us consider next the following particular solution of (1.1). We define $U(P)$ as that solution which on C has the constant boundary value one. By means of $U(P)$ we can immediately formulate the following theorem: *Let $u(P)$ satisfy on* C *the inequality*

$$\text{(3.3)} \qquad m \leqslant u(P) \leqslant M.$$

Then throughout D *it satisfies the inequality*

$$\text{(3.4)} \qquad m\, U(P) \leqslant u(P) \leqslant M\, U(P).$$

This result is an immediate consequence of our first theorem applied to the solutions $M\,U - u$ and $u - m\,U$, respectively. In the theory of (1.1) the function $U(P)$ plays the same role as the harmonic measure functions play in the theory of harmonic functions in multiply-connected domains. Because of the subharmonic character of $U(P)$ the above inequality may be replaced for $M \geqslant 0$ by

$$u(P) \leqslant M \tag{3.4'}$$

and for $m \leqslant 0$ by

$$m \leq u(P) \tag{3.4''}$$

In particular we derive from (3.4) the following theorem: *Every $u \in \Sigma$ which vanishes everywhere on* C *vanishes identically in* D.

It is also clear that this result can be derived from the first theorem and is, therefore, independent of the existence of the particular solution U.

If there were a point $Q \in$ D where $U(Q) = 0$, we could deduce from (3.4) that every solution $u(P)$ of (1.1) with bounded boundary values must vanish at the same point Q. We shall show in Section V.2 that such a point Q cannot exist; it is useful to state this fact in the form: *at every point $P \in$ D there exists at least one solution of* (1.1) *which is different from zero at this point.*

Finally, let us point out the interesting role which $U(P)$ plays with respect to the Dirichlet metric within the space Σ. By virtue of (2.6), we have for each solution $u(P)$ in Σ the identity

$$\mathrm{E}\{U, u\} = -\int_{C} U \frac{\partial u}{\partial \nu}\, ds = -\int_{C} \frac{\partial u}{\partial \nu}\, ds. \tag{3.5}$$

The flux-integral $\int_{C} \frac{\partial u}{\partial \nu}\, ds$ related to a solution $u \in \Sigma$ plays an important role in various applications of the differential equation (1.1). It is, therefore, remarkable that Dirichlet multiplication with the particular solution $U(P)$ effects the calculation of this important linear functional.

E. Hopf (H 3), (H 4), Picard [60].

4. Existence theorems for certain solutions: In this section we shall establish important transformations of the differential equation (1.1) and its corresponding inhomogeneous form

$$\Delta\varphi - q\varphi = f(P) \tag{4.1}$$

into an integral equation. We shall reduce the difficult question of existence of solutions with prescribed boundary conditions to one and the same existence theorem in the theory of integral equations. In this way, a better insight into the nature of the solutions will be obtained, and important particular solutions will be constructed which will play a central role in the sequel. For the fundamental theorem in the theory of integral equations we refer the reader to the standard treatises.

At first we introduce two functions (cf. A.II.13) $\Gamma(P,Q)$ and $H(P,Q)$ with the following properties:

a) Γ and H are harmonic in $\mathsf{D}+\mathsf{C}$ as functions of P, except at the point $P=Q$.

b) At the point Q, $\Gamma+\frac{1}{2\pi}\log r$, and $H+\frac{1}{2\pi}\log r$ are harmonic, $r=\overline{PQ}$.

c) For fixed $Q\in\mathsf{D}$, we have for $P\in\mathsf{C}$:

$$\Gamma(P,Q)=0, \qquad \frac{\partial H(P,Q)}{\partial\nu}=\frac{1}{L}, \qquad L=\text{total length of } \mathsf{C}. \tag{4.2}$$

The existence of the two fundamental functions Γ and H is well known from potential theory.[1] Γ is called *Green's function of* D *with respect to Laplace's equation* $\Delta u=0$ and H is called *Neumann's function of* D *with respect to the same differential equation.* By the requirements a) — c), Neumann's function is determined only up to an additive constant which may still depend on Q. It is usually determined by the additional condition

$$\int_{\mathsf{C}} H(P,Q)\,ds_P=0. \tag{4.3}$$

It can then be easily shown that Green's and Neumann's functions are symmetric in both argument points and, therefore, are also harmonic functions of Q except for $P=Q$.

Let us write

$$\Gamma(P,Q)=\frac{1}{2\pi}\log\frac{1}{r}+\gamma(P,Q), \qquad H(P,Q)=\frac{1}{2\pi}\log\frac{1}{r}+\eta(P,Q), \tag{4.4}$$

where γ and η are symmetric harmonic functions of both argument points. Let $\mu(P)$ be a continuously differentiable function in $\mathsf{D}+\mathsf{C}$, except for at

[1] See, e. g., Kellogg [30], Sternberg-Smith [77].

most a finite number of points Q_ν where it may become infinite like $a_\nu \log \frac{1}{r_\nu}$, $r_\nu = \overline{PQ_\nu}$. Consider the functions

$$\Phi(Q) = -\iint_D \Gamma(P,Q)\,\mu(P)\,d\tau_P, \qquad \psi(Q) = -\iint_D H(P,Q)\,\mu(P)\,d\tau_P,$$

$$d\tau = \text{area element in } \mathsf{D}. \tag{4.5}$$

It is obvious that Φ and ψ are twice continuously differentiable functions of Q except for $Q = Q_\nu$ which, moreover, in view of the Poisson-Laplace equation satisfy the conditions

$$\Delta\Phi(Q) = \mu(Q), \qquad \Delta\psi(Q) = \mu(Q), \tag{4.6}$$

and which, in view of the characteristic properties of Green's and Neumann's functions, satisfy the following boundary conditions:

$$\Phi(Q) = 0, \qquad \frac{\partial\psi(Q)}{\partial\nu} = -\frac{1}{L}\iint_D \mu(P)\,d\tau_P \qquad \text{for} \qquad Q \in \mathsf{C}. \tag{4.7}$$

Let us now ask for a solution $u(P)$ of (1.1) with prescribed values on the boundary C of D. If such a solution $u(P)$ exists, the function

$$\Phi(Q) = -\iint_D q(P)\,\Gamma(P,Q)\,u(P)\,d\tau_P \tag{4.5'}$$

will vanish on C and satisfy the equation

$$\Delta\Phi(Q) = q(Q)\,u(Q). \tag{4.6'}$$

Hence, the function $u(Q) - \Phi(Q) = v(Q)$ will satisfy Laplace's equation $\Delta v = 0$ and have the prescribed boundary values of u on C. We shall suppose that the fundamental existence theorems for harmonic functions are known, and we can therefore assert that such a harmonic function $v(Q)$ exists. Thus, we obtain finally:

$$u(Q) = v(Q) - \iint_D q(P)\,\Gamma(P,Q)\,u(P)\,d\tau_P. \tag{4.8}$$

Conversely, if we could find a function $u(P)$ which satisfied the integral equation (4.8), it would obviously be a solution of (1.1) with the correct boundary values.

Thus, we must investigate whether or not the integral equation (4.8) possesses a solution. In the general theory of integral equations the following alternative is proved:[1] *the inhomogeneous integral equation (with kernel whose iterates of some order are continuous)*

$$u(Q) = \varphi(Q) + \iint_D K(Q, P)\, \varphi(P)\, d\tau_P \tag{4.9}$$

has a unique solution for every choice of the left-hand side $u(Q)$, *or the homogeneous integral equation*

$$0 = \varphi(Q) + \iint_D K(Q, P)\, \varphi(P)\, d\tau_P \tag{4.10}$$

possesses a solution φ *which is not identically zero.*

Hence, in order to show that (4.8) possesses a solution for every choice of $v(Q)$, i. e., arbitrary boundary values, we have to show that the homogeneous integral equation

$$u(Q) = -\iint_D \Gamma(P, Q)\, q(P)\, u(P)\, d\tau_P \tag{4.11}$$

possesses only the solution $u \equiv 0$. In fact, if there were a solution $u(Q)$ of (4.11), it would satisfy the conditions:

$$\Delta u = q u, \qquad u(Q) = 0 \qquad \text{for} \qquad Q \text{ on } \mathsf{C}. \tag{4.12}$$

But in view of the third theorem of Section 3 this leads to $u \equiv 0$ in D. Hence by the above alternative, we have the result that (4.8) has a solution for every choice of $v(Q)$. This proves that the boundary value problem for (1.1) always has a solution.

Let us next consider the differential equation (1.1) and prescribe for a solution $u(P)$ the values $\partial u/\partial \nu$ of the normal derivative on C. If such a function $u(P)$ exists, let us construct

$$\psi(Q) = -\iint_D H(P, Q)\, q(P)\, u(P)\, d\tau_P. \tag{4.5''}$$

This function satisfies

$$\Delta \psi = q u \qquad \text{and} \qquad \frac{\partial \psi}{\partial \nu} = \text{const. on } \mathsf{C}. \tag{4.6''}$$

[1] Courant-Hilbert [13], Goursat [16], Lovitt [44], etc.

Hence $v = u - \psi$ will be a harmonic function in D and have a normal derivative which differs from the prescribed values $\partial u / \partial \nu$ by a fixed constant. This constant is uniquely determined; for by Gauss' theorem we have

$$\int_{C} \frac{\partial v}{\partial \nu} \, ds = 0 \tag{4.13}$$

which enables us to calculate the constant value of $\frac{\partial \psi}{\partial \nu}$ on C in terms of the given values $\frac{\partial u}{\partial \nu}$ on C. Thus, by well-known existence theorems for harmonic functions $v(Q)$ is given up to an additive constant K which must still be determined. We thus obtain the following integral equation for u:

$$u(Q) = v(Q) + \mathrm{K} - \iint_{D} H(P, Q) \, q(P) \, u(P) \, d\tau_P. \tag{4.14}$$

Here $v(Q)$ is any harmonic function with the prescribed normal derivatives and can be supposed normalized by the condition

$$\int_{C} v \, ds = 0. \tag{4.14'}$$

At first let us prove that the integral equation (4.14) always has a solution $u(Q)$ for arbitrary choice of the term $v(Q) + \mathrm{K}$. For this purpose, we have to show that the homogeneous integral equation

$$u(Q) = - \iint_{D} H(P, Q) \, q(P) \, u(P) \, d\tau_P \tag{4.15}$$

has the identically vanishing solution only. In fact, we derive from (4.6), (4.7) and (4.3) for every solution of the homogeneous integral equation (4.15) the conditions

$$\Delta u = q u, \qquad \frac{\partial u}{\partial \nu} = \text{const.}, \qquad \int_{C} u \, ds = 0. \tag{4.16}$$

Now using the identity (2.6), we derive from (4.16)

$$\mathrm{E}\{u\} = - \int_{C} u \frac{\partial u}{\partial \nu} \, ds = 0. \tag{4.17}$$

This proves $u \equiv 0$ in D and hence shows that the inhomogeneous equation (4.14) always has a solution.

We consider the particular function $V(P)$ defined by the integral equation

(4.18) $$V(Q) = 1 - \iint_{\mathsf{D}} H(P,Q)\, q(P)\, V(P)\, d\tau_P.$$

Clearly, $V(P)$ is a solution of (1.1) and has a constant normal derivative $\frac{\partial V}{\partial \nu}$ on C. Let now $u(Q)$ be a solution of (4.14), say for $\mathrm{K} = 0$. We see immediately that $u(Q)$ is a solution of (1.1) and on C has a normal derivative which differs from that of v by a constant. The same then holds for the combination $u(Q) + \mathrm{K}\, V(Q)$ and by proper choice of K we can show that this combination has exactly the prescribed normal derivative on C. Thus, we have proved that we are always able to solve the boundary value problem of the second kind for the differential equation (1.1).

Let us next consider the inhomogeneous differential equation (4.1) where the right-hand side is a continuously differentiable function in $\mathsf{D} + \mathsf{C}$, except for possibly a finite number of points Q_ν, where it may become infinite like $a_\nu \log \frac{1}{r_\nu}$, $r_\nu = \overline{P Q_\nu}$. We prescribe certain boundary values for φ on C and let $v(P)$ be that harmonic function in D which on C has these boundary values. Then, clearly $\varphi(P)$ will be determined by the integral equation:

$$\varphi(Q) = \left[v(Q) - \iint_{\mathsf{D}} \Gamma(P,Q)\, f(P)\, d\tau_P \right] - \iint_{\mathsf{D}} \Gamma(P,Q)\, q(P)\, \varphi(P)\, d\tau_P.$$

(4.19)

By our above considerations we know that (4.19) possesses a solution $\varphi(P)$ and we have thus obtained an existence proof for solutions of the inhomogeneous differential equation (4.1) with prescribed boundary values. It is obvious that we could similarly show the existence of solutions of (4.1) with prescribed values for the normal derivative on C.

A more general type of boundary condition for solutions of (1.1) is obtained if instead of $u(P)$ or $\frac{\partial u(P)}{\partial \nu}$, we prescribe *the values of the combination* $-\lambda u + \frac{\partial u}{\partial \nu}$ *on the boundary* C. Here λ may be a positive constant or even a non-negative continuous function of the arc length on C. Again we may reduce this so-called boundary value problem of the third kind to the analogous question for harmonic functions. In this case, we will have to introduce the so-called *Robin's functions for Laplace's equation* which are defined in the same way as Green's and Neumann's functions but satisfy the boundary condition

$$\frac{\partial R_\lambda(P,Q)}{\partial \nu} = \lambda\, R_\lambda(P,Q). \tag{4.20}$$

Using the above method we can prove the existence of solutions of (1.1) under boundary conditions of the third kind by using integral equation theory.

We have thus established the important existence theorems for the differential equation (1.1), but there still remains the problem of actually constructing required solutions by means of feasible procedures and of studying their properties. This is our program for the following sections.

Goursat [16], Gunther [17], Hamel [20], Hellinger-Toeplitz [21], Hilbert [22], Julia [26], Kneser [32], Lichtenstein [41], Lovitt [44], Mikhlin [47], Murnaghan [53], Smirnoff [69].

5. Fundamental singularities and fundamental solutions: In addition to solutions $u(P) \in \Sigma$ of (1.1) we shall also consider solutions $S(P,Q)$ which depend on a parameter point $Q \equiv (\xi, \eta)$ where they are to become logarithmically infinite. The point Q is called the source point of the solution $S(P,Q)$. In order to establish the existence of such solutions we consider the inhomogeneous differential equation

$$\Delta u - qu = \frac{1}{2\pi}\, q \log \frac{1}{r}, \qquad r = \overline{PQ}, \qquad Q \in \mathsf{D} \qquad \text{fixed.} \tag{5.1}$$

Using the results of Section 4, and, in particular, integral equation (4.19), we can assert that (5.1) possesses a solution $u(P) = s(P,Q)$ which is twice continuously differentiable in $\mathsf{D} + \mathsf{C}$ except at the point Q where it is still continuously differentiable. $s(P,Q)$ depends, of course, on the source point of the right-hand term in (5.1). Let us now define

$$S(P,Q) = \frac{1}{2\pi} \log \frac{1}{r} + s(P,Q). \tag{5.2}$$

This function is, by construction, a solution of (1.1) and at the point Q has a logarithmic infinity. Let C be a circle around Q of radius ρ; we have

$$\lim_{\rho \to 0} \int_{\mathsf{C}} \frac{\partial S(P,Q)}{\partial \nu_P}\, ds_P = -1. \tag{5.3}$$

A solution of (1.1) which has at one fixed point $Q \in \mathsf{D}$ a singularity with the property (5.3) is called *a fundamental singularity* of the differential equation considered. In the thermodynamical interpretation, as given in (A.1.7), a fundamental singularity represents a heat source of strength one. In (V.4) we shall give another existence proof for such fundamental singularities together with a convenient method for constructing them.

In the important special case where the term $q(P)$ on the right-hand side of (1.1) is an analytic function of the coordinates x, y of P, we can make much stronger statements about $S(P, Q)$. In this case, we know that every solution of (1.1) is an analytic function of the variables x, y at each point $Q \in \mathsf{D}$. Furthermore, we can show that $S(P, Q)$ has the form

$$S(P,Q) = A(P,Q) \log \frac{1}{r} + B(P,Q) \tag{5.4}$$

where A and B are analytic functions of x and y. From requirement (5.3) it follows that

$$A(Q,Q) = \frac{1}{2\pi} \tag{5.5}$$

and from the fact that $S(P, Q)$ is a solution of (1.1) one deduces that $A(P, Q)$ is, as a function of P, a solution of (1.1) and that, moreover, grad A vanishes at the point Q. All these properties show the close relation between $A(P, Q)$ and the Riemann function[1] of the partial differential equation of hyperbolic type which one obtains from (1.1) by replacing the variable y by $i\,y$. We shall not enter here into a detailed discussion of this relation since no use will be made of it later on.

The significance of $S(P, Q)$ for our theory comes from the identity

$$v(Q) = \int_{\mathsf{C}} v(P) \frac{\partial S(P,Q)}{\partial \nu_P} ds_P + \mathrm{E}\{S(P,Q), v(P)\} \tag{5.6}$$

which is valid for any $v \in \Omega$. This is an immediate consequence of Green's identity (2.6) and of the behavior of $S(P, Q)$ near Q as expressed by (5.3). Thus each fundamental singularity $S(P, Q)$ determines any function $v \in \Omega$ by scalar multiplication and by an integral over C depending only on the boundary values of v. It should be remarked that $\mathrm{E}\{S, v\}$ *is an improper integral and is to be understood as the limiting value as* $n \to \infty$ *of a sequence of integrals over the domain* D *from which circles of radius* $1/n$ *around the*

[1] Courant-Hilbert [13], vol. 2, p. 314.

point Q have been removed. We mention another application of the identity (2.6) valid for any $u \in \Sigma$:

$$\int_C S(P,Q) \frac{\partial u(P)}{\partial \nu_P} ds_P + \mathrm{E}\{S(P,Q), u(P)\} = 0 \tag{5.7}$$

whence, by combination with (5.6) we derive Green's identity

$$u(Q) = \int_C \left[u(P) \frac{\partial S(P,Q)}{\partial \nu_P} - S(P,Q) \frac{\partial u(P)}{\partial \nu_P} \right] ds_P. \tag{5.8}$$

Now let $S(P,Q)$ and $T(P,R)$ be two fundamental singularities in D with source points at Q and R, respectively. We may easily derive the following identities for $Q \neq R$:

$$\begin{aligned} \mathrm{E}\{S(P,Q), T(P,R)\} &= S(R,Q) - \int_C S(P,Q) \frac{\partial T(P,R)}{\partial \nu_P} ds_P = \\ &= T(Q,R) - \int_C T(P,R) \frac{\partial S(P,Q)}{\partial \nu_P} ds_P. \end{aligned} \tag{5.9}$$

Combining the two identities (5.9), we obtain the important relation

$$S(R,Q) - T(Q,R) = \int_C \left[S(P,Q) \frac{\partial T(P,R)}{\partial \nu_P} - T(P,R) \frac{\partial S(P,Q)}{\partial \nu_P} \right] ds_P. \tag{5.10}$$

In the sequel *we shall understand by $S(P,Q)$ an arbitrarily chosen but fixed fundamental singularity.* The general theory of boundary value problems of equation (1.1) guarantees the existence of a function $g(P,Q) \in \Sigma$ which has the boundary values $-S(P,Q)$ for fixed $Q \in$ D and $P \in$ C. Thus, the function

$$G(P,Q) = S(P,Q) + g(P,Q) \tag{5.11}$$

is a solution of (1.1) and is twice continuously differentiable in D + C except for the point Q where it behaves like $S(P,Q)$. Moreover it vanishes for $P \in$ C. $G(P,Q)$ is called *Green's function of the differential equation* (1.1) *with respect to the domain* D.

Green's function $G(P,Q)$ is, of course, a special instance of a fundamental singularity. Hence, identity (5.10) may be applied with $S(P,Q) = G(P,Q)$ and $T(P,R) = G(P,R)$. In view of the vanishing of Green's function on the boundary C of D, (5.10) now takes the special form

$$G(R,Q) = G(Q,R), \tag{5.12}$$

i. e., Green's function is symmetric in parameter Q and argument R. It is therefore a fundamental singularity of (1.1) also when considered as a function of its parameter point Q. Thus, *Green's function is a fundamental singularity, symmetric in both its argument points and vanishing on the boundary* **C** *of* **D**.

Identity (5.8) which has been proved for every fundamental singularity holds in particular for Green's function, and because of the vanishing of the latter on **C** has the simple form:

$$u(Q) = \int_{\mathbf{C}} u(P) \frac{\partial G(P,Q)}{\partial \nu_P} ds_P. \tag{5.13}$$

Thus (5.13) provides a representation of each $u \in \Sigma$ in terms of its boundary values. Hence, in order to solve the general boundary value problem of the first kind with respect to (1.1) and **D**, it is sufficient to determine a fundamental singularity $S(P,Q)$ and to solve the special boundary value problem of the first kind of finding a $g(P,Q)$ with boundary values $S(P,Q)$ in **C**. A detailed study of Green's function will give us a complete understanding of the theory of the boundary value problem of the first kind.

We next solve the following special boundary value problem of the second kind. Determine a function $n(P,Q) \in \Sigma$ which on **C** has the normal derivative $-\dfrac{\partial S(P,Q)}{\partial \nu_P}$ for fixed $Q \in \mathbf{D}$. Then the function

$$N(P,Q) = S(P,Q) + n(P,Q) \tag{5.14}$$

is a solution of (1.1) which is twice continuously differentiable in **D** except for the point Q where it behaves like $S(P,Q)$. Moreover it possesses a vanishing normal derivative on **C**. $N(P,Q)$ is called *Neumann's function of the differential equation* (1.1) *with respect to the domain* **D**. Again we may deduce from (5.10) that $N(P,Q)$ *is symmetric in* P *and* Q, and hence is also a fundamental singularity of (1.1) with respect to Q. Applying (5.8) to an arbitrary $u \in \Sigma$, we have

$$u(Q) = -\int_{\mathbf{C}} N(P,Q) \frac{\partial u(P)}{\partial \nu} ds_P. \tag{5.15}$$

Thus, Neumann's function provides a representation of each $u \in \Sigma$ in terms of the values of its normal derivative on **C**, and solves the general boundary value problem of the second kind.

Let $\lambda(s)$ be a continuous non-negative function of the arc length s along **C**. It is well known that the boundary value problem of the third kind always has a solution. This problem is that of finding a function $u \in \Sigma$ which on C satisfies the condition

$$\frac{\partial u}{\partial \nu} - \lambda u = f(s) \tag{5.16}$$

for any given continuous function $f(s)$. We may solve a particular problem of this kind with $f(s) = -\dfrac{\partial S(P,Q)}{\partial \nu_P} + \lambda(s)\, S(P,Q)$ for $Q \in$ D. Thus, we obtain a function $r_\lambda(P,Q) \in \Sigma$ such that

$$R_\lambda(P,Q) = S(P,Q) + r_\lambda(P,Q) \tag{5.17}$$

is a solution of (1.1) which is twice continuously differentiable in D, except for the point Q where it behaves like $S(P,Q)$ and which on C satisfies the requirement

$$\frac{\partial R_\lambda(P,Q)}{\partial \nu_P} = \lambda(s)\, R_\lambda(P,Q), \qquad Q \in \mathrm{D} \quad \text{fixed.} \tag{5.18}$$

$R_\lambda(P,Q)$ is called *Robin's function with respect to the differential equation* (1.1), *the function* λ, *and to the domain* D. *It is symmetric in* P *and* Q as may again be verified from (5.10). In view of (5.8), we have for $u \in \Sigma$ the identity

$$u(Q) = -\int_{\mathrm{C}} \left(\frac{\partial u(P)}{\partial \nu_P} - \lambda\, u(P) \right) R_\lambda(P,Q)\, ds_P \tag{5.19}$$

and using (5.16)

$$u(Q) = -\int_{\mathrm{C}} f(s)\, R_\lambda(P,Q)\, ds. \tag{5.20}$$

Thus, Robin's function enables us to solve the general boundary value problem of the third kind.

We shall call the three important functions of Green, Neumann and Robin the *fundamental functions* for the differential equation (1.1) and the domain D.

The term *fundamental solution* is used to denote a fundamental singularity which is defined for a fixed domain and has prescribed behavior on the boundary. In particular, the fundamental functions are fundamental solutions.

We remark that there exist only one Green's and one Neumann's function but that we have infinitely many Robin's functions depending on the particular choice of the non-negative weight function $\lambda(s)$ on C.

It will be convenient to assume from the beginning that $S(P, Q)$ is symmetric in P and Q. We know that such fundamental singularities exist, for example Green's, Neumann's or Robin's function of D or of any domain $\mathsf{D}_1 \supset \mathsf{D}$. Under this assumption the functions $g(P, Q)$, $n(P, Q)$ and $r_\lambda(P, Q)$ also become symmetric in their argument points.

Courant-Hilbert [13], Frank-Mises [14], Goursat [16], Gunther [17], Hadamard [19], Hilbert [22], Kneser [32], Lichtenstein [41], Sommerfeld [71], [73].

6. Dirichlet integrals and fundamental functions: In view of (5.6), for any $v \in \Omega$ we have the identity:

$$v(Q) = \mathrm{E}\{N(P, Q), v(P)\}, \qquad v \in \Omega. \tag{6.1}$$

Thus, the scalar multiplication of any vector in Ω with Neumann's function reproduces the vector. *Neumann's function appears as the unit multiplier in the vector algebra induced by the Dirichlet integral.*

Similarly, for every $v \in \Omega^0$ we have the identity

$$v(Q) = \mathrm{E}\{G(P, Q), v(P)\}, \qquad v \in \Omega^0. \tag{6.2}$$

Green's function represents a unit multiplier in the subspace Ω^0 of Ω, consisting of all functions v which vanish on C as does Green's function itself. If $u \in \Sigma$, we have, on the other hand, in view of (5.7):

$$\mathrm{E}\{G(P, Q), u(P)\} = 0, \qquad u \in \Sigma, \tag{6.3}$$

i. e., *Green's function is orthogonal to the space Σ of all solutions.*

It is easily seen that Neumann's and Green's functions are uniquely determined by the requirement that $N - S \in \Omega$ and $G - S \in \Omega$, and the properties:

a) Neumann's function reproduces every function $v \in \Omega$.

b) Green's function reproduces every function $v \in \Omega^0$ and is orthogonal to every $u \in \Sigma$.

In fact, suppose there were another fundamental singularity $M(P, Q)$ with the same properties as $N(P, Q)$. Then $N - M \in \Omega$ would be orthogonal to all functions in Ω, hence also to itself and would therefore be of norm zero. A similar argument holds for the case b).

If we wish to establish similar results for Robin's functions, we must introduce new Dirichlet integrals which also possess the differential equation (1.1) as their Euler-Lagrange condition. In fact, let us define

$$\mathrm{E}_\lambda\{u, v\} = \mathrm{E}\{u, v\} + \int_{\mathsf{C}} \lambda(s)\, u\, v\, ds. \tag{6.4}$$

This integral differs from E only by a boundary integral and has, therefore, the same Euler-Lagrange equations. It may be interpreted as the scalar product between two functions u and v which are continuously differentiable in $\mathsf{D}+\mathsf{C}$; this comes from the fact that $E_\lambda\{u\} = E_\lambda\{u, u\}$ is positive-definite. In particular, we may introduce among all vectors of Ω a new metric based on E_λ and obtain a new vector space Ω_λ which consists of the same vectors as Ω. For each $v \in \Omega$ (or Ω_λ), we have in view of (5.6) and (5.18):

$$v(Q) = E\{R_\lambda(P,Q), v(P)\} + \int_{\mathsf{C}} \lambda(s) R_\lambda(P,Q)\, v(P)\, ds_P = E_\lambda(R_\lambda, v). \tag{6.5}$$

Thus, *in the vector space Ω_λ Robin's function plays the same role of unit multiplier* as did Neumann's function in the space Ω; we may even consider Neumann's function as a very special Robin's function, namely for $\lambda = 0$. Its importance for the general theory comes from the fact that it belongs to a particularly simple Dirichlet integral. We observe further that in all these spaces Green's function plays the same role as in Ω since it vanishes on C. Thus, it is clear that it reproduces every $v \in \Omega^0$ and is orthogonal to every $u \in \Sigma$ even in the E_λ-metric.

Let us finally study the effect of Dirichlet multiplication by the fundamental functions upon a function $t(P,Q)$ which is twice continuously differentiable in $\mathsf{D}+\mathsf{C}$, except for one point Q where it becomes logarithmically infinite, but such that $t(P,Q) - S(P,Q) \in \Omega$. The fundamental singularities of (1.1) are special instances of such functions $t(P,Q)$. For any fundamental singularity $T(P,Q)$ we have still identity (5.6), i. e.,

$$E\{t(P,Q), T(P,R)\} = t(R,Q) - \int_{\mathsf{C}} t(P,Q) \frac{\partial T(P,R)}{\partial \nu_P} ds_P, \quad Q \neq R. \tag{6.6}$$

In particular, choosing $T(P,Q)$ to be Neumann's function, and in view of $\dfrac{\partial N}{\partial \nu} = 0$ on C we clearly obtain

$$E\{t(P,Q), N(P,R)\} = t(R,Q). \tag{6.7}$$

Thus, *Neumann's function also reproduces functions with logarithmic infinities*, and in particular Green's, Robin's and Neumann's functions. One must, of course, take care to keep Q and R apart, since otherwise the above improper integrals do not converge.

One can show similarly that Robin's function $R_\lambda (P, R)$ has the same reproducing property with respect to the E_λ-metric. One has only to insert into (6.6) the boundary behavior (5.18) of R_λ.

If $t (P, Q)$ has the additional property of vanishing on C, we deduce from (6.6) that it is reproduced by any fundamental singularity. In particular, by choosing $t (P, Q) = G (P, Q)$, we arrive at the identity

$$\text{E} \{G (P, Q), T (P, R)\} = G (R, Q). \tag{6.8}$$

If we choose in (6.6) $T (P, R) = G (P, R)$ and notice that the function $H (R, Q)$ defined by

$$H (R, Q) = \int_{\mathsf{C}} t (P, Q) \frac{\partial G (P, R)}{\partial \nu_P} ds_P \tag{6.9}$$

is in Σ with the boundary values $t (R, Q)$, we arrive at

$$\text{E} \{t (P, Q), G (P, R)\} = t (R, Q) - H (R, Q) \tag{6.10}$$

which gives us an interpretation of the Dirichlet product considered. Analogous statements can be made with respect to the E_λ-metric since $G \equiv 0$ on C.

Bergman-Schiffer (B 21), (B 22), (B 23).

Chapter II

THE KERNEL FUNCTIONS AND THEIR PROPERTIES

1. Kernel functions: Let $u (x, y) \in \Sigma$ be an arbitrary solution of (I.1.1). In view of (I.6.1) and (I.6.3), we have

$$\text{E} \{K (P, Q), u (P)\} = u (Q), \qquad u \in \Sigma \tag{1.1}$$

with

$$K (P, Q) = N (P, Q) - G (P, Q). \tag{1.2}$$

Thus, $K (P, Q)$ is a new *function* which *is a unit multiplier in the space* Σ, just as N and G were in Ω and Ω^0. We notice that the geometric relation between spaces

$$\Omega = \Sigma + \Omega^0$$

has now been translated into precisely the same relation between their unit multipliers

$$N = K + G. \tag{1.2'}$$

However, K is greatly distinguished from the other unit multipliers by the property that it itself is a function of the class for which it serves as unit multiplier. In fact, since N and G have the representations (I.5.11) and (I.5.14), we find

$$K(P,Q) = n(P,Q) - g(P,Q) \tag{1.3}$$

where both n and g lie in Σ. We call $K(P,Q)$ *the reproducing kernel of the class* Σ *with respect to the metric* E.

The importance of the kernel becomes clear if we notice that for $P \in \mathsf{C}$ we have

$$K(P,Q) = N(P,Q), \qquad \frac{\partial K(P,Q)}{\partial \nu_P} = -\frac{\partial G(P,Q)}{\partial \nu_P}, \qquad Q \in \mathsf{D}. \tag{1.4}$$

and hence, in view of (I.5.13) and (I.5.15), for any $u \in \Sigma$:

$$u(Q) = -\int_{\mathsf{C}} K(P,Q) \frac{\partial u}{\partial \nu_P} ds_P = -\int_{\mathsf{C}} u \frac{\partial K(P,Q)}{\partial \nu_P} ds_P. \tag{1.5}$$

Thus, if we succeed in determining the kernel K with respect to (I.1.1) and the domain D, we are able to solve the boundary value problems of both the first and of the second kind. It is a principal aim of this exposition to derive numerical procedures for the computation of this kernel. The importance of this study has been made quite obvious by the preceding facts. We shall now show that $K(P,Q)$ has interesting theoretical properties as well.

Let $w \in \Omega$; according to (I.2.8) we may split it up into functions $u \in \Sigma$ and $v \in \Omega^0$, i. e., $w = u + v$, in a unique way. From (I.6.1), (I.6.2), and the definition (1.2) of the kernel we derive:

$$E\{K(P,Q), v(P)\} = 0 \qquad \text{for every} \qquad v \in \Omega^0. \tag{1.6}$$

Hence:

$$E\{K(P,Q), w(P)\} = u(Q). \tag{1.7}$$

Since $u(Q)$ is that solution of (I.1.1) which has on C the same boundary value as $w(Q)$, we have shown that *scalar multiplication by* K *of any* $w \in \Omega$ *yields that solution of* (I.1.1) *which has the same boundary values.* In formulas (1.5) and (1.7) we possess two alternative methods for solving the boundary value problem of the first kind by means of the kernel function. The kernel appears in (1.7) as the projector of Ω into Σ which preserves the boundary values on C.

Consider now the somewhat more general type of function $t(P,Q)$ introduced at the end of (I.6). From (I.6.7), (I.6.10) and from definition (I.6.9), we deduce

$$\mathrm{E}\{t(P,Q), K(P,R)\} = H(R,Q), \tag{1.8}$$

i. e., the Dirichlet product of t with the kernel K yields the function H with the same boundary values as t. Thus, K preserves its characteristic property even with respect to functions with a logarithmic singularity.

This result enables us to construct Green's and Neumann's functions, once the kernel $K(P,Q)$ and the fundamental singularity $S(P,Q)$ are known. In fact, the function

$$H(R,Q) = \mathrm{E}\{S(P,Q), K(P,R)\} \tag{1.9}$$

is of class Σ and has the same boundary values as $S(R,Q)$. Hence

$$G(R,Q) = S(R,Q) - \mathrm{E}\{S(P,Q), K(P,R)\} \tag{1.10}$$

is a representation of Green's function in terms of S and K. From the definition (1.2) of the kernel K, we further infer

$$N(R,Q) = S(R,Q) + K(R,Q) - \mathrm{E}\{S(P,Q), K(P,R)\}. \tag{1.10'}$$

Let us apply the Schwarz inequality (I.2.4) to the identity (1.1). We obtain

$$\big(u(Q)\big)^2 \leqslant \mathrm{E}\{u\} \cdot \mathrm{E}\{K(P,Q), K(P,Q)\}. \tag{1.11}$$

Since $K(P,Q)$ is itself in the class Σ, we may apply (1.1) again and find

$$\mathrm{E}\{K(P,Q), K(P,Q)\} = K(Q,Q) \tag{1.11'}$$

and hence

$$\big(u(Q)\big)^2 \leqslant \mathrm{E}\{u\} \cdot K(Q,Q). \tag{1.12}$$

Thus, we may estimate any function $u \in \Sigma$ by means of its E-norm and the kernel. This estimate is the best possible, for taking $u(P) = K(P,Q)$ it becomes an equality. This remark yields a characterization of the kernel $K(P,Q)$ which is independent of any boundary value problem:

Of all functions $u \in \Sigma$ which at a point $Q \in \mathrm{D}$ have the value $u(Q) = 1$, the function $u = \dfrac{K(P,Q)}{K(Q,Q)}$ has the least norm $\mathrm{E}\{u\}$; *namely* $\big(K(Q,Q)\big)^{-1}$.

Applying inequality (1.12) to $u = K(P,T)$, we obtain the inequality

$$K(Q,T)^2 \leqslant K(T,T) \cdot K(Q,Q). \tag{1.13}$$

This gives an estimate of the kernel with different argument points in terms of the function $K(Q, Q)$ of one argument point.

Inequality (1.13) can be immediately generalized by the following method. Let Q_i, $(i = 1, 2, \ldots, N)$, be an arbitrary set of points in D and let x_i be N arbitrary real numbers. The function

$$u(P) = \sum_{i=1}^{N} K(P, Q_i)\, x_i \tag{1.14}$$

belongs to Σ and in view of (1.1) has the non-negative norm

$$\mathrm{E}\{u\} = \sum_{i,k=1}^{N} K(Q_i, Q_k)\, x_i\, x_k \geqslant 0. \tag{1.15}$$

Because of the arbitrariness in the choice of the real coefficients x_i, we conclude that the matrix $(K(Q_i, Q_k))$ *determines a positive-semidefinite quadratic form*. Inequality (1.13) is the condition for semi-definiteness in the case $N = 2$. For $N > 2$ numerous necessary conditions can be obtained.

Let us suppose that for certain points Q_i and for properly chosen values x_i equality can hold in (1.15). This implies that the norm of the function (1.14) is zero, i. e.,

$$\sum_{i=1}^{N} K(P, Q_i)\, x_i \equiv 0 \qquad \text{for all} \qquad P \in \mathrm{D}. \tag{1.16}$$

Taking the Dirichlet product of this identity with an arbitrary function $u \in \Sigma$, we obtain, in view of the reproducing property of the kernel,

$$\sum_{i=1}^{N} u(Q_i)\, x_i = 0. \tag{1.17}$$

Thus, if the matrix $(K(Q_i, Q_k))$ is not definite, i. e., if its determinant vanishes, the corresponding $u(Q_i)$ are linearly dependent functionals on the whole class Σ.

This remark shows the central role played by the kernel $K(P, Q)$ in the interpolation problem for the class Σ of solutions of (I.1.1). A necessary and sufficient condition in order that we can prescribe arbitrary values a_i at N points Q_i and find a function $u(Q) \in \Sigma$ such that $u(Q_i) = a_i$ is that the determinant $|K(Q_i, Q_k)|$ satisfies

$$|K(Q_i, Q_k)| \neq 0, \qquad i, k = 1, \ldots, N. \tag{1.18}$$

More generally one sees by elementary linear algebra that *an interpolation problem* $u(Q_i) = a_i$, $(i = 1, 2, \ldots, N)$, *is possible if and only if it can be solved by an expression* $u(P) = \sum_{i=1}^{N} x_i K(P, Q_i)$.

This particular interpolation function may be characterized by a certain extremum property relative to all functions of Σ which solve the same interpolation problem. In fact, each such function may be written in the form

$$v(P) = \sum_{i=1}^{N} x_i K(P, Q_i) + w(P) = u(P) + w(P) \tag{1.19}$$

where $w(P) \in \Sigma$ vanishes at the N points of interpolation Q_i. Let us now compute the norm of $v(P)$ taking into consideration the reproducing property of K and the equations $w(Q_i) = 0$. We obtain:

$$\mathrm{E}.\{v\} = \sum_{i,k=1}^{N} x_i x_k K(Q_i, Q_k) + \mathrm{E}\{w\} = \mathrm{E}\{u\} + \mathrm{E}\{w\}. \tag{1.20}$$

Thus $u(P)$ *is the solution of the interpolation problem with minimum norm and* $\sum_{i,k=1}^{N} x_i x_k K(Q_i, Q_k)$ *is that minimum norm.* Clearly, this characterization is an extension of the aforementioned minimum property of the kernel $K(P, Q)$.

The question may be raised as to whether the determinant of the $K(Q_i, Q_k)$ can ever vanish and thus make the above quadratic form actually semi-definite. We shall show that this possibility may be excluded if the coefficient $q(P)$ is analytic in x and y throughout the region $\mathsf{D} + \mathsf{C}$. In this case, there exists a domain $\mathsf{D}_1 \supset \mathsf{D}$ in which $q(P)$ is still positive and analytic and we denote its corresponding Green's function by $G_1(P, Q)$. For $Q \in \mathsf{D}_1$ but outside of D this represents a function of class Σ with respect to D and hence, in view of (1.17), we would have

$$\sum_{i=1}^{N} G_1(Q_i, Q) x_i = 0, \qquad \text{with not all } x_i = 0. \tag{1.21}$$

The left-hand side of (1.21) is now analytic in the coordinates ξ, η of Q, except at the points $Q_i \in \mathsf{D}$. Thus, we may conclude by analytic continuation that (1.21) holds not only outside D but everywhere in D also. But for $Q = Q_i$

this expression becomes logarithmically infinite; this is obviously a contradiction and hence the assumption of the vanishing of the above determinant which led to it is wrong. Thus, *in the case of an analytic coefficient* $q(P)$ *the quadratic form* (1.15) *is positive-definite.*

In a similar fashion, we may introduce the regular kernel

$$K_\lambda(P,Q) = R_\lambda(P,Q) - G(P,Q) \tag{1.22}$$

which possesses properties analogous to those of the kernel $K(P,Q)$ provided the metric E is replaced by the metric E_λ. In the following we shall concentrate upon the first kernel $K(P,Q)$, but it should be borne in mind that all results and methods can be extended to the more general K_λ-kernels and that the boundary value problems of the third kind can be attacked in a way analogous to that which will now be described for the first two types of boundary value problems.

Bergman-Schiffer (B 21), (B 22), (B 23).

2. Orthonormal systems and construction of the kernel: The typical difference between the theories of ordinary and partial differential equations is that in the first case the main problem lies in the determination of solutions, while in the second case the fitting of solutions to the boundary conditions is, in general, of at least the same order of difficulty. In many important cases of partial differential equations one possesses an infinity of particular solutions without being able to make general statements in boundary value theory. We need only mention the fact that a complete basis for all solutions of Laplace's equation is available in classical potential theory but that nevertheless boundary value problems as, for example, in conformal mapping are still of great difficulty.

We shall show now how the knowledge of sufficiently many particular solutions of (I.1.1) may be used to construct the kernel $K(P,Q)$ and thus to solve the boundary value problems of the first and second kind. We assume that an infinity of functions $u_\nu(P) \in \Sigma$ is given which are complete within this space, in the sense that each $u \in \Sigma$ can be approximated to an arbitrary degree in the E-metric:

$$E\left\{u - \sum_{\nu=1}^{n} c_{n\nu} u_\nu(P)\right\} < \varepsilon \quad \text{for} \quad n > N(\varepsilon). \tag{2.1}$$

We may assume also without restriction of generality that the $u_\nu(P)$ are orthonormalized in the E-metric, i. e., they satisfy the conditions

(2.2) $$E\{u_\mu, u_\nu\} = \delta_{\mu\nu} = \begin{cases} 1, & \mu = \nu \\ 0, & \mu \neq \nu \end{cases}.$$

Each system $\{u_\nu(P)\}$ may be brought into this form by the Gram-Schmidt process of orthonormalization.

By means of the orthonormality of the system $\{u_\nu(P)\}$ we can express the left-hand side of (2.1) as follows:

(2.3) $$E\left\{u - \sum_{\nu=1}^{n} c_{n\nu} u_\nu(P)\right\} = E\{u\} - 2\sum_{\nu=1}^{n} c_{n\nu} E\{u, u_\nu\} + \sum_{\nu=1}^{n} c_{n\nu}{}^2 =$$
$$= E\{u\} - \sum_{\nu=1}^{n} E\{u, u_\nu\}^2 + \sum_{\nu=1}^{n} [c_{n\nu} - E\{u, u_\nu\}]^2.$$

It is obvious that the best approximation of $u(P)$ by means of the n first $u_\nu(P)$ is attained if we choose

(2.3′) $$c_{n\nu} = E\{u, u_\nu\} = a_\nu,$$

and we recognize the important fact that this choice of the best coefficient $c_{n\nu}$ does not depend on the degree n of approximation.

In view of inequality (1.12) and (2.1) we have

(2.4) $$\left(u(P) - \sum_{\nu=1}^{n} a_\nu u_\nu(P)\right)^2 \leqslant \varepsilon K(P, P)$$

which shows that the series

(2.5) $$u(P) = \sum_{\nu=1}^{\infty} a_\nu u_\nu(P), \qquad a_\nu = E\{u, u_\nu\},$$

converges uniformly in each closed subdomain of D.

We may apply this result, in particular, to the function $K(P, Q)$, and in view of the reproducing property (1.1) of the kernel, we obtain:

(2.6) $$K(P, Q) = \sum_{\nu=1}^{\infty} u_\nu(P)\, u_\nu(Q).$$

This formula provides a simple but important identity for the construction of the kernel $K(P, Q)$ in terms of an arbitrary complete orthonormal set of solutions of (I.1.1) in D.

If we have a complete orthonormal system $\{u_\nu(P)\}$ and a fundamental singularity $S(P,Q)$, we can construct Green's and Neumann's functions by the formulas (1.10) and (1.10'). In fact, by virtue of (2.6) we can calculate the kernel $K(P,Q)$, and from $K(P,Q)$ and $S(P,Q)$ the above fundamental functions can be constructed. Similarly, we can express the Robin's functions by using complete systems of solutions orthonormalized with respect to the metric E_λ, defined in (I.6.4).

Thus, the knowledge of a complete system of particular solutions and of a fundamental singularity permits the construction of the fundamental functions. It should be remarked, however, that the boundary value problems can be solved even without a fundamental singularity, since we showed in (1.5) that for this purpose one needs only the kernel $K(P,Q)$.

On the other hand, the knowledge of a fundamental singularity in many cases leads to an easy construction of a complete system of solutions of the class Σ. Suppose that the domain D can be embedded in a larger domain D_1 where $q(P)$ still satisfies the conditions of continuous differentiability and positiveness, and suppose that we know a fundamental singularity $S(P,Q)$ in D_1 which is a solution of (I.1.1) in both argument points, e. g., Green's or Neumann's function of D_1. These latter functions are symmetric in their argument points and are thus of the required type. We now select a countable set of points Q_ν in the domain $D_1 - \bar{D}$, $(\bar{D} = D + C)$, which has every point of $D_1 - D$ as limit point. Consider the sequence of functions

$$U_{3\nu}(P) = S(P,Q_\nu),\; U_{3\nu+1}(P) = \frac{\partial S(P,Q_\nu)}{\partial \xi_\nu} = \left.\frac{\partial S(x,y;\xi,\eta)}{\partial \xi}\right|_{\xi=\xi_\nu,\ \eta=\eta_\nu}$$
$$(2.7)\qquad U_{3\nu+2}(P) = \frac{\partial S(P,Q_\nu)}{\partial \eta_\nu} = \left.\frac{\partial S(x,y;\xi,\eta)}{\partial \eta}\right|_{\xi=\xi_\nu,\ \eta=\eta_\nu}$$

which are, considered as functions of P, in the class Σ.

In view of (I.5.8), every function $u \in \Sigma$ may be written in the form

$$(2.8)\qquad u(P) = \int_C \left[u(Q)\frac{\partial S(P,Q)}{\partial \nu_Q} - S(P,Q)\frac{\partial u(Q)}{\partial \nu_Q}\right] ds_Q$$

since $S(P,Q)$ is, by assumption, a fundamental singularity when considered as a function of Q. The integral in (2.8) may be approximated by a finite sum, uniformly in any given closed subdomain Δ of D. Thus, we find:

$$(2.9)\qquad u(P) = \sum_{\mu=1}^{N}\left[u(T_\mu)\frac{\partial S(P,T_\mu)}{\partial \nu_\mu} - S(P,T_\mu)\frac{\partial u(T_\mu)}{\partial \nu_\mu}\right]\Delta s_\mu + \eta(N)$$

where the T_μ are points on C chosen sufficiently close to each other and where $|\eta|$ can be made arbitrarily small in Δ for large enough N. Next, we remark that $S(P, Q)$ and $\text{grad}_Q S(P, Q)$ are uniformly continuous functions of $Q \in \mathsf{D}_1 - \mathsf{D}$ if P lies in the closed subdomain $\Delta \subset \mathsf{D}$. Thus, the terms

$$S(P, T_\mu) \quad \text{and} \quad \frac{\partial S(P, T_\mu)}{\partial \nu_\mu} = \frac{\partial S(P, T_\mu)}{\partial \xi_\mu} \cos(\nu_\mu, \xi_\mu) + \frac{\partial S(P, T_\mu)}{\partial \eta_\mu} \cos(\nu_\mu, \eta_\mu)$$

can be approximated arbitrarily closely by linear combinations of functions (2.7), uniformly with respect to $P \in \Delta$. Thus, we have proved that every function $u(P) \in \Sigma$ can be approximated uniformly in each closed subdomain $\Delta \subset \mathsf{D}$ by linear combinations of the functions $U_\nu(P)$ to any desired degree of precision. Similarly, we can show that $\dfrac{\partial u}{\partial x}$ and $\dfrac{\partial u}{\partial y}$ can be approximated at the same time by the gradients of the corresponding linear combinations of functions (2.7).

We shall show that the *system of solutions* (2.7) *is complete in the space of solutions of* (I.1.1). This means that every $u \in \Sigma$ can be approximated arbitrarily closely by a combination of functions $U_\nu(P)$ in the sense of the Dirichlet metric (I.2.2) defined in Σ. In other words, given a number $\varepsilon > 0$ we must show that a combination $\sum_{\nu=1}^{N} a_{N\nu} U_\nu(P)$ exists such that

$$\text{(2.10)} \qquad \mathrm{E}\left\{u - \sum_{\nu=1}^{N} a_{N\nu} U_\nu(P)\right\} < \varepsilon.$$

The completeness property can be derived from our preceding results as follows.

We remark at first that every function $u(P) \in \Sigma$ which is still a twice continuously differentiable solution of (I.1.1) in a domain D^* such that $\overline{\mathsf{D}} \subset \mathsf{D}^* \subset \mathsf{D}_1$ can be approximated in the form (2.10). In fact, we may apply our above reasoning to the domains D_1 and D^*. $\overline{\mathsf{D}}$ being a closed subdomain of D^*, we can approximate u and grad u uniformly by a combination of functions (2.7) and their gradients, respectively; hence inequality (2.10) can be satisfied.

We consider next a sequence of domains D_n such that $\mathsf{D}_n \supset \mathsf{D} + \mathsf{C}$ and $\mathsf{D}_n \supset \mathsf{D}_{n+1}$ which converges towards the domain D in the sense of Carathéodory.[1] Let $K_n(P, Q)$ be the kernel functions of these domains for

[1] Bieberbach [8], vol. 2, pp. 12—15.

the corresponding classes Σ_n of solutions of (I.1.1). If $u(P) \in \Sigma$ is given arbitrarily, the functions

(2.11) $$u_n(P) = \mathrm{E}\{K_n(P,Q), u(Q)\}$$

also belong to the class Σ and even to the class Σ_n related to the domain D_n. Hence each $u_n(P)$ can be approximated by functions $U_\nu(P)$ in the sense of the Dirichlet metric. If we could show that the $u_n(P)$ converge towards $u(P)$ in the same sense, the completeness of $\{U_\nu(P)\}$ with respect to Σ would be established; for, given an $\varepsilon > 0$, we could first determine a value n so large that

(2.12) $$\mathrm{E}\{u - u_n\} < \frac{\varepsilon}{4}$$

and next find a combination $V_n(P)$ of functions (2.7) such that

(2.13) $$\mathrm{E}\{u_n - V_n\} < \frac{\varepsilon}{4}.$$

Hence, in view of the triangle inequality (I.2.5), we would have

(2.14) $$\mathrm{E}\{u - V_n\} \leqq \varepsilon$$

which shows the completeness of the U_n in Σ.

We need therefore only prove that the $u_n(P)$ converge towards the given function $u(P) \in \Sigma$ in the sense of the Dirichlet metric. From the definition of the kernel function in terms of Green's and Neumann's functions and the continuous dependence of the latter upon the domain it can easily be shown that $u_n(P)$ and grad u_n converge to $u(P)$ and grad u uniformly in each closed subdomain Δ of D. In III.1, we shall show, furthermore, that we always have

(2.15) $$\mathrm{E}\{u_n\} \leqslant \mathrm{E}\{u\}.$$

If the integrals $\mathrm{E}\{u\}$ over D are taken in the Lebesgue sense, we obtain from the two facts mentioned above the result:

(2.16) $$\lim_{n \to \infty} \mathrm{E}\{u_n\} = \mathrm{E}\{u\}.$$

Now let a number $\varepsilon > 0$ be prescribed. We determine a closed subdomain $\Delta \subset \mathsf{D}$ such that

(2.17) $$\mathrm{E}_{D-\Delta}\{u\} < \varepsilon.$$

We choose $N(\varepsilon)$ so large that for $n > N(\varepsilon)$ we have

(2.17 a) $$|\mathrm{E}_\Delta\{u\} - \mathrm{E}_\Delta\{u_n\}| < \varepsilon,$$

(2.17 b) $$\mathrm{E}_\Delta\{u - u_n\} < \varepsilon.$$

For every $u_n(P)$ with $n > N(\varepsilon)$, we clearly have in view of (2.15), (2.17), and (2.17a)

$$
\begin{aligned}
\mathrm{E}_{D-\Delta}\{u_n\} &= \mathrm{E}\{u_n\} - \mathrm{E}_\Delta\{u_n\} \\
&= \mathrm{E}\{u_n\} - \mathrm{E}\{u\} - [\mathrm{E}_\Delta\{u_n\} - \mathrm{E}_\Delta\{u\}] + \mathrm{E}_{D-\Delta}\{u\} \\
&< 2\varepsilon.
\end{aligned} \tag{2.18}
$$

Now we are able to give a final estimate for the expression

$$\mathrm{E}\{u - u_n\} = \mathrm{E}_\Delta\{u - u_n\} + \mathrm{E}_{D-\Delta}\{u - u_n\}. \tag{2.19}$$

Using (2.17b), the triangle inequality (I.2.5), and in view of (2.17) and (2.18) we obtain

$$\mathrm{E}\{u - u_n\} < \varepsilon + \varepsilon(1 + \sqrt{2})^2. \tag{2.19'}$$

This shows that $u_n \to u$ in the sense of the Dirichlet metric. Thus our proof of the completness of the system (2.7) is established.

The main difficulty which had to be overcome in the above reasoning was the transition from uniform convergence in each closed subdomain to the convergence in the Hilbert space Σ with the Dirichlet metric $\mathrm{E}\{u\}$. Our proof is modelled on an analogous proof by Farrell in the case of analytic functions. The new feature in it is provided by the definition (2.11) of approximating solutions which are regular beyond $\mathbf{D} + \mathbf{C}$ and the fact that $\mathrm{E}\{u_n\} \leqslant \mathrm{E}\{u\}$. The importance of the latter inequality to the success of the proof is obvious and the formal considerations of (III.1) which lead to it are thus given additional interest.

From a practical point of view the above proof ensures that by proper choice of functions $S(P, Q_\nu)$ and $\operatorname{grad}_{Q_\nu} S(P, Q_\nu)$ each solution $u \in \Sigma$ can be approximated in the Dirichlet sense. The choice of the Q_ν will depend on the skill of the computer and various considerations based on the physical meaning of the problem treated. Suppose, for example, that a function $u(P) \in \Sigma$ is to be determined with prescribed boundary values and constructed in terms of a system $\{U_\nu(P)\}$. One may start with any set of points Q_ν and try to fit linear combinations of $U_\nu(P)$ to the given boundary values; one then would look for those points on $\mathbf{C}$ where the deviation is maximal and introduce as next point Q_ν a point very near to the place of maximum deviation. The corresponding functions $U_\nu(P)$ will be large near Q_ν and may be used to correct the deviation near Q_ν without destroying the good approximation to the given boundary values elsewhere. Thus, one may reduce the discrepancy on the boundary step by step and at the same time obtain a natural selection of points Q_ν.

The only difficulty in the practical application of (2.6) to boundary value problems comes from the fact that no simple criterion for the quality of the convergence of this series is known. We know that the convergence is uniform in each closed subdomain of D; but given a finite set of orthonormal functions $u_\nu(P)$ and a subdomain, we have no general rule for estimating the remainder term in the K-development. This difficulty can often be overcome by special considerations adapted to the particular orthonormal set considered. In Section 6 we shall, however, develop another numerical procedure for the construction of the kernel K where the convergence theory is more convenient.

Farrell (F 1), Kaczmarz-Steinhaus [27].

3. Integral operators and the construction of complete sets of solutions: In Section 2 it was shown how a knowledge of a fundamental singularity leads to the construction of a complete system of solutions for the class Σ. It is of importance to be able to construct complete systems without assuming a knowledge of a fundamental singularity. In the present section, we shall show how this can be done by a method of integral operators in the case where the coefficient $q(x, y)$ (Cf. I.1.1) is an analytic function. We shall deal with operators $\operatorname{Re} \boldsymbol{P}$

$$(3.1) \qquad u(x, y) = \operatorname{Re} \boldsymbol{P}\big(f(z)\big), \qquad \operatorname{Re} = \text{Real part}$$

defined on some set of analytic functions of a complex variable which converts each $f(z)$ into a solution $u(x, y)$ of (1.1.1). While a number of operators $\boldsymbol{P}$ may be found which convert each $f(z)$ into a complex solution, we shall confine ourselves here to one such operator $\boldsymbol{P}_1$, the so-called integral operator of the first kind. The operator $\operatorname{Re} \boldsymbol{P}_1$ may be regarded as a generalization of the operator "Re" which, under the correspondence $u(x, y) = \operatorname{Re} f(z)$ assigns to each analytic function $f(z)$ a harmonic function $u(x, y)$; if the coefficient $q(x, y)$ vanishes, then $\boldsymbol{P}_1$ reduces to a mapping of the space of analytic functions onto itself (defined by (3.20)). In the case in which the coefficient $q(x, y)$ is an entire function of x and y, and for the case of a simply-connected domain bounded by simple curves, the integral operator of the first kind yields a complete set of solutions which are entire functions of their arguments, and this set may be regarded as a generalization of the set $\operatorname{Re}(z^n)$, $\operatorname{Im}(z^n)$, $n = 0, 1, 2, \ldots$ for the case of Laplace's equation. The theory of integral operators is of importance in that it yields not only particular solutions of (I.1.1) but also many properties of these solutions. In the present work we shall not be able to pursue these matters beyond the construction of complete systems. It should be added that the present section may be read independently and is not needed for the subsequent development of Part B.

For the work of the present section, it will be convenient to extend the real variables x and y into the complex plane. We shall employ the notation

$$z_1 = x + i\,X, \qquad z_2 = y + i\,Y. \tag{3.2}$$

In addition we shall write

$$\begin{aligned} z &= z_1 + i\,z_2 = (x - Y) + i\,(X + y); \\ z^* &= z_1 - i\,z_2 = (x + Y) + i\,(X - y). \end{aligned} \tag{3.3}$$

The symbols z and z^* are to be regarded in general as two independent complex variables. However, when $X = Y = 0$, we have $z^* = \bar{z}$. The operators $\frac{\partial}{\partial z}$ and $\frac{\partial}{\partial z^*}$ are introduced by (cf. A. II.18)

$$\frac{\partial}{\partial z} = \frac{1}{2}\left(\frac{\partial}{\partial z_1} - i\,\frac{\partial}{\partial z_2}\right); \quad \frac{\partial}{\partial z^*} = \frac{1}{2}\left(\frac{\partial}{\partial z_1} + i\,\frac{\partial}{\partial z_2}\right). \tag{3.4}$$

Throughout the present section, we shall assume that $q\,(x, y)$ is an analytic function of x and y and may be continued analytically to yield $q\,(z_1, z_2)$ which will be presumed analytic in a sufficiently large neighborhood of $z_1 = 0$, $z_2 = 0$. The introduction of z and z^* now reduces (I.1.1) to

$$\begin{aligned} &\mathrm{L}\,(\hat{u}) \equiv \frac{\partial^2 \hat{u}}{\partial z\,\partial z^*} + \hat{q}\,(z, z^*)\,\hat{u} = 0; \\ &\hat{u}\,(z, z^*) \equiv u\,(z_1, z_2), \qquad \hat{q}\,(z, z^*) \equiv -\frac{1}{4}\,q\,(z_1, z_2). \end{aligned} \tag{3.5}$$

The consideration of the differential equation (3.5) will occupy our attention in the present section, although all our methods are immediately applicable to the more general equation $\frac{\partial^2 \hat{u}}{\partial z\,\partial z^*} + a\frac{\partial \hat{u}}{\partial z} + b\frac{\partial \hat{u}}{\partial z^*} + c\,\hat{u} = 0.$

Let $\mathbf{E}\,(z, z^*, t)$ *be a function of the three complex variables* z, z^*, t *which is analytic for* $|t| \leqslant 1$ *and in some region of the* z, z^**-space which includes* $z = 0$, $z^* = 0$. *The function* $\mathbf{E}$ *is assumed to satisfy the partial differential equation*

$$-(1 - t^2)\,E_{z^*t} + \frac{1}{t}\,E_{z^*} - 2\,t\,z\,\mathrm{L}\,(E) = 0 \tag{3.6}$$

and in addition is such that $E_{z^*}/z\,t$ is continuous at $z = 0$, $t = 0$; then if $f(z)$ is an analytic function of z regular in a neighborhood of $z = 0$,

$$\hat{u}(z, z^*) = P_1(f) \equiv \int_{-1}^{1} E(z, z^*, t)\, f\left(\frac{z}{2}(1-t^2)\right) \frac{dt}{(1-t^2)^{1/2}} \tag{3.7}$$

will be a solution of (3.5) which is regular in a sufficiently small neighborhood of $z = 0$, $z^* = 0$.

Here we have assumed that the integration is carried out along a rectifiable curve $\mathfrak{l}$ joining $t = -1$ and $t = 1$ and lying in $|t| \leqslant 1$. If $\mathfrak{l}$ does not pass through $t = 0$, we need only require that E_{z^*}/z be continuous at $z = 0$.

To prove the above theorem, we note that by formal differentiation of (3.7) we find

$$\hat{u}_{zz^*}(z, z^*) = \tag{3.8}$$

$$= \int_{-1}^{1} \left(E_{zz^*}(z, z^*, t)\, f\left(\frac{z}{2}(1-t^2)\right) + E_{z^*}(z, z^*, t) \frac{\partial f\left(\frac{z}{2}(1-t^2)\right)}{\partial z} \right) \frac{dt}{(1-t^2)^{1/2}}.$$

Since the argument of f is $\frac{z}{2}(1-t^2)$, we have $f_z = -f_t(1-t^2)/2\,z\,t$, so that

$$\hat{u}_{zz^*}(z, z^*) = \int_{-1}^{1} \left(E_{zz^*} f - E_{z^*}(1-t^2)(2\,z\,t)^{-1} f_t\right) \frac{dt}{(1-t^2)^{1/2}}. \tag{3.9}$$

Integrating the second term by parts

$$\hat{u}_{zz^*} = \int_{-1}^{1} E_{zz^*} f \frac{dt}{(1-t^2)^{1/2}} - \left(\frac{E_{z^*}(1-t^2)^{1/2}}{2\,z\,t} f\left(\frac{z}{2}(1-t^2)\right)\right)\Bigg|_{t=-1}^{t=+1} +$$

$$+ \int_{-1}^{1} \left(\frac{E_{z^*}(1-t^2)^{1/2}}{2\,z\,t}\right)_t f\,dt = \int_{-1}^{1} \left(\frac{E_{zz^*}}{(1-t^2)^{1/2}} + \left(\frac{E_{z^*}(1-t^2)^{1/2}}{2\,z\,t}\right)_t\right) f\left(\frac{z}{2}(1-t^2)\right) dt,$$

in view of the continuity condition on $E_{z^*}/z\,t$. It is now evident from (3.5), (3.7), and (3.8) that if E satisfies (3.6), then $\hat{u}$ will satisfy (3.5).

We shall now show that it is possible to find a generating function $E(z, z^*, t)$ which satisfies all the requirements of the previous theorem and is such that

$$E(0, z^*, t) = 1, \qquad E(z, 0, t) = 1. \tag{3.10}$$

These additional requirements will insure that our integral operator $\operatorname{Re} \boldsymbol{P}_1$ will possess many properties of the operator "Re". We tentatively adopt the form

$$E(z, z^*, t) = 1 + \sum_{n=1}^{\infty} t^{2n} z^n \int_0^{z^*} P^{(2n)}(z, z^*)\, dz^* \tag{3.11}$$

which clearly satisfies (3.10) and the continuity condition on $E_{z^*}/z\,t$. Substituting (3.11) into the partial differential equation (3.6) and comparing powers of t, we find that the functions $P^{(2n)}(z, z^*)$ must be subjected to the recursion relations

$$P^{(2)}(z, z^*) = -2\,\hat{q}\,(z, z^*), \tag{3.12 a}$$

$$(2n+1)\,P^{(2n+2)}(z, z^*) = \tag{3.12 b}$$

$$= -2\left(P_z^{(2n)} + \hat{q}\,(z, z^*) \int_0^{z^*} P^{(2n)}(z, z^*)\, dz^*\right), \qquad (n = 1, 2, \ldots,).$$

Thus, a knowledge of $\hat{q}\,(z, z^*)$ determines $P^{(2)}$ through (3.12a) and successively all the $P^{(2n)}$ through (3.12b).

If (3.11) converges uniformly for $|t| \leqslant 1$ and z, z^* in a neighborhood of the origin, then it will be a representation of a generating function for the differential equation (3.5). We shall call the integral operator (3.7) which utilizes the generating function (3.11), *the integral operator of the first kind.* We turn now to the proof of the convergence of (3.11). This will be accomplished by the method of dominants [cf. (A. II.22) where this method was applied to an equation with a singular coefficient. This method of generating solutions of the compressibility equation is effectively an integral operator of a second kind]. If we are given two series

$$L = \sum_{m,\,n=0} a_{mn} z^m z^{*n}, \qquad \tilde{L} = \sum_{m,\,n=0} \tilde{a}_{mn} z^m z^{*n},$$

where $\tilde{a}_{mn} \geqslant 0$, then we shall say that the series $\tilde{L}$ *dominates* the series L if $|a_{mn}| \leqslant \tilde{a}_{mn}$, $(m, n = 0, 1, \ldots,)$, and we shall write $L \ll \tilde{L}$. This definition is equivalent to the one which was already introduced in (A.II.22). The following properties of dominant series are easily established. If $L \ll \tilde{L}$, then

$$\frac{\partial L}{\partial z} \ll \frac{\partial \tilde{L}}{\partial z}, \qquad \int_0^{z^*} L(z, z^*)\, dz^* \ll \int_0^{z^*} \tilde{L}(z, z^*)\, dz^*, \qquad L \ll \frac{\tilde{L}}{(1 - a\,z)}, \qquad a \geqslant 0.$$

By hypothesis, $\hat{q}\,(z, z^*)$ is regular for $z = 0$, $z^* = 0$. Hence, we have $\hat{q}\,(z, z^*) = \sum_{m,\,n=0}^{\infty} a_{mn}\, z^m z^{*n}$ convergent uniformly and absolutely in $|z| \leqslant r$, $|z^*| \leqslant r$ for some $r > 0$. It follows that for some $M > 0$, $|a_{mn}\, r^m r^n| < M$, $(m, n = 0, 1, 2, \ldots,)$, and hence

$$\hat{q}\,(z, z^*) \ll M \left(1 - \frac{z}{r}\right)^{-1} \left(1 - \frac{z^*}{r}\right)^{-1} \equiv \tilde{q}\,(z, z^*). \tag{3.13}$$

We shall now introduce functions $\tilde{P}^{(2n)}\,(z, z^*)$, $(n = 1, 2, \ldots,)$, by recursion as follows

$$\tilde{P}^{(2)}\,(z, z^*) = 2\,\tilde{q}\,(z, z^*), \tag{3.14 a}$$

$$(2\,n + 1)\,\tilde{P}^{(2\,n+2)}\,(z, z^*) = \tag{3.14 b}$$

$$= 2 \left(\tilde{P}_z^{(2\,n)} \left(1 - \frac{z^*}{r}\right)^{-1} + \tilde{q} \int_0^{z^*} \tilde{P}^{(2\,n)} \left(1 - \frac{z^*}{r}\right)^{-1} dz^* + \right.$$

$$\left. + \, c^{(2\,n)}\, r\, M\, n^{-1} \left(1 - \frac{z}{r}\right)^{-n-1} \left(1 - \frac{z^*}{r}\right)^{-1} \right), \qquad (n = 1, 2, \ldots,),$$

where

$$c^{(2)} = 2\,M \tag{3.15 a}$$

$$c^{(2n+2)} = c^{(2\,n)} \left(\frac{2\,n}{2\,n+1} \cdot \frac{1}{r} + \frac{2\,M\,r}{n\,(2\,n+1)} \right), \qquad (n = 1, 2, \ldots,). \tag{3.15 b}$$

The functions $\tilde{P}^{(2n)}\,(z, z^*)$ are uniquely determined by (3.14), (3.15), and in view of our previous remarks we have $P^{(2n)}\,(z, z^*) \ll \tilde{P}^{(2n)}\,(z, z^*)$. Furthermore, by means of (3.14), (3.15), it is easily shown by induction that

$$\tilde{P}^{(2\,n)}\,(z, z^*) = c^{(2\,n)} \left(1 - \frac{z}{r}\right)^{-n} \left(1 - \frac{z^*}{r}\right)^{-n}, \qquad (n = 1, 2, \ldots,). \tag{3.16}$$

In view of the fact that the bracketed expression in (3.15b) approaches r^{-1} as $n \to \infty$, we have, for every $\varepsilon > 0$, $c^{(2n)} \leqslant N \left(\frac{1+\varepsilon}{r}\right)^n$, $(n = 1, 2, \ldots,)$, for some $N = N\,(\varepsilon)$. Thus, finally we have

$$\tilde{P}^{(2\,n)} \ll \frac{N\,(1+\varepsilon)^n}{r^n \left(1 - \frac{z}{r}\right)^n \left(1 - \frac{z^*}{r}\right)^n}, \qquad (n = 1, 2, \ldots,). \tag{3.17}$$

It is now clear that

$$1 + N \int_0^{z^*} \sum_{n=1}^{\infty} \frac{z^n (1+\varepsilon)^n}{r^n \left(1 - \frac{z}{r}\right)^n \left(1 - \frac{z^*}{r}\right)^n} dz^* \tag{3.18}$$

is a dominant for (3.11) with $|t| \leqslant 1$. But since ε is arbitrary, (3.18) will converge uniformly and absolutely provided

$$\left| \frac{z}{r\left(1 - \frac{z}{r}\right)\left(1 - \frac{z^*}{r}\right)} \right| \leqslant \eta < 1. \tag{3.19}$$

The region satisfying (3.19) includes the origin $z = 0$, $z^* = 0$, so that the series (3.11) for the generating function of the first kind converges in at least this same region. It should be pointed out that *if the coefficient* $q(z_1, z_2)$ *is an entire function of* z_1, z_2, *i. e., is analytic for* $|z_1| < \infty$, $|z_2| < \infty$, *then the representation* (3.11) *is valid over the entire plane.*

From (3.7) and (3.10), we recognize that

$$\hat{u}(z, 0) = \int_{-1}^{1} f\left(\frac{z}{2}(1 - t^2)\right) \frac{dt}{(1 - t^2)^{1/2}} \equiv g(z). \tag{3.20}$$

It is easily seen that this formula can be inverted in the form

$$f\left(\frac{z}{2}\right) = -\frac{1}{2\pi} \int_{-1}^{1} g\left(z(1 - t^2)\right) \frac{dt}{t^2} \tag{3.21}$$

and instead of considering u as a linear functional of f we can as well consider it a linear functional of g, and in this context we shall write $P_1(f) \equiv p_1(g)$. The importance of g lies in the fact that the differential equation (3.5) can be considered to be formally of hyperbolic type and $g(z)$ appears as the initial value of $\hat{u}(z, z^*)$ at $z^* = 0$. We also derive from (3.7), (3.10), and (3.20) that

$$\hat{u}(0, z^*) = g(0). \tag{3.22}$$

These two initial conditions determine the solution uniquely. The classical method of successive approximations leads to the following additional representation of the integral operator of the first kind as a Neumann type series

$$\hat{u}(z, z^*) = g(z) - \int_0^z \int_0^{z^*} \hat{q}(z_1, z_1^*)\, g(z_1)\, dz_1\, dz_1^* + \\ + \int_0^z \int_0^{z^*} \hat{q}(z_1, z_1^*) \int_0^{z_1} \int_0^{z_1^*} \hat{q}(z_2, z_2^*)\, g(z_2)\, dz_2\, dz_2^*\, dz_1\, dz_1^* - \ldots \tag{3.23}$$

If $g(z)$ is regular in a region R containing $z = 0$ and if $\hat{q}(z, z^*)$ is regular in $\mathsf{R} \times \mathsf{R}$ (i. e., in the four-dimensional region consisting of points $z \in \mathsf{R}$, $z^* \in \mathsf{R}$), then the series (3.23) is easily shown to converge uniformly and absolutely in every closed subregion of $\mathsf{R} \times \mathsf{R}$ and will be a solution of (3.5). Since furthermore, $\hat{u}(0, z^*) = g(0)$ and $\hat{u}(z, 0) = g(z)$, a property which is shared by p_1, it follows that we may identify the series (3.23) with $p_1(g)$. The use of the integral operator of the first kind may therefore be regarded as equivalent to the Riemann-Picard method in the theory of linear hyperbolic equations.[1] In the case of a *fixed* differential equation, the explicit formula (3.7) replaces the series development (3.23) by the calculation of one fixed function $E(z, z^*, t)$ from which all solutions can be obtained by a single integration.

The Riemann-Picard method may be applied (in the case of an analytic q) to yield an explicit representation of a fundamental singularity for (3.5). To this end, let us introduce the additional complex variables

$$\zeta = \zeta_1 + i\,\zeta_2; \quad \zeta^* = \zeta_1 - i\,\zeta_2; \quad \zeta_1 = \xi + i\,\Xi; \quad \zeta_2 = \eta + iH. \tag{3.24}$$

Let $\hat{q}(z, z^*)$ be regular in a sufficiently large domain B^4. Then

$$\hat{S}(z, z^*; \zeta, \zeta^*) = \frac{1}{2} \chi(z, z^*; \zeta, \zeta^*) \left(\log(z - \zeta) + \log(z^* - \zeta^*)\right) + \\ + v(z, z^*; \zeta, \zeta^*), \tag{3.25}$$

where

$$\chi(z, z^*; \zeta, \zeta^*) = 1 - \int_\zeta^z \int_{\zeta^*}^{z^*} \hat{q}(z_1, z_1^*)\, dz_1\, dz_1^* + \\ + \int_\zeta^z \int_{\zeta^*}^{z^*} \hat{q} \left(\int_\zeta^{z_1} \int_{\zeta^*}^{z_1^*} \hat{q}\, dz_2\, dz_2^* \right) dz_1\, dz_1^* - \ldots, \tag{3.26}$$

---

[1] Cf., e. g., Courant-Hilbert [13], vol. 2, Ch. V, § 5.

$$\nu(z, z^*; \zeta, \zeta^*) = \int_{\zeta}^{z}\int_{\zeta^*}^{z^*} G\, dz_1\, dz_1^* - \int_{\zeta}^{z}\int_{\zeta^*}^{z^*} \hat{q}\left(\int_{\zeta}^{z_1}\int_{\zeta^*}^{z_1^*} G\, dz_2\, dz_2^*\right) dz_1\, dz_1^* + \tag{3.27}$$
$$+ \int_{\zeta}^{z}\int_{\zeta^*}^{z^*} \hat{q}\left(\int_{\zeta}^{z_1}\int_{\zeta^*}^{z_1^*} \hat{q}\left(\int_{\zeta}^{z_2}\int_{\zeta^*}^{z_2^*} G\, dz_3\, dz_3^*\right) dz_2\, dz_2^*\right) dz_1\, dz_1^* - \ldots$$

and

$$G(z, z^*; \zeta, \zeta^*) = -\left(\frac{1}{z^* - \zeta^*}\frac{\partial \chi}{\partial z} + \frac{1}{z - \zeta}\frac{\partial \chi}{\partial z^*}\right), \tag{3.28}$$

is a fundamental singularity for (3.5). It is clear from (3.26) that χ is an analytic function of z, z^* in $\mathbf{B}^4$. A similar result will hold for ν providing we can show that G is regular in $\mathbf{B}^4$. Now,

$$\frac{\partial \chi}{\partial z} = - \int_{\zeta^*}^{z^*} \hat{q}\, dz_1^* + \int_{\zeta^*}^{z^*} \hat{q}\left(\int_{\zeta}^{z_1}\int_{\zeta^*}^{z_1^*} \hat{q}\, dz_2\, dz_2^*\right) dz_1^* - \ldots. \tag{3.29}$$

Since $\hat{q}(z, z^*)$ (and the other integrands) can be developed in the series

$$\hat{q}(z, z^*) = \sum_{m,n=0}^{\infty} a_{mn} z^m z^{*n}, \quad \text{so that} \quad \int_{\zeta^*}^{z^*} \hat{q}\, dz_1^* = \sum_{m,n=0}^{\infty} \frac{a_{mn}}{n+1} z^m (z^{*n+1} - \zeta^{*n+1}),$$

it is clear that the first term of (3.29) (and also the other terms) have the factor $(z^* - \zeta^*)$. Thus $\frac{1}{z^* - \zeta^*}\frac{\partial \chi}{\partial z}$ is regular in $\mathbf{B}^4$. A similar argument holds for $\frac{1}{z - \zeta}\frac{\partial \chi}{\partial z^*}$ and therefore by (3.28), G is regular in $\mathbf{B}^4$, and by (3.27) ν must also be regular there. It is now clear that $\hat{S}$ can be singular only for $z = \zeta$ and for $z^* = \zeta^*$ and possesses a logarithmic singularity there. To complete the proof, we need only show that $\hat{S}$ is a solution of (3.5). Substituting in (3.5) there is obtained,

$$\frac{1}{2}\Big(\log(z - \zeta) + \log(z^* - \zeta^*)\Big)(\chi_{zz^*} + \hat{q}\,\chi) + \tag{3.30}$$
$$+ \frac{1}{2}\frac{\chi_{z^*}}{z - \zeta} + \frac{1}{2}\frac{\chi_z}{z^* - \zeta^*} + \nu_{zz^*} + \hat{q}\,\nu = 0.$$

But from (3.26) and (3.27) we have $\chi_{zz^*} + \hat{q}\,\chi = 0$ while $\nu_{zz^*} + \hat{q}\,\nu = G$. Equation (3.5) is therefore satisfied identically. This proves that $\hat{S}$ is a fundamental singularity defined for $(z, z^*) \in \mathsf{B}^4$, $(\zeta, \zeta^*) \in \mathsf{B}^4$. Let us observe that we have just proved that S may be continued analytically to complex values of x, y.

We shall now show that *if the coefficient* $q(z_1, z_2)$ *is regular in a sufficiently large region, then any real solution* $u(x, y)$ *of* (I.1.1) *which is regular in a simply-connected domain* B *of the real* x, y*-plane can be continued analytically to yield a solution* $u(z_1, z_2) \equiv \hat{u}(z, z^*)$ *which is regular in a four-dimensional domain* B^4 *of* z_1, z_2*-space. The domain* B^4 *depends on* B *but is independent of* $q(z_1, z_2)$. B^4 *is the product domain* $\mathsf{B} \times \mathsf{B}$. To prove this, we write by (I.5.8)

$$u(x, y) = \hat{u}(x + iy, x - iy) = \tag{3.31}$$

$$= \frac{1}{2\pi} \int_{\mathsf{b}} \left(u(\xi, \eta) \frac{\partial S(x, y; \xi, \eta)}{\partial \nu_{\xi, \eta}} - \frac{\partial u(\xi, \eta)}{\partial \nu_{\xi, \eta}} S(x, y; \xi, \eta) \right) ds_{\xi, \eta}$$

where b is the boundary of B. The normal differentiation and integration in (3.31) are to be considered with respect to the variables ξ, η. The solution u may therefore be continued analytically by means of the formula

$$u(z_1, z_2) = \frac{1}{2\pi} \int_{\mathsf{b}} \left(u(\xi, \eta) \frac{\partial S(z_1, z_2; \xi, \eta)}{\partial \nu_{\xi, \eta}} - \frac{\partial u(\xi, \eta)}{\partial \nu_{\xi, \eta}} S(z_1, z_2; \xi, \eta) \right) ds_{\xi, \eta}. \tag{3.32}$$

In (3.32), it should be emphasized that the z's are complex variables while the variables ζ_1 and ζ_2 are real. Now S becomes singular only if

$$z_1 + i z_2 - \xi - i\eta = 0 \qquad (\xi, \eta) \in \mathsf{b}, \tag{3.33 a}$$

$$z_1 - i z_2 - \xi + i\eta = 0 \qquad (\xi, \eta) \in \mathsf{b}. \tag{3.33 b}$$

If we start at a point $z, z^* \in \mathsf{B} \times \mathsf{B}$ we may continue $u(z_1, z_2)$ analytically till (3.33 a) or (3.33 b) is fulfilled, i. e., until we reach the boundary of $\mathsf{B} \times \mathsf{B}$. This shows that $u(z_1, z_2)$ is regular in the domain $\mathsf{B}^4 = \mathsf{B} \times \mathsf{B}$.

In addition to the operator $\boldsymbol{P}_1$, it will be convenient to introduce an operator $\boldsymbol{P}_2$ such that for real values of $z_1, z_2, \boldsymbol{P}_2$ is conjugate to $\boldsymbol{P}_1$. This may be accomplished by interchanging the roles of z and z^* in (3.11), (3.12a), (3.12b) and taking the conjugates of all coefficients. Our previous proof shows that $\boldsymbol{P}_2$ is also defined in a neighborhood of the origin. The corresponding operator defined on g will be denoted by $\boldsymbol{p}_2$ and the corresponding $\boldsymbol{E}$ function by $\boldsymbol{E}_2$.

For a given analytic function $f(z)$, the analytic function $\bar{f}(z)$ will be defined by $\bar{f}(z) \equiv \overline{f(\bar{z})}$. For a fixed $f(z)$, $\boldsymbol{P}_1(f(z))$ and $\boldsymbol{P}_2(\bar{f}(z^*))$ will be two functions of the complex variables z and z^*. In order to exhibit their explicit dependence upon z and z^*, we shall write $P_1(f(z); z, z^*)$ and $P_2(\bar{f}(z^*); z, z^*)$. These two functions are now conjugate in the real plane, i. e., for $z^* = \bar{z}$. More explicitly we have,

$$\text{(3.34)} \quad P_1(f(x+iy); x+iy, x-iy) = \overline{P_2(\bar{f}(x-iy); x+iy, x-iy)}.$$

It follows that

$$\text{(3.35)} \quad u(x, y) = \\ = \frac{1}{2}\Big(P_1(f(x+iy); x+iy, x-iy) + P_2(\bar{f}(x-iy); x+iy, x-iy)\Big)$$

is therefore a *real* solution of (I.1.1) which is regular in a neighborhood of $x=0$, $y=0$. For, consider the solution $P_1(f(x+iy); x+iy, x-iy)$. This is, in general, a complex function of the two real variables x, y which satisfies a differential equation (I.1.1) with real coefficients. Similarly, $P_2(\bar{f}(x-iy); x+iy, x-iy)$ is such a complex solution and the two solutions may be shown independent. Inasmuch as the coefficients of the differential equation are real, it follows that the real and imaginary parts of these solutions are real solutions which are regular in a neighborhood of the origin. It is easily shown that *assuming $q(x, y)$ is regular in a sufficiently large region (when continued to the complex values z_1, z_2), then $P_1(f(x+iy); x+iy, x-iy)$ is regular in the regularity domain of $f(z)$, the latter being supposed simply connected.* By our hypothesis on $q(x, y)$, r may be chosen arbitrarily large in (3.18) and (3.19), so that we may drop the assumption $|t| \leqslant 1$ and still have the convergence of (3.11) in as large a domain as is needed. We use the representation

$$\text{(3.36)} \quad P_1(f(x+iy); x+iy, x-iy) = \\ = \int_{-1}^{1} E(x+iy, x-iy, t)\, f\left(\frac{x+iy}{2}(1-t^2)\right) \frac{dt}{(1-t^2)^{1/2}}.$$

If, now, $f(z)$ is regular in a simply-connected domain B which contains $z=0$, then to every $z_1 \in \mathsf{B}$, we may select a path $\mathsf{p} = \mathsf{p}_{z_1}$ in the complex t-plane which joins $t=-1$ and $t=+1$ so that $z(1-t^2)$ lies in B for all $t \in \mathsf{p}$ and for all z in a sufficiently small neighborhood of z_1. Since q and hence E is regular in a sufficiently large domain, the statement now follows.

We have just seen that $u(x, y)$ given by (3.35) is a real solution of (I.1.1) which is regular in the regularity domain of f and $\bar{f}$. Conversely, *every real solution $u(x, y)$ of (I.1.1) can be represented in a sufficiently small neighborhood of $x=0$, $y=0$ in the form (3.35) for an appropriate $f(z)$.*

For, since our differential equation is of elliptic type and possesses an analytic coefficient $q(x, y)$, any solution $u(z_1, z_2)$ must, by a classical result, possess an expansion of the form

$$(3.37) \qquad u(z_1, z_2) = \sum_{m,n=0}^{\infty} a_{mn} z^m z^{*n}; \qquad a_{mn} = \overline{a_{nm}}$$

which is valid in the small. In particular, if we put in turn $z^* = 0$ and $z = 0$, we obtain

$$(3.38) \qquad \begin{aligned} u(z_1, -i z_1) &= \sum_{m=0}^{\infty} a_{m0} z^m \equiv G_1(z), \qquad z = 2 z_1; \\ u(-i z_2, z_2) &= \sum_{m=0} a_{0m} z^{*m} \equiv G_2(z^*), \qquad z^* = -2 i z_2. \end{aligned}$$

Here G_1 and G_2 are two analytic functions of the complex variables z and z^* which are regular in a neighborhood of the origin. We note also that since $a_{m0} = \overline{a_{0m}}$, we have $G_2(\overline{z}) = \overline{G_1(z)}$ and $G_1(0) = G_2(0)$. On the other hand, if functions $G_1(z)$ and $G_2(z^*)$ are given, $G_1(0) = G_2(0)$, there exists one and only one solution $u(z_1, z_2)$ which satisfies (I.1.1) and such that (3.38) holds. We can determine two functions $g_1(z)$ and $g_2(z^*)$ such that $g_2(\overline{z}) = \overline{g_1(z)}$ and such that

$$(3.39) \qquad g_1(z) + g_2(0) = G_1(z), \qquad g_2(z^*) + g_1(0) = G_2(z^*);$$

then it may be immediately verified that

$$(3.40) \qquad u(x, y) = \\ = \frac{1}{2} [p_1 \big(g_1(x + i y); x + i y, x - i y\big) + p_2 \big(g_2(x - i y); x + i y, x - i y\big)].$$

Let us introduce the particular set of solutions

$$(3.41) \qquad \begin{aligned} u_{2\nu-1}(x, y) &= \mathrm{Re}\, [p_1 \big((x + i y)^\nu;\ x + i y, x - i y\big)] \\ u_{2\nu}(x, y) &= \mathrm{Im}\, [p_1 \big((x + i y)^\nu;\ x + i y, x - i y\big)], \quad (\nu = 0, 1, \ldots,). \end{aligned}$$

We shall show that *the system* $\{u_\nu(x, y)\}$ *is complete with respect to solutions of* (I.1.1) *which are regular in* $\overline{\mathsf{B}}$. Let $u(x, y)$ be a regular solution in a simply-connected domain $\overline{\mathsf{B}}$. By our previous result, it may be continued analytically to yield $\hat{u}(z, z^*)$ which is regular in $\overline{\mathsf{B}} \times \overline{\mathsf{B}}$. The functions $\hat{u}(0, z^*)$ and $\hat{u}(z, 0)$ are therefore regular in B. By (3.38)—(3.39), we have $g_1(z) = \hat{u}(z, 0) + \text{const.}$, $g_2(z^*) = \hat{u}(0, z^*) + \text{const.}$ Thus g_1 and g_2

are regular in $\overline{\mathsf{B}}$, $g_2(\overline{z}) = \overline{g_1(z)}$, and (3.40) holds. By Runge's theorem, given an ε, $\varepsilon > 0$, there exist coefficients $A_{N\nu}$ such that

$$g_1(z) = \sum_{\nu=0}^{N} A_{N\nu} z^\nu + \varepsilon_N(z); \quad g_2(z^*) = \sum_{\nu=0}^{N} \overline{A_{N\nu}} z^{*\nu} + \varepsilon_N'(z^*) \tag{3.42 a}$$

where

$$|\varepsilon_N(z)| \leqslant \varepsilon, \qquad z \in \overline{\mathsf{B}}, \qquad |\varepsilon_N'(z^*)| \leqslant \varepsilon, \qquad z^* \in \overline{\mathsf{B}}. \tag{3.42 b}$$

Thus, it appears from (3.40) and (3.42a), and the integral representation (3.7) that $u(x, y)$ may be approximated arbitrarily closely in $\overline{\mathsf{B}}$ by a linear combination of the solutions

$$p_1((x+iy)^\nu; x+iy, x-iy), \qquad p_2((x-iy)^\nu; x+iy, x-iy).$$

Our statement now follows in view of (3.34). It also may be shown that the set (3.41) *is complete with respect to solutions of the class* Σ.

Bergman (B 6), (B 10), (B 14), (B 15).

4. Dirichlet identities: In the present section we present a number of formal results which will be required in the sequel and which are of considerable interest in themselves. Formula (2.6) applied to two functions v and $w \in \Sigma$ gives

$$\mathrm{E}\{v, w\} = -\int_{\mathsf{C}} v \frac{\partial w}{\partial \nu} ds = -\int_{\mathsf{C}} w \frac{\partial v}{\partial \nu} ds, \qquad v, w \in \Sigma. \tag{4.1}$$

By means of these formulas and the boundary behavior of Green's and Neumann's functions, we can obtain various identities for the Dirichlet product between the functions n and g defined in I.5. We start with the product:

$$\mathrm{E}\{g(T,P), g(T,Q)\} = -\int_{\mathsf{C}} g(T,P) \frac{\partial g(T,Q)}{\partial \nu_T} ds_T = \int_{\mathsf{C}} S(T,P) \frac{\partial g(T,Q)}{\partial \nu_T} ds_T. \tag{4.2}$$

By virtue of (I.5.8) and (I.5.11), we may transform this latter integral and obtain

$$\mathrm{E}\{g(T,P), g(T,Q)\} = -g(P,Q) - \int_{\mathsf{C}} S(T,Q) \frac{\partial S(T,P)}{\partial \nu_T} ds_T. \tag{4.3}$$

In order to clarify the aim of our transformation, it should be understood that *we will consider a symmetric fundamental singularity* $S(P,Q)$ *as known*, while the quantities g and n are related to S by means of a boundary value problem with respect to (I.1.1) and the domain D and are of a more involved character. We set

$$I(P,Q) = \int_{\mathsf{C}} S(T,Q) \frac{\partial S(T,P)}{\partial \nu_T} ds_T \tag{4.4}$$

and consider it a *geometric quantity*, i. e., a quantity which depends only on the geometry of D once a fundamental singularity $S(P,Q)$ is known and fixed. Thus:

$$\mathrm{E}\{g(T,P), g(T,Q)\} = -g(P,Q) - I(P,Q) \tag{4.3'}$$

i. e., the g-functions reproduce themselves under Dirichlet multiplication except for an additive geometric quantity and the minus sign.

Similarly, we find from (4.1) and the boundary values of g and $\dfrac{\partial n}{\partial \nu}$:

$$\begin{aligned} \mathrm{E}\{g(T,P), n(T,Q)\} &= -\int_{\mathsf{C}} g(T,P) \frac{\partial n(T,Q)}{\partial \nu_T} ds_T = \\ &= -\int_{\mathsf{C}} S(T,P) \frac{\partial S(T,Q)}{\partial \nu_T} ds_T \end{aligned} \tag{4.4'}$$

i. e.,

$$\mathrm{E}\{g(T,P), n(T,Q)\} = -I(Q,P) = -I(P,Q), \tag{4.4''}$$

is a *geometric quantity*. The symmetry of $I(P,Q)$ can immediately be seen from (4.3') where all other terms are symmetric in P and Q, or from (I.5.10).

Finally, in the same way we compute, using (I.5.8),

$$\mathrm{E}\{n(T,P), n(T,Q)\} = -\int_{\mathsf{C}} n(T,P) \frac{\partial n(T,Q)}{\partial \nu_T} ds_T = \tag{4.5}$$

$$= \int_{\mathsf{C}} n(T,P) \frac{\partial S(T,Q)}{\partial \nu_T} ds_T = n(Q,P) + \int_{\mathsf{C}} S(T,Q) \frac{\partial n(T,P)}{\partial \nu_T} ds_T =$$

$$= n(Q,P) - \int_{\mathsf{C}} S(T,Q) \frac{\partial S(T,P)}{\partial \nu_T} ds_T = n(P,Q) - I(P,Q).$$

The identities (4.3′), (4.4″), and (4.5) are a source of valuable information for the important functions $n(P,Q)$ and $g(P,Q)$. We mention the following application. Let $P_1, P_2, \ldots, P_m$ be an arbitrary set of points in D; let $x_i, \ldots, x_m$ be a set of real numbers. Then from (4.3′) and (4.5) we obtain

$$(4.6)\qquad -\sum_{i,k=1}^{m} [g(P_i,P_k)+I(P_i,P_k)]\,x_i x_k = \mathrm{E}\left\{\sum_{i=1}^{m} x_i g(T,P_i)\right\} \geqslant 0,$$

$$(4.7)\qquad \sum_{i,k=1}^{m} [n(P_i,P_k)-I(P_i,P_k)]\,x_i x_k = \mathrm{E}\left\{\sum_{i=1}^{m} x_i n(T,P_i)\right\} \geqslant 0.$$

On the other hand, we derive from (4.4″)

$$(4.8)\qquad \mathrm{E}\left\{\sum_{i=1}^{m} x_i g(T,P_i), \sum_{i=1}^{m} x_i n(T,P_i)\right\} = -\sum_{i,k=1}^{m} I(P_i,P_k)\,x_i x_k.$$

Hence, by the Schwarz inequality, we can combine (4.6), (4.7), and (4.8) and obtain

$$(4.9)\qquad \left(\sum_{i,k=1}^{m} I(P_i,P_k)\,x_i x_k\right)^2 \leqslant \sum_{i,k=1}^{m} [n(P_i,P_k)-I(P_i,P_k)]\,x_i x_k \cdot \sum_{i,k=1}^{m} [-g(P_i,P_k)-I(P_i,P_k)]\,x_i x_k.$$

Thus, the values of n and g satisfy a great number of inequalities in which the geometric integrals $I(P,Q)$ are involved.

Since inequality (4.6) holds for an arbitrary choice of the points $P_i \in$ D and the weight factor x_i, we can extend it to a continuous distribution of weight $\varphi(P)$ over all points $P \in$ D; we thus obtain the inequality

$$\iint_D \iint_D g(P,Q)\varphi(P)\varphi(Q)\,d\tau_P d\tau_Q + \iint_D \iint_D I(P,Q)\varphi(P)\varphi(Q)\,d\tau_P d\tau_Q =$$

$$(4.10)\qquad = -\mathrm{E}\left\{\iint_D \varphi(P)\,g(T,P)\,d\tau_P\right\} \leqslant 0.$$

which is valid for any continuous function $\varphi(P)$ in D + C.

This result is closely related to the theory of the inhomogeneous differential equation connected with (I.1.1). Let us consider an arbitrary continuous function φ in $\mathsf{D}+\mathsf{C}$ and the partial differential equation

$$\Delta\Phi - q\Phi = \varphi, \qquad \Phi = 0 \text{ on } \mathsf{C}, \qquad q > 0. \tag{4.11}$$

By means of Green's function we can solve this problem in the form

$$\Phi(P) = -\iint_{\mathsf{D}} G(P,Q)\,\varphi(Q)\,d\tau_Q. \tag{4.12}$$

Now, using (4.11) and Green's identity, we find

$$-\iint_{\mathsf{D}}\iint_{\mathsf{D}} G(P,Q)\,\varphi(P)\,\varphi(Q)\,d\tau_P\,d\tau_Q = \iint_{\mathsf{D}} \Phi(P)\,\varphi(P)\,d\tau_P = \tag{4.13}$$

$$= \iint_{\mathsf{D}} \Phi(P)\,[\Delta\Phi - q\Phi]\,d\tau_P = -\mathrm{E}\{\Phi\}.$$

Thus, we have proved the following inequality valid for Green's function and any continuous function $\varphi(P)$:

$$\iint_{\mathsf{D}}\iint_{\mathsf{D}} G(P,Q)\,\varphi(P)\,\varphi(Q)\,d\tau_P\,d\tau_Q = \mathrm{E}\left\{\iint_{\mathsf{D}} G(P,Q)\,\varphi(Q)\,d\tau_Q\right\} \geqslant 0. \tag{4.14}$$

If we decompose Green's function according to (I.5.11) we arrive at

$$\begin{aligned}&\iint_{\mathsf{D}}\iint_{\mathsf{D}} g(P,Q)\,\varphi(P)\,\varphi(Q)\,d\tau_P\,d\tau_Q + \\ &+ \iint_{\mathsf{D}}\iint_{\mathsf{D}} S(P,Q)\,\varphi(P)\,\varphi(Q)\,d\tau_P\,d\tau_Q = \mathrm{E}\{\Phi\}.\end{aligned} \tag{4.14'}$$

Now let

$$\psi(P) = -\iint_{\mathsf{D}} S(P,Q)\,\varphi(Q)\,d\tau_Q. \tag{4.15}$$

Clearly, $\psi(P)$ also satisfies the differential equation (4.11) but does not vanish on C. We transform the second left-hand term in (4.14′) as follows:

$$-\iint_{\mathsf{D}} \psi\varphi\,d\tau = -\iint_{\mathsf{D}} \psi\,[\Delta\psi - q\psi]\,d\tau = \mathrm{E}\{\psi\} + \int_{\mathsf{C}} \psi\,\frac{\partial\psi}{\partial\nu}\,ds. \tag{4.16}$$

Using definitions (4.4) and (4.15), we have further

$$\int_C \psi \frac{\partial \psi}{\partial \nu} ds = \iint_D \iint_D I(P,Q)\,\varphi(P)\,\varphi(Q)\,d\tau_P\,d\tau_Q. \tag{4.17}$$

Thus, (4.14′) attains the form

$$\iint_D \iint_D [g(P,Q) + I(P,Q)]\,\varphi(P)\,\varphi(Q)\,d\tau_P\,d\tau_Q = \mathrm{E}\{\Phi\} - \mathrm{E}\{\psi\}. \tag{4.18}$$

In view of (4.10), we arrive at

$$\mathrm{E}\{\Phi\} - \mathrm{E}\{\psi\} = \mathrm{E}\left\{\iint_D G(P,Q)\,\varphi(Q)\,d\tau_Q\right\} - \mathrm{E}\left\{\iint_D S(P,Q)\,\varphi(Q)\,d\tau_Q\right\} =$$

$$= -\mathrm{E}\left\{\iint_D g(P,Q)\,\varphi(Q)\,d\tau_Q\right\} \leqslant 0. \tag{4.19}$$

Thus, in particular:

$$\mathrm{E}\{\Phi\} \leqslant \mathrm{E}\{\psi\} \tag{4.20}$$

i. e., *among all the solutions* (4.15) *of the differential equation* $\Delta\psi - q\psi = \varphi$ *the solution which vanishes on* C *has the least energy integral.*

This last result can also be verified directly as follows. Let ψ be an arbitrary solution of the inhomogeneous differential equation. Then $u(P) = \psi(P) - \Phi(P)$ will be a solution of the homogeneous equation (I.1.1). Hence, in view of (I.2.6) and the vanishing of Φ on C, we have

$$\mathrm{E}\{\psi\} = \mathrm{E}\{\Phi\} + \mathrm{E}\{u\} + 2\,\mathrm{E}\{u,\Phi\} = \mathrm{E}\{\Phi\} + \mathrm{E}\{u\} - 2\int_C \Phi \frac{\partial u}{\partial \nu} ds =$$

$$= \mathrm{E}\{\Phi\} + \mathrm{E}\{u\} \geqslant \mathrm{E}\{\Phi\}, \tag{4.21}$$

which proves the result in question. We can derive an alternative proof of the inequality (4.6) by reversing our reasoning.

Schiffer-Szegö (S 6).

5. Choice of the fundamental singularity: The functions $n(P,Q)$ and $g(P,Q)$ are determined only after a fixed singularity function $S(P,Q)$ has been chosen. The kernel $K(P,Q)$, on the other hand, is uniquely determined by the differential equation (I.1.1) and the domain D. Sometimes the form of $S(P,Q)$ is suggested by reasons of simplicity, as for example, in the case of the differential equation

$$\Delta u = c^2 u, \qquad c = \text{const.}, \tag{5.1}$$

a natural choice for $S(P,Q)$ is

$$S(P,Q) = N_0(icr) \qquad r = \overline{PQ}. \tag{5.2}$$

Here $N_0(Z)$ denotes the Neumann function of order zero in the theory of the Bessel equation.

However, let $u(P) \in \Sigma$ be chosen arbitrarily; then the function

$$S^*(P,Q) = S(P,Q) - u(P)\,u(Q) \tag{5.3}$$

is also a symmetric fundamental singularity, giving rise to the functions

$$n^*(P,Q) = n(P,Q) + u(P)\,u(Q), \quad g^*(P,Q) = g(P,Q) + u(P)\,u(Q). \tag{5.4}$$

We shall now make certain assumptions as to $S(P,Q)$ which will restrict somewhat the degree of freedom in its choice. *We shall assume that the geometric integral $I(P,Q)$ connected with $S(P,Q)$ (cf. (4.4)) is a positive semi-definite quadratic kernel,* i. e., *that for each choice of points P_i in* D *and real numbers x_i*

$$\sum_{i,k=1}^{m} I(P_i, P_k)\, x_i x_k \geqslant 0 \tag{5.5}$$

holds. Such a choice of $S(P,Q)$ can, under assumptions indicated below, be made in the following way:

Let D_1 be a domain which contains D in its interior and let $q(P)$ still be continuously differentiable and positive in $D_1 + C_1$, C_1 = boundary of D_1. Let $N_1(P,Q)$ be Neumann's function with respect to D_1 and the differential equation (I.1.1). Then $N_1(P,Q)$ is a fundamental singularity for D with the required definite character. In fact, using Green's formula, we find (putting $T \equiv (\xi, \eta)$):

$$I(P,Q) = \int_C N_1(T,Q) \frac{\partial N_1(T,P)}{\partial \nu_T}\, ds_T = \iint_{D_1 - D} \Big[\frac{\partial N_1(T,Q)}{\partial \xi} \frac{\partial N_1(T,P)}{\partial \xi} + \frac{\partial N_1(T,Q)}{\partial \eta} \frac{\partial N_1(T,P)}{\partial \eta} + q(T)\, N_1(T,Q)\, N_1(T,P) \Big] d\xi\, d\eta + \int_{C_1} N_1(T,Q) \frac{\partial N_1(T,P)}{\partial \nu_T}\, ds_T. \tag{5.6}$$

Because of the vanishing of $\dfrac{\partial N_1}{\partial \nu_T}$ on C_1, we see that

$$I(P,Q) = E_{\mathsf{D}_1 - \mathsf{D}}\{N_1(T,P), N_1(T,Q)\} \tag{5.7}$$

which exhibits the positive semi-definite character of I. It is also obvious that we might equally well have chosen $G_1(P,Q)$, i. e., Green's function of D_1, for our fundamental singularity.

If our assumptions about $I(P,Q)$ are fulfilled, we have, in view of (4.3′) and (4.5) the result that $n(P,Q)$ and $-g(P,Q)$ generate positive semi-definite matrices as well. Now consider the kernel

$$l(P,Q) = n(P,Q) + g(P,Q); \tag{5.8}$$

in view of (4.3′), (4.4″) and (4.5), we have

$$E\{l(T,P), l(T,Q)\} = K(P,Q) - 4I(P,Q). \tag{5.9}$$

This leads to an interesting estimate for the kernel in terms of $I(P,Q)$. In fact, *for any choice of* $P_\nu \in \mathsf{D}$ *and real numbers* x_ν we find:

$$\sum_{i,k=1}^{m} K(P_i, P_k)\, x_i x_k \geqq 4 \sum_{i,k=1}^{m} I(P_i, P_k)\, x_i x_k \geqq 0. \tag{5.10}$$

In particular, let us note the inequality

$$K(P,P) \geqq 4I(P,P). \tag{5.11}$$

6. The regularity of $l(P,Q)$: By construction, the functions $n(P,Q)$ and $g(P,Q)$ belong to the class Σ as functions of P for a fixed parameter point $Q \in \mathsf{D}$. However, if both P and Q are permitted to vary over D these functions are by no means bounded. For example, $S(P,Q) = -g(P,Q)$ for fixed $P \in \mathsf{C}$, and hence we see that for $Q = P \in \mathsf{C}$ the function $g(P,Q)$ becomes logarithmically infinite. The kernel $K(P,Q) = n(P,Q) - g(P,Q)$ is also irregular near the boundary C as follows from the fact that because of the reproducing property of the kernel, the homogeneous integro-differential equation

$$\varphi_\nu(Q) = \lambda_\nu E\{K(P,Q), \varphi_\nu(P)\} \tag{6.1}$$

possesses for $\lambda_\nu = 1$ all functions $u \in \Sigma$ as eigenfunctions. Thus, $K(P,Q)$ has $\lambda_\nu = 1$ as eigenvalue of infinite order.

It is now a remarkable fact that *the combination* $l(P,Q)$ *of the functions* n *and* g *is continuously differentiable in* $\mathsf{D}+\mathsf{C}$ *with respect to both argument points* P *and* Q. We shall prove this important result in several steps:

a) Let

(6.2) $\Gamma(P,Q) = \frac{1}{2\pi}\log\frac{1}{r} + \gamma(P,Q), \qquad H(P,Q) = \frac{1}{2\pi}\log\frac{1}{r} + \eta(P,Q)$

be Green's and Neumann's functions of the domain D with respect to Laplace's equation $\Delta u = 0$ which were introduced in (I.4).

We will show at first that

(6.3) $$\lambda(P,Q) = \gamma(P,Q) + \eta(P,Q)$$

has the asserted regularity in $\mathsf{D} + \mathsf{C}$. If D is the unit circle $|z| < 1$ and P, Q have the complex coordinates z, ζ, we have

(6.4) $\Gamma(P,Q) = \frac{1}{2\pi}\log\left|\frac{1-z\bar{\zeta}}{z-\zeta}\right|, \qquad -H(P,Q) = \frac{1}{2\pi}\log|z-\zeta|\cdot|1-z\bar{\zeta}|.$

In this case, clearly $\lambda(P,Q) = 0$ and everything is proved.

Next let R be another point in $|z| < 1$. The function $H(P,Q) - H(P,R)$ has logarithmic poles at Q and R and has a vanishing normal derivative for $P \in \mathsf{C}$. Let us now effect a conformal mapping of the unit circle by means of a univalent function $w = f(z)$ which is still univalent and analytic for $|z| = 1$. The unit circle goes over into a simply connected domain D in the w-plane bounded by an analytic curve C. Let $\Gamma^*(P^*, Q^*)$ and $H^*(P^*, Q^*)$ be the Green's and Neumann's functions of the domain D where P^* and Q^* correspond to P and Q respectively under the conformal mapping. Since harmonic functions remain harmonic under conformal transformation $\Gamma^*(P^*, Q^*)$ is a harmonic function of P and Q in the unit circle. It has a logarithmic pole for $P = Q$ and vanishes if either argument point is on the boundary $|z| = 1$. Hence

(6.5) $$\Gamma^*(P^*, Q^*) = \Gamma(P,Q),$$

i. e., *Green's function of the Laplace equation is a conformal invariant.* Similarly, $H^*(P^*, Q^*) - H^*(P^*, R^*)$ is a harmonic function of P and Q in the unit circle except for the logarithmic poles Q and R; if P^* and P are corresponding points on C and the unit circumference, respectively, we have, in view of the conformality:

(6.6) $$\frac{\partial}{\partial \nu_{P^*}} = |f'(z)|^{-1}\frac{\partial}{\partial \nu_P}.$$

Hence, since the normal derivative of $H^*(P^*, Q^*) - H^*(P^*, R^*)$ vanishes on C it must also vanish on the unit circumference. From all these facts we conclude the invariance relation for the Neumann's function $H(P,Q)$:

(6.5′) $$H^*(P^*, Q^*) - H^*(P^*, R^*) = H(P,Q) - H(P,R).$$

Now let D be any simply-connected domain with analytic boundary C. D can always be obtained by a conformal map from the unit circle by means of a function $w = f(z)$ which is univalent and analytic for $|z| \leqslant 1$. Therefore we derive from (6.5) and (6.5′) the identity

$$\lambda^*(P^*,Q^*) = \gamma^*(P^*,Q^*) + \eta^*(P^*,Q^*) = \Gamma^*(P^*,Q^*) + \tag{6.7}$$

$$+ H^*(P^*,Q^*) - \frac{1}{\pi}\log\frac{1}{P^*Q^*} =$$

$$= \Gamma(P,Q) + H(P,Q) + H^*(P^*,R^*) - H(P,R) - \frac{1}{\pi}\log\frac{1}{P^*Q^*} =$$

$$= H^*(P^*,R^*) - H(P,R) - \frac{1}{\pi}\left[\log\frac{1}{P^*Q^*} - \log\frac{1}{PQ}\right].$$

We hold the arbitrary point R fixed inside the unit circle and conclude from (6.7) that $\lambda^*(P^*,Q^*)$ is continuously differentiable (and even analytic) in D + C.

Consider next a multiply-connected domain D with analytic boundary C and distinguish the boundary curve C_1. Let D_1 be that domain bounded by C_1 which contains D, and $\Gamma^{(1)}(P,Q)$, $H^{(1)}(P,Q)$ the corresponding Green's and Neumann's functions of D_1. Clearly, $\Gamma(P,Q) - \Gamma^{(1)}(P,Q)$ is a regular harmonic function in D which vanishes on C_1; hence, we may represent it in the form

$$\Gamma(P,Q) - \Gamma^{(1)}(P,Q) = \int\limits_{C-C_1} [\Gamma(T,Q) - \Gamma^{(1)}(T,Q)] \frac{\partial \Gamma(T,P)}{\partial \nu_T}\, ds_T \tag{6.8}$$

and similarly

$$H(P,Q) - H^{(1)}(P,Q) = \tag{6.9}$$

$$= -\int\limits_{C-C_1} H(T,P)\frac{\partial[H(T,Q) - H^{(1)}(T,Q)]}{\partial\nu_T}\, ds_T + k\int\limits_{C-C_1} H(T,P)\, ds_T.$$

Since $\Gamma^{(1)}(P,Q) + H^{(1)}(P,Q) + \frac{1}{\pi}\log r$ behaves regularly if P and Q converge to any point in C, and since the integrations in (6.8) and (6.9) avoid the contour C_1 we recognize that $\lambda(P,Q)$ behaves regularly on the boundary contour C_1. Since this reasoning can be applied to every boundary component C_ν, we have proved our statement for $\lambda(P,Q)$.

b) We now return to the general differential equation (I.1.1) and our original domain D. Again let $\boldsymbol{H}(P,Q)$ and $\Gamma(P,Q)$ denote Neumann's and Green's functions with respect to Laplace's equation. According to our assumptions in I.5 about the fundamental singularities, the difference $N(P,Q)-\boldsymbol{H}(P,Q)$ and $G(P,Q)-\Gamma(P,Q)$ are continuously differentiable in D + C. We have furthermore:

$$\Delta_P\,[G(P,Q)-\Gamma(P,Q)] = q(P)\,G(P,Q) \tag{6.10}$$
$$\text{and}\qquad G(P,Q)-\Gamma(P,Q)=0 \qquad \text{for} \qquad P\in \mathsf{C}.$$

Hence, we have the representation

$$G(P,Q) = \Gamma(P,Q) - \iint_{\mathsf{D}} q(T)\,G(T,Q)\,\Gamma(T,P)\,d\xi\,d\eta, \qquad T\equiv(\xi,\eta). \tag{6.11}$$

Similarly, we prove for a fixed arbitary $R\in\mathsf{D}$:

$$N(P,Q)-N(R,Q) = \boldsymbol{H}(P,Q)-\boldsymbol{H}(R,Q) - \iint_{\mathsf{D}} q(T)\,N(T,Q)\,[\boldsymbol{H}(T,P)-\boldsymbol{H}(T,R)]\,d\xi\,d\eta. \tag{6.12}$$

Thus, we finally arrive at

$$l(P,Q) = \lambda(P,Q) + 2\left(\frac{1}{2\pi}\log\frac{1}{r} - S(P,Q)\right) + N(R,Q) - \boldsymbol{H}(R,Q) - \iint_{\mathsf{D}} q(T)\,[G(T,Q)\,\Gamma(T,P) + N(T,Q)\big(\boldsymbol{H}(T,P)-\boldsymbol{H}(T,R)\big)]\,d\xi\,d\eta. \tag{6.13}$$

The right-hand side of this equation is continuously differentiable with respect to P or to Q if P and Q vary over D + C for fixed R. Thus, we have proved the asserted regularity of $l(P,Q)$ in the closed region D + C.

This result implies that

$$\mathrm{E}\,\{l(T,P),l(T,Q)\} = -\int_{\mathsf{C}} l(T,P)\,\frac{\partial l(T,Q)}{\partial \nu_T}\,ds_T = -\int_{\mathsf{C}} l(T,Q)\,\frac{\partial l(T,P)}{\partial \nu_T}\,ds_T \tag{6.14}$$

is also continuously differentiable with respect to P or to Q in D + C. Thus in view of (5.9) we have proved: *The expression* $K(P,Q) - 4\,I(P,Q)$ *is continuously differentiable in either variable in the closed region* D + C. The latter kernel has the further important property of being positive semi-definite according to (5.10).

In the sequel, we shall also need some information on the behavior of the mixed derivatives of $l(P, Q)$ with respect to both argument points. We consider again a domain D_1 which includes D in its interior and such that $q(t)$ is still positive and continuously differentiable in $D_1 + C_1$, $C_1 =$ boundary of D_1, and let us suppose that $S(P, Q)$ is still a fundamental singularity for D_1. From Green's identity we derive the following integral equation:

$$s(P,Q) \equiv S(P,Q) - \frac{1}{2\pi}\log\frac{1}{r} = -\frac{1}{2\pi}\int_{C_1}\left\{\log\frac{1}{TQ}\frac{\partial S(T,P)}{\partial\nu_T} - S(T,P)\frac{\partial}{\partial\nu_T}\log\frac{1}{TQ}\right\}ds - \frac{1}{4\pi^2}\iint_{D_1} q(T)\log\frac{1}{TQ}\log\frac{1}{TP}\,d\tau_T - \frac{1}{2\pi}\iint_{D_1}\log\frac{1}{TQ}\,q(T)\,s(T,P)\,d\tau_T. \tag{6.15}$$

At first, we derive from the symmetry of $S(P, Q)$ that $s(P, Q)$ is continuously differentiable in either argument point in D_1. Thus, the last right-hand integral is continuously differentiable with respect to both points P and Q simultaneously. However, the second right-hand integral

$$-\frac{1}{4\pi^2}\iint_{D_1} q(T)\log\frac{1}{TP}\log\frac{1}{TQ}\,d\tau_T = J(P,Q) \tag{6.16}$$

is continuously differentiable with respect to P and Q simultaneously only if P and Q are separate. In fact, it is easily seen that the mixed second derivatives of $J(P, Q)$ become logarithmically infinite for $P \to Q$. The first right-hand integral in (6.15), finally, is twice continuously differentiable throughout $D + C$.

Thus, we have shown: the terms $\dfrac{\partial^2 s}{\partial x\,\partial\xi}$, etc., become logarithmically infinite for $P = Q$ and are otherwise continuous in $D + C$. The same reasoning leads to the same conclusion for the expression $N(R, Q) - H(R, Q)$ which occurs in (6.13). Finally, we derive from the asymptotic behavior of the expression (6.16) and the singular behavior of the Green's and Neumann's functions that the right-hand side integral in (6.13) has continuous mixed second derivatives with respect to P and Q everywhere in $D + C$, except for $P = Q$. In the case $P \to Q$, these mixed derivatives will become infinite logarithmically.

Thus we have proved:

The function $l(P, Q)$ is continuously differentiable in $\mathsf{D} + \mathsf{C}$ with respect to either argument point; in the same region it possesses continuous mixed derivatives with respect to both argument points as long as P and Q are different. For $P \to Q$ the mixed derivatives become infinite but such that $\dfrac{\partial^2 l}{\partial x\, \partial \xi} \left(\log \dfrac{1}{\overline{PQ}}\right)^{-1}$ *etc., remain bounded.*

If P and Q converge to the same boundary point of D, the continuity of $l(P, Q)$ up to the boundary C of D shows that the two functions $n(P, Q)$ and $g(P, Q)$ become infinite, but in such a way that their sum remains bounded. It is very illuminating to give a physical interpretation of this phenomenon.

We interpret (I.1.1) as the differential equation for the field of temperatures $\varphi(P)$ in a stationary flow of heat with accompanying chemical reactions as discussed in A.I. $S(P, Q)$ is then to be interpreted as the field of temperatures obtained if a heat source of strength one is located at the point $Q \in \mathsf{D}$. Suppose now that within the heat conductor D a heat source of strength one is established but that the walls C of this region are always cooled to the fixed temperature 0; the temperature field will be described in this case by Green's function $G(P, Q)$. The representation (I.5.11) for Green's function may be interpreted as follows: the walls C create a line of infinitesimal sinks $g(P, Q)$ which absorbs all the heat created at Q by the heat source $S(P, Q)$. If Q approaches the wall C, $g(P, Q)$ will become very nearly a sink of strength -1 at a point Q', behind the wall very near to Q. Thus, $g(P, Q)$ will differ little from $-S(P, Q)$.

Consider, on the other hand, the heat conduction problem where the domain D has a heat source of unit strength at the point Q and has isolated walls C through which no flow of heat can pass. In this case it is required that $\dfrac{\partial \varphi}{\partial \nu} = 0$ on C and the temperature field is described by Neumann's function. Now, the decomposition (I.5.14) means that the walls C reflect the heat flow back into D and give rise to an additional source $n(P, Q)$. If Q approaches the wall, obviously $n(P, Q)$ will behave like the temperature field due to a heat source of strength one at a point Q' behind the wall C and near Q. Thus, $n(P, Q)$ will behave nearly like $S(P, Q)$. We thus recognize that $n(P, Q)$ and $g(P, Q)$ have infinities of opposite signs if P and Q converge to the boundary. This physical illustration, therefore, makes the continuity of $l(P,Q)$ in $\mathsf{D}+\mathsf{C}$ understandable. The first investigation on the asymptotic properties of $n(P,Q)$ and $g(P,Q)$ in C is due to Lichtenstein[1] whose results contain the continuity of $l(P,Q)$ in $\mathsf{D}+\mathsf{C}$.

Bergman-Schiffer (B 24), (B 25), (B 27).

7. An integral equation for the kernel: In this section, we shall express the kernel $K(P,Q)$ as a series of geometric quantities as defined in Section 4. More specifically, we shall develop $K(P,Q)$ in a series of iterated integrals of the elementary kernel $S(P,Q)$.

If we apply the reproduction formula (1.1) to the particular function $u(P) = [K(P,Q) - 4I(P,Q)] \in \Sigma$, we obtain

$$4I(P,Q) = K(P,Q) - \mathrm{E}\{K(T,Q) - 4I(T,Q), K(T,P)\}. \tag{7.1}$$

This may also be transformed by means of (4.1) into

$$4I(P,Q) = K(P,Q) + \int_{\mathsf{C}} \frac{\partial}{\partial \nu_T} [K(T,Q) - 4I(T,Q)] \cdot K(T,P)\, ds_T. \tag{7.2}$$

In the last section we have proved that the kernel

$$\mathbf{K}(Q,T) = \frac{\partial}{\partial \nu_T} [K(T,Q) - 4I(T,Q)] \tag{7.3}$$

is a continuous function of T and Q on C. Thus, choosing a fixed $P \in \mathsf{D}$, we may consider

$$4I(Q,P) = K(Q,P) + \int_{\mathsf{C}} \mathbf{K}(Q,T)\, K(T,P)\, ds_T \tag{7.3'}$$

as an *integral equation for the unknown function* $K(Q,P)$, $Q \in \mathsf{C}$ *with continuous kernel* $\mathbf{K}(Q,T)$.

In order to study the inhomogeneous integral equation (7.3′), we shall first investigate the corresponding homogeneous integral equation

$$0 = \varphi(Q) + \lambda \int_{\mathsf{C}} \mathbf{K}(Q,T)\, \varphi(T)\, ds_T. \tag{7.4}$$

---

[1]L. Lichtenstein (L 12).

We have already observed in (I.4) that the inhomogeneous equation (7.3′) will surely have a solution if the homogeneous equation (7.4) does not possess the value $\lambda = 1$ as an eigenvalue. We shall now show that all eigenvalues of (7.4) satisfy the inequality $\lambda > 1$.

Since we can always solve the boundary value problem for the class Σ, we may consider $\varphi(Q)$ for $Q \in \mathsf{C}$ as the boundary values of a solution $u(Q)$ of (I.1.1) in D and instead of (7.4) we may consider the following eigenvalue problem with respect to D:

$$u(Q) = \lambda \mathrm{E}\{K(P,Q) - 4I)P,Q), u(P)\}. \tag{7.5}$$

Because of the reproducing property of the kernel, we may put this integro-differential equation in the form

$$(\lambda - 1)\, u(Q) = \mathrm{E}\{4I(P,Q), u(P)\}. \tag{7.6}$$

We next compute $\mathrm{E}\{u\}$ by means of (7.6); let us suppose that $S(P,Q)$ was chosen according to Section 5 such that $I(P,Q)$ is given by (5.7). Let

$$u_1(T) = \mathrm{E}\{N_1(Q,T), u(Q)\}. \tag{7.7}$$

Clearly $u_1(T)$ is then defined in the domain $\mathsf{D}_1 - \mathsf{D}$ as well as in D. We make use of the formal identity

$$\mathrm{E}_1\{\mathrm{E}_2\{\varphi(T,P), \psi(T)\}, \chi(P)\} = \mathrm{E}_2\{\mathrm{E}_1\{\varphi(T,P), \chi(P)\}, \psi(T)\}.$$

Then in view of (7.6) and (5.7), we obtain

$$(\lambda - 1)\, \mathrm{E}\{u\} = 4\, \mathrm{E}_{\mathsf{D}_1 - \mathsf{D}}\{u_1\} \geqslant 0 \tag{7.8}$$

which proves that every eigenvalue λ of the problem (7.5) satisfies the inequality

$$\lambda \geqslant 1. \tag{7.9}$$

We wish to exclude the possibility of an equality sign in (7.8) and (7.9). This equality can be attained only if for all points T of the open domain $\mathsf{D}_1 - \bar{\mathsf{D}}$

$$u_1(T) = \mathrm{E}\{N_1(Q,T), u(Q)\} = -\int_{\mathsf{C}} \frac{\partial N_1(Q,T)}{\partial \nu_Q}\, u(Q)\, ds_Q = 0 \tag{7.10}$$

holds identically.

Now consider the function

$$v(P) = \int_{\mathsf{C}} \frac{\partial N_1(Q,P)}{\partial \nu_Q}\, u(Q)\, ds_Q \qquad \text{for} \qquad P \in \mathsf{D}. \tag{7.11}$$

It is obviously of class Σ in D. The right-hand integral, however, represents a solution of (I.1.1) not only in D but also in $\mathsf{D}_1 - \overline{\mathsf{D}}$. It is not continuous when the point P crosses the integration curve C. Because of the fact that $N_1(Q, P)$ behaves like $\frac{1}{2\pi}\log\frac{1}{PQ}$ for P near to Q, this discontinuity behavior is the same as that of the following function:

$$h(P) = \frac{1}{2\pi}\int_{\mathsf{C}} u(Q)\,\frac{\partial}{\partial \nu_Q}\left(\log\frac{1}{r}\right) ds_Q, \qquad r = \overline{PQ}. \tag{7.12}$$

$h(P)$ is a harmonic function in the whole plane, except on the curve C. Physically, it may be interpreted as the logarithmic potential of a dipole distribution with density $u(Q)/2\pi$ along C. It is well known[1] that if P_i and P_e are two points in the interior and exterior of D converging to the point P_0 on C, the following relation holds:

$$\lim_{P_e,\, P_i \to P_0} [h(P_i) - h(P_e)] = u(P_0). \tag{7.13}$$

For later use, let us also consider the harmonic function

$$h^*(P) = \frac{1}{2\pi}\int_{\mathsf{C}} \sigma(Q)\log\frac{1}{r}\, ds_Q, \qquad r = \overline{PQ}. \tag{7.12'}$$

This represents the logarithmic potential of a simple charge distribution on C with density $\frac{1}{2\pi}\sigma(Q)$. It can be shown[2] to be continuous through the line of charge C, but the normal derivative of $h^*(P)$ has a jump of the amount $\sigma(Q)$.

Because of (7.10) and (7.13) we find

$$\lim_{P \to P_0 \in \mathsf{C}} v(P) = u(P_0), \qquad P \in \mathsf{D} \tag{7.14}$$

and hence, because of the uniqueness theorem for the boundary value problem $u(P) \equiv v(P)$, i. e.,

$$u(P) = \int_{\mathsf{C}} u(Q)\,\frac{\partial N_1(Q, P)}{\partial \nu_Q}\, ds_Q \qquad \text{for} \qquad P \in \mathsf{D}. \tag{7.15}$$

---

[1] Courant-Hilbert [13], vol. 2, pp. 237—9.
[2] Ibid. Kellogg [30], Chapter 6.

We conclude from this that $u(P)$ has continuous first derivatives in $\mathsf{D}+\mathsf{C}$ and hence by virtue of (I.5.8):

(7.16)
$$\int_{\mathsf{C}} N_1(Q,P)\frac{\partial u(Q)}{\partial \nu_Q}\,ds_Q \equiv 0 \quad \text{for} \quad P \in \mathsf{D}.$$

Because of the continuity of single layer potentials through C, we find that

(7.17)
$$\int_{\mathsf{C}} N_1(Q,T)\frac{\partial u(Q)}{\partial \nu_Q}\,ds_Q = V(T) \quad \text{for} \quad T \in \mathsf{D}_1 - \bar{\mathsf{D}}$$

satisfies the differential equation (I.1.1) in $\mathsf{D}_1 - \bar{\mathsf{D}}$, has on C the boundary values zero, and on C_1 the normal derivative zero. Thus, by Green's identity

(7.18)
$$E_{\mathsf{D}_1-\mathsf{D}}\{V\} = -\int_{\mathsf{C}_1+\mathsf{C}} V\frac{\partial V}{\partial \nu}\,ds = 0$$

i. e.,

(7.18′)
$$V(T) \equiv 0.$$

Since the jump of the normal derivative of the single layer potential through C is zero and, on the other hand, must equal $\frac{\partial u}{\partial \nu}$, we find:

(7.19)
$$\frac{\partial u}{\partial \nu} \equiv 0 \quad \text{on } \mathsf{C}.$$

The uniqueness theorem for the boundary value problem of the second kind now yields

(7.19′)
$$u \equiv 0.$$

Thus, the eigenvalue $\lambda = 1$ has been excluded. We have proved that *the integral equation* (7.4) *has only eigenvalues* $\lambda > 1$.

Consider, in general, the inhomogeneous integral equation

(7.20)
$$f(t) = \varphi(t) + \lambda\int_a^b K(t,s)\,\varphi(s)\,ds$$

where $f(t)$ and the kernel $K(t,s)$ are known and the function $\varphi(s)$ is to be determined. It is well known that for sufficiently small values of λ the following iterative process leads to a determination of $\varphi(s)$. Put

(7.21)
$$\varphi_n(t) = f(t) - \lambda\int_a^b K(t,s)\,\varphi_{n-1}(s)\,ds, \qquad \varphi_0(t) = f(t).$$

This iteration leads to the series representation

$$\varphi(t) = f(t) + \sum_{\nu=1}^{\infty} (-1)^{\nu} \lambda^{\nu} \int_a^b K^{(\nu)}(t, s) f(s)\, ds \tag{7.22}$$

where

$$K^{(\nu)}(t, s) = \int_a^b K^{(\nu-1)}(t, r) K(r, s)\, dr, \qquad K^{(1)}(t, s) = K(t, s), \tag{7.22'}$$

is the ν-th iterated kernel. The series (7.22) was given by Liouville and Neumann many years before the modern theory of integral equations was developed and is called the Neumann series for the solution of (7.20). We define the resolvent kernel

$$K^{(-1)}(t, s; \lambda) = \sum_{\nu=1}^{\infty} (-1)^{\nu} \lambda^{\nu} K^{(\nu)}(t, s) \tag{7.23}$$

in terms of which we may express (7.22) in the elegant form

$$\varphi(t) = f(t) + \int_a^b K^{(-1)}(t, s; \lambda) f(s)\, ds. \tag{7.22''}$$

The great progress made by Fredholm in the theory of integral equations was the discovery that the resolvent kernel $K^{(-1)}(t, s; \lambda)$ is a meromorphic function of λ which can be expressed in simple analytic form for all complex values of λ which are not eigenvalues of (7.20). In particular, we conclude that the series (7.23) for the reciprocal kernel will converge for all values λ which have a modulus smaller than that of the first eigenvalue of (7.20).

We have sketched the fundamental results of the theory of integral equations for the case that the domain of integration is an interval [a, b]. The same results are true, of course, if we integrate along a curve C and even if the integration is carried out over a domain D.

We therefore know that the Neumann series for the unknown kernel $K(P, Q)$, arising from (7.3′), converges. We shall put this series in an elegant form which will exhibit clearly its significance. Let us introduce the notation

$$\begin{aligned} M^{(n)}(P, Q) &= \mathrm{E}\,\{M(T, P), M^{(n-1)}(T, Q)\}, \\ M^{(1)}(P, Q) &= M(P, Q) = K(P, Q) - 4\, I(P, Q). \end{aligned} \tag{7.24}$$

We have by (7.3)

$$K(Q,P) = \frac{\partial M(P,Q)}{\partial \nu_P} \tag{7.25}$$

and in view of identity (4.1):

$$K^{(2)}(Q,P) = \int_C K(Q,T)K(T,P)\,ds_T = -\frac{\partial}{\partial \nu_P}\bigl(\mathrm{E}\,\{M(T,Q), M(T,P)\}\bigr) =$$

$$= -\frac{\partial M^{(2)}(P,Q)}{\partial \nu_P}. \tag{7.25'}$$

Generally:

$$K^{(n)}(Q,P) = \int_C K^{(n-1)}(Q,T)\,K(T,P)\,ds_T = \tag{7.26}$$

$$= -\frac{\partial}{\partial \nu_P}\bigl(\mathrm{E}\,\{M(T,P), (-1)^{n-2} M^{(n-1)}(T,Q)\}\bigr) = (-1)^{n-1}\frac{\partial M^{(n)}(P,Q)}{\partial \nu_P}.$$

Thus, we may write the resolvent kernel of $K(Q,T)$ in the following form:

$$K^{(-1)}(Q,T) = K(Q,T) - K^{(2)}(Q,T) + K^{(3)}(Q,T) - \ldots = \tag{7.27}$$

$$= \frac{\partial}{\partial \nu_T}[M(T,Q) + M^{(2)}(T,Q) + M^{(3)}(T,Q) + \ldots]$$

and hence:

$$K(Q,P) = 4I(Q,P) - \int_C K^{(-1)}(Q,T)\,4I(T,P)\,ds_T = \tag{7.28}$$

$$= 4I(Q,P) + \mathrm{E}\,\{4I(T,P), M(T,Q)\} + \mathrm{E}\,\{4I(T,P), M^{(2)}(T,Q)\} + \ldots.$$

This identity, proved for $Q \in \mathsf{C}$ and $P \in \mathsf{D}$ can now be continued also for $Q \in \mathsf{D}$ because of the uniqueness theorem of the boundary value problem of the first kind. We find:

$$K(Q,P) = \sum_{\nu=0}^{\infty} \mathrm{E}\,\{4I(T,P), M^{(\nu)}(T,Q)\}; \quad M^{(0)}(T,Q) = K(T,Q). \tag{7.29}$$

This series development for $K(Q,P)$ permits us to compute the kernel in terms of a geometrically convergent series of geometric expressions. It must be remarked that in spite of the fact that $M(P,Q)$ contains the unknown kernel K, each of the terms in the right-hand side of (7.29) is expressible as an iterated integral over the fundamental singularity $S(P,Q)$. We have, for example,

(7.30) $$M^{(2)}(P,Q) = \mathrm{E}\{K(T,P) - 4I(T,P), K(T,Q) - 4I(T,Q)\} = \\ = K(P,Q) - 8I(P,Q) + \mathrm{E}\{4I(T,P), 4I(T,Q)\}$$

and

(7.30′) $$\mathrm{E}\{4I(T,P), M^{(2)}(T,Q)\} = 4I(P,Q) - 8\,\mathrm{E}\{4I(T,P), I(T,Q)\} + \\ + \mathrm{E}\{4I(T,P), \mathrm{E}\{4I(R,T), 4I(R,Q)\}\}.$$

In general, the reproducing property of the kernel function will permit its elimination from the right-hand side of (7.29).

In fact, let us define the following iterated integrals:

(7.31) $$i^{(\nu)}(P,Q) = \mathrm{E}\{i^{(\nu-1)}(P,T), i^{(1)}(T,Q)\}, \qquad i^{(1)}(P,Q) = 4I(P,Q).$$

All integrals $i^{(\nu)}(P,Q)$ are geometric quantities since they can be obtained from the known term $I(P,Q)$ by integration and differentiation processes alone. We can easily express

(7.32) $$M^{(n)}(P,Q) = \sum_{\nu=0}^{n} (-1)^{\nu} \binom{n}{\nu} i^{(\nu)}(P,Q)$$

if we denote $K(P,Q) = i^{(0)}(P,Q)$. Introducing (7.32) and (7.29) we finally obtain the desired series development for the kernel function:

(7.33) $$K(P,Q) = \sum_{\rho=0}^{\infty} \left[\sum_{\nu=0}^{\rho} (-1)^{\nu} \binom{\rho}{\nu} i^{(\nu+1)}(P,Q) \right].$$

All terms $i^{(\nu+1)}(P,Q)$ are iterated integrals of $I(P,Q)$.

The series development (7.33) for the kernel function shows the central role of $K(P,Q)$ in the general theory of the differential equation (I.1.1). On the one hand, we have a rapidly convergent series for the kernel which has various convenient features which will be discussed below; on the other hand, we have already shown that the knowledge of this kernel leads immediately to the numerical solution of all boundary value problems of the first and second kind connected with the differential equation (I.1.1) and the domain **D**.

Bergman-Schiffer (B 25), (B 27), Courant [12], Appendix, Plemelj (P 4), Privaloff (P 9), E. Schmidt (S 7), Schiffer-Spencer [68].

8. The eigenvalues of the kernel $l(P,Q)$: In Section I.5 we have proved that the function $M(P,Q) = K(P,Q) - 4I(P,Q)$ is continuously differentiable with respect to either argument in the closed region $\mathbf{D} + \mathbf{C}$. Using the following formula for the iterated kernels $M^{(\rho)}(P,Q)$ defined in (7.24):

$$M^{(\rho)}(P,Q) = -\int\limits_{C} M^{(\rho-1)}(T,Q)\,\frac{\partial M(T,P)}{\partial \nu_T}\,ds_T = \tag{8.1}$$

$$= -\int\limits_{C} M(T,P)\,\frac{\partial M^{(\rho-1)}(T,Q)}{\partial \nu_T}\,ds_T$$

we can prove by recursion that all $M^{(\rho)}(P,Q)$ have the same continuity property as $M(P,Q)$.

Let us define the linear transformation

$$T_u(P) = \mathrm{E}\,\{l(R,P), u(R)\} \tag{8.2}$$

of the linear space Σ. Because of the identity (5.9) and the definition of $M(P,Q)$ we have

$$\mathrm{E}\,\{T_u\} = \mathrm{E}\big\{\mathrm{E}\,\{M(P,Q), u(P)\}, u(Q)\big\} \tag{8.3}$$

which shows that the right-hand side of (8.3) considered as a quadratic functional of u is non-negative. We can apply the reproducing property of the kernel $K(P,Q)$ and the property (5.7) of $I(P,Q)$ in order to transform this quadratic functional. We obtain

$$\mathrm{E}\,\{T_u\} = \mathrm{E}\,\{u\} - 4\,\mathrm{E}_{\mathsf{D}_1-\mathsf{D}}\,\{u_1\}, \quad u_1(P) = \mathrm{E}_{\mathsf{D}}\,\{N_1(R,P), u(R)\}. \tag{8.4}$$

This clearly shows that the transformation (8.2) is norm-decreasing.

Let us ask for the eigenfunctions of the integro-differential equation

$$u_\nu(P) = \lambda_\nu\, T_{u_\nu}(P). \tag{8.5}$$

From (8.4) we deduce immediately that $|\lambda_\nu| \geqslant 1$ and that $|\lambda_\nu| = 1$ is only possible in the case that $u_1(P) \equiv 0$ in $\mathsf{D}_1 - \mathsf{D}$. However, as we have shown in the previous section, this is possible only if $u \equiv 0$. Hence, we are sure that *all the eigenvalues of* (8.5) *have modulus* > 1.

We shall now show that a real symmetric kernel which is not identically zero has a finite eigenvalue. We carry through the argument here for the kernel $M(P,Q)$ but the same reasoning applies in general.

From the definition (7.24) we derive the following identity by induction

$$\mathrm{E}\,\{M^{(\mu)}(R,P), M^{(\nu)}(R,Q)\} = M^{(\mu+\nu)}(P,Q) \tag{8.6}$$

and in particular

$$\mathrm{E}\,\{M^{(\nu-1)}(R,P), M^{(\nu+1)}(R,Q)\} = M^{(2\nu)}(P,Q). \tag{8.6'}$$

Using the Schwarz inequality, we derive from (8.6) and (8.6′):

$$M^{(2\nu)}(P,Q)^2 \leqslant M^{(2\nu-2)}(P,P)\cdot M^{(2\nu+2)}(Q,Q), \tag{8.7}$$

and if $M^{(2\nu)}(Q,Q) \neq 0$, we conclude

$$M^{(2\nu+2)}(Q,Q)/M^{(2\nu)}(Q,Q) \geqslant M^{(2\nu)}(Q,Q)/M^{(2\nu-2)}(Q,Q). \tag{8.8}$$

Hence, we have proved that the sequence of numbers

$$\omega_\nu(Q) = M^{(2\nu)}(Q,Q)/M^{(2\nu-2)}(Q,Q) \tag{8.9}$$

is non-decreasing. Thus, we have

$$M^{(2\nu)}(Q,Q) \geqslant M^{(2)}(Q,Q)\,[\omega_2(Q)]^{\nu-1} \tag{8.10}$$

and hence

$$\overline{\lim_{\nu\to\infty}} \sqrt[2\nu]{M^{(2\nu)}(Q,Q)} \geqslant \sqrt{\omega_2(Q)}. \tag{8.11}$$

Consider now the power series in the complex variable λ

$$M^{(-1)}(P,Q;\lambda) = \sum_{\nu=1}^{\infty} \lambda^\nu M^{(\nu)}(P,Q) \tag{8.12}$$

and the corresponding normal derivative on the boundary

$$K^{(-1)}(Q,R;\lambda) = \frac{\partial M^{(-1)}(R,Q;\lambda)}{\partial \nu_R}, \qquad R \in \mathsf{C}. \tag{8.13}$$

$K^{-1}(Q,R;\lambda)$ is the resolvent kernel of the integral equation

$$f(Q) = \varphi(Q) + \lambda \int_{\mathsf{C}} K(Q,R)\,\varphi(R)\,ds_R \tag{8.13'}$$

closely related to (7.3′). We proved in Section 7 that it will converge for all values $|\lambda| < |\lambda_1|$ where λ_1 is the first eigenvalue of the homogeneous integral equation (7.4). Now, the function (8.12) can be defined as that solution of the differential equation (I.1.1) which on C has the normal derivative (8.13). Hence, by virtue of (I.5.15), we obtain

$$M^{(-1)}(P,Q;\lambda) = -\int_{\mathsf{C}} N(R,P)\,K^{(-1)}(Q,R;\lambda)\,ds_R. \tag{8.14}$$

Consequently, the uniform convergence of the series (8.12) is assured in the closed region $\mathsf{D}+\mathsf{C}$ for all values λ with $|\lambda| < |\lambda_1|$.

On the other hand, by means of the Cauchy-Hadamard formula for the radius of convergence of a power series, we derive from (8.11) that (8.12) will converge in a circle of radius at most $[\operatorname{Max}\omega_2(Q)]^{-1/2}$, the maximum taken for $Q \in \mathsf{D} + \mathsf{C}$. This proves the existence of a finite eigenvalue λ of the integral equation (7.4), except in the case, thus far excluded, where for some ν and some $Q \in \mathsf{D} + \mathsf{C}$ we have $M^{(2\nu)}(Q, Q) = 0$.

In order to study the significance of this occurrence, we use the identity

$$\mathrm{E}\{M^{(\nu)}(P,Q), M^{(\nu)}(P,Q)\} = M^{(2\nu)}(Q,Q) \tag{8.15}$$

which is a particular instance of (8.6). We recognize that $M^{(2\nu)}(Q, Q) = 0$ would imply

$$M^{(\nu)}(P,Q) \equiv 0 \qquad \text{for all} \qquad P \in \mathsf{D}, \qquad Q \text{ fixed.} \tag{8.16}$$

Let ν be the smallest index for which identity (8.16) occurs for this fixed Q. ν must obviously be odd, for otherwise we could descend from $M^{(\nu)}(Q, Q) = 0$ to $M^{(\nu/2)}(P, Q) \equiv 0$ by the same reasoning. If, therefore, we put $\nu = 2\mu + 1$ and apply the identity

$$\mathrm{E}\{M(P,Q), M^{(2\mu+1)}(P,Q)\} = M^{(2\mu+2)}(Q,Q) \equiv 0, \tag{8.17}$$

we may conclude $M^{(\mu+1)}(P, Q) \equiv 0$. Thus, we have the inequality

$$\mu + 1 = \frac{\nu+1}{2} \geqslant \nu, \qquad \text{i. e.,} \qquad \nu \leqslant 1. \tag{8.18}$$

But $M^{(1)}(P, Q) = K(P, Q) - 4I(P, Q) \equiv 0$ implies, because of (5.9), that $l(P, Q) \equiv 0$. By the definition of $l(P, Q)$ this means that $S(P, Q) = \frac{1}{2}[N(P, Q) + G(P, Q)]$. In this case we have, moreover, $K(P, Q) = N(P, Q) - G(P, Q) = 4I(P, Q)$. Hence, we can easily express the fundamental solutions N and G in terms of $S(P, Q)$ and no further investigation is necessary. If $l(P, Q)$ is not identically zero, we can never have $M^{(2\nu)}(Q, Q) = 0$ and in this case we have proved that the integral equation (7.4) has at least one eigenvalue λ_1^2. We have shown in Section 7 that it is necessarily positive and greater than one. We may assume that λ_1^2 is the least eigenvalue. We have also shown that in this case the integro-differential equation

$$u_1(Q) = \lambda_1^2 \mathrm{E}\{M(P,Q), u_1(P)\} \tag{8.19}$$

has an eigenfunction of the class Σ with the same eigenvalue λ_1^2.

It is easily seen directly that $u_1(Q)$ is continuously differentiable in the closed region $\mathsf{D} + \mathsf{C}$. In fact, we have by (4.1)

$$u_1(Q) = -\lambda_1^2 \int_{\mathsf{C}} u_1(P) \frac{\partial M(P,Q)}{\partial \nu_P} ds_P. \tag{8.19'}$$

From (6.13) and (6.14) we can easily show that if Q converges towards a point $P \in \mathsf{C}$, $\operatorname{grad}_Q \left[\frac{\partial M(P, Q)}{\partial \nu_P}\right]$ becomes at most logarithmically infinite and that, therefore, the integral (8.19′) is continuously differentiable in $\mathsf{D} + \mathsf{C}$. We may further normalize $u_1(P)$ by the requirement $\mathrm{E}\{u_1\} = 1$.

Consider next the kernel

$$M_1(P,Q) = M(P,Q) - \frac{u_1(P)\, u_1(Q)}{\lambda_1^2}. \tag{8.20}$$

It has precisely those properties of $M(P, Q)$ which were needed in order to show the existence of eigenvalues. It is continuously differentiable in $\mathsf{D} + \mathsf{C}$ and symmetric in P and Q; it belongs to the class Σ with respect to each variable. If, therefore, we do not happen to have $M_1(P,Q) \equiv 0$, then a function $u_2(P)$ in Σ will exist such that

$$u_2(Q) = \lambda_2^2\, \mathrm{E}\{M_1(P,Q), u_2(P)\}. \tag{8.21}$$

We clearly have, by construction, in view of (8.19), (8.20), and the normalization of u_1

$$\mathrm{E}\{M_1(P,Q), u_1(P)\} \equiv 0 \tag{8.22}$$

and hence from (8.21)

$$\mathrm{E}\{u_1, u_2\} = 0. \tag{8.22′}$$

Thus, (8.21) and (8.20) together with (8.22′) imply

$$\lambda_2^2\, \mathrm{E}\{M(P,Q), u_2(P)\} = u_2(Q), \tag{8.23}$$

i. e., we have obtained a new eigenfunction of the integro-differential equation (7.5). Since λ_1^2 was supposed to be the least eigenvalue of this integro-differential equation, we have $\lambda_2^2 \geqslant \lambda_1^2$. We may assume $u_2(P)$ to be normalized again by the requirement $\mathrm{E}\{u_2\} = 1$.

In this way, we can go on and derive further eigenfunctions $u_\nu(P)$ with eigenvalues λ_ν^2. Without loss of generality we may assume that the system is orthonormalized by the requirement

$$\mathrm{E}\{u_\nu, u_\mu\} = \delta_{\nu\mu}. \tag{8.24}$$

To each eigenvalue λ_ν^2 belong only a finite number of eigenfunctions and the λ_ν^2 have no finite limit point. This follows from the fact that the same values λ_ν^2 are the eigenvalues of the ordinary integral equation (7.4) and have the same order of multiplicity with respect to it and the integro-differential equation (7.5). It was precisely the close connection between the ordinary integral equation (7.4) and the integro-differential equation (7.5) which permitted us to carry out the above treatment of the eigenvalue theory of the latter.

It is of great importance to notice that the system $\{u_\nu(P)\}$ may be chosen in such a way that each function $u_\nu(P)$ is an eigenfunction of the integro-differential equation

$$u_\nu(Q) = \lambda_\nu \mathrm{E}\{l(P,Q), u_\nu(P)\} = \lambda_\nu T_{u_\nu}. \tag{8.25}$$

In fact, let $u_\nu(P)$ be an eigenfunction of (7.5) with the eigenvalue λ_ν^2. Define

$$v_\nu(Q) = \lambda_\nu \mathrm{E}\{l(P,Q), u_\nu(P)\} = \lambda_\nu T_{u_\nu}; \tag{8.25'}$$

in view of (5.9), we easily derive

$$\lambda_\nu T_{v_\nu} = \lambda_\nu^2 \mathrm{E}\{M(P,Q), u_\nu(P)\} = u_\nu(Q) \tag{8.26}$$

and introducing (8.26) again in (8.25′), we obtain by means of (5.9)

$$v_\nu(Q) = \lambda_\nu^2 \mathrm{E}\{M(P,Q), v_\nu(P)\}. \tag{8.27}$$

Thus, $v_\nu(P)$ is itself an eigenfunction of (7.5) corresponding to the same eigenvalue λ_ν^2, and the transformation T_u leaves invariant the subspaces of all $u_\nu \in \Sigma$ which are eigenfunctions of (7.5) with the same eigenvalue λ_ν^2. By simple linear algebra one can prove that in each such subspace an orthonormal basis $u_\nu(P)$ can be selected such that the transformation T_u becomes simply a division by the eigenvalue $\pm \lambda_\nu$. For such choice of the $u_\nu(P)$ the equation (8.25) will be fulfilled. Conversely, each eigenfunction of (8.25) is, in view of

$$u_\nu(Q) = \lambda_\nu T_{u_\nu} = \lambda_\nu^2 T_{T_{u_\nu}} = \lambda_\nu^2 \mathrm{E}\{M(P,Q), u_\nu(P)\}, \tag{8.28}$$

an eigenfunction of the integro-differential equation (7.5). We will assume in the following that the $u_\nu(P)$ have been chosen to be eigenfunctions of (7.5) and (8.25) simultaneously.

Consider now the function

$$L_n(P,Q) = l(P,Q) - \sum_{\nu=1}^{n} \frac{u_\nu(P)\, u_\nu(Q)}{\lambda_\nu}. \tag{8.29}$$

We clearly have for fixed $Q \in \mathrm{D} + \mathrm{C}$

$$\mathrm{E}\{L_n(P,Q)\} = M(Q,Q) - \sum_{\nu=1}^{n} \frac{u_\nu(Q)^2}{\lambda_\nu^2} \geqslant 0 \tag{8.30}$$

because of the integro-differential equation satisfied by the $u_\nu(P)$ and their orthonormality (8.24). Suppose there are infinitely many eigenfunctions $u_\nu(Q)$; then we derive from (8.30) that the series of positive terms

$$\sum_{\nu=1}^{\infty} \frac{u_\nu(Q)^2}{\lambda_\nu^2} \tag{8.31}$$

converges uniformly in the closed region D + C and hence, by the Schwarz inequality, the same must be true of

$$\sum_{\nu=1}^{\infty} \frac{u_\nu(P)\, u_\nu(Q)}{\lambda_\nu^2}.$$

Consider now the expression

$$\Delta(P,Q) = M(P,Q) - \sum_{\nu=1}^{\infty} \frac{u_\nu(P)\, u_\nu(Q)}{\lambda_\nu^2}. \tag{8.32}$$

Its first iterate has the form

$$\Delta^{(2)}(P,Q) = \mathrm{E}\{\Delta(R,P), \Delta(R,Q)\} = M^{(2)}(P,Q) - \sum_{\nu=1}^{\infty} \frac{u_\nu(P)\, u_\nu(Q)}{\lambda_\nu^4}. \tag{8.32'}$$

Similarly

$$\sum_{\nu=1}^{\infty} \frac{u_\nu(P)\, u_\nu(Q)}{\lambda_\nu^4} = \mathrm{E}\left\{ M(R,P), \sum_{\nu=1}^{\infty} \frac{u_\nu(R)\, u_\nu(Q)}{\lambda_\nu^2} \right\} = \tag{8.33}$$

$$= -\int_C \sum_{\nu=1}^{\infty} \frac{u_\nu(R)\, u_\nu(Q)}{\lambda_\nu^2} \frac{\partial}{\partial \nu_R} M(R,P)\, ds_R.$$

This representation shows that the left-hand sum is continuously differentiable in the closed region D + C and the same holds, consequently, for $\Delta^{(2)}(P,Q)$ also. Since this quantity is symmetric in P and Q and is of the class Σ, we may conclude as before (see (8.6) ff.) that either $\Delta^{(2)}(P,Q) \equiv 0$ or that there exists an eigenfunction for the equation

$$v_\nu(Q) = \varkappa_\nu^2\, \mathrm{E}\{\Delta^{(2)}(P,Q), v_\nu(P)\}. \tag{8.34}$$

Since $\Delta^{(2)}(P,Q)$ is, by construction, orthogonal to all eigenfunctions $u_\nu(Q)$ the same holds also for all eigenfunctions $v_\nu(Q)$ of (8.34). Hence, in view of (8.32′), they must also satisfy the equation

$$v_\nu(Q) = \varkappa_\nu^2\, \mathrm{E}\{M^{(2)}(P,Q), v_\nu(P)\}; \tag{8.34'}$$

without loss of generality we may assume the $v_\nu(Q)$ to be chosen in such a way that they satisfy at the same time

$$(8.34'') \qquad v_\nu(Q) = \varkappa_\nu \mathrm{E}\{M(P,Q), v_\nu(P)\}$$

and are thus eigenfunctions of the integro-differential equation (7.5) with finite eigenvalue $\varkappa_\nu$. But we have assumed that in the system $\{u_\nu(P)\}$ all such eigenfunctions have already been enumerated and thus the $v_\nu(Q)$ cannot lead to additional ones. There remains, therefore, only the first alternative

$$(8.35) \qquad \Delta^{(2)}(P,Q) \equiv 0, \qquad \text{i. e.,} \qquad \Delta(P,Q) \equiv 0.$$

Thus, *we have proved the representation:*

$$(8.36) \qquad M(P,Q) = K(P,Q) - 4I(P,Q) = \sum_{\nu=1}^{\infty} \frac{u_\nu(P)\, u_\nu(Q)}{\lambda_\nu^2}.$$

This series development converges uniformly in the closed region $\mathsf{D} + \mathsf{C}$.

It is not certain that infinitely many eigenfunctions $u_\nu(P)$ of (7.5) will exist; and if there are even infinitely many, they need not necessarily form a complete orthonormal system with respect to the class Σ. It might happen that there exist additional functions $u(P)$ orthogonal to all the $u_\nu(P)$ considered. Each such $u(P)$ is then also orthogonal to the kernels $M(P,Q)$ and $l(P,Q)$. In order to simplify the statements of our results, we shall call such functions $u(P)$ eigenfunctions of (7.5) and (8.25) with infinite eigenvalue. With this convention we may assume that all eigenfunctions of (7.5) and (8.25) form a complete orthonormal system for the class Σ of solutions of the differential equation (I.1.1) in D.

We can arrive at the series development (8.36) *directly by using a fundamental theorem of the theory of linear transformations in Hilbert space.* In order to apply this theorem, we shall have to make a few preliminary definitions. We shall call a linear transformation $L(u)$ *continuous* if for any sequence u_n of elements of the Hilbert space which converges in the corresponding metric towards u, the limit relation $L(u_n) \to L(u)$ holds in the same metric; i. e., we require that

$$(8.37) \quad \lim_{n\to\infty} \mathrm{E}\{u_n - u\} = 0 \quad \text{implies} \quad \lim_{n\to\infty} \mathrm{E}\{L(u_n) - L(u)\} = 0.$$

In the theory of Hilbert space, another (weaker) type of convergence, the so-called weak convergence, is often of great use. We shall say that a sequence of elements u_ν in the Hilbert space $\Sigma^\blacktriangle$ *converges weakly* towards u, if the norms of the elements are uniformly bounded, and if for any fixed element $v \in \Sigma^{\blacktriangle}$ we have

$$\lim_{n \to \infty} \mathrm{E}\{u_n - u, v\} = 0. \tag{8.38}$$

Clearly, ordinary convergence will imply weak convergence; but weak convergence does not, in general, imply convergence.

Let us consider, for example, a complete orthonormal system $\{u_\nu\}$ in $\Sigma^{\blacktriangle}$. If v is any element of $\Sigma^{\blacktriangle}$, $\mathrm{E}\{u_\nu, v\}$ represents its Fourier coefficient in the orthogonal development in terms of the u_ν and by Parseval's identity

$$\mathrm{E}\{v\} = \sum_{\nu=1}^{\infty} (\mathrm{E}\{u_\nu, v\})^2. \tag{8.39}$$

Thus, we always have $\mathrm{E}\{u_\nu, v\} \to 0$, i. e., each complete orthonormal system converges weakly to zero. On the other hand,

$$\mathrm{E}\{u_\nu - u_\mu\} = 2 \qquad \text{for} \qquad \nu \neq \mu \tag{8.40}$$

and hence there cannot exist any $u \in \Sigma^{\blacktriangle}$ such that $\mathrm{E}\{u_\nu - u\} \to 0$. For by the triangle inequality (I.2.5) we have

$$\mathrm{E}\{u_\mu - u_\nu\}^{1/2} \leqslant \mathrm{E}\{u - u_\nu\}^{1/2} + \mathrm{E}\{u - u_\mu\}^{1/2} \tag{8.40'}$$

and if the u_ν converged to u the left-hand side in (8.40') could be made arbitrarily small.

We shall call the linear operator $L(u)$ *completely continuous* if for every sequence of elements $u \in \Sigma^{\blacktriangle}$ which converges weakly towards $u_n \in \Sigma^{\blacktriangle}$ the following holds:

$$\lim_{n \to \infty} \mathrm{E}\{L(u_n) - L(u)\} = 0; \tag{8.41}$$

i. e., if from the weak convergence of the u_n the ordinary convergence of the transformed elements follows. Obviously, complete continuity is a stronger requirement on the linear operator L than mere continuity since the concept of weak convergence is more inclusive than that of convergence.

We call a linear operator $L(u)$ *symmetric* if for every element v

$$\mathrm{E}\{L(u), v\} = \mathrm{E}\{u, L(v)\} \tag{8.42}$$

holds. Obviously, the linear integral operator defined by equation (8.2) is a symmetric operator, since its kernel $l(P, Q)$ is symmetric.

We now have the following fundamental theorem with respect to symmetric and completely continuous linear operators:

Let $L(u)$ be a linear operator defined for all elements $u \in \Sigma^{\blacktriangle}$, symmetric and completely continuous. Then there exist infinitely many eigenelements $u_\nu \in \Sigma^{\blacktriangle}$ satisfying the relation

$$u_\nu = \lambda_\nu L(u_\nu) \tag{8.43}$$

with real eigenvalues λ_ν which do not have finite limit points but which may also be infinite. These u_ν may be chosen in such a way that they form a complete orthonormal system in $\Sigma^{\blacktriangle}$.

In order to apply the theory of Hilbert space to the particular linear transformation (8.2), we must first complete the linear space Σ to a Hilbert space $\Sigma^{\blacktriangle}$. This is effected by considering all fundamental sequences $u_\nu \in \Sigma$; i. e., sequences such that $|u_\mu - u_\nu| < \varepsilon$ for $\nu, \mu > N(\varepsilon)$. We define an abstract element u as their limit if there does not already exist an element in Σ which is the limit of this sequence. In this way, the linear space Σ is completed to the Hilbert space $\Sigma^{\blacktriangle}$. It can easily be shown that $\Sigma^{\blacktriangle}$ consists of all solutions u of the differential equation (I.1.1) which possess a finite Dirichlet integral $E\{u\}$. The solutions need not be twice continuously differentiable in $\mathsf{D} + \mathsf{C}$. The transformation (8.2) can clearly be extended to all elements of $\Sigma^{\blacktriangle}$ and represents a symmetric linear transformation in this Hilbert space.

We can now show that this symmetric linear transformation (8.2) is completely continuous.[1] In fact, let $w_n(P)$ be a sequence of functions in $\Sigma^{\blacktriangle}$ which converges in the weak sense to a function $w(P) \in \Sigma^{\blacktriangle}$. Then, for each $v(P) \in \Sigma^{\blacktriangle}$, the inequality

$$|E\{v, w_n - w\}| < \varepsilon \quad \text{for} \quad n > N(\varepsilon) \tag{8.44}$$

holds. We may assume further that we have

$$E\{w_n\} \leqslant 1, \qquad E\{w\} \leqslant 1. \tag{8.45}$$

We then have to show that the corresponding transforms $\omega_n = T_{w_n}$ converge towards $\omega = T_w$ in the Dirichlet metric.

At first we remark that if we take $v(P) = K(P, Q)$, we have

$$E\{K(P,Q), w_n(P) - w(P)\} = w_n(Q) - w(Q) \tag{8.46}$$

and that this sequence is equicontinuous in each closed subdomain Δ of D. Hence, we may derive from (8.44) by the usual reasoning that there exists a number $N(\varepsilon, \Delta)$ such that

$$|w_n(Q) - w(Q)| < \varepsilon \quad \text{for} \quad n > N(\varepsilon, \Delta) \quad \text{and} \quad Q \in \Delta. \tag{8.46'}$$

[1] Indeed, a linear integral operator whose kernel is continuous in the closure of a domain is completely continuous.

Since, in view of (I.5.13)

$$w_n(Q) - w(Q) = \int_\gamma [w_n(R) - w(R)] \frac{\partial G_\Delta(R,Q)}{\partial \nu_R} ds_R \tag{8.47}$$

where γ is the boundary of Δ and G_Δ the corresponding Green's function, we also see that

$$|\mathrm{grad}\,(w_n - w)| < \varepsilon \quad \text{for} \quad n > N_1(\varepsilon, \Delta) \tag{8.48}$$

Thus, from (8.46′), (8.48), and the definition of the $\omega_n = T_{w_n}$, we find

$$|\omega_n(Q) - \omega(Q)| \leqslant |E_{D-\Delta}\{l(P,Q), w_n(P) - w(P)\}| + \varepsilon\,\alpha(\Delta) \tag{8.49}$$

for all $Q \in D$, where $\alpha(\Delta)$ is a constant depending on the closed subdomain $\Delta \subset D$.

We can choose Δ so near to D that

$$E_{D-\Delta}\{l(P,Q)\} < \varepsilon^2 \quad \text{for all} \quad Q \in D \tag{8.50}$$

and hence in view of the Schwarz inequality and (8.45), we obtain

$$|E_{D-\Delta}\{l(P,Q), w_n(P) - w(P)\}| < 2\varepsilon. \tag{8.50′}$$

Thus, we obtain uniformly in D:

$$|\omega_n(Q) - \omega(Q)| < \varepsilon_1 \quad \text{for} \quad n > N_2(\varepsilon_1). \tag{8.51}$$

Similarly, it is possible to show that one can obtain uniformly in D

$$|\mathrm{grad}\,\omega_n(Q) - \mathrm{grad}\,\omega(Q)| < \varepsilon_1, \quad \text{for} \quad n > N_3(\varepsilon_1) \tag{8.51′}$$

since the integrals $E\left\{\frac{\partial l(P,Q)}{\partial \xi}\right\}$ and $E\left\{\frac{\partial l(P,Q)}{\partial \eta}\right\}$ still converge. In fact, we have

$$E\left\{\frac{\partial l(P,Q)}{\partial \xi}\right\} = -\int_C \frac{\partial l(R,Q)}{\partial \xi} \frac{\partial^2 l(R,Q)}{\partial n_R\, \partial \xi} ds_R. \tag{8.52}$$

It is clear that this integral converges for Q in D; but it still converges for $Q \in C$; for we have proved in Section 6 that $\frac{\partial l(R,Q)}{\partial \xi}$ is continuous in the closed region $D + C$ and that $\frac{\partial^2 l(R,Q)}{\partial n_R\, \partial \xi}$ becomes infinite only logarithmically for $Q \to R$. Hence, the term (8.52) converges for all $Q \in D + C$, and similarly, we may prove the convergence of $E\left\{\frac{\partial l(P,Q)}{\partial \eta}\right\}$.

Finally from (8.51) and (8.51′) we deduce that

$$\mathrm{E}\,\{\omega_n - \omega\} < \varepsilon \qquad \text{for} \qquad n > N_4(\varepsilon). \tag{8.53}$$

This proves the convergence of the T-transforms of the w_n. Thus, the complete continuity of the linear operator (8.2) is established.

We may now apply the fundamental theorem with respect to symmetric, completely continuous operators. We obtain a complete orthonormal system of eigenfunctions $u_\nu(P)$ with corresponding eigenvalues λ_ν which, in view of the definition (8.2) of the operator, satisfy the integro-differential equations

$$u_\nu(P) = \lambda_\nu \mathrm{E}\,\{l(R,P), u_\nu(R)\}. \tag{8.54}$$

For fixed R, let us develop $l(R, P)$ in a series of this complete orthonormal system. Since the Fourier coefficients are easily computed from (8.54), we arrive at the following series development for $l(P,Q)$:

$$l(P,Q) = \sum_{\nu=1}^{\infty} \frac{u_\nu(P)\, u_\nu(Q)}{\lambda_\nu}, \tag{8.55}$$

the series converging uniformly in each closed subdomain of D. In view of (5.9) and the orthonormality of the $u_\nu(P)$, we may again obtain the development (8.36) from (8.55) by iteration.

By virtue of our general theorem, the eigenfunctions $u_\nu(P)$ lie in the Hilbert space Σ▲. However, in view of (8.54) and the continuity properties of the l-kernel we can now assert, a posteriori, that they must also belong to Σ. Thus, we have regained all previous results by means of the theory of linear operators in a Hilbert space.

Courant-Hilbert [13], vol. 2, Hellinger-Toeplitz [21], Julia [26], Kneser [32], Lichnerowicz [39], v. Neumann [56], Stone [78].

9. Series developments and integral equations: The eigenfunctions $u_\nu(P)$ of the integro-differential equation (7.5) yield a convenient representation for the iterated kernels $M^{(n)}(P,Q)$ which have been defined in Section 7 and which play an important role in the computation of the kernel $K(P,Q)$. In view of (8.36) and the recursive definition (7.24) of the $M^{(n)}$, we have

$$M^{(n)}(P,Q) = \sum_{\nu=1}^{\infty} \frac{1}{\lambda_\nu^{2n}}\, u_\nu(P)\, u_\nu(Q). \tag{9.1}$$

This representation exhibits the symmetry of all kernels $M^{(n)}$ and also their semi-definite character. In fact, let Q_i, $(i = 1, 2, \ldots, N)$, be an arbitrary set of points in D and x_i, $(i = 1, 2, \ldots, N)$, any set of real numbers. We clearly have

$$(9.2) \qquad \sum_{i,k=1}^{N} M^{(n)}(Q_i, Q_k)\, x_i\, x_k = \sum_{\nu=1}^{\infty} \frac{1}{\lambda_\nu^{2n}} \left(\sum_{i=1}^{N} u_\nu(Q_i)\, x_i \right)^2 \geqslant 0.$$

In particular, we note the inequality

$$(9.2') \qquad M^{(n)}(Q, Q) \geqslant 0.$$

Let us define the kernel

$$(9.3) \qquad \mathfrak{M}(P, Q) = \sum_{\rho=0}^{\infty} M^{(\rho)}(P, Q) = \sum_{\nu=1}^{\infty} \left(1 - \frac{1}{\lambda_\nu^2}\right)^{-1} u_\nu(P)\, u_\nu(Q).$$

In the system $\{u_\nu(P)\}$ the kernel $K(P, Q)$ has, as in every complete orthonormal system, the development

$$(9.4) \qquad K(P, Q) = \sum_{\nu=1}^{\infty} u_\nu(P)\, u_\nu(Q),$$

whence, in view of (8.36), we deduce

$$(9.5) \qquad 4\, I(P, Q) = \sum_{\nu=1}^{\infty} \left(1 - \frac{1}{\lambda_\nu^2}\right) u_\nu(P)\, u_\nu(Q).$$

Combining (9.3) and (9.5), and in view of (9.4), we obtain

$$(9.6) \qquad \mathrm{E}\{4\, I(R, P), \mathfrak{M}(R, Q)\} = \sum_{\nu=1}^{\infty} u_\nu(P)\, u_\nu(Q) = K(P, Q)$$

which is precisely the identity (7.29). In Section 7, we have already remarked that the practical importance of this identity comes from the fact that the left-hand side of (9.6) can be computed in terms of geometric expressions. On the other hand, it is evident that the introduction of the orthonormal system $\{u_\nu(P)\}$ helps considerably in clarifying all formal relationships obtained before.

It is also interesting to observe that the eigenfunctions $u_\nu(P)$ have been defined as solutions of the homogeneous integro-differential equation (7.5) with kernel $K(P, Q) - 4\, I(P, Q)$. In view of (9.5), we may also consider them as eigenfunctions of the equation

$$(9.7) \qquad u_\nu(P) = \left(1 - \frac{1}{\lambda_\nu^2}\right)^{-1} \mathrm{E}\{4\, I(P, Q), u_\nu(Q)\}.$$

The kernel $4I(P,Q)$ of (9.7) is a simple geometric quantity in contradistinction to that of (7.5). On the other hand, $K(P,Q) - 4I(P,Q)$ is continuous in the closed region $\mathsf{D} + \mathsf{C}$, while it is easily seen that $4I(P,Q)$ becomes infinite if P and Q converge to the same boundary point of D.

From the representation (9.1) for the iterated kernels $M^{(n)}$, we may draw some important conclusions with regard to the character of convergence of the series development (7.29) for the kernel. Consider the n-th approximation to the kernel $K(P,Q)$ defined by the n-th partial sum.

$$K_n(P,Q) = \sum_{\rho=0}^{n} \mathrm{E}\,\{4I(R,Q), M^{(\rho)}(R,P)\}. \tag{9.8}$$

In view of (9.1) and (9.5), this may be written in the form

$$K_n(P,Q) = \sum_{\nu=1}^{\infty} \left(1 - \frac{1}{\lambda_\nu^{2n+2}}\right) u_\nu(P) u_\nu(Q) \tag{9.9}$$

and hence we obtain for the remainder term

$$K(P,Q) - K_n(P,Q) = \sum_{\nu=1}^{\infty} \frac{1}{\lambda_\nu^{2n+2}} u_\nu(P)\, u_\nu(Q) = M^{(n+1)}(P,Q). \tag{9.10}$$

The right-hand side of this identity cannot be reduced to a geometric expression, and (9.10) is of no immediate value for the numerical calculation of the kernel $K(P,Q)$. But it is of great use for estimating the error committed if we break off the series development (7.29) after the n-th step. $M^{(n)}(P,Q)$ is a symmetric definite kernel, and hence we have for every choice of points $Q_i \in \mathsf{D}$ and real numbers x_i, the inequality

$$\sum_{i,k=1}^{N} K(Q_i,Q_k)\, x_i x_k \geqslant \sum_{i,k=1}^{N} K_n(Q_i,Q_k)\, x_i x_k. \tag{9.11}$$

Thus, the partial sums $K_n(P,Q)$ approximate the kernel $K(P,Q)$ in such a way that their corresponding quadratic forms increase monotonically toward their limit. Each approximation leads, therefore, to an interesting inequality for the kernel K in terms of geometric quantities. For example, let $n = 0$; comparing (9.5) and (9.9), we derive $K_0(P,Q) = 4I(P,Q)$, and introducing this in (9.11), we arrive at inequality (5.10). This result appears as the first of an infinite sequence of estimates for the quadratic form

$$\sum_{i,k=1}^{N} K(Q_i,Q_k)\, x_i x_k$$

in terms of geometric expressions.

If we have some estimate for the lowest eigenvalue λ_1^2 of the integro-differential equation (7.5), we may make additional statements as to the rapidity of convergence of the series (7.29) for the kernel. To this end, let us remark at first that

$$M^{(n)}(P,P) \leqslant \frac{4}{\lambda_1^{2(n-1)}(\lambda_1^2-1)} I(P,P) \tag{9.12}$$

as is easily seen from (9.1) and (9.5), and the monotonicity of the functions $\dfrac{x^n}{1-x}$ in the interval $0 \leqslant x < 1$. Next we obtain from (9.1) and the Schwarz inequality,

$$|M^{(n)}(P,Q)|^2 \leqslant M^{(n)}(P,P)\, M^{(n)}(Q,Q) \leqslant \left(\frac{4}{\lambda_1^{2(n-1)}(\lambda_1^2-1)}\right)^2 I(P,P)\, I(Q,Q). \tag{9.13}$$

Thus, in view of (9.10) we have the following estimate:

$$|K(P,Q) - K_n(P,Q)| \leqslant \frac{4}{\lambda_1^{2n}(\lambda_1^2-1)} (I(P,P)\, I(Q,Q))^{1/2}, \tag{9.14}$$

for the convergence of the partial sums to their limit. We see that *the convergence is that of a geometric series and can be expressed in terms of* λ_1 *and geometric terms alone.*

Let us next combine the series development (8.55) for the kernel $l(P,Q)$ with the representation (9.4) for the kernel $K(P,Q)$. Using the fact that in view of (I.5.11), (I.5.14), and (1.2), we have

$$K(P,Q) = n(P,Q) - g(P,Q) \tag{9.15}$$

and the definition (5.8) of $l(P,Q)$, we derive the following series for the important kernels $n(P,Q)$ and $g(P,Q)$:

$$n(P,Q) = \frac{1}{2} \sum_{\nu=1}^{\infty} \left(1 + \frac{1}{\lambda_\nu}\right) u_\nu(P)\, u_\nu(Q), \tag{9.16}$$

$$g(P,Q) = -\frac{1}{2} \sum_{\nu=1}^{\infty} \left(1 - \frac{1}{\lambda_\nu}\right) u_\nu(P)\, u_\nu(Q). \tag{9.17}$$

The reader can easily check all Dirichlet identities derived in Section 4 which now become simple formal consequences of the series development of this section. The series developments (9.16) and (9.17) also exhibit the semi-definite character of the quadratic forms connected with the kernels

n and g; this character is due to the particular choice of the fundamental singularity $S(P,Q)$ as discussed in Section 5. Thus, various results which have been derived before by repeated application of Green's identity and the boundary behavior of the functions n and g, can now be read off immediately from the formulas involving the complete orthonormal system $\{u_\nu(P)\}$.

We recognize from (9.16) and (9.17) and the orthonormality relations between the $\{u_\nu(P)\}$ that these functions may also be considered as solutions of the homogeneous integro-differential equations

$$\frac{1}{2}\left(1+\frac{1}{\lambda_\nu}\right) u_\nu(P) = \mathrm{E}\,\{n(P,Q), u_\nu(Q)\}, \tag{9.18}$$

$$-\frac{1}{2}\left(1-\frac{1}{\lambda_\nu}\right) u_\nu(P) = \mathrm{E}\,\{g(P,Q), u_\nu(Q)\}. \tag{9.19}$$

In Sections 7 and 8 we made frequent use of the fact that our special type of integro-differential equations in the E-metric over D can be transformed by integration by parts into ordinary equations where the basic domain of integration is the boundary curve C of D. We shall now carry out the same transformation of the equations (9.18) and (9.19), in order to obtain a better insight into their significance. We notice that all eigenfunctions $u_\rho(P)$ considered are continuously differentiable in the closed region $\mathsf{D}+\mathsf{C}$. This is best seen from equation (8.54), and from the continuity character of $l(P,Q)$ which was discussed extensively in Section 6. Thus, we may transform equations (8.18) and (8.19) by integration by parts to

$$\frac{1}{2}\left(1+\frac{1}{\lambda_\rho}\right) u_\rho(P) = -\int_{\mathsf{C}} u_\rho(Q)\,\frac{\partial n(P,Q)}{\partial \nu_Q}\,ds_Q \tag{9.20}$$

and

$$-\frac{1}{2}\left(1-\frac{1}{\lambda_\rho}\right) u_\rho(P) = -\int_{\mathsf{C}} g(P,Q)\,\frac{\partial u_\rho(Q)}{\partial \nu_Q}\,ds_Q. \tag{9.21}$$

Equations (9.20) and (9.21) are not yet ordinary integral equations, since the variable point Q runs over the curve system C, while the point P lies in D. In order to obtain integral equations in the ordinary sense, we must let P tend to the boundary C of D; but the character of the discontinuity of the right-hand integrals in (9.20) and (9.21) which arises from infinities of the integrand for $P=Q$ is to be taken into account. We may use, at first, the boundary behavior of $n(P, Q)$ and $g(P, Q)$ in order to replace them in the above integrals by the fundamental singularity $S(P, Q)$ which is much easier to deal with. We obtain

(9.22) $$\frac{1}{2}\left(1+\frac{1}{\lambda_\rho}\right) u_\rho(P) = \int_C u_\rho(Q) \frac{\partial S(P,Q)}{\partial \nu_Q} ds_Q,$$

(9.23) $$-\frac{1}{2}\left(1-\frac{1}{\lambda_\rho}\right) u_\rho(P) = \int_C S(P,Q) \frac{\partial u_\rho(Q)}{\partial \nu_Q} ds_Q.$$

Since $S(P, Q)$ becomes infinite for $P \to Q$ as $\frac{1}{2\pi} \log \frac{1}{PQ}$, the behavior of the right-hand integrals is the same as that of the integrals

(9.24) $$A_\rho(P) = \frac{1}{2\pi} \int_C u_\rho(Q) \frac{\partial}{\partial \nu_Q}\left(\log \frac{1}{r}\right) ds_Q, \qquad r = \overline{PQ}$$
$$B_\rho(P) = \frac{1}{2\pi} \int_C \log \frac{1}{r} \frac{\partial u_\rho(Q)}{\partial \nu_Q} ds_Q,$$

if P approaches the integration curve C. It is well known[1] that if $P_0 \in C$,

(9.25) $$A_\rho(P_0) = \lim_{P \to P_0} A_\rho(P) - \frac{1}{2} u_\rho(P_0), \qquad P \in D.$$

In other words, the potential of a dipole distribution of density $\frac{1}{2\pi} u_\rho(Q)$ on a curve system C is discontinuous and has a jump $-\frac{1}{2} u_\rho(Q)$ at the point $Q \in C$. This result is, of course, closely related to the saltus condition (7.13) which expresses the jump of the same potential across the curve C. The simple charge potential $B_\rho(P)$ is continuous in D + C, but its derivatives are not. Let P_0 be any point in C, and let $\boldsymbol{\nu}$ denote the normal direction at P_0; then we have

(9.26) $$\frac{\partial B_\rho(P_0)}{\partial \nu} = \lim_{P \to P_0} \frac{\partial B_\rho(P)}{\partial \nu} + \frac{1}{2} \frac{\partial u(P_0)}{\partial \nu}, \qquad P \in D.$$

Using (9.25) and (9.26), we may carry out the transition to the limit $P \in C$ in (9.22) and (9.23) and obtain the ordinary integral equations:

[1] Courant-Hilbert [13], vol. 2, pp. 237—9; Kellogg [30], Chapter 6.

$$u_\rho(P) = 2\lambda_\rho \int_C \frac{\partial S(P,Q)}{\partial \nu_Q} u_\rho(Q)\, ds_Q, \tag{9.27}$$

$$\frac{\partial u_\rho(P)}{\partial \nu_P} = 2\lambda_\rho \int_C \frac{\partial S(P,Q)}{\partial \nu_P} \frac{\partial u_\rho(Q)}{\partial \nu_Q}\, ds_Q. \tag{9.28}$$

Here the functions $u_\rho(P)$ and $\dfrac{\partial u_\rho(P)}{\partial \nu}$ on C are to be considered as the unknown functions. We may simplify equations (9.27) and (9.28) by defining the kernel

$$\mathfrak{K}(P,Q) = 2\frac{\partial S(P,Q)}{\partial \nu_Q}, \qquad \text{for} \qquad P, Q \in \mathsf{C}, \tag{9.29}$$

which is asymmetric in its argument points, and putting (9.27) and (9.28) in the form

$$\varphi_\rho(P) = \lambda_\rho \int_C \mathfrak{K}(P,Q)\, \varphi_\rho(Q)\, ds_Q, \qquad \varphi_\rho(P) = u_\rho(P), \tag{9.30}$$

$$\psi_\rho(P) = \lambda_\rho \int_C \mathfrak{K}(Q,P)\, \psi_\rho(Q)\, ds_Q, \qquad \psi_\rho(P) = \frac{\partial u_\rho(P)}{\partial \nu}. \tag{9.31}$$

Formulas (9.30) and (9.31) form a system of two adjoint integral equations with an asymmetric kernel. It is well known[1] from the general theory of these integral equations that they both have the same set of eigenvalues.

Let $\psi_\sigma(P)$ be any solution of (9.31); multiplying (9.30) by this function and integrating the resulting equation over C we obtain

$$\int_C \varphi_\rho \psi_\sigma\, ds = \lambda_\rho \int_C \int_C \mathfrak{K}(P,Q)\, \varphi_\rho(Q)\, \psi_\sigma(P)\, ds_Q\, ds_P = \frac{\lambda_\rho}{\lambda_\sigma} \int_C \varphi_\rho \psi_\sigma\, ds \tag{9.32}$$

which shows that

$$\int_C \varphi_\rho \psi_\sigma\, ds = 0 \qquad \text{if} \qquad \lambda_\rho \neq \lambda_\sigma. \tag{9.33}$$

Furthermore, it can be shown that the eigenfunctions of (9.30) and (9.31) can be arranged in such an order $\{\varphi_\rho\}$ and $\{\psi_\rho\}$ that the following biorthogonality relations hold:

[1] Courant-Hilbert [13], vol. 1, Ch. 3, § 3; Kellogg [30], Ch. 11, § 7.

(9.34)
$$\int_{C} \varphi_\rho \psi_\sigma \, ds = - \delta_{\rho\sigma}.$$

For, remembering now that $\varphi_\rho = u_\rho(P)$ and $\psi_\rho = \frac{\partial u_\rho(P)}{\partial \nu}$, we can transform (9.34) by means of (3.1) to

(9.35)
$$-\int_{C} \varphi_\rho \psi_\sigma \, ds = -\int_{C} u_\rho \frac{\partial u_\sigma}{\partial \nu} \, ds = \mathrm{E}\{u_\rho, u_\sigma\} = \delta_{\rho\sigma}.$$

Thus, (9.34) is just the orthonormalization of the solution system $\{u_\rho(P)\}$ of the integro-differential equation (7.5). Summarizing, we may state that *the integro-differential equation (7.5) which determines functions $u_\rho(P) \in \Sigma$ can be transformed into two adjoint ordinary integral equations for the boundary values of $u_\rho(P)$ and $\frac{\partial u_\rho(P)}{\partial \nu}$ on the boundary* C *of* D.

The integral equations (9.30) and (9.31) play a central role in the theory of the boundary value problem of (I.1.1) as developed by Poincaré, Fredholm, and Hilbert. This development is based on the theory of integral equations with an asymmetric kernel and will be sketched briefly in order to allow a comparison with our approach. Suppose that a solution $u(P)$ is to be determined with given values $u(P)$ on the boundary C. Following Poincaré, we may set up this function in the form

(9.36)
$$u(P) = \int_{C} \mu(Q) \frac{\partial S(P,Q)}{\partial \nu_Q} \, ds_Q$$

where $\mu(Q)$ is a continuous weight function on C which is to be chosen appropriately. Clearly, each expression of the right-hand type represents a solution of (I.1.1); the only problem is to fit $\mu(Q)$ to the boundary requirements with respect to $u(P)$. Now let P converge to a point $P_0 \in$ C; we can then derive the following equation from (9.36) and (9.25):

(9.37)
$$u(P_0) = \frac{1}{2}\mu(P_0) + \int_{C} \mu(Q) \frac{\partial S(P_0,Q)}{\partial \nu_Q} \, ds_Q.$$

Since $u(P_0)$ is given for every point $P_0 \in$ C, (9.37) is an inhomogeneous integral equation for the unknown function $\mu(P)$. In view of the fundamental alternative in the theory of integral equations with kernels whose iterates of some order are continuous, we can assert that the equation (9.37) has a solution if the corresponding homogeneous integral equation

$$0 = \mu(P) + 2\lambda \int_{C} \mu(Q) \frac{\partial S(P,Q)}{\partial \nu_Q} ds_Q \tag{9.37'}$$

does not possess the eigenvalue $\lambda = 1$. But (9.37') is only an alternative form of equation (9.30). Thus, the Poincaré theory of the first boundary value problem leads naturally to a study of our eigenfunctions $u_\rho(P)$ and their eigenvalues λ_ρ. Similarly, the second boundary value problem will lead to the eigenvalue problem (9.31) and thus, finally, to the same system $u_\rho(P)$. Since we know that all eigenvalues λ_ρ are greater than one in absolute value, we may assert that the solution of the inhomogeneous Fredholm equation (9.37) can be developed in a Neumann series.

While in the Poincaré-Fredholm theory of the boundary value problems the eigenfunctions $u_\rho(P)$ play an incidental role and only the fact that $|\lambda_\rho| > 1$ is used, these eigenfunctions are of fundamental importance in our approach. The kernels $K(P,Q)$ and $l(P,Q)$ possess the elegant representations (9.4) and (8.55) in terms of these important orthogonal functions, and the central role of the geometric term $I(P,Q)$ is clearly illustrated by its representation (9.5). These observations will clarify the relative position of the kernel function approach and the integral equation method in the theory of boundary value problems. We may also contrast the two methods as follows: In the integral equation approach *each particular* boundary value problem is transformed into an integral equation which is solved by a geometrically convergent Neumann series. The solution of the differential equation (I.1.1) in question is then finally expressed as the potential of a charge distribution along C the density of which is determined by the integral equation.

The kernel method works directly with the solution of (I.1.1) *inside* the domain D. The central role of the particular solution $K(P,Q)$ is recognized and *one single development* with particularly useful properties is derived for this fundamental function. Once this function has been constructed, the solutions of the first and second boundary value problems can be obtained by simple integrations. Our preceding considerations have shown that this approach also leads to a theoretical understanding of the formal relations between various important solutions and fundamental functions.

Goursat [16], Hilbert [22], Kneser [32], Lichtenstein [41], Plemelj [62], Smirnoff [69] vol. 4, § 123, Sternberg-Smith [77].

Chapter III

VARIATIONAL AND COMPARISON THEORY

1. Relations between kernels of different domains: In II.5 we used the Neumann's function of a domain D_1 in order to obtain a convenient fundamental singularity for a subdomain $D \subset D_1$. In this section, *we shall establish useful and interesting relations between various fundamental functions with respect to two domains* D *and* D_1 *for which* $D \subset D_1$. We assume that both domains D and D_1 are analytically bounded, say by the curve systems C and C_1. The coefficient $q(P)$ of the differential equation (I.1.1) is assumed to be positive and continuously differentiable in the closed region $D_1 + C_1$. We shall denote all the functions belonging to D_1 by the corresponding subscript, as, e. g., K_1, l_1, n_1, g_1, etc.

In addition to the kernels

$$K(P,Q) = N(P,Q) - G(P,Q), \qquad K_1(P,Q) = N_1(P,Q) - G_1(P,Q), \tag{1.1}$$

it will be convenient to introduce the singular kernels

$$L(P,Q) = N(P,Q) + G(P,Q), \qquad L_1(P,Q) = N_1(P,Q) + G_1(P,Q). \tag{1.2}$$

We may use $\frac{1}{2} L_1(P,Q)$ as the fundamental singularity $S(P,Q)$ for the domain D. In this case we clearly have

$$l(P,Q) = L(P,Q) - L_1(P,Q). \tag{1.3}$$

At first, let us calculate the following Dirichlet integral:

$$E\{l(R,P), l(R,Q)\} = K(P,Q) - 4I(P,Q) \tag{1.4}$$

where

$$I(P,Q) = \frac{1}{4} \int_C L_1(R,P) \frac{\partial L_1(R,Q)}{\partial \nu_R} ds_R, \tag{1.5}$$

and E { } denotes as before integration over the domain D. This is easily derived from the Dirichlet identities of Section II.4. We may now transform the term $I(P,Q)$ by integration by parts with respect to the difference domain

$$\mathsf{D}_0 = \mathsf{D}_1 - \overline{\mathsf{D}}. \tag{1.6}$$

Assuming that P and Q lie in D, we may put

$$4\,I(P,Q) = \mathrm{E}_0\{L_1(R,P), L_1(R,Q)\} + \int_{\mathsf{C}_1} L_1(R,P)\frac{\partial L_1(R,Q)}{\partial \nu_R}\,ds_R \tag{1.7}$$

where E_i denotes the Dirichlet integral extended over D_i. The last integral in (1.7) may be evaluated further since the boundary behavior of L_1 on C_1 is well known. In fact, on C_1 we have $G_1 = 0$ and $\frac{\partial N_1}{\partial \nu} = 0$, so that in view of (II.1.4) and the reproducing property of the kernel K_1, we may write

$$\int_{\mathsf{C}_1} L_1(R,P)\frac{\partial L_1(R,Q)}{\partial \nu_R}\,ds_R = \int_{\mathsf{C}_1} N_1(R,P)\frac{\partial G_1(R,Q)}{\partial \nu_R}\,ds_R = \tag{1.8}$$

$$= -\int_{\mathsf{C}_1} K_1(R,P)\frac{\partial K_1(R,Q)}{\partial \nu_R}\,ds_R = \mathrm{E}_1\{K_1(R,P), K_1(R,Q)\} = K_1(P,Q).$$

Thus, we obtain finally

$$4\,I(P,Q) = \mathrm{E}_0\{L_1(R,P), L_1(R,Q)\} + K_1(P,Q). \tag{1.9}$$

From (1.9) we immediately derive that $I(P,Q)$ represents the kernel of a semidefinite quadratic form; this is evident for the first right-hand term in (1.9) and is guaranteed for $K_1(P,Q)$ by our general result of Section II.1 on the semidefinite character of kernel functions. In Section II.5 we have required that the fundamental singularity $S(P,Q)$ should be chosen in such a way that $I(P,Q)$ be definite, i. e., that it satisfy (II.5.5). We showed there that the choice of N_1 or G_1 as fundamental singularity is permissible. Now, we can determine a more symmetric fundamental singularity, namely $\frac{1}{2}(N_1 + G_1)$, which still satisfies the requirements of II.5.

Introducing (1.9) in (1.4), we obtain the identity:

$$\begin{aligned}\mathrm{E}\{L(R,P) - L_1(R,P), L(R,Q) - L_1(R,Q)\} &= \\ = K(P,Q) - K_1(P,Q) - \mathrm{E}_0\{L_1(R,P), L_1(R,Q)\}&.\end{aligned} \tag{1.10}$$

Let us interpret this formula in the following sense; *we shall assume that all the fundamental functions with respect to the domain* D_1 *are known and that the corresponding functions for all subdomains* $\mathsf{D} \subset \mathsf{D}_1$ *are to be investigated. In this sense*

$$B(P,Q) = \mathrm{E}_0 \{L_1(R,P), L_1(R,Q)\} \tag{1.11}$$

is to be considered as a known "geometric" quantity. Formula (1.10) then expresses the increment of the K-kernel in terms of the increments of the L-kernel; it is a comparison formula describing the relation between the fundamental kernels of two domains lying within each other.

The following application may be made of identity (1.10); let $Q_i \in \mathsf{D}$ be an arbitrary set of points in D and x_i a set of real numbers. Then from (1.10) we obtain

$$\sum_{i,k=1}^{N} K(Q_i,Q_k)\, x_i x_k - \sum_{i,k=1}^{N} K_1(Q_i,Q_k)\, x_i x_k = \sum_{i,k=1}^{N} B(Q_i,Q_k)\, x_i x_k + \tag{1.12}$$
$$+ \mathrm{E}\left\{ \sum_{i=1}^{N} \big(L(R,Q_i) - L_1(R,Q_i)\big)\, x_i \right\}.$$

This shows that *for fixed points* Q_i *and coefficients* x_i *the quadratic forms*

$$\sum_{i,k=1}^{N} K(Q_i,Q_k)\, x_i x_k$$

are monotonically decreasing if the basic domain D *increases.* The change of the quadratic form can be estimated by the geometric B-integral. In particular, we have

$$K(Q,Q) - K_1(Q,Q) \geqslant B(Q,Q). \tag{1.13}$$

Next we introduce the following two linear transformations in the space Σ:

$$T_u(P) = \mathrm{E}\{l(P,Q), u(Q)\}, \qquad S_u(P) = \mathrm{E}\{K_1(P,Q), u(Q)\}. \tag{1.14}$$

The S-transform of $u(P)$ is a function of the class Σ_1 of all solutions of (I.1.1) in the domain D_1. The T-transform is defined only in the domain D since $l(P,Q)$ has sense only in this domain. We may, however, extend its definition to the domain D_0 by defining

$$l(P,Q) = -L_1(P,Q) \quad \text{for} \quad P \in \mathsf{D}_0, \quad Q \in \mathsf{D}. \tag{1.15}$$

The significance of this notation becomes clear when we notice that we may now rewrite (1.10) in the form

$$(1.10') \quad E_1\{l(R,P), l(R,Q)\} = K(P,Q) - K_1(P,Q), \qquad P,Q \in \mathsf{D}.$$

Because of the reproducing property of the kernel $K_1(P,Q)$ with respect to the E_1-metric, we can also write (1.10) in the form

$$(1.10'') \quad E_1\{l(R,P), l(R,Q)\} + E_1\{K_1(R,P), K_1(R,Q)\} = K(P,Q).$$

Now let $u(P)$ be an arbitrary element of Σ; we multiply (1.10″) with $u(P)$ in the E-metric and also with $u(Q)$. Using the reproducing property of K and the definitions (1.14), we arrive at:

$$(1.16) \qquad E_1\{T_u\} + E_1\{S_u\} = E\{u\}.$$

Thus, we have shown that to a function $u \in \Sigma$ we may adjoin two functions S_u and T_u defined in D_1 (T_u being in general discontinuous over C) which are both solutions of (I.1.1) and such that the sum of their norms in D_1 equals the norm of u. In particular, we have proved:

$$(1.17) \qquad E\{T_u\} \leqslant E_1\{T_u\} \leqslant E\{u\},$$

$$(1.17') \qquad E\{S_u\} \leqslant E_1\{S_u\} \leqslant E\{u\}.$$

The fact that the norm of u is decreased under an S-transformation played an important role in the proof in Section II.2 that a complete system in Σ can be constructed from a fundamental singularity in D_1. The great importance of identity (1.10) is its close relation to the transformations (1.14) which will yield a number of very interesting properties.

Let us consider the Dirichlet product (for P and R in D)

$$(1.18) \qquad E_1\{l(P,Q), K_1(Q,R)\} = E\{l(P,Q), K_1(Q,R)\} - E_0\{L_1(P,Q), K_1(Q,R)\},$$

the equality following from the definition (1.15). Using integration by parts, as given by (II.4.1), we can transform (1.18) into

$$(1.19) \qquad E_1\{l(P,Q), K_1(Q,R)\} = -\int_{\mathsf{C}} l(P,Q) \frac{\partial K_1(Q,R)}{\partial \nu_Q} ds_Q$$

$$- \int_{\mathsf{C}} L_1(P,Q) \frac{\partial K_1(Q,R)}{\partial \nu_Q} ds_Q + \int_{\mathsf{C}_1} L_1(P,Q) \frac{\partial K_1(Q,R)}{\partial \nu_Q} ds_Q.$$

Using definition (1.3) and the fact that $L(P, Q) = K(P, Q)$ on C and $L_1(P, Q) = K_1(P, Q)$ on C_1, we find

$$(1.20) \qquad \mathrm{E}_1\{l(P,Q), K_1(Q,R)\} = -\int_{\mathsf{C}} K(P,Q) \frac{\partial K_1(Q,R)}{\partial \nu_Q} ds_Q +$$

$$+\int_{\mathsf{C}_1} K_1(P,Q) \frac{\partial K_1(Q,R)}{\partial \nu_Q} ds_Q = \mathrm{E}\{K(P,Q), K_1(Q,R)\}$$

$$-\mathrm{E}_1\{K_1(P,Q), K_1(Q,R)\} = K_1(P,R) - K_1(P,R) = 0$$

We have thus proved that the *functions* $l(P, Q)$, as defined by (1.3) and (1.15), *and* $K_1(P, Q)$ *are orthogonal with respect to the* E_1*-metric.* This leads immediately to the result:

$$(1.21) \qquad \mathrm{E}_1\{T_u, S_u\} = 0 \qquad \text{for all} \qquad u \in \Sigma.$$

Moreover, since every function $w \in \Sigma_1$ can be expressed in the form

$$(1.22) \qquad w(P) = \mathrm{E}_1\{K_1(P,Q), w(Q)\},$$

we conclude from (1.20) that every T-transform of a function $u \in \Sigma$ is orthogonal to every function $w \in \Sigma_1$, i. e.,

$$(1.23) \qquad \mathrm{E}_1\{T_u, w\} = 0.$$

From definition (1.14) and (1.22), we may draw the further conclusion

$$(1.24) \qquad \mathrm{E}_1\{S_u, w\} = \mathrm{E}\{u, w\},$$

i. e., S_u *has the same scalar product in the* E_1*-metric with each* $w \in \Sigma_1$ *as has the corresponding function* u *in the* E*-metric.*

We have defined the kernel $l(P, Q)$ by (1.3) and (1.15) in a discontinuous way in order to obtain convenient properties for the operator T_u. We may also define this operator in a slightly different way in order to clarify its significance further. Using the definition (1.2) of $L(P, Q)$ and the identities (I.6.1) and (I.6.3), we obtain for every $u \in \Sigma$

$$(1.25) \qquad \mathrm{E}\{L(P,Q), u(Q)\} = u(P).$$

Hence, in view of (1.3), (1.14), and (1.15), we find

$$(1.25') \qquad \begin{aligned} T_u(P) &= u(P) - \mathrm{E}\{L_1(P,Q), u(Q)\} && \text{for} \quad P \in \mathsf{D}, \\ &= -\mathrm{E}\{L_1(P,Q), u(Q)\} && \text{for} \quad P \in \mathsf{D}_0. \end{aligned}$$

By means of (1.25′), we are able to extend the definition of the operator T_u to all functions which are defined in D and in D_0 and of the class Σ and Σ_0 in these domains; the functions considered will, in general, be discontinuous on the boundary C between D and D_0. Let Σ^* be the class of these functions; we may extend each $u \in \Sigma$ to the class Σ^* by defining it as identically zero in D_0. For each $u \in \Sigma^*$ we shall define

$$T_u(P) = u(P) - E_1\{L_1(P,Q), u(Q)\}. \tag{1.26}$$

For functions $u \in \Sigma$ this definition is consistent with (1.14); the discontinuity of the operator has now been replaced by the discontinuity of u, considered as a function in the entire domain D_1. We further define the operator S_u for functions of the class Σ^* by

$$S_u(P) = E_1\{K_1(P,Q), u(Q)\}. \tag{1.27}$$

The operator S_u has the important property of transforming every element $w \in \Sigma^*$ into an element of the subclass Σ_1. It reproduces every element of the class Σ_1, while T_u vanishes for each element of the same class.

The operator T_u has now been defined for all elements of Σ^* by an improper integral with a discontinuous integrand. For a further study of its properties it will be convenient to express it as a proper integral. We observe that since $u(P)$ is of class Σ in D and of class Σ_0 in D_0, we have:

$$u(P) = \begin{cases} E\{L(P,Q), u(Q)\} & \text{for} \quad P \in D, \\ E_0\{L_0(P,Q), u(Q)\} & \text{for} \quad P \in D_0, \end{cases}$$

where L_0 is the L-kernel with respect to the domain D_0. Thus, if we define:

$$l(P,Q) = \begin{cases} L(P,Q) - L_1(P,Q) & \text{for } P \in D,\ Q \in D, \\ -L_1(P,Q) & \text{for } P \in D,\ Q \in D_0 \text{ or } P \in D_0,\ Q \in D, \\ L_0(P,Q) - L_1(P,Q) & \text{for } P \in D_0,\ Q \in D_0, \end{cases} \tag{1.28}$$

we may put (1.26) in the form

$$T_u(P) = E_1\{l(P,Q), u(Q)\}. \tag{1.29}$$

Clearly definition (1.28) is consistent with (1.3) and (1.15) and is a natural extension of this definition to the case in which both argument points of l lie in D_0.

In the new definition (1.28) of the l-kernel, we can extend the identity (1.10′) to the case where the argument points considered lie anywhere in $D_1 - C$. For this purpose we define

$$k(P,Q) = \begin{cases} K(P,Q) - K_1(P,Q) & \text{for } P \in D,\ Q \in D, \\ -K_1(P,Q) & \text{for } P \in D,\ Q \in D_0 \text{ or } P \in D_0,\ Q \in D, \\ K_0(P,Q) - K_1(P,Q) & \text{for } P \in D_0,\ Q \in D_0. \end{cases} \tag{1.30}$$

In this notation we have the identity

$$E_1\{l(P,Q), l(P,R)\} = k(Q,R), \tag{1.31}$$

valid for all points Q and R in $\mathsf{D}_1 - \mathsf{C}$. For Q and R in D or in D_0, this result is identical with formula (1.10′); we must prove (1.31) only for the case in which $Q \in \mathsf{D}$ and $R \in \mathsf{D}_0$. Under these assumptions, we have

$$\begin{aligned} E_1\{l(P,Q), l(P,R)\} &= -E\{l(P,Q), L_1(P,R)\} \\ -E_0\{L_1(P,Q), l(P,R)\} &= -E\{L(P,Q), L_1(P,R)\} \\ -E_0\{L_1(P,Q), L_0(P,R)\} &+ E_1\{L_1(P,Q), L_1(P,R)\}. \end{aligned} \tag{1.32}$$

The function $L_1(P,R)$ is of class Σ and $L_1(P,Q)$ is of class Σ_0; hence, in view of (1.25), the first two right-hand terms in (1.32) have the value $-L_1(Q,R)$. In view of (I.6.7) and (I.6.8) applied to the domain D_1, we have furthermore

$$\begin{aligned} E_1\{L_1(P,Q), L_1(P,R)\} &= N_1(Q,R) + 3G_1(Q,R) \\ &= 2L_1(Q,R) - K_1(Q,R). \end{aligned} \tag{1.33}$$

Finally we obtain the result:

$$E_1\{l(P,Q), l(P,R)\} = -K_1(Q,R) = k(Q,R). \tag{1.34}$$

Thus, *identity* (1.31) *has been proved generally.*

We also notice that the *identity* (1.20) *now holds for an arbitrary location of the argument points P and R in $\mathsf{D}_1 - \mathsf{C}$.* To prove this fact, we have only to consider the case where $P \in \mathsf{D}$ and $R \in \mathsf{D}_0$. In this case we have

$$\begin{aligned} E_1\{l(P,Q), K_1(Q,R)\} &= E\{L(P,Q) - L_1(P,Q), K_1(Q,R)\} \\ -E_0\{L_1(P,Q), K_1(Q,R)\} &= K_1(P,R) - E_1\{L_1(P,Q), K_1(Q,R)\} = \\ &= K_1(P,R) - K_1(P,R) = 0. \end{aligned} \tag{1.35}$$

From (1.31) and (1.35) we draw the following conclusions: *Let $u(P)$ and $v(P)$ be two functions in Σ^*; the four transforms T_u, S_u and T_v, S_v again lie in the same function space Σ^* and satisfy the equations:*

$$E_1\{T_u, T_v\} + E_1\{S_u, S_v\} = E_1\{u, v\} \tag{1.36}$$

and

$$E_1\{T_u, S_v\} = E_1\{S_u, T_v\} = 0. \tag{1.37}$$

In particular, we observe that the *two linear transformations of Σ^**

$$\gamma_u^+ = T_u + S_u \quad \text{and} \quad \gamma_u^- = S_u - T_u \tag{1.38}$$

have the property of norm preservation

$$E_1\{\gamma_u^{\pm}\} = E_1\{u\}. \tag{1.39}$$

The linear transformations γ_u have further interesting properties. Let us start with any function $u \in \Sigma^*$; then $w = \gamma_u^+$ is again an element of the same space with the same norm and the question of expressing γ_w^+ in terms of u arises. We have:

$$\gamma_w^+(P) = S_w + T_w = \mathrm{E}_1\{K_1(P,Q), S_u + T_u\} + \mathrm{E}_1\{l(P,Q), S_u + T_u\}. \tag{1.40}$$

Using the identities (1.31) and (1.35) we can easily calculate

$$\begin{gathered}\mathrm{E}_1\{K_1(P,Q), S_u(Q)\} = S_u(P), \quad \mathrm{E}_1\{K_1(P,Q), T_u(Q)\} = 0, \\ \mathrm{E}_1\{l(P,Q), S_u(Q)\} = 0, \quad \mathrm{E}_1\{l(P,Q), T_u(Q)\} = \mathrm{E}_1\{k(P,Q), u(Q)\}.\end{gathered} \tag{1.41}$$

Inserting these relations in (1.40) and using the definition (1.30) of $k(P,Q)$, we find

$$\gamma_w^+(P) = u(P). \tag{1.42}$$

Thus, we have proved that the γ^+ transformation applied twice reproduces every element of Σ^*; the same is also true for the γ^- transformation as is easily verified.

Let us now interpret the operators γ^+ and γ^-. Let $u \in \Sigma^*$; using the definitions (1.1), (1.2), (1.26), (1.27), and (1.38), we obtain

$$\begin{aligned}\gamma_u^+(P) &= u(P) + \mathrm{E}_1\{K_1(P,Q) - L_1(P,Q), u(Q)\} = \\ &= u(P) - 2\,\mathrm{E}_1\{G_1(P,Q), u(Q)\}.\end{aligned} \tag{1.43}$$

Let us apply Green's formula (I.5.7) with respect to the domains D and D_0 and let us denote by $\frac{\partial u(Q+)}{\partial \nu}$, $\frac{\partial u(Q-)}{\partial \nu}$ the limits of $\frac{\partial u(P)}{\partial \nu}$ as $P \to Q \in \mathsf{C}$ from D and D_0 respectively, where $\boldsymbol{\nu}$ is the interior normal of D at Q. Then we find

$$\gamma_u^+(P) = u(P) + 2\int_{\mathsf{C}} G_1(P,Q)\left(\frac{\partial u(Q+)}{\partial \nu} - \frac{\partial u(Q-)}{\partial \nu}\right) ds_Q. \tag{1.44}$$

Similarly

$$\begin{aligned}\gamma_u^-(P) &= -u(P) + \mathrm{E}_1\{K_1(P,Q) + L_1(P,Q), u(Q)\} = \\ &= -u(P) + 2\,\mathrm{E}_1\{N_1(P,Q), u(Q)\}\end{aligned} \tag{1.45}$$

i. e.,

$$\gamma_u^-(P) = u(P) - 2\int_{\mathsf{C}} \frac{\partial N_1(P,Q)}{\partial \nu_Q}\big(u(Q+) - u(Q-)\big)\, ds_Q. \tag{1.45'}$$

In view of the character of the discontinuity of the integrals in (1.44) and (1.45′) which behave like simple and dipole charge potentials along C, we may characterize the γ_u^+ and γ_u^- transforms as follows:

If $u \in \Sigma^*$, then γ_u^+ is of the same class. On C_1 it has the same boundary values as u; along C it has the same jump $u(Q^+) - u(Q^-)$ while the jump of its normal derivative is opposite to that of u, namely $-\left(\frac{\partial u(Q^+)}{\partial \nu} - \frac{\partial u(Q^-)}{\partial \nu}\right)$.

On C_1 γ_u^- has the same normal derivative as u; its jump across C is opposite to that of u, namely $-(u(Q^+) - u(Q^-))$ while its normal derivatives have just the same jump as those of u.

From this characterization of the operators γ^+ and γ^- we immediately obtain a new proof of their involutory character, i. e., that their iterated application reproduces the original function. In fact, for each function $u \in \Sigma^*$

$$E_1\{u\} = -\int_{C_1} u \frac{\partial u}{\partial \nu} ds - \int_{C} \left[u \frac{\partial u}{\partial \nu}\right] ds \tag{1.46}$$

where the symbol $[f]$ denotes the saltus of the expression f across C. Now let $v = \gamma_u^+$ and $w = \gamma_v^+$; $w = \gamma_v^+$ will have the same boundary values on C_1 as u and the same jump of u and of $\frac{\partial u}{\partial \nu}$ across C. Hence, $u - w$ will also belong to the class Σ^*, be continuous in D_1, have continuous derivatives there and vanish on C_1. Hence, in view of (1.46), we have $E_1\{u - w\} = 0$, $u \equiv w$. This proves that the application of γ^+ to γ_u^+ reproduces u. Similarly, we can prove that γ^- applied twice to u reproduces this function.

If u and v are both of class Σ^*, we can generalize (1.46) to

$$E_1\{u, v\} = -\int_{C_1} u \frac{\partial v}{\partial \nu} ds - \int_{C} \left[u \frac{\partial v}{\partial \nu}\right] ds. \tag{1.47}$$

From this result we can easily derive the norm preservation under the γ^- transformations. In fact, $w = u - \gamma_u^+$ is continuous in D_1, vanishes on C_1, and its normal derivative has the jump $2\left[\frac{\partial u}{\partial \nu}\right]$ across C. Hence, by (1.46), we have

$$E_1\{u - \gamma_u^+\} = -2\int_{C} (u - \gamma_u^+) \left[\frac{\partial u}{\partial \nu}\right] ds = -2\int_{C} \left[u \frac{\partial u}{\partial \nu}\right] ds + 2\int_{C} \left[\gamma_u^+ \frac{\partial u}{\partial \nu}\right] ds. \tag{1.48}$$

Since $u = \gamma_u^+$ on C_1, we may transform the previous formula to

$$(1.49)\qquad E_1\{u-\gamma_u^+\} = -2\int_{C_1} u\frac{\partial u}{\partial \nu}ds - 2\int_{C}\left[u\frac{\partial u}{\partial \nu}\right]ds + 2\int_{C_1}\gamma_u^+\frac{\partial u}{\partial \nu}ds + 2\int_{C}\left[\gamma_u^+\frac{\partial u}{\partial \nu}\right]ds$$

whence, in view of (1.46) and (1.47):

$$(1.50)\qquad E_1\{u\} + E_1\{\gamma_u^+\} - 2E_1\{u,\gamma_u^+\} = 2E_1\{u\} - 2E_1\{u,\gamma_u^+\}.$$

Thus, we finally conclude

$$(1.51)\qquad E_1\{\gamma_u^+\} = E_1\{u\}.$$

Similarly, we can prove

$$(1.51')\qquad E_1\{\gamma_u^-\} = E_1\{u\}.$$

As we have seen in all our previous considerations, the E-metric is closely related to the theory of Green's and Neumann's functions. We can obtain analogous results with respect to general Robin's functions by the use of an appropriate metric. Let us define the following metric within the class Σ^*:

$$(1.52)\qquad \begin{gathered} E_{\mu,\lambda}\{u,v\} = E_1\{u,v\} + \int_{C_1}\lambda(s)\,u\,v\,ds + \int_{C}\mu(s)\,[u\,v]\,ds, \\ \lambda(s) > 0, \qquad \mu(s) > 0. \end{gathered}$$

We observe that if u and v belong to the subclass Σ of Σ^* the metric (1.52) becomes simply

$$(1.52')\qquad E_\mu\{u,v\} = E\{u,v\} + \int_{C}\mu(s)\,u\,v\,ds.$$

This was considered in Section I.6 in connection with the Robin function R_μ of the class Σ. Similarly, if u and v belong to the subclass $\Sigma_1 \subset \Sigma^*$, we obtain the metric

$$(1.52'')\qquad E_{1,\lambda}\{u,v\} = E_1\{u,v\} + \int_{C_1}\lambda(s)\,u\,v\,ds$$

leading to the Robin function with subscript λ of the class Σ_1. Let us denote this Robin function by $\mathfrak{R}_\lambda(P,Q)$.

We now define the following linear transformation of Σ^*:

$$\mathfrak{T}_u(P) = u(P) + 2\int_{\mathbf{C}} \left(\mu(s)\,\mathfrak{R}_\lambda(P,Q) - \frac{\partial \mathfrak{R}_\lambda(P,Q)}{\partial \nu_Q}\right)[u(Q)]\,ds_Q \tag{1.53}$$

and study its characteristic properties:

a) Because of the equation (I.5.18) satisfied by $\mathfrak{R}_\lambda$ on $\mathbf{C}_1$, we find

$$\frac{\partial \mathfrak{T}_u}{\partial \nu} - \lambda\,\mathfrak{T}_u = \frac{\partial u}{\partial \nu} - \lambda u, \qquad \text{on } \mathbf{C}_1. \tag{1.54}$$

b) From the character of the discontinuity of the integral in (1.53) we obtain the following formulas expressing the jump of $\mathfrak{T}_u$ through $\mathbf{C}$:

$$[\mathfrak{T}_u] = -[u], \qquad \left[\frac{\partial \mathfrak{T}_u}{\partial \nu}\right] = -2\mu\,[u] + \left[\frac{\partial u}{\partial \nu}\right]. \tag{1.55}$$

c) In particular, we need the following combination of equations (1.55):

$$\left[\frac{\partial \mathfrak{T}_u}{\partial \nu}\right] - \mu\,[\mathfrak{T}_u] = \left[\frac{\partial u}{\partial \nu}\right] - \mu\,[u]. \tag{1.56}$$

From the properties a) — c) of $\mathfrak{T}_u$ it is easy to show that it is an involutory linear transformation of Σ^* which preserves the norm $E_{\mu,\lambda}$. In fact, let $v = \mathfrak{T}_u$ and $w = \mathfrak{T}_v$. Clearly, we have $\frac{\partial w}{\partial \nu} - \lambda w = \frac{\partial u}{\partial \nu} - \lambda u$ on $\mathbf{C}_1$ and $[w] = [u]$, $\left[\frac{\partial w}{\partial \nu}\right] - \mu\,[w] = \left[\frac{\partial u}{\partial \nu}\right] - \mu\,[u]$ on $\mathbf{C}$. Hence, the function $u - w$ will be continuous in $\mathbf{D}_1$ and the operator $\frac{\partial}{\partial \nu} - \lambda$ will destroy it entirely on $\mathbf{C}_1$. Hence, in view of

$$\mathrm{E}_{\mu,\lambda}\{u, v\} = \int_{\mathbf{C}_1} \left(\lambda(s)\,v - \frac{\partial v}{\partial \nu}\right) u\,ds + \int_{\mathbf{C}} \left(\mu\,[u\,v] - \left[u\frac{\partial v}{\partial \nu}\right]\right) ds \tag{1.57}$$

we find $\mathrm{E}_{\mu,\lambda}\{u - w\} = 0$. Since $u - w$ is continuous in $\mathbf{D}_1$ we see by (1.52) that its $\mathrm{E}_{\mu,\lambda}$-norm can vanish only if $u \equiv w$; this proves the involutory character of the $\mathfrak{T}$-transformation.

Next, consider the norm of $u - \mathfrak{T}_u$ in the $\mathrm{E}_{\mu,\lambda}$-metric. In view of the properties a) — c) of $\mathfrak{T}_u$, the formula (1.57) can be written as

$$(1.58)\qquad \mathrm{E}_{\mu,\lambda}\{u-\mathfrak{T}_u\} = 2\int_{\mathsf{C}} [u]\left(\mu\,(u-\mathfrak{T}_u) - \frac{\partial(u-\mathfrak{T}_u)}{\partial\nu}\right) ds$$

$$= 2\int_{\mathsf{C}}\left(\mu\,[u^2] - \left[u\frac{\partial u}{\partial\nu}\right]\right) ds - 2\int_{\mathsf{C}}\left(\mu\,[u\,\mathfrak{T}_u] - \left[u\frac{\partial\mathfrak{T}_u}{\partial\nu}\right]\right) ds$$

$$= 2\,\mathrm{E}_{\mu,\lambda}\{u\} - 2\,\mathrm{E}_{\mu,\lambda}\{u,\mathfrak{T}_u\}.$$

From (1.58), we conclude as before

$$(1.59)\qquad \mathrm{E}_{\mu,\lambda}\{u\} = \mathrm{E}_{\mu,\lambda}\{\mathfrak{T}_u\}$$

which proves the *norm preservation of the* $\mathfrak{T}$*-transform in the* $\mathrm{E}_{\mu,\lambda}$*-metric.*

Let $u(P)$ be an arbitrary function of class Σ^*; one easily derives the identity

$$u(P) = -\int_{\mathsf{C}_1} \mathfrak{N}_\lambda(P,Q)\left(\frac{\partial u}{\partial\nu} - \lambda u\right) ds_Q - \int_{\mathsf{C}}\left(\frac{\partial\mathfrak{N}_\lambda(P,Q)}{\partial\nu_Q}[u] - \mathfrak{N}_\lambda(P,Q)\left[\frac{\partial u}{\partial\nu}\right]\right) ds_Q.$$
(1.60)

This identity allows us to express each function in Σ^* by means of its boundary values $\frac{\partial u}{\partial\nu} - \lambda u$ on C_1 and its discontinuities across C. Conversely, if $\frac{\partial u}{\partial\nu} - \lambda u$ on C_1 and $[u]$, $\left[\frac{\partial u}{\partial\nu}\right]$ on C are prescribed arbitrarily, the expression (1.60) yields an element of Σ^* with just these boundary values on C_1 and discontinuities on C. Thus the problem of determining a function $u\in\Sigma^*$ by its boundary values on C_1 and discontinuities on C can always be solved if the fundamental functions with respect to D_1 are known.

Bergman-Schiffer (B 25), (B 26), Schiffer-Spencer [68].

2. Eigenfunctions of the γ-transformation: Let us consider the functions u and γ_u as functions in the domain D only. In this case, both may be considered as elements of Σ, and γ_u may be considered as a linear transformation of Σ into itself. It is therefore of interest to ask for the eigenfunctions of this transformation. At first let us consider the operator γ_u^+; we are looking for those functions $u_\nu(P)\in\Sigma$ which satisfy the equation

$$(2.1)\qquad u_\nu(P) = \lambda_\nu\gamma^+_{u_\nu}(P)\qquad \text{for}\qquad P\in\mathsf{D}.$$

Since we are working only in the domain D, we may use the representations (1.14) for the operators T and S in the definition (1.38) and we may write (2.1) as the integro-differential equation

$$(2.2)\qquad u_\nu(P) = \lambda_\nu \mathrm{E}\{l(P,Q) + K_1(P,Q), u_\nu(Q)\}.$$

In Section II.8 we proved that for proper choice of the fundamental singularity $S(P,Q)$ the linear operator $E\{l(P,Q), u(Q)\}$ is completely continuous. This is the case for our present choice of $S(P,Q)$, and since K_1 is continuous in the closure of D, $E\{K_1(P,Q), u(Q)\}$ is a completely continuous transformation in Σ, so that $E\{l + K_1, u\}$ is completely continuous in Σ. It is also symmetric.

Hence, using the fundamental theorem quoted in Section II.8, we may assert that there exists a complete set of eigenfunctions $u_\nu(P)$ of (2.1) with eigenvalues λ_ν. We may assume these $u_\nu(P)$ to be orthonormalized according to the conditions

$$E\{u_\nu, u_\mu\} = \delta_{\nu\mu}. \tag{2.3}$$

Having arrived at this complete orthonormal set of eigenfunctions $\{u_\nu\}$ in Σ, we now consider the functions $v_\nu(P) = \overset{+}{\gamma}_{u_\nu}$ in Σ^*. Because of the norm-preserving property (1.51) of the γ-transformation, these functions form an orthonormal set in Σ^*, with respect to the metric defined by E_1. In particular, we shall consider the functions $v_\nu(P)$ in D_0, i. e., as elements of Σ_0. For this purpose we notice that in view of (2.1) we have

$$E_1\{v_\nu, v_\mu\} = E_0\{v_\nu, v_\mu\} + E\{v_\nu, v_\mu\} = E_0\{v_\nu, v_\mu\} + \frac{1}{\lambda_\nu \lambda_\mu} E\{u_\nu, u_\mu\}. \tag{2.4}$$

Hence, in view of (2.3) and the norm-preserving property of the γ-transform

$$E_0\{v_\nu, v_\mu\} = \left(1 - \frac{1}{\lambda_\nu^2}\right) \delta_{\nu\mu}. \tag{2.5}$$

Thus, we have shown that the γ-transforms of the u_ν form an orthogonal system in Σ_0.

From (2.5) we conclude that $|\lambda_\rho| \geqslant 1$ and that $\lambda_\rho = \pm 1$ is possible only for $v_\rho \equiv 0$. But in this case, the normal derivative of $\overset{+}{\gamma}_u$ would have the jump $\pm \left[\dfrac{\partial u}{\partial \nu}\right]$ across C. From our characterization of the γ^+ transform we conclude that only the negative sign is permissible, i. e., $\lambda = -1$. But then $\overset{+}{\gamma}_{u_\rho}$ would have the jump $-[u_\rho]$ across C which would lead to $[u_\rho] = 0$ on C. But $u_\rho = 0$ in D_0, hence $u_\rho = 0$ on C. Thus $u_\rho \equiv 0$ in D by the uniqueness theorem in the boundary value theory and hence $|\lambda_\rho| = 1$ is impossible for any normalized u_ρ. We have therefore proved that $|\lambda_\rho| > 1$.

Let us next determine $w_\nu(P) = \overset{+}{\gamma}_{v_\nu}(P)$. If $P \in D_0$, we have by the involutory character of the γ-transformation $w_\nu(P) - u_\nu(P) = 0$. Thus we obtain

$$E_0\{l(P,Q)+K_1(P,Q),v_\nu(Q)\}+\frac{1}{\lambda_\nu}E\{l(P,Q)+K_1(P,Q),u_\nu(Q)\}=0 \tag{2.6}$$

Here $l(P,Q)$ is to be understood in the general sense as defined in (1.28). In view of the fact that $v_\nu = \overset{+}{\gamma}_{u_\nu}$, we may write (2.6) in the form

$$v_\nu(P) = -\lambda_\nu E_0\{l(P,Q)+K_1(P,Q),v_\nu(Q)\}. \tag{2.7}$$

Thus, $v_\nu(P)$ considered as a function of Σ_0, i. e., assumed zero in D, satisfies the equation

$$v_\nu(P) = -\lambda_\nu \gamma_{v_\nu}^+(P). \tag{2.8}$$

The above result shows that the *complete set of eigenfunctions with respect to the domain* D *is transformed by the elementary operation* γ^+ *into an orthogonal set of eigenfunctions with respect to the complementary domain* D_0.

The question arises whether this set $\{v_\nu\}$ is complete in Σ_0. We can no longer appeal to the fundamental theorem on completely continuous transformations; for, the kernel $K_1(P,Q)$ is no longer bounded on the boundary curve C_1 of D_1. In fact, by a characteristic property of the transformation γ_u^+ all functions $v_\nu(P)$ vanish on C_1. Hence,

$$E_0\{v_\rho, v\} = -\int_C v_\rho \frac{\partial v}{\partial \nu}\, ds \tag{2.9}$$

vanishes for every function $v \in \Sigma_0$ whose normal derivative is zero on C. This fact shows that the set $\{v_\rho\}$ is not complete in Σ_0 since there exist non-vanishing functions $v \in \Sigma_0$ with normal derivative zero on C.

We shall show, however, that the $\{v_\rho(P)\}$ *form a complete set in the subspace* $O_0 \subset \Sigma_0$ *consisting of all functions which vanish on* C_1. Suppose a function $v \in O_0$ were orthogonal to all functions v_ρ. Consider its transform $w = \gamma_v^+$ which is of the class Σ^*, i. e., defined in D and D_0. The function $\overset{+}{\gamma}_{u_\rho}$ which equals v_ρ in D_0 and $\frac{1}{\lambda_\rho} u_\rho$ in D is also of the same class. We have

$$E_1\{\gamma_w^+, \gamma_{u_\rho}^+\} = E_1\{w, u_\rho\} = E\{w, u_\rho\} \tag{2.10}$$

since $u_\rho \in \Sigma$ vanishes in D_0. Finally, $\gamma_w^+ = v$ will vanish in D, whence

$$E_0\{v, v_\rho\} = E\{w, u_\rho\}. \tag{2.11}$$

Since v is orthogonal in the E_0-metric to all functions v_ρ, w will be orthogonal in the E-metric to all functions u_ρ. But since the set $u_\rho(P)$ is complete $w(P) \equiv 0$ in D. Since $v = \gamma_w^+$, and $v = 0$ in D, we conclude that $w = v$

on the boundary C of D_0; on the boundary C_1 of D_0 both functions vanish. Hence, by the uniqueness theorem in the boundary value theory, we conclude $v(P) \equiv w(P)$ in D_0. But the jump of $\frac{\partial v}{\partial \nu}$ and $\frac{\partial \gamma_v^+}{\partial \nu}$ should have opposite signs across C and this clearly leads to $\frac{\partial v}{\partial \nu} \equiv 0$ on C. In view of

$$(2.12) \qquad \mathrm{E}_0\{v\} = -\int_{C_1} v \frac{\partial v}{\partial \nu}\, ds - \int_{C} v \frac{\partial v}{\partial \nu}\, ds = 0$$

we finally conclude $v \equiv 0$ in D_0. Hence, the completeness of the set $\{v_\rho(P)\}$ in the subclass $O_0 \subset \Sigma_0$ is established.

It is clear that the kernels $K(P,Q)$ and $l(P,Q) + K_1(P,Q)$ can be developed in a Fourier series with respect to the complete orthonormal set $\{u_\nu\}$ in D; we have, in view of the reproducing property of K and the equation (2.2):

$$(2.13) \quad K(P,Q) = \sum_{\nu=1}^{\infty} u_\nu(P)\, u_\nu(Q), \quad l(P,Q) + K_1(P,Q) = \sum_{\nu=1}^{\infty} \frac{u_\nu(P)\, u_\nu(Q)}{\lambda_\nu}.$$

In the domain D_0 we may use the system $\{v_\nu\}$ to develop the function $G_0(P,Q) - G_1(P,Q)$ which is obviously in the subclass O_0 of Σ_0. We have, in view of (1.1) and (1.28)

$$(2.14) \qquad G_0(P,Q) - G_1(P,Q) = \frac{1}{2}[l(P,Q) + K_1(P,Q)] - \frac{1}{2} K_0(P,Q).$$

Hence, using the reproducing property of the K_0-kernel and equation (2.7), we can immediately calculate the Fourier coefficients

$$(2.15) \qquad \mathrm{E}_0\{G_0(P,Q) - G_1(P,Q), v_\nu(Q)\} = -\frac{1}{2}\left(1 + \frac{1}{\lambda_\nu}\right) v_\nu(P).$$

We notice that because of (2.5), the $v_\nu(P)$ are not normalized in the E_0-metric. Hence, we obtain the development

$$(2.16) \qquad G_0(P,Q) - G_1(P,Q) = -\frac{1}{2} \sum_{\nu=1}^{\infty} \frac{v_\nu(P)\, v_\nu(Q)}{1 - \lambda_\nu^{-1}}.$$

Using the analogous identity

$$(2.14') \qquad G(P,Q) - G_1(P,Q) = \frac{1}{2}[l(P,Q) + K_1(P,Q)] - \frac{1}{2} K(P,Q),$$

we derive from (2.13) the corresponding identity

$$(2.16') \qquad G(P,Q) - G_1(P,Q) = -\frac{1}{2}\sum_{\nu=1}^{\infty}\left(1 - \frac{1}{\lambda_\nu}\right) u_\nu(P)\, u_\nu(Q)$$

which is, of course, only a special instance of (II.9.17). In fact, since

$$(2.17) \qquad l(P,Q) + K_1(P,Q) = N(P,Q) + G(P,Q) - 2G_1(P,Q)$$

we may consider the integro-differential equation (2.2) as a special case of the equation (II.8.54) for the particular choice of $G_1(P, Q)$ as the fundamental singularity. The importance of the special case considered lies in the interesting relations to which one is led and which connect the fundamental functions of the complementary domains D and D_0.

Let us now consider the significance of the eigenfunctions $u_\nu(P)$ of the integro-differential equation (2.1). Using the fact that we are dealing with a particular instance of the general theory of eigenfunctions as developed in Sections II.8 and II.9 with the particular choice of $G_1(P,Q)$ as fundamental singularity, we may characterize the $\{u_\nu\}$ as follows. Let

$$(2.18) \qquad \psi_\rho(P) = \frac{\partial u_\rho(P)}{\partial \nu}, \qquad P \in \mathsf{C},$$

be the normal derivative of the eigenfunction $u_\rho(P)$ on C; then, in view of (II.9.29) and (II.9.31), we find

$$(2.19) \qquad \psi_\rho(P) = 2\lambda_\rho \int_{\mathsf{C}} \frac{\partial G_1(P,Q)}{\partial \nu_P}\, \psi_\rho(Q)\, ds_Q.$$

The values of the normal derivative of our eigenfunctions are thus characterized by an integral equation of the general type considered in Section II.9. The particular form (2.19) of the integral equation is, however, closely related to a problem which arises in numerous applications.

We require a function $u(P) \in \Sigma^*$ which is continuous in D_1, has prescribed boundary values on C_1 and on C satisfies the discontinuity relation for its normal derivatives

$$(2.20) \qquad \frac{\partial u(P)}{\partial \nu^+} = a\frac{\partial u(P)}{\partial \nu^-}, \qquad a = \text{given constant}.$$

Using a representation of the form (1.60) for the required solution, we find

$$(2.21) \qquad u(P) = \int_{\mathsf{C}_1} \frac{\partial G_1(P,Q)}{\partial \nu_Q}\, u(Q)\, ds + \int_{\mathsf{C}} G_1(P,Q)\left[\frac{\partial u}{\partial \nu}\right] ds_Q.$$

We have, in view of (2.20)

(2.20′)
$$\left[\frac{\partial u}{\partial \nu}\right] = \frac{\partial u\,(P)}{\partial \nu^+}\left(1 - \frac{1}{a}\right);$$

allowing P to approach C through D and computing $\dfrac{\partial u\,(P)}{\partial \nu^+}$ by means of (2.21), we obtain, in view of (II.9.26), for $\chi\,(P) = \dfrac{\partial u\,(P)}{\partial \nu^+}$:

$$\left(\frac{1}{2} + \frac{a}{a-1}\right)\chi\,(P) - \int_{C} \frac{\partial G_1(P,Q)}{\partial \nu_P}\,\chi\,(Q)\,ds_Q = \frac{a}{a-1}\int_{C_1} \frac{\partial^2 G_1(P,Q)}{\partial \nu_P\,\partial \nu_Q}\,u\,(Q)\,ds_Q.$$
(2.22)

This represents an inhomogeneous integral equation for the unknown function $\chi\,(P)$. If we develop the known right-hand side of (2.22) in a series of eigenfunctions $\psi_\rho\,(P)$ of (2.19)

(2.23)
$$\sum_{\rho=1}^{\infty} \beta_\rho\,\psi_\rho\,(P) = \frac{a}{a-1}\int_{C_1} \frac{\partial^2 G_1(P,Q)}{\partial \nu_P\,\partial \nu_Q}\,u\,(Q)\,ds_Q$$

we may express the function $\chi\,(P)$ as follows:

(2.24)
$$\chi\,(P) = \sum_{\rho=1}^{\infty}\left(\frac{1}{2} + \frac{a}{a-1} - \frac{1}{2\,\lambda_\rho}\right)^{-1}\beta_\rho\,\psi_\rho\,(P).$$

This series will converge as long as $\dfrac{1}{2\,\lambda_\rho} \neq \dfrac{1}{2} + \dfrac{a}{a-1}$. We know from our considerations at the beginning of this section that $|\lambda_\rho| > 1$. Hence, as long as $a \geqslant 1/2$, $a \neq 1$, or $a \leqslant 0$, we can assert that the problem in question has a solution and that this solution can be expressed in terms of the eigenfunctions ψ_ρ of our above integral equations.

Completely analogous considerations hold for the case of the operator γ^- and its corresponding eigenfunctions and eigenvalues. We leave the development of the corresponding formulas to the reader.

Bergman-Schiffer (B 26).

3. Doubly orthogonal systems: In this section we shall investigate the eigenfunctions of the equation

(3.1)
$$d_\nu\,(P) = \varkappa_\nu\,S_{d_\nu}\,(P) = \varkappa_\nu\,\mathrm{E}\,\{K_1\,(P,Q),\,d_\nu\,(Q)\}.$$

Since $K_1\,(P,Q)$ is twice continuously differentiable in the closed region $\mathsf{D} + \mathsf{C}$ with respect to both arguments, it is easily seen that the linear transformation S_u is completely continuous in the Hilbert space $\Sigma^\blacktriangle$.

$S_u(P)$ is, moreover, a symmetric transformation and hence we may apply the fundamental theorem of Section II.8. We can assert that the eigenfunctions $d_\nu(P)$ of the integro-differential equation (3.1) form a complete orthonormal system in Σ. We have, therefore, the development theorems for the kernels K and K_1:

$$(3.2)\quad K_1(P,Q) = \sum_{\nu=1}^{\infty} \frac{1}{\varkappa_\nu} d_\nu(P)\, d_\nu(Q), \qquad K(P,Q) = \sum_{\nu=1}^{\infty} d_\nu(P)\, d_\nu(Q).$$

Clearly, the functions $d_\nu(P)$ are of the class Σ_1 since the kernel K_1 belongs to this class. Using the reproducing property of K_1 in the E_1-metric, we derive from (3.1)

$$(3.3)\qquad E_1\{d_\nu, d_\mu\} = \varkappa_\nu E\{d_\nu, d_\mu\}.$$

We thus deduce that the system $\{d_\nu\}$ is also an orthogonal system with respect to the metric E_1, i. e.,

$$(3.3')\qquad E\{d_\nu, d_\mu\} = \delta_{\nu\mu}, \qquad E_1\{d_\nu, d_\mu\} = \varkappa_\nu \delta_{\nu\mu}.$$

We shall call the system $\{d_\nu\}$ *doubly-orthogonal with respect to the domains* D *and* D_1, *or with respect to the metrics* E *and* E_1. Various interesting applications of this set are possible; in particular, the problem of continuation of a function $u \in \Sigma$ into D_1 can conveniently be studied by means of the $\{d_\nu\}$.

From (3.1) we deduce immediately that

$$(3.4)\qquad \varkappa_\nu \geqslant 1.$$

The equality sign can hold only if $d_\nu(P) \equiv 0$ in D_0. But $d_\nu(P)$ is of the class Σ_1 and in view of the uniqueness theorem of the boundary value theory this leads to $d_\nu(P) \equiv 0$ in D which contradicts the assumption on the normalization of $d_\nu(P)$. We therefore conclude the sharper inequality:

$$(3.4')\qquad \varkappa_\nu > 1.$$

There arises now the question as to whether the system $\{d_\nu\}$ is also complete with respect to the space Σ_1. In this space the $\{d_\nu\}$ form an orthogonal system and if they are not complete they may be completed by addition of further functions d_ν^*. Thus, we will have the series development for K_1:

$$(3.5)\qquad K_1(P,Q) = \sum_{\nu=1}^{\infty} \frac{1}{\varkappa_\nu} d_\nu(P)\, d_\nu(Q) + \sum_{\nu} d_\nu^*(P)\, d_\nu^*(Q)$$

valid in D_1. It must coincide with the series (3.2) in D; hence we conclude

$$d_\nu^* (P) \equiv 0 \qquad \text{for} \qquad P \in \mathsf{D}. \tag{3.6}$$

In the case of an analytic coefficient $q(P)$ the identity (3.6) clearly implies $d_\nu^*(P) \equiv 0$ all over D_1 since d_ν^* is an analytic function of P. Thus, the system $\{d_\nu(P)\}$ is also complete with respect to the linear space Σ_1. In the general case, we can complete the system $\{d_\nu\}$ in Σ_1 by the addition of an appropriate set of orthogonal functions in Σ_1 which are identically zero in D.

We notice that the functions $\{d_\nu\}$ also form an orthogonal set with respect to the E_0-metric. In fact, for every pair of functions $u, v \in \Sigma_1$, we have

$$\mathrm{E}_1\{u, v\} = \mathrm{E}_0\{u, v\} + \mathrm{E}\{u, v\}, \tag{3.7}$$

whence in view of (3.3′)

$$\mathrm{E}_0\{d_\nu, d_\mu\} = (\varkappa_\nu - 1)\,\delta_{\nu\mu}. \tag{3.8}$$

Because of inequality (3.4′), we can therefore normalize the $d_\nu(P)$ with respect to the E_0-metric. We may characterize the functions $d_\nu(P)$ in D_0 as the eigenfunctions of the integro-differential equation

$$d_\nu(P) = \left(1 - \frac{1}{\varkappa_\nu}\right)^{-1} \mathrm{E}_0\{K_1(P, Q), d_\nu(Q)\} \tag{3.9}$$

as follows again by application of (3.7) to the functions $K_1(P, Q)$ and $d_\nu(Q)$.

The domains D_1 and D_0 have the boundary C_1 in common and $K_1(P, Q)$ becomes infinite if P and Q converge towards the same boundary point on C_1. This implies that the linear transformation $\mathrm{E}_0\{K_1(P, Q), u(Q)\}$ is not completely continuous in $\Sigma_0^\blacktriangle$; thus, we cannot conclude from (3.9) that the $d_\nu(P)$ form a complete set of orthogonal functions in Σ_0. We may, however, complete the set $\{d_\nu(P)\}$ by addition of the above mentioned set $\{d_\nu^*(P)\}$ if such functions exist. There might be functions $d_\nu^{**}(P)$ in $\Sigma_0^\blacktriangle$ which are orthogonal to all the functions $d_\nu(P)$ and $d_\nu^*(P)$ which are all elements of Σ_1. Since $K_1(P, Q)$ has the series representation (3.5) in D_0, we conclude that each such d_ν^{**} must satisfy the equation

$$0 = \mathrm{E}_0\{K_1(P, Q), d_\nu^{**}(Q)\}. \tag{3.10}$$

We may consider the general integro-differential equation

$$d_\nu(P) = \sigma_\nu\, \mathrm{E}_0\{K_1(P, Q), d_\nu(Q)\}. \tag{3.9′}$$

For $1 < \sigma_\nu < \infty$ we obtain all eigenfunctions $d_\nu(P) \in \Sigma_1$ which form a complete set in Σ. For $\sigma_\nu = \infty$ we obtain the functions $d_\nu^{**}(Q)$ which satisfy (3.10). The functions $d_\nu^*(P)$ may be characterized as the eigenfunctions of (3.9') with the eigenvalue one. Thus, we have shown that *we can find a complete orthonormal set of eigenfunctions of* (3.9') *in* Σ_0. *This set contains a complete set in* Σ_1 *which in turn contains a complete set in* Σ *as a subset.*

We assume, as usual, the eigenvalues $\varkappa_\nu$ to be arranged in increasing order so that $\varkappa_\nu \geqslant \varkappa_{\nu-1}$. We may deduce from (3.2) the inequality

$$K_1(P, P) \leqslant \frac{1}{\varkappa_1} K(P, P) \leqslant K(P, P). \tag{3.11}$$

In Section 1 we have already proved the monotonicity of the expression $K(P, P)$ with respect to the domain (see formula (1.13)). The value of the inequality (3.11) consists in the fact that it gives an estimate for the lowest eigenvalue $\varkappa_1$ of (3.1). Suppose that a domain $\mathsf{D}_2 \subset \mathsf{D}$ is known with a well-determined kernel $K_2(P, Q)$. Then we have $K(P, P) \leqslant K_2(P, P)$ and hence:

$$\varkappa_1 \leqslant \frac{K_2(P, P)}{K_1(P, P)} \tag{3.12}$$

i. e., we may estimate the lowest eigenvalue of D without knowing the corresponding kernel K exactly.

Suppose that a function $u(P) \in \Sigma_1$ has been developed in a Fourier series of the eigenfunctions $d_\nu(P)$ and the additional set of functions $d_\nu^*(P)$ in Σ_1. We have

$$u(P) = \sum_{\nu=1}^{\infty} c_\nu d_\nu(P) + \sum_{\nu=1}^{\infty} c_\nu^* d_\nu^*(P) \tag{3.13}$$

valid in the whole domain D_1. In D, however, this series development reduces to

$$u(P) = \sum_{\nu=1}^{\infty} c_\nu d_\nu(P) \tag{3.13'}$$

since the $d_\nu^*(P)$ vanish identically there. From the fact that $u(P) \in \Sigma_1$ we conclude that it has a finite Dirichlet integral over D_1, i. e., in view of (3.3'):

$$\mathrm{E}_1\{u\} = \sum_{\nu=1}^{\infty} c_\nu^2 \varkappa_\nu + \sum_{\nu=1}^{\infty} c_\nu^{*2} < \infty. \tag{3.14}$$

Conversely, let us suppose that a function $u(P) \in \Sigma$ has been prescribed with the Fourier development (3.13'). *A necessary and sufficient condition in order that the function u can be extended to a function of the class Σ_1 is*

$$\sum_{\nu=1}^{\infty} c_\nu^2 \varkappa_\nu < \infty. \tag{3.15}$$

This extension is, in general, not uniquely determined since any combination of functions $d_\nu^*(P)$ may be added without affecting the values of $u(P)$ in D. In the case of an analytic coefficient $q(P)$ in (I.1.1) the extension is uniquely determined by the series (3.13').

Bergman (B 1), (B 4), Davis (D 2), Hilbert [22], Stone [78].

4. An application of the operators to the theory of orthogonal functions: We have shown in Section II.2 that the kernel $K(P, Q)$ can be obtained by means of a complete orthonormal system. In practical applications the investigator has a certain finite number of orthogonal functions at his disposal and there arises the problem of determining how well the unknown kernel can be approximated by the given finite set of functions. Let us assume that N orthonormal functions $u_\nu(P)$ of the class Σ have been given and denote the expression

$$K_N(P,Q) = \sum_{\nu=1}^{N} u_\nu(P)\, u_\nu(Q) \tag{4.1}$$

as the N-th approximation to the real kernel $K(P, Q)$. Our problem reduces to an estimate for the error term

$$F_N(P,Q) = K(P,Q) - K_N(P,Q). \tag{4.2}$$

The first step in the solution of the problem consists in the recognition of the fact that the functions S_{F_N} and T_{F_N} (cf. (1.14)) can be computed explicitly without knowing the kernel $K(P, Q)$ which plays an essential part in the definition of F_N. In fact, because of the reproducing property of the K-kernel, we find

$$S_{F_N} = \mathrm{E}\{K_1(P,Q), K(P,R) - K_N(P,R)\} = K_1(Q,R) - \mathrm{E}\{K_1(P,Q), K_N(P,R)\}. \tag{4.3}$$

Similarly, we determine for $Q \in \mathsf{D}_0$

$$T_{F_N} = -\mathrm{E}\{L_1(P,Q), K(P,R) - K_N(P,R)\} = -L_1(Q,R) + \mathrm{E}\{L_1(P,Q), K_N(P,R)\}. \tag{4.4}$$

It will be sufficient for our purpose to operate with T_F only in D_0 and we need not calculate this transform in D.

Let us next compute the norm of S_u for any function $u \in \Sigma$:

$$\mathrm{E}_1\{S_u\} = \mathrm{E}_1\big\{\mathrm{E}\{K_1(P,Q), u(Q)\}, \mathrm{E}\{K_1(P,R), u(R)\}\big\}. \tag{4.5}$$

Rearranging and using the reproducing property of K_1 in the E_1-metric, we arrive at

$$\mathrm{E}_1\{S_u\} = \mathrm{E}\big\{u(Q), \mathrm{E}\{K_1(Q,R), u(R)\}\big\}. \tag{4.6}$$

Similarly, we find

$$\mathrm{E}_0\{T_u\} = \mathrm{E}_0\big\{\mathrm{E}\{L_1(P,Q), u(Q)\}, \mathrm{E}\{L_1(P,R), u(R)\}\big\}. \tag{4.7}$$

Rearranging and using the notation (1.11), we obtain

$$\mathrm{E}_0\{T_u\} = \mathrm{E}\big\{u(Q), \mathrm{E}\{B(Q,R), u(R)\}\big\}. \tag{4.8}$$

Let now $\{u_\nu(P)\}$ denote the set of eigenfunctions in D of the equation

$$u_\nu(P) = \lambda_\nu \mathrm{E}\{l(P,Q), u_\nu(Q)\}, \qquad P \in \mathsf{D}. \tag{4.9}$$

According to our general theory, we have the series development

$$l(P,Q) = \sum_{\nu=1}^{\infty} \frac{u_\nu(P)\, u_\nu(Q)}{\lambda_\nu} \tag{4.10}$$

and hence, in view of identity (1.10) and definition (1.11)

$$\sum_{\nu=1}^{\infty} \frac{1}{\lambda_\nu^2} u_\nu(P)\, u_\nu(Q) = \sum_{\nu=1}^{\infty} u_\nu(P)\, u_\nu(Q) - K_1(P,Q) - B(P,Q), \tag{4.11}$$

i. e.,

$$K_1(P,Q) + B(P,Q) = \sum_{\nu=1}^{\infty} \left(1 - \frac{1}{\lambda_\nu^2}\right) u_\nu(P)\, u_\nu(Q). \tag{4.11'}$$

Since the system $\{u_\nu\}$ is complete in Σ, we may develop every $u \in \Sigma$ in a Fourier series of the form

$$u(P) = \sum_{\nu=1}^{\infty} c_\nu u_\nu(P). \tag{4.12}$$

Introducing (4.12) and (4.11') in (4.6) and (4.8), we obtain

$$\mathrm{E}_1\{S_u\} + \mathrm{E}_0\{T_u\} = \sum_{\nu=1}^{\infty} \left(1 - \frac{1}{\lambda_\nu^2}\right) c_\nu^2. \tag{4.13}$$

Assuming the eigenvalues arranged in order of increasing magnitude, we derive from (4.13) the inequality

$$\text{(4.14)} \qquad E_1\{S_u\} + E_0\{T_u\} \geqslant \left(1 - \frac{1}{\lambda_1{}^2}\right) E\{u\}.$$

Thus, *knowing the lowest eigenvalue of the equation* (4.9) *we may estimate the norm of any function* $u \in \Sigma$ *by means of the operator norms* $E_0\{T_u\}$ *and* $E_1\{S_u\}$. We have pointed out that for the function $F_N = K - K_N$, these expressions can be computed explicitly. Thus, we are able to obtain an estimate for the norm of the error term if λ_1 can be estimated in a convenient way. In Section V.3 we shall indicate how such estimates can be obtained for a large number of cases.

5. Comparison formulas for Green's and Neumann's functions: Formula (1.10) expresses the change of the kernel $K(P, Q)$ under the transition from the domain D_1, considered as known, to the new domain D. In these formulas, functionals of both compared domains will appear in a rather involved form, but interesting inequalities can be derived immediately. If we wish to express explicitly a functional of one domain in terms of the corresponding function of the other, we must use the series developments which will be discussed in Section 6. In Section 6, we shall assume the compared domains lie in an ε-neighborhood of each other, and we shall neglect terms of higher order of magnitude than ε in the developments. In this way, variational formulas will be obtained which express the growth of a functional in terms of the functional of the varying domain only.

We start from the Dirichlet identity (II.4.3′) where we shall assume that the fundamental singularity $S(P, Q)$ has been chosen as $G_1(P, Q)$, the Green's function of the larger domain D_1. In this case we find that the geometric quantity $I(P, Q)$ may be transformed as follows:

$$\text{(5.1)} \quad I(P,Q) = \int_{\mathsf{C}} G_1(R, P) \frac{\partial G_1(R, Q)}{\partial \nu_R} ds_R = E_0\{G_1(R, P), G_1(R, Q)\}$$

where the last Dirichlet integral is to be extended over the difference domain $\mathsf{D}_0 = \mathsf{D}_1 - \bar{\mathsf{D}}$. Thus, (II.4.3′) assumes the form

$$\text{(5.2)} \qquad \begin{aligned} &E\{G(R, P) - G_1(R, P), G(R, Q) - G_1(R, Q)\} = \\ &= -[G(P, Q) - G_1(P, Q)] - E_0\{G_1(R, P), G_1(R, Q)\}. \end{aligned}$$

This is obviously a comparison formula for $G(P, Q)$ of the same type as (1.10). It may be brought into a more concise form if we define the function

$$g(P,Q)=\begin{cases} G(P,Q)-G_1(P,Q) & \text{for } P,\ Q\in \mathsf{D} \\ \quad\quad\quad\ \ -G_1(P,Q) & \text{for } P\in\mathsf{D},\ Q\in\mathsf{D}_0 \text{ or } P\in\mathsf{D}_0,\ Q\in\mathsf{D} \\ G_0(P,Q)-G_1(P,Q) & \text{for } P,\ Q\in\mathsf{D}_0. \end{cases}$$

(5.3)

With this notation we may write (5.2) in the form

$$g(P,Q)=-E_1\{g(R,P),g(R,Q)\}. \tag{5.4}$$

This formula has been proved only for $P,Q\in\mathsf{D}$; it can, however, be easily verified for arbitrary location of P and Q in D or D_0.

Similarly, we may apply (II.4.5) but now with $N_1(P,Q)$ instead of the general fundamental singularity $S(P,Q)$. In this case, we have again

$$I(P,Q)=\int_{\mathsf{C}} N_1(R,P)\frac{\partial N_1(R,Q)}{\partial\nu_R}ds_R=E_0\{N_1(R,P),N_1(R,Q)\} \tag{5.5}$$

and hence the comparison formula

$$\begin{aligned} &E\{N(R,P)-N_1(R,P),N(R,Q)-N_1(R,Q)\}= \\ &=N(P,Q)-N_1(P,Q)-E_0\{N_1(R,P),N_1(R,Q)\}. \end{aligned} \tag{5.6}$$

This formula can again be simplified and at the same time generalized by defining

$$n(P,Q)=\begin{cases} N(P,Q)-N_1(P,Q) & \text{for } P,\ Q\in \mathsf{D} \\ \quad\quad\quad\ \ -N_1(P,Q) & \text{for } P\in\mathsf{D},\ Q\in\mathsf{D}_0 \text{ or } P\in\mathsf{D}_0,\ Q\in\mathsf{D} \\ N_0(P,Q)-N_1(P,Q) & \text{for } P,\ Q\in\mathsf{D}_0. \end{cases}$$

(5.7)

With this notation, we obtain, instead of (5.6),

$$n(P,Q)=E_1\{n(R,P),n(R,Q)\}. \tag{5.8}$$

One may verify that this formula holds for every choice of P and Q in D and D_0.

Having given the scalar products of the g-functions and the n-functions in the E_1-metric in (5.4) and (5.8), we shall complete our results by calculating the scalar product of n and g in the E_1-metric. By Green's identity we have

$$E_1\{n(R,P),g(R,Q)\}=-\int g(R,Q)\frac{\partial n(R,P)}{\partial\nu_R}ds_R \tag{5.9}$$

where the line integral is to be extended over the boundary C_1 of D_1 and both "sides" of C which is to be considered as the boundary of D_0 and of D. Clearly, $g(R,Q)\equiv 0$ on C_1, and on C we have

$$g(R,Q)\frac{\partial n(R,P)}{\partial\nu_R}=G_1(R,Q)\frac{\partial N_1(R,P)}{\partial\nu_R}.$$

Thus, we see that the sum of all line integrals on the right-hand side of (5.9) vanishes and we obtain

$$\mathrm{E}_1 \{n(R, P), g(R, Q)\} = 0. \tag{5.10}$$

In view of (1.1—3), (1.28), and (1.30), we may write

$$l(P,Q) = n(P,Q) + g(P,Q), \qquad k(P,Q) = n(P,Q) - g(P,Q). \tag{5.11}$$

Thus, formula (1.31) which is the most general form of the comparison formula (1.10) is an immediate consequence of (5.4), (5.8), and (5.10). From the same formulas, we may also derive the following analogues to (1.31):

$$\mathrm{E}_1 \{k(R, P), k(R, Q)\} = k(P, Q), \tag{5.12}$$

$$\mathrm{E}_1 \{k(R, P), l(R, Q)\} = l(P, Q). \tag{5.13}$$

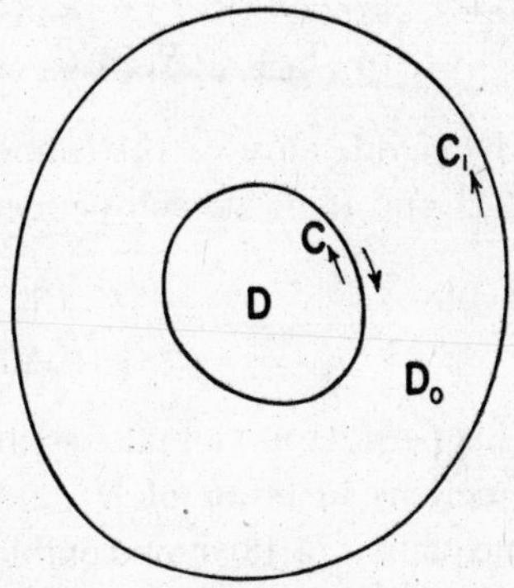

Figure 10

Let us now consider the inequality

$$\mathrm{E}_1 \left\{ \sum_{i=1}^{N} x_i\, l(P, Q_i) + \lambda \sum_{i=1}^{N} x_i\, k(P, Q_i) \right\} \geqq 0 \tag{5.14}$$

which is valid for arbitrary choice of the N points Q_i in $\mathbf{D}$ or $\mathbf{D}_0$, and of the real numbers x_i and λ. Transforming it by means of identities (1.31), (5.12), and (5.13), we obtain

$$0 \leqslant \sum_{i,k=1}^{N} x_i x_k\, k(Q_i, Q_k) + 2\lambda \sum_{i,k=1}^{N} x_i x_k\, l(Q_i, Q_k) + \lambda^2 \sum_{i,k=1}^{N} x_i x_k\, k(Q_i, Q_k) \tag{5.15}$$

whence, finally

$$\left| \sum_{i,k=1}^{N} l(Q_i, Q_k)\, x_i x_k \right| \leqslant \sum_{i,k=1}^{N} k(Q_i, Q_k)\, x_i x_k. \tag{5.16}$$

From (5.4), (5.8), and (5.12) we deduce immediately that the quadratic forms

$$\sum n(Q_i, Q_k)\, x_i x_k, \qquad -\sum g(Q_i, Q_k)\, x_i x_k, \qquad \sum k(Q_i, Q_k)\, x_i x_k$$

are positive-semidefinite. Formula (5.16) leads to an easy estimate for the only quadratic form arising here which is not definite.

Assuming that P and Q both lie in D, we may write identity (5.10) in the form

$$\text{(5.17)} \qquad \begin{aligned} &\mathrm{E}\{N(R,P) - N_1(R,P), G(R,Q) - G_1(R,Q)\} = \\ &= -\mathrm{E}_0\{N_1(R,P), G_1(R,Q)\}. \end{aligned}$$

Applying Schwarz' inequality and formulas (5.2) and (5.6), we obtain

$$\text{(5.18)} \qquad \begin{aligned} &[n(P,P) - \mathrm{E}_0\{N_1(R,P), N_1(R,P)\}]\,[-g(Q,Q) \\ &- \mathrm{E}_0\{G_1(R,Q), G_1(R,Q)\}] \geqslant [\mathrm{E}_0\{N_1(R,P), G_1(R,Q)\}]^2. \end{aligned}$$

The significance of this somewhat lengthy formula is the following: From (5.2) and (5.6) we can deduce that

$$\text{(5.19)} \qquad \begin{aligned} n(P,P) &\geqslant \mathrm{E}_0\{N_1(R,P), N_1(R,P)\}, \\ -g(R,Q) &\geqslant \mathrm{E}_0\{G_1(\mathrm{R},Q), G_1(R,Q)\}. \end{aligned}$$

This permits us to make estimates of the changes of Green's and Neumann's functions in terms of N_1 and G_1 which are considered as known functions. Inequality (5.18) now combines with the two inequalities (5.19) and shows that we can estimate the product of their deviations in terms of N_1 and G_1. Various other estimates and inequalities may be derived from the special form of the comparison formulas established.

Schiffer-Szegö (S 6).

6. Variational theory: In a general study of the fundamental solutions of the differential equation (I.1.1), the importance of the theory of the variation of the fundamental functions with a varying domain D cannot be overrated. In fact, one can determine the fundamental functions explicitly only in a very few particularly convenient cases. In all other cases, only approximate formulas for these functions will be available so that a more penetrating study of the fundamental functions will have to start from the well-known fundamental functions of special domains and will have to derive their properties in the general case by continuity arguments. Just as elementary functions such as the trigonometric and elliptic functions are best understood on the basis of their differential equations, so in our much more complex problems the fundamental functions will be understood by their functional-derivative equations which we shall now establish.

Let us start with the integro-differential equation

$$\text{(6.1)} \qquad u_\rho(P) = \lambda_\rho \mathrm{E}\{L(P,Q) - L_1(P,Q), u_\rho(Q)\}$$

with L and L_1 defined in (1.2). This is an equation of the general type (II.8.54) with the particular choice $S(P,Q) = 1/2\, L_1(P,Q)$ of the fundamental singularity. By Green's identity we transform this equation into

$$u_\rho(P) = -\lambda_\rho \int_{\mathsf{C}} \frac{\partial}{\partial \nu_Q} [L(P,Q) - L_1(P,Q)]\, u_\rho(Q)\, ds_Q. \tag{6.2}$$

By the Schwarz inequality, we derive from (6.2) the inequality

$$u_\rho(P)^2 \leqslant \lambda_\rho^2 \int_{\mathsf{C}} \left(\frac{\partial}{\partial \nu_Q} [L(P,Q) - L_1(P,Q)] \right)^2 ds_Q \int_{\mathsf{C}} u_\rho^2\, ds. \tag{6.3}$$

Integrating this result again, we arrive at the following estimate for λ_ρ:

$$\frac{1}{\lambda_\rho^2} \leqslant \int_{\mathsf{C}} \int_{\mathsf{C}} \left(\frac{\partial}{\partial \nu_Q} [L(P,Q) - L_1(P,Q)] \right)^2 ds_P\, ds_Q. \tag{6.4}$$

In view of the definition of L and the fact that G and $\dfrac{\partial N}{\partial \nu}$ vanish on C, we may put (6.4) in the form:

$$\frac{1}{\lambda_\rho^2} \leqslant \int_{\mathsf{C}} \int_{\mathsf{C}} \left(\frac{\partial}{\partial \nu_Q} [N_1(P,Q) + G_1(P,Q)] \right)^2 ds_P\, ds_Q. \tag{6.5}$$

Since $l(P,Q) = L(P,Q) - L_1(P,Q)$ is continuously differentiable in $\mathsf{D} + \mathsf{C}$ as was shown in Section II.6, we conclude that $\dfrac{\partial}{\partial \nu_Q} [N_1(P,Q) + G_1(P,Q)]$ is continuous on C and that the right-hand integral in (6.5) converges despite an apparent infinity for $P = Q$.

Let us now assume that the curve system C is obtained from the curve system C_1 in the following way. If s is the length parameter on C_1, we define a three times continuously differentiable non-negative function $\varphi(s)$ on C_1; at each point $P_1 \in \mathsf{C}_1$ we erect the normal and proceed along it by an amount $\varepsilon \varphi(s) = \delta\nu$, in the direction of the interior normal, where $\varepsilon > 0$ is a smallness parameter. In this way, to each point P_1 on C_1 we associate a shifted point P on the normal. The points $P(s)$ will define a curve system C which will, for small enough ε, be non-self-intersecting and in a Fréchet ε-neighborhood of the original curves C_1. We shall say that the curves C have been obtained from C_1 by a normal shift $\delta\nu = \varepsilon\varphi(s)$. Our problem is to determine the change of the fundamental functions under such a variation.

Let us now apply formula (6.5) for this particular choice of C and C_1. Since each point P of C has a corresponding point $P_1 \in C_1$ at a distance $\varepsilon \varphi(s)$, since $G_1(P, Q)$, $\frac{\partial N_1(P, Q)}{\partial \nu}$ vanish on C_1 and since, finally, the normal at P to C is turned from the normal at P_1 to C_1 only by an angle of order ε, we can easily calculate that

$$(6.6) \qquad -\frac{\partial l(P,Q)}{\partial \nu_Q} = \frac{\partial}{\partial \nu_Q}[N_1(P,Q) + G_1(P,Q)] = O(\varepsilon) \qquad \text{for } P, Q \in C.$$

Hence, we arrive at the following fundamental theorem: *If the curves* C *are obtained from the curves* C_1 *by a normal shift* $\delta\nu = \varepsilon\varphi(s)$ *where* $\varphi(s)$ *is three times continuously differentiable, then the lowest eigenvalue* λ_1 *of the integro-differential equation* (6.1) *satisfies*

$$(6.7) \qquad \frac{1}{\lambda_1} = O(\varepsilon).$$

In the complete set of orthonormal functions $\{u_\nu(P)\}$ the function $l(P,Q) = L(P,Q) - L_1(P,Q)$ has the following Fourier development:

$$(6.8) \qquad l(P,Q) = L(P,Q) - L_1(P,Q) = \sum_{\nu=1}^{\infty} \frac{1}{\lambda_\nu} u_\nu(P)\, u_\nu(Q).$$

We have, therefore, by the Schwarz inequality and (6.7) the estimate

$$(6.9) \qquad |l(P,Q)| \leqslant \frac{1}{\lambda_1}(K(P,P)\,K(Q,Q))^{1/2} = O(\varepsilon)$$

i. e.,

$$(6.9') \qquad L(P,Q) - L_1(P,Q) = O(\varepsilon).$$

Next we introduce the series (6.8) for $l(P,Q)$ in the identity (1.10). Using the orthonormality conditions for the $u_\nu(P)$, we may put (1.10) in the form:

$$(6.10) \quad K(P,Q) - K_1(P,Q) = \mathrm{E}_0\{L_1(R,P), L_1(R,Q)\} + \sum_{\nu=1}^{\infty} \frac{1}{\lambda_\nu^2} u_\nu(P)\, u_\nu(Q).$$

In view of (6.7), we put (6.10) in the form

$$(6.10') \qquad K(P,Q) - K_1(P,Q) = \mathrm{E}_0\{L_1(R,P), L_1(R,Q)\} + O(\varepsilon^2)$$

where the remainder term $O(\varepsilon^2)$ can be estimated uniformly in each closed subdomain of D. Formula (6.10′) is a typical variational formula for the kernel $K(P,Q)$. It is assumed that the fundamental functions of the domain D_1 are known, and the problem is to express the fundamental functions of the slightly varied domain D in terms of the former except for error terms of order ε^2. This has just been achieved for the K-kernel in formula (6.10′).

A similar result can be obtained for the difference of the L-kernels. For this purpose we start with formula (5.13) which leads to

$$L(P,Q) - L_1(P,Q) = \mathrm{E}_0\{K_1(R,P), L_1(R,Q)\} + \\ + \mathrm{E}\{k(R,P), l(R,Q)\}. \tag{6.11}$$

It is easily seen from (6.9′) and (6.10) that the second right-hand integral is of order ε^2, whence

$$L(P,Q) - L_1(P,Q) = \mathrm{E}_0\{K_1(R,P), L_1(R,Q)\} + O(\varepsilon^2) \tag{6.12}$$

uniformly in each closed subdomain of D. Thus, a variational formula for the L-kernel has been obtained.

It is possible to write formulas (6.10′) and (6.12) in an alternate form which exhibits more clearly the role of the boundary C_1 of D_1. The integration which is necessary for the computation of the E_0-terms in both formulas is extended over a narrow strip along C_1 the width of which is everywhere of order ε. Every point within this strip can be characterized by the following two coordinates: the length parameter s on C_1 which determines the normal with respect to C_1 on which the point lies, and the length σ along the normal to the point. Clearly, σ is always of order ε only. Let us introduce s and σ as new variables of integration in the calculation of the E_0-terms. Without great difficulty the following forms of (6.10′) and (6.12) are obtained:

$$K(P,Q) - K_1(P,Q) = \int_{\mathsf{C}_1} \big(\operatorname{grad} L_1(R,P) \cdot \operatorname{grad} L_1(R,Q) + \\ + q(R)\, L_1(R,P)\, L_1(R,Q)\big)\, \delta\nu\, ds + O(\varepsilon^2), \tag{6.13}$$

$$L(P,Q) - L_1(P,Q) = \int_{\mathsf{C}_1} \big(\operatorname{grad} K_1(R,P) \cdot \operatorname{grad} L_1(R,Q) + \\ + q(R)\, K_1(R,P)\, L_1(R,Q)\big)\, \delta\nu\, ds + O(\varepsilon^2). \tag{6.13′}$$

These formulas are particularly useful since they depend only on the boundary values of the kernels K_1 and L_1, and since by (1.1) and (1.2) the latter depend in an elementary way on Green's and Neumann's functions, use can be made of the characteristic boundary behavior of these fundamental solutions. We notice that on C_1 we have

$$(6.14)\quad G_1(R,P)\equiv 0,\qquad \frac{\partial N_1(R,P)}{\partial \nu_R}\equiv 0,\qquad \operatorname{grad} G_1(R,P)=\frac{\partial G_1(R,P)}{\partial \nu_R}\boldsymbol{\nu},$$
$$\operatorname{grad} G_1(R,P)\perp \operatorname{grad} N_1(R,Q),\quad R\in \mathsf{C}_1,\quad P,Q\in \mathsf{D}_1.$$

In fact, $\dfrac{\partial G_1}{\partial s}=0$ and $\dfrac{\partial N_1}{\partial \nu}=0$ on C_1; hence the gradient of Green's function has the direction of the normal vector at $R\in\mathsf{C}_1$ while that of Neumann's function has tangential direction there.

We can make use of these identities in order to obtain elegant variational formulas for Green's and Neumann's functions. Using (1.1—2) and (6.14), we obtain from (6.13) and (6.13′):

$$(6.15)\quad N(P,Q)-N_1(P,Q)=\int_{\mathsf{C}_1}\bigl(\operatorname{grad} N_1(R,P)\cdot\operatorname{grad} N_1(R,Q)+$$
$$+\,q(R)\,N_1(R,P)\,N_1(R,Q)\bigr)\,\delta\nu\,ds+O(\varepsilon^2),$$

$$(6.16)\quad G(P,Q)-G_1(P,Q)=-\int_{\mathsf{C}_1}\operatorname{grad} G_1(R,P)\cdot\operatorname{grad} G_1(R,Q)\,\delta\nu\,ds+O(\varepsilon^2)$$
$$=-\int_{\mathsf{C}_1}\frac{\partial G_1(R,P)}{\partial \nu_R}\,\frac{\partial G_1(R,Q)}{\partial \nu_R}\,\delta\nu\,ds+O(\varepsilon^2).$$

We see that *we can express the variation of Neumann's function in terms of* $N_1(R,P)$ *only and the variation of Green's function in terms of* $G_1(R,P)$. For the sake of completeness, we give the following variational formulas for the kernels K and L which can immediately be derived from (6.13) and (6.13′) in view of the boundary relations (6.14) of Green's and Neumann's functions:

$$(6.17)\quad K(P,Q)-K_1(P,Q)=\int_{\mathsf{C}_1}\bigl(\operatorname{grad} K_1(R,P)\cdot\operatorname{grad} K_1(R,Q)+$$
$$+\,q(R)\,K_1(R,P)\,K_1(R,Q)\bigr)\,\delta\nu\,ds+O(\varepsilon^2),$$

$$(6.17')\quad L(P,Q)-L_1(P,Q)=\int_{\mathsf{C}_1}\bigl(\operatorname{grad} L_1(R,P)\cdot\operatorname{grad} K_1(R,Q)+$$
$$+\,q(R)\,L_1(R,P)\,L_1(R,Q)\bigr)\,\delta\nu\,ds+O(\varepsilon^2).$$

We see that the K-kernel has a variational formula depending on K_1 only while the variation of the L-kernel depends on both the K_1- and L_1-kernels. It is of practical value in actual computations to obtain variational formulas for important functions which depend only on the boundary values of these functions and their derivatives; such formulas allow a step-by-step calculation of the function in question for a series of consecutively changing domains. Formulas which give the variation of a domain function in terms of the boundary values of several domain functions also permit step-by-step calculation of the domain function considered; in this case, however, one must carry out simultaneously the calculation of all other domain functions which occur in the variational formula which makes the computational work in the process prohibitive. From this point of view, formulas (6.15—17) are far superior to the variational formula (6.17′) for the L-kernel.

Variational formulas of the type (6.15—17′) were first derived by Hadamard for the fundamental functions of Laplace's equation with respect to a given domain. It is remarkable that the variational fromula (6.16) for the Green's function has a form which is independent of the coefficient $q(P)$ in the differential equation (I.1.1). For this reason Hadamard obtained exactly the same formula (6.16) in his special case. The variational formula for Neumann's function is actually more complicated in the harmonic case than in the case of the differential equation (I.1.1); the reason lies in the fact that in the latter case Neumann's function possesses a much simpler definition than in the former.

Variational formulas of the Hadamard type give the change of the domain function under a shift of the boundary of the domain. Green's, Neumann's, and Robin's functions depend on two argument points P and Q; but, in addition, given the fixed differential equation (I.1.1), they depend on the domain D or, what is equivalent, the boundary curves C of D. It is the latter dependence which is investigated by the variational approach. It is well known from the calculus of several variables that a differentiable function $F(x_1, \ldots, x_N)$ of N independent variables is characterized by its total differential

$$dF = \sum_{\nu=1}^{N} \frac{\partial F}{\partial x_\nu} dx_\nu. \tag{6.18}$$

A domain function (or functional) Φ depends on the infinitely many points of the boundary curve C and has correspondingly a total differential of the form

$$\delta\Phi = \int_{\mathsf{C}} \psi(s)\, \delta\nu\, ds \tag{6.18'}$$

which is the natural generalization of (6.18) as $N \to \infty$. The close relation between differentials of the type (6.18) and variational formulas (6.18′)

has been emphasized by Volterra in his approach to functional analysis. In his notation the formulas (6.15) and (6.16) would appear in the form

$$\delta N(P,Q) = \int_{\mathsf{C}} [\operatorname{grad} N(R,P) \cdot \operatorname{grad} N(R,Q) + q(R) N(R,P) N(R,Q)] \, \delta\nu \, ds, \tag{6.15'}$$

$$\delta G(P,Q) = -\int_{\mathsf{C}} \frac{\partial G(R,P)}{\partial \nu_R} \frac{\partial G(R,Q)}{\partial \nu_R} \delta\nu \, ds. \tag{6.16'}$$

If one desires to avoid the use of infinitesimals, one may interpret the above formulas as follows. Consider a family of curve systems $\mathsf{C}(t)$ which depends on the real parameter t; as t varies from 0 to 1 the system $\mathsf{C}(t)$ changes continuously from C_1 to C. Let each point P on $\mathsf{C}(t)$ move with the normal velocity $\varphi(s;t)$. Each curve system $\mathsf{C}(t)$ determines a domain $\mathsf{D}(t)$ with corresponding Green's and Neumann's functions $G(P,Q;t)$ and $N(P,Q;t)$. We deduce from (6.15) and (6.16) the following differential equations for the fundamental functions:

$$\frac{\partial N(P,Q;t)}{\partial t} = \int_{\mathsf{C}(t)} [\operatorname{grad} N(R,P;t) \cdot \operatorname{grad} N(R,Q;t) + q(R) N(R,P;t) N(R,Q;t)] \, \varphi(s;t) \, ds, \tag{6.15''}$$

$$\frac{\partial G(P,Q;t)}{\partial t} = -\int_{\mathsf{C}(t)} \frac{\partial G(R,P;t)}{\partial \nu_R} \frac{\partial G(R,Q;t)}{\partial \nu_R} \varphi(s;t) \, ds. \tag{6.16''}$$

Let us now show how, in the case of the particularly simple formula (6.16) for Green's function, some results for this domain function can be read off from the variational formula. At first we need some elementary remarks regarding Green's function and its normal derivatives on the boundary.

Since $G_1(P,Q)$ vanishes for fixed $Q \in \mathsf{D}_1$ for all values of $P \in \mathsf{C}_1$ and since it becomes positively infinite for $P \to Q$, we deduce easily from the first theorem of (I.3) the inequality

$$G_1(P,Q) \geqslant 0 \quad \text{for all points } P \text{ and } Q \text{ in } \mathsf{D}_1. \tag{6.19}$$

For $P \in \mathsf{C}_1$, Green's function vanishes by definition and for $P \in \mathsf{D}_1$ it is non-negative. Hence, its derivative with respect to the interior normal at $P \in \mathsf{C}_1$ must be non-negative, i. e.,

$$\frac{\partial G_1(P,Q)}{\partial \nu_P} \geqslant 0 \quad \text{for} \quad P \in \mathsf{C}_1, \quad Q \in \mathsf{D}_1. \tag{6.20}$$

Let us now hold P fixed in C_1 and consider $\dfrac{\partial G_1(P,Q)}{\partial \nu_P}$ as a function of Q. This function represents a solution of (I.1.1) which is non-negative in D_1 by virtue of (6.20). If Q converges to any boundary point on C_1 which is different from P, this function will converge to zero as is immediately seen by differentiating the identity $G_1(P,Q) \equiv 0$ for $Q \in \mathsf{C}_1$ normally with respect to P. Thus, $\dfrac{\partial G_1(P,Q)}{\partial \nu_P}$ is zero for $Q \in \mathsf{C}_1$ and non-negative in D_1; as before we may derive, therefore, the inequality

$$\frac{\partial^2 G_1(P,Q)}{\partial \nu_P\, \partial \nu_Q} \geqslant 0 \quad \text{for} \quad P \in \mathsf{C}_1, \quad Q \in \mathsf{C}_1, \quad P \neq Q. \tag{6.21}$$

After these preliminaries, we can now use formula (6.16′) as follows. We remark at first that since $\delta\nu \geqslant 0$ along C_1 we have in view of (6.20)

$$\delta G(P,Q) \leqslant 0. \tag{6.22}$$

This means that if the domain D_1 is shrunk by moving every boundary point into the interior by a normal shift $\delta\nu$, the value of Green's function decreases. This result is also an immediate consequence of the first theorem in Section I.3. In fact, if $\mathsf{D} \subset \mathsf{D}_1$ the function $G_1(P,Q) - G(P,Q)$ will be of class Σ and on the boundary C of D, we shall have $G_1(P,Q) - G(P,Q) = G_1(P,Q) \geqslant 0$. Hence, by the above-mentioned theorem this difference will be non-negative throughout D, and this again proves the monotonicity of Green's function in dependence upon the domain.

We may, however, derive from (6.16′) a deeper result which cannot be obtained in an elementary way. Let us assume that a domain D is contained in the closure of a domain D_1 but that both domains have a boundary arc γ in common. On γ, we have $G(P,Q) = G_1(P,Q) = 0$ while in view of the monotonic property of Green's function we have inside of D, $G(P,Q) \leqslant G_1(P,Q)$. Hence, we obtain the following inequality for the normal derivatives of the Green's functions:

$$\frac{\partial G(P,Q)}{\partial \nu_P} \leqslant \frac{\partial G_1(P,Q)}{\partial \nu_P}, \quad \text{for} \quad P \in \gamma, \quad Q \in \mathsf{D}. \tag{6.23}$$

If we now vary the domains D *and* D_1 *by letting them decrease simultaneously by an interior shift* $\delta\nu > 0$ *of* γ, *we will have,* in view of (6.16′) and (6.23):

$$\delta G_1(P,Q) \leqslant \delta G(P,Q) \leqslant 0. \tag{6.24}$$

Hence, we have shown that Green's function of the larger domain is more sensitive to a shift of the common boundary than Green's function of the smaller one.

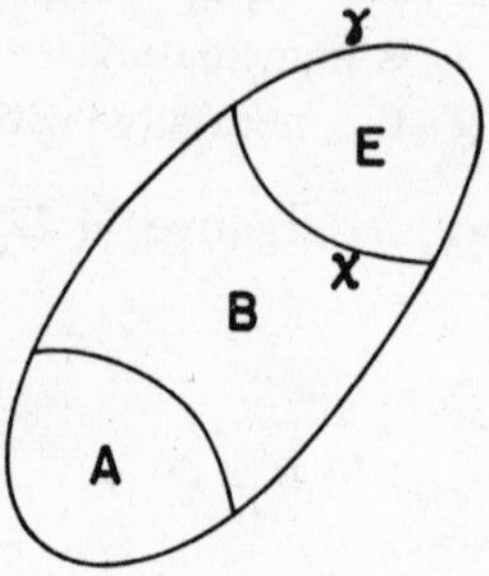

Figure 11

Suppose, for example, that we have three domains A, B, and E as indicated in the figure. Let us denote $B + E = D$ and $A + B + E = D_1$; then the assumptions of our preceding considerations will hold and we may assert that if we shrink the arc γ of the boundary of E into the arc χ of the same boundary, the Green's function of the domain D_1 will decrease more rapidly than that of D. But at the end of the shrinking process, D will have become B and D_1 will have become A + B.

Thus, we have proved:

$$G_{A+B+E}(P,Q) - G_{A+B}(P,Q) \geqslant G_{B+E}(P,Q) - G_B(P,Q). \tag{6.25}$$

This inequality can also be interpreted as follows. Let $A + B = \mathfrak{N}$ and $B + E = \mathfrak{L}$. Then $B = \mathfrak{N} \cap \mathfrak{L}$, $A + B + E = \mathfrak{N} \cup \mathfrak{L}$. Thus, we have proved:

$$G_{\mathfrak{N} \cup \mathfrak{L}} + G_{\mathfrak{N} \cap \mathfrak{L}} \geqslant G_{\mathfrak{N}} + G_{\mathfrak{L}}, \tag{6.26}$$

an interesting superadditivity property of Green's function.

Various generalizations of the variational formula (6.16′) are possible. We have derived this formula under the assumption $\delta\nu \geqslant 0$ on C_1. We shall now show that (6.16′) will be valid even if this sign restriction is dropped, i. e., if the monotonicity of the variation is no longer required. In fact, let C and C_1 be two curve systems in an ε-Fréchet neighborhood which bound two domains D and D_1. We introduce a third domain D^* which contains D and D_1 and the boundary curve system C^* which lies also in an ε-neighborhood of C and C_1. Let $\delta\nu^*$ be the normal shift on C^* which shrinks C^* into C and let, similarly, $\delta\nu_1{}^*$ shrink C^* into C_1; clearly, $\delta\nu^* \geqslant 0$ and $\delta\nu_1{}^* \geqslant 0$ and the variational formula (6.16) becomes applicable with respect to the variation of $G^*(P,Q)$. Applying (6.16) in order to compute $G^* - G$ and $G^* - G_1$ and subtracting both formulas, we obtain:

$$G(P,Q) - G_1(P,Q) = \tag{6.27}$$

$$= -\int_{C^*} \frac{\partial G^*(R,P)}{\partial \nu_R} \frac{\partial G^*(R,Q)}{\partial \nu_R} (\delta\nu^* - \delta\nu_1{}^*)\, ds + O(\varepsilon^2).$$

By a simple geometric argument we derive

$$\delta\nu = \delta\nu^* - \delta\nu_1^* + O(\varepsilon^2)$$

whence (6.16′) follows immediately but now without any restriction with respect to the sign of $\delta\nu$.

If we apply formula (6.16′) with respect to P and Q near C and take the normal derivative of the identity with respect to P and Q, we obtain

$$\delta\left(\frac{\partial^2 G(P,Q)}{\partial\nu_P\,\partial\nu_Q}\right) = -\int_{\mathsf{C}} \frac{\partial^2 G(R,P)}{\partial\nu_R\,\partial\nu_P}\,\frac{\partial^2 G(R,Q)}{\partial\nu_R\,\partial\nu_Q}\,\delta\nu\, ds_R. \tag{6.28}$$

This formula is not to be considered proved by this formal procedure; for we have derived the variational formula (6.16′) only for points P and Q in the interior of D. Moreover, the integrand on the right-hand side of (6.28) becomes infinite for $R = P$ and for $R = Q$ and the integral can be defined only in a Cauchy principal value sense. By a finer argument one may show that if the variation $\delta\nu$ of the boundary curve vanishes in the neighborhood of the points P and Q on C, the formula (6.28) is, in fact, applicable. The consideration of the function $\mathfrak{G}(P,Q) = \dfrac{\partial^2 G(P,Q)}{\partial\nu_P\,\partial\nu_Q}$, [cf. (A.II.18.4) et seq.], on C is from many points of view rather interesting. The function has the elegant variational formula

$$\delta\mathfrak{G}(P,Q) = -\int_{\mathsf{C}} \mathfrak{G}(R,P)\,\mathfrak{G}(R,Q)\,\delta\nu\, ds_R. \tag{6.29}$$

By (6.21) it is non-negative and therefore, in view of (6.29), varies monotonically with the domain D; one must only keep a neighborhood of the points P and Q fixed in order that the integral on the right-hand side in (6.29) be a proper integral. $\mathfrak{G}(P,Q)$, being defined on C only, depends on two real parameters while $G(P,Q)$ depends on four real parameters, namely the coordinates of P and Q in D. Thus, the treatment of the $\mathfrak{G}$-function is in many respects simpler than that of Green's function itself. It can be shown that the knowledge of $\mathfrak{G}(P,Q)$ yields a solution of the boundary value problem of the first kind for the class Σ so that $\mathfrak{G}(P,Q)$ renders the same service as Green's function. The disadvantage of the treatment of the $\mathfrak{G}$-function comes from the high degree of singularity of this kernel for $P = Q$ and for this reason we shall content ourselves with these few remarks.

If an analytic function F of N variables $x_1, \ldots, x_N$ is given, we may express its value $F + \triangle F$ at the point $x_i + \triangle x_i$ by means of the Taylor series:

$$\triangle F = \sum_{i=1}^{N} \frac{\partial F}{\partial x_i} \triangle x_i + \frac{1}{2!} \sum_{i,k=1}^{N} \frac{\partial^2 F}{\partial x_i \, \partial x_k} \triangle x_i \triangle x_k + \ldots . \tag{6.30}$$

The total differential of F as defined by (6.18) appears as the linear term in this series development and this property is frequently used in order to define this expression. It is now natural to ask for a generalized Taylor series for our fundamental functions such that the variational formulas obtained will appear as the linear terms in the development. We can actually give such a series development for the kernel $K(P, Q)$ by means of the general formula (II.7.28). This formula enabled us to express the kernel $K(P, Q)$ in terms of an infinite series of iterated integrals over a fundamental singularity $S(P, Q)$. Let us now choose $S(P, Q) = (1/2)\, L_1(P, Q)$ as we did at the beginning of this section and of Section 1. In this case, we computed the term $I(P, Q)$ in (1.9) to be (cf. (1.11)):

$$\begin{aligned} I(P,Q) &= \frac{1}{4}\big(K_1(P,Q) + \mathrm{E}_0\{L_1(R, P), L_1(R,Q)\}\big) = \\ &= \frac{1}{4}[K_1(P,Q) + B(P,Q)]. \end{aligned} \tag{6.31}$$

Thus, *we obtain from* (II.7.29) *the series development*

$$\begin{aligned} K(P,Q) &= \sum_{\nu=0}^{\infty} \mathrm{E}\,\{K_1(R, P) + B(R, P), M^{(\nu)}(R,Q)\} = \\ &= K_1(P,Q) + B(P,Q) + \sum_{\nu=1}^{\infty} \mathrm{E}\,\{K_1(R, P) + B(R, P), M^{(\nu)}(R,Q)\}. \end{aligned} \tag{6.32}$$

By virtue of (II.9.1) and in view of our choice of $S(P, Q)$ we have:

$$M^{(\nu)}(P,Q) = \sum_{\rho=1}^{\infty} \frac{1}{\lambda_\rho^{2\nu}} u_\rho(P)\, u_\rho(Q) \tag{6.33}$$

where the $u_\rho(P)$ and λ_ρ are the eigenfunctions and eigenvalues of the integro-differential equation (6.1). If the domains D and D_1 lie in an ε-neighborhood of each other, we have by (6.7)

$$M^{(\nu)}(P,Q) = O(\varepsilon^{2\nu}) \tag{6.34}$$

uniformly in each closed subdomain of **D**. Thus, the series

$$\Delta K(P,Q) = \mathrm{E}_0\{L_1(R,P), L_1(R,Q)\} + \\ + \sum_{\nu=1}^{\infty} \mathrm{E}\{K_1(R,P) + B(R,P), M^{(\nu)}(R,Q)\} \tag{6.32'}$$

is precisely of the Taylor type required. The first right-hand term in (6.32′) coincides with the variational expression (6.10′) and the series which follows is in the higher powers of the Fréchet distance between the two domains considered. Thus, (6.32′) contains not only the first variation of the K-kernel but also all higher variations as well.

In general, it is considered an easier problem to study infinitesimal variations of the fundamental functions than to attack the problem of finite change. It appears now that *theoretically there is no difference between the variational theory and the method of series development for the kernels in finite neighborhoods.* The first method is less laborious since only the first term of the infinite series needs to be computed. On the other hand, all terms in the infinite series (6.32′) are obtained by the same elementary processes of integration and are, therefore, of the same character as the first (the variational) term. Thus, the computation of an arbitrarily high order variation differs from the determination of the first order variation only in the number but not in the kind of operations necessary.

Bergman-Schiffer (B 21), Courant [12], Appendix, Hadamard [18].

Chapter IV

EXISTENCE THEORY

1. Boundary value problem and orthogonal projection: In I.2 we introduced the space Ω of all functions $v(x, y)$ which are twice continuously differentiable in the closure of a given domain **D**. We considered two subspaces Σ and Ω^0 of Ω which contained the solutions of (I.1.1) and functions vanishing on the boundary **C**, respectively. Using the existence of functions in Σ with prescribed boundary values on **C**, we were able to show that every function $v \in \Omega$ can be represented in the form

$$v = u + w \quad \text{with} \quad u \in \Sigma, \quad w \in \Omega^0. \tag{1.1}$$

Since we showed that the two spaces Σ and Ω^0 are orthogonal to each other, this decomposition has a simple interpretation in the space of functions. We may consider u as the orthogonal projection of v into the linear space Σ and w as the difference vector connecting u with v; alternatively, we can consider w as the orthogonal projection of v into Ω^0 and u as the difference vector $v - w$.

Conversely, starting with geometric considerations of this nature we might begin with an arbitrarily given function $v \in \Omega$ and using orthogonal projection, prove the existence of a function $u \in \Sigma$ with the same boundary values on C as v. This method is an elegant formulation of a classical method in analysis, the Dirichlet principle. In its application, one is still free to decide whether to project a function of Ω into Σ or Ω^0, and thus one has two different methods of existence proof by orthogonal projection. It has been customary to base the existence proof for the boundary value problem on the projection of a given function v into the space Ω^0. One reason for this is the desire not to assume the existence of even a single solution of the differential equation considered and consequently to avoid the concept of the space Σ of all these solutions. On the other hand, the space Σ consists of regular solutions of a simple differential equation and has various important properties which the more general and larger subspace Ω^0 lacks. It is, therefore, much more convenient to operate with the projection into Σ and we shall develop this method in the sequel.

Let $v \in \Omega$ be given arbitrarily; let us ask for the minimum value of the expression $E\{v - u\}$ where u is an arbitrary element of Σ. We know that this expression is, at any rate, non-negative and has, therefore, a greatest lower bound $d \geqslant 0$. There then exists a sequence $u_1, u_2, \ldots, u_n, \ldots$ of elements of Σ such that

$$\lim_{n \to \infty} E\{v - u_n\} = d. \tag{1.2}$$

Now let U be an arbitrary element of Σ and λ a real parameter. Clearly

$$E\{v - u_n - \lambda U\} = E\{v - u_n\} - 2\lambda E\{v - u_n, U\} + \lambda^2 E\{U\} \geqslant d \tag{1.3}$$

and hence we find the discriminant condition

$$E\{v - u_n, U\}^2 \leqslant (E\{v - u_n\} - d) \cdot E\{U\}. \tag{1.4}$$

Applying (1.4) for two arbitrary indices n and m and subtracting, we find

$$E\{u_n - u_m, U\} \leqslant E\{U\}^{1/2} [(E\{v - u_n\} - d)^{1/2} + (E\{v - u_m\} - d)^{1/2}]. \tag{1.5}$$

Let us set $U = u_n - u_m$. This is obviously a function of Σ and is therefore a permissible choice. We obtain

$$(1.6) \qquad \mathrm{E}\{u_n - u_m\}^{1/2} \leqslant (\mathrm{E}\{v - u_n\} - d)^{1/2} + (\mathrm{E}\{v - u_m\} - d)^{1/2}.$$

From (1.2) and (1.6) we finally deduce

$$(1.7) \qquad \mathrm{E}\{u_n - u_m\} \to 0 \quad \text{with} \quad n, m \to \infty.$$

The sequence $\{u_\nu\}$ of functions which leads to the lower limit of $\mathrm{E}\{v - u\}$ forms, therefore, a Cauchy sequence.

We shall now show that *there exists a function* u *solving the equation* (I.1.1) *with finite norm and such that*

$$(1.8) \qquad \lim_{n \to \infty} \mathrm{E}\{u - u_n\} = 0.$$

From the triangle inequality (I.2.5) it is then immediately clear that $\mathrm{E}\{v - u\} = d$, i. e., that the minimum problem considered actually possesses a solution and that u can be considered as the orthogonal projection of v into the closure $\Sigma^\blacktriangle$ of Σ. $\Sigma^\blacktriangle$ consists of all solutions of (I.1.1) having finite norm with no assumptions on boundary behavior.

The proof of the existence of the limit function u is based upon the important inequality

$$(1.9) \qquad (U(P))^2 \leqslant C(P) \cdot \mathrm{E}\{U\}$$

which is valid for all functions $U \in \Sigma$ where $C(P)$ is a positive function of P. If the boundary value problem had already been solved and the existence of the K-kernel had thus been established, then by virtue of (II.1.12), we could choose for $C(P)$ the best possible value $K(P, P)$. Since, however, we wish to prove the possibility of solving the boundary value problem we must derive the inequality (1.9) in a different way. For our purpose, the value of the factor $C(P)$ does not have to be best possible.

Around a given point $P \in \mathsf{D}$ we choose a circle C_R of radius R such that C_R lies in D and consider the function

$$(1.10) \qquad \chi_R(P) = \frac{1}{2\pi} \log\left(\frac{r}{R}\right) + \frac{1}{4\pi}\left(1 - \frac{r^2}{R^2}\right), \qquad r = \overline{P\,P_0}.$$

$\chi_R(P)$ vanishes on the circumference of C_R, has a vanishing normal derivative there, and inside C_R satisfies the equation

$$(1.11) \qquad \Delta \chi_R(P) = -\frac{1}{\pi R^2}.$$

Hence, applying Green's identity with respect to U and χ_R and taking into account the singularity of $\chi_R(P)$ at P_0, we obtain

$$(1.12) \qquad U(P_0) = \frac{1}{\pi R^2} \iint_{C_R} U(Q)\, d\tau_Q + \iint_{C_R} \chi_R(Q)\, \Delta U(Q)\, d\tau_Q,$$

i. e., in view of the differential equation (I.1.1) satisfied by U:

$$(1.12') \qquad U(P_0) = \iint_{C_R} \left[q(Q)\, \chi_R(Q) + \frac{1}{\pi R^2} \right] U(Q)\, d\tau_Q.$$

Using the Schwarz inequality, we derive from (1.12')

$$(1.13) \qquad U(P_0)^2 \leqslant \iint_{C_R} \left[(q(Q)\, \chi_R(Q) + \frac{1}{\pi R^2} \right]^2 d\tau_Q \cdot \iint_{C_R} U(Q)^2\, d\tau_Q.$$

Now let m denote the minimum of $q(P)$ in D; we clearly have

$$(1.14) \qquad \iint_{C_R} ((U(Q))^2\, d\tau \leqslant \iint_{D} U^2\, d\tau \leqslant \frac{1}{m} E\{U\}.$$

Thus, we have proved inequality (1.9) with

$$(1.14') \qquad C(P_0) = \iint_{C_R} \left[q\, \chi_R + \frac{1}{\pi R^2} \right]^2 d\tau / m.$$

We are now able to show the existence of the limit function $u \in \Sigma^{\blacktriangle}$ for the sequence u_n. In fact, from (1.7) and (1.9) we may conclude:

$$(1.15) \qquad |u_n - u_m| \to 0$$

uniformly in each closed subdomain of D. There exists, therefore, a continuous function $u(P)$ such that

$$(1.16) \qquad u_n \to u(P)$$

uniformly in each closed subdomain of D. Let $S(P, Q)$ be a symmetric fundamental singularity of (I.1.1) and γ a closed smooth curve around the point $P_0 \in D$. Then we have by (I.5.8)

$$(1.17) \qquad u_n(P_0) = \int_{\gamma} \left[u_n(Q) \frac{\partial S(P_0, Q)}{\partial \nu_Q} - S(P_0, Q) \frac{\partial u_n(Q)}{\partial \nu} \right] ds_Q,$$

and hence because of the uniform convergence of the u_n towards u on γ:

$$(1.17') \qquad u(P_0) = \int_{\gamma} \left[u(Q) \frac{\partial S(P_0, Q)}{\partial \nu_Q} - S(P_0, Q) \frac{\partial u(Q)}{\partial \nu} \right] ds_Q.$$

This result shows that the limit function $u(P)$ satisfies the differential equation (I.1.1) in **D**.

Finally, by virtue of the triangle inequality each u_n satisfies

$$E\{u_n\}^{1/2} \leq E\{v\}^{1/2} + E\{v - u_n\}^{1/2}. \tag{1.18}$$

In view of (1.2) this proves that all u_n have an equally bounded E-norm. Hence, applying the fundamental result on bounded convergence in the Lebesgue integration theory, we arrive at the result that $E\{u\}$ exists and is finite which proves that u belongs to the class $\Sigma^{\blacktriangle}$. This completes the proof that there exists a projection u in $\Sigma^{\blacktriangle}$ of any given function $v \in \Omega$. From (1.2) and (1.4) one easily concludes

$$E\{v - u, U\} = 0, \qquad \text{for all} \qquad U \in \Sigma, \tag{1.19}$$

which is the characteristic property of the orthogonal projection.

We come now to the more difficult part of our existence proof. *We must show that the difference function* $w = v - u$, which is, according to (1.19), orthogonal to all functions $U \in \Sigma$, *actually vanishes on* **C**. This is by no means obvious since the unique decomposition of Ω into the orthogonal spaces Σ and Ω^0 is still to be proved and since, moreover, the subspace Ω^0 is clearly not a compact space. We can assert, however, that w has continuous second derivatives in **D** since this holds for v and for u.

In our proof we must evidently make use of the characterization of w as being orthogonal to all functions U of Σ. We choose for U a fundamental singularity $S(P, Q)$ where Q is a point outside of **D**. Hence:

$$E\{w(P), S(P, Q)\} = 0. \tag{1.20}$$

The integral (1.20) exists even when Q is chosen to be a point inside **D**, since grad S is integrable and grad w even continuous there. But, of course, its value is no longer zero, and so we define

$$\varphi(Q) = E\{w(P), S(P, Q)\}. \tag{1.21}$$

$\varphi(Q)$ is defined for all values of Q inside of **D** and everywhere in the exterior where $S(P, Q)$ is defined. Simple estimates show that it is a continuous function of Q both in the interior and exterior of **D**. The surprising fact is that $\varphi(Q)$ *is continuous even as* Q *crosses the boundary* **C** *of* **D**.

This can be proved by the following consideration: Let P be any point in **D**; denote by R the nearest boundary point. It is easily seen from the analyticity of the boundary **C** that there exist two circles γ and $\bar{\gamma}$ through R, both of radius d, such that γ lies in **D** and $\bar{\gamma}$ outside. Assume that P is so close to R that it lies in γ. Since R is the nearest boundary point to P, P

lies on the diameter of γ through R. Assume further that P and R are so close that P lies on the radius between the center of γ and R, and moreover that $\overline{P}$, the image of P inverted with respect to γ, lies in $\overline{\gamma}$.

We shall now estimate the difference

$$\varphi(P) - \varphi(\overline{P}) = \mathrm{E}\{w(T), S(T,P) - S(T,\overline{P})\}. \tag{1.22}$$

If we decompose $S(T,P) = \dfrac{1}{2\pi}\log\dfrac{1}{r} + s(T,P)$ with $r = \overline{TP}$, the term $\mathrm{E}\{w(T), s(T,P)\}$ will be a continuous function of P and need not be considered in the estimate (1.22). Similarly, $\displaystyle\iint_{\mathrm{D}} q(T)\, w(T) \log\frac{1}{r}\, ds_T$ is obviously continuous even when P crosses the boundary C of D. We need, therefore, only show that the integral

$$\iint_{\mathrm{D}} \operatorname{grad}_T w \cdot \operatorname{grad}_T \left[\log\frac{1}{\overline{TP}} - \log\frac{1}{\overline{T\overline{P}}}\right] d\tau_T \tag{1.23}$$

can be made arbitrarily small if P and $\overline{P}$ move together.

Describe a circle Γ of radius ρ with center R and divide D into the three parts γ, $(\mathrm{D}-\gamma)\cap\Gamma$, and $\mathrm{D}-\gamma-\Gamma$. We shall show that the integral (1.23) extended over each of these parts tends to zero as P and hence $\overline{P}$ tend to R. Choose the radius ρ of Γ so small that the integral

$$\iint_{\Gamma-\gamma-\overline{\gamma}} \frac{1}{\overline{TR}^2}\, d\tau$$

is smaller than a preassigned number. This is possible since $\Gamma-\gamma-\overline{\gamma}$ forms a horn-angle at $T = R$ and the integral therefore converges. For P and $\overline{P}$ in Γ and for T in $\Gamma-\gamma-\overline{\gamma}$ the following estimates hold:

$$\left|\operatorname{grad}\left(\log\frac{1}{\overline{TP}}\right)\right|^2 = \frac{1}{\overline{TP}^2} \leqslant \frac{4}{\overline{TR}^2}, \quad \left|\operatorname{grad}\left(\log\frac{1}{\overline{T\overline{P}}}\right)\right|^2 \leqslant \frac{4}{\overline{TR}^2}. \tag{1.24}$$

Thus, we can show by Schwarz' inequality that the contribution of $(\mathrm{D}-\gamma)\cap\Gamma$ to the integral (1.23) can be made less than a preassigned number. Having fitted the radius ρ of Γ to this requirement, we keep it fixed in the following estimates.

Concerning the part of (1.23) extended over $\mathrm{D}-\gamma-\Gamma$, we can assert that the difference $\left(\operatorname{grad}\left(\log\dfrac{1}{\overline{TP}}\right) - \operatorname{grad}\left(\log\dfrac{1}{\overline{T\overline{P}}}\right)\right)$ converges uniformly to zero in $D - \gamma - \Gamma$ if $\overline{PR}$ tends to zero. Hence, the integral extended over $D - \gamma - \Gamma$ also tends to zero.

It remains only to show that the integral extended over γ tends to zero if P tends to R. At this stage we should like to apply integration by parts, but we encounter the difficulty that $w = v - u$ need not be continuously differentiable up to the boundary at R. We describe, therefore, a little circle of radius δ with center R and remove all points inside this circle from γ. Let S be the circular arc which separates the truncated domain γ_S from R. The boundary β of γ_S consists of S and the remainder of the γ-circle. Using Green's identity, we may write

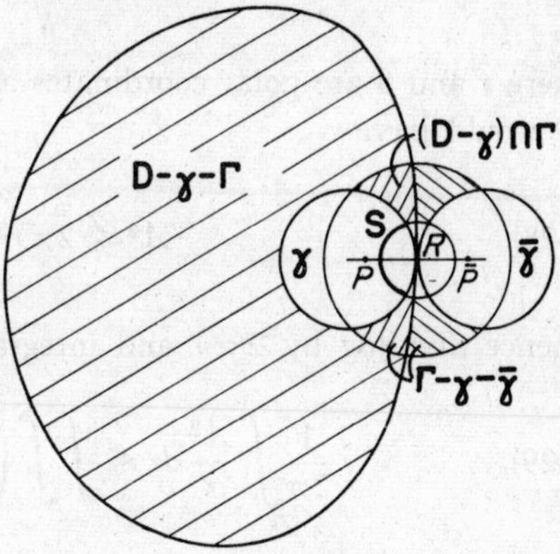

Figure 12

$$(1.25) \qquad \iint_{\gamma_S} \operatorname{grad} w \cdot \operatorname{grad}\left(\log \frac{1}{\overline{TP}} - \log \frac{1}{\overline{T\overline{P}}}\right) d\tau =$$

$$= -\int_{\beta}\left(\log \frac{1}{\overline{TP}} - \log \frac{1}{\overline{T\overline{P}}} - k\right) \frac{\partial w}{\partial \nu}\, ds$$

$$- \iint_{\gamma_S}\left(\log \frac{1}{\overline{TP}} - \log \frac{1}{\overline{T\overline{P}}} - k\right) \Delta w \, d\tau.$$

Here k is a constant of integration which will immediately be determined in a convenient way. Since P and $\overline{P}$ are inverse points with respect to the circle γ, the difference $\log \frac{1}{\overline{TP}} - \log \frac{1}{\overline{T\overline{P}}}$ has for fixed P a constant value on the circumference and we choose k to be this number. Thus the integral over β in (1.25) actually has only to be extended over the arc S.

We shall now show that we can select a sequence of radii δ_i such that $\delta_i \to 0$ and for the corresponding circular arcs S_i

$$(1.26) \qquad \lim_{i\to\infty} \int_{S_i} \left| \frac{\partial w}{\partial \nu} \right| ds = 0.$$

In fact, suppose this were not the case. There would then exist a positive constant A such that for every radius r

$$A \leqslant \int_0^{2\pi} \left| \frac{\partial w}{\partial r} \right| r \, d\theta \tag{1.27}$$

where r and θ are polar coordinates around R. By the Schwarz inequality we would have

$$A^2 \leqslant 2\pi r^2 \int_0^{2\pi} \left(\frac{\partial w}{\partial r} \right)^2 d\theta \tag{1.28}$$

whence dividing by $2\pi r$ and integrating from $r = r_0$ to r_1 we obtain:

$$\frac{1}{2\pi} \int_{r_0}^{r_1} \frac{A^2}{r} \, dr \leqslant \int\!\!\int \left(\frac{\partial w}{\partial r} \right)^2 r \, dr \, d\theta \leqslant \mathrm{E}\,\{w\}. \tag{1.29}$$

Now letting $r_0 \to 0$, we obtain a contradiction since the left-hand side would diverge to infinity and must, on the other hand, always be bounded by $\mathrm{E}\,\{w\}$. Thus the existence of a sequence of arcs S_i with property (1.26) has been proved.

We now let δ tend to zero through this particular sequence δ_i. Passing to the limit in (1.25), we arrive at the equation

$$\begin{aligned} \int\!\!\int_{\Upsilon} \operatorname{grad} w . \operatorname{grad} \left[\log \frac{1}{\overline{\overline{TP}}} - \log \frac{1}{\overline{\overline{T\overline{P}}}} \right] d\tau = \\ = - \int\!\!\int_{\Upsilon} \left[\log \frac{1}{\overline{\overline{TP}}} - \log \frac{1}{\overline{\overline{T\overline{P}}}} - k \right] \Delta w \, d\tau. \end{aligned} \tag{1.30}$$

We remark that $\Delta w = \Delta v - \Delta u = \Delta v - q u$ is square integrable over D. Hence, by the Schwarz inequality we find:

$$\begin{aligned} \left(\int\!\!\int_{\Upsilon} \operatorname{grad} w \cdot \operatorname{grad} \left[\log \frac{1}{\overline{\overline{TP}}} - \log \frac{1}{\overline{\overline{T\overline{P}}}} \right] d\tau \right)^2 \leqslant \\ \leqslant \int\!\!\int_{\Upsilon} (\Delta w)^2 \, d\tau \cdot \int\!\!\int_{\Upsilon} \left(\log \frac{1}{\overline{\overline{TP}}} - \log \frac{1}{\overline{\overline{T\overline{P}}}} - k \right)^2 d\tau. \end{aligned} \tag{1.30'}$$

If P converges to R, the last right-hand integral converges to zero since k and $\log \frac{1}{\overline{\overline{TP}}} - \log \frac{1}{\overline{\overline{T\overline{P}}}}$ tend to zero; in fact, the constant k depends continuously on P and will vanish if $P = \overline{P}$. Thus, we have proved that the expression (1.23) converges to zero if P approaches the boundary C of D. Because of the analytic character of the boundary C, it is possible to derive from our above inequalities a uniform estimate for the difference $\varphi(P) - \varphi(\overline{P})$ which depends only on the distance of P from its nearest boundary point R.

At this point we take into account the fact that outside of D the function $\varphi(P)$ is identically zero by virtue of (1.20). Hence we have $\varphi(\overline{P}) \equiv 0$, and thus we have proved: $\varphi(P)$ *is continuous in* $\mathsf{D} + \mathsf{C}$ *and assumes the boundary values zero on* C.

Let us now study the analytic nature of $\varphi(P)$ in more detail. Let D' be a proper subdomain of D which contains P and let C' be its boundary. We integrate (1.21) by parts, but this time apply the differentiation to the singularity terms. By an easy calculation we obtain

$$\text{(1.31)} \qquad \varphi(P) = E_{\mathsf{D}-\mathsf{D}'}\{w(T), S(T, P)\} - \int_{\mathsf{C}'} w(T) \frac{\partial S(T, P)}{\partial \nu_T} ds_T + w(P).$$

From (1.31) we conclude that the function

$$\text{(1.32)} \qquad U(P) = \varphi(P) - w(P)$$

is for every point $P \in \mathsf{D}$, a regular solution of the differential equation (I.1.1); for around every such point we can find a subdomain D' containing it, and it is obvious that the integrals in (1.31) are solutions of the differential equation.

Using (1.32) and the definition $w = v - u$, we obtain

$$\text{(1.33)} \qquad v(P) = [u(P) - U(P)] + \varphi(P).$$

$v(P)$ was an arbitrary element in Ω; $\varphi(P)$ has been shown to be continuous in $\mathsf{D} + \mathsf{C}$ and to vanish on C. Hence, $u(P) - U(P)$ is a solution of the differential equation (I.1.1) which on C has the same boundary values as the prescribed function $v(P)$. Thus, we have proved that *the boundary value problem has a solution.*

We have not yet shown that the solution of the boundary value problem is continuously differentiable in $\mathsf{D} + \mathsf{C}$; this property is very important if any application of Green's identity is required. In order to prove the continuous differentiability of the solution, we will assume that Green's function for Laplace's equation with respect to D exists and will denote this function by $\Gamma(P, Q)$ as in Section I.4. Let us now compute the Laplacian of φ; in view of (I.1.1), we find

$$\text{(1.34)} \qquad \Delta\varphi = \Delta v - q(u - U)$$

and recognize that $\Delta\varphi$ is continuous in D + C. Since $\varphi = 0$ on C, we have

$$(1.35)\qquad \varphi(P) = -\iint_{D} \Gamma(P,Q)\cdot[\Delta v(Q) - q(Q)(u(Q) - U(Q))]\,d\tau_Q.$$

in view of the Poisson-Laplace equation. From this representation, it follows immediately that $\varphi(P)$ is continuously differentiable in D + C, and in view of (1.33) this holds also for $u(P) - U(P)$. If we transform (1.35) by a simple application of Green's formula into

$$(1.36)\qquad \varphi(P) = v(P) - \int_{C} v(Q)\frac{\partial\Gamma(P,Q)}{\partial\nu_Q}\,ds_Q + \\ + \iint_{D} q(Q)\,\Gamma(P,Q)(u(Q) - U(Q))\,d\tau_Q$$

we recognize that φ possesses two continuous derivatives in D + C and thus belongs to Ω^0. By virtue of (1.33), this implies that *$u - U$ is twice continuously differentiable in D + C and therefore belongs to Σ*. Thus, the final result of our investigation is that each *function $v \in \Omega$ can be decomposed into a sum of one function of the space Σ and another function of the space Ω^0.*

We have arrived at the decomposition $v = (u - U) + \varphi$ in a somewhat roundabout fashion; the original solution of our extremum problem connected with orthogonal projection was $u(P)$. Now, we are able to state actually that $U \equiv 0$ and that the orthogonal projection of v into Σ really leads to a function of the space Σ itself. In fact, let $u_n(P)$ be any element of the minimum sequence considered in our projection problem; clearly

$$(1.37)\qquad E\{v - u_n\} = E\{v - (u - U) + (u - U - u_n)\} = \\ = E\{v - (u - U)\} + E\{u - U - u_n\}$$

since $v - (u - U) \in \Omega^0$ and $u - U - u_n \in \Sigma$. This shows that the lower limit d for all $E\{v - u_n\}$ is attained for $u - U$:

$$(1.38)\qquad E\{v - (u - U)\} = d\ .$$

Consider now the inequality (1.6) which is valid for any two functions of the class Σ. Put $u_m = u - U$ and let $u_n \to u$. In view of (1.8) and (1.38) we obtain

$$(1.39)\qquad E\{U\} = 0, \qquad \text{i. e.,} \qquad U \equiv 0.$$

Returning now to (1.32), we recognize that $\varphi(P) = -w(P)$ which, in view of the definition (1.21) for $\varphi(P)$, yields the interesting integral equation for $w(P)$

$$w(P) - \mathrm{E}\{S(T, P), w(T)\} = 0. \tag{1.40}$$

This equation can also be easily derived by means of an elementary application of Green's identity from the fact that $w \in \Omega^0$.

The above arrangement of argument was first given in the theory of conformal mapping by Garabedian and Schiffer. It was extended to the theory of harmonic functions by P. Lax who communicated his proof to the authors. His method was general enough to be immediately applicable to the type of differential equations considered in this book. The method fits well into the general approach of our present theory in that great simplification and elegance of treatment can be obtained by operating within the class Σ of solutions of the differential equation (I.1.1) instead of within the wider classes Ω^0 and Ω which form the usual basis of approach in the Dirichlet principle and in numerical approximations.

Garabedian-Schiffer (G 4), P. Lax (L 4), Lehto (L 5), Lokki (L 21).

CHAPTER V

DEPENDENCE OF KERNELS ON BOUNDARY CONDITIONS AND THE DIFFERENTIAL EQUATION

1. The positiveness of the fundamental functions: In Section II.6, use was made of the fact that *Green's function* $G(P, Q)$ *is non-negative* in the whole domain of its definition. This was an immediate consequence of its boundary behavior, its singularity character, and of the first theorem of Section I.3. It is now interesting to observe that not only Green's function, but *all Robin's functions,* as defined in Section I.5, *have the same property* and that inequalities among various Robin's functions $R_\lambda(P, Q)$ may be established if inequalities between their characterizing functions $\lambda(s)$ are prescribed. Considering Green's and Neumann's functions as limiting cases of Robin's functions, namely for $\lambda = \infty$ and $\lambda = 0$, we obtain, in particular, useful estimates for these important solutions.

Let us consider the Robin function $R_\lambda(P, Q)$ defined in Section I.5. It becomes positively infinite at Q and we shall show that it is nowhere negative in D. In fact, let D_- be that part of D where R_λ is non-positive; such a domain must surely exist if, for fixed $Q \in D$, $R_\lambda(P,Q)$ becomes negative for some point $P \in D$. The domain D_- is bounded by curves $\gamma_i \in D$ on which $R_\lambda = 0$ or by parts δ_i of the boundary on which by definition of the Robin function

$$\frac{\partial R_\lambda}{\partial \nu} = \lambda R_\lambda. \tag{1.1}$$

Let us now compute by means of Green's identity

$$E_{D_-}\{R_\lambda(T,Q)\} = -\sum_i \int_{\delta_i} \frac{\partial R_\lambda(T,Q)}{\partial \nu_T} R_\lambda(T,Q)\, ds_T = \tag{1.2}$$

$$= -\sum_i \int_{\delta_i} \lambda (R_\lambda(T,Q))^2 \, ds_T.$$

This equation between the non-negative left-hand side and the non-positive right-hand side can hold only if both terms vanish. [By the definition of R_λ (see I.5), λ is non-negative.] But then we must necessarily have $R_\lambda \equiv 0$ in D_-, while we have assumed that somewhere in D_-, $R_\lambda < 0$ holds. This contradiction shows that

$$R_\lambda(P,Q) \geq 0 \quad \text{in } D. \tag{1.3}$$

In particular, taking $\lambda(s) = 0$, we arrive at the inequality for Neumann's function

$$N(P,Q) \geq 0 \quad \text{in } D. \tag{1.4}$$

Let now

$$0 \leq \varkappa(s) \leq \lambda(s). \tag{1.5}$$

and compare the corresponding Robin functions $R_\lambda(P,Q)$ and $R_\varkappa(P,Q)$. Let D_- denote the domain where $R_\varkappa(P,Q) - R_\lambda(P,Q) \leq 0$. Its boundary C_- consists of curves on which either $R_\varkappa - R_\lambda = 0$, or else

$$R_\varkappa - R_\lambda \leq 0, \ \frac{\partial}{\partial \nu}(R_\varkappa - R_\lambda) = \varkappa R_\varkappa - \lambda R_\lambda \leq \lambda (R_\varkappa - R_\lambda) \leq 0 \tag{1.6}$$

because of inequalities (1.3) and (1.5). Thus we find

$$E_{D_-}\{R_\varkappa(T,Q) - R_\lambda(T,Q)\} = -\int_{C_-} \frac{\partial}{\partial \nu}(R_\varkappa - R_\lambda) \cdot (R_\varkappa - R_\lambda)\, ds \leq 0. \tag{1.7}$$

Thus, we again arrive at the result $R_\varkappa - R_\lambda \equiv 0$ in D_-; hence, we have proved

$$R_\varkappa (P,Q) \geqslant R_\lambda (P,Q) \quad \text{in } \mathsf{D}, \quad \text{if } 0 \leqslant \varkappa \leqslant \lambda. \tag{1.8}$$

The most interesting instance of this inequality arises for $\varkappa = 0$, $\lambda = \infty$. This yields

$$K (P,Q) = N (P,Q) - G (P,Q) \geqslant 0, \quad \text{in } \mathsf{D}. \tag{1.9}$$

We have proved, therefore, the important theorem: *The kernel K is non-negative in* D.

We also note the inequality

$$N (P,Q) \geqslant R_\lambda (P,Q) \geqslant G (P,Q) \geqslant 0 \quad \text{in } \mathsf{D}. \tag{1.10}$$

From inequality (1.4) and the representation (I.5.15) of a function $u \in \Sigma$ by means of its normal derivative on C, we draw the following conclusion: *If the function $u \in \Sigma$ has everywhere on* C *a non-negative normal derivative, then in* D *it satisfies the inequality* $u (P) \leqslant 0$. This result suggests the introduction of the following test function for the class Σ. We define

$$V (P) = - \int_{\mathsf{C}} N (P,Q) \, ds_Q. \tag{1.11}$$

This is a non-positive function in the class Σ which has, by virtue of (I.5.15), the constant normal derivative one on C.

Now let $u (P)$ be an arbitrary function of the class Σ and suppose that its normal derivative on C satisfies the inequalities

$$\mu \leqslant \frac{\partial u}{\partial \nu} \leqslant M. \tag{1.12}$$

Then the combinations $M\,V (P) - u (P)$ and $u (P) - \mu\, V (P)$ will have non-negative normal derivatives on C and will, by our preceding result, be non-positive in D. Thus, we obtain the estimates for $u \in \Sigma$:

$$M\,V (P) \leqslant u (P) \leqslant \mu\, V (P). \tag{1.13}$$

This inequality is a useful analogue to the estimate (I.3.4) which permits us to estimate the same function u in D by means of its boundary values on C.

In the Dirichlet metric the function $V (P)$ has the following interesting significance. For any $u \in \Sigma$ we have by (II.4.1)

$$\mathrm{E}\{V, u\} = - \int_{\mathsf{C}} u \, ds. \tag{1.14}$$

Thus scalar multiplication of u with V has the same result as taking the negative integral of u over the boundary. By means of this interpretation we are able to define a mean boundary value not only for functions of the class Σ, but also for all functions in the closure $\Sigma^{\blacktriangle}$ of this class.

Bergman-Schiffer (B 23).

2. Stability of fundamental functions: In Section III.6, we studied the continuous change of the fundamental functions belonging to a fixed differential equation (I.1.1) under a continuous change of the domain D. Another important problem arises if for a fixed domain D the differential equation (I.1.1) is varied.

This problem arises in practical applications, principally in connection with questions of stability. If a certain physical situation is described by the solution of a partial differential equation, it is natural to inquire how this situation is affected by a slight perturbation, i. e., a small change of the differential equation.

We shall show that for a very general type of variation, the change of the fundamental functions may easily be determined. The fact that a particularly elegant theory has just been obtained for these fundamental functions is a new justification of our point of view in which the general study of solutions of (I.1.1) is reduced to these central expressions.

Let

$$\Delta v = (q + \varepsilon p)\, v, \qquad \varepsilon > 0, \tag{2.1}$$

be a differential equation which will be compared to our original equation (I.1.1). We assume that p is continuously differentiable and positive in $D + C$. We are then sure that a Green's function $G_\varepsilon(P, Q)$ and Neumann's function $N_\varepsilon(P, Q)$ with respect to (2.1) and the domain D exist. Now consider the following identities which are an immediate consequence of Green's theorem and the boundary behavior of the fundamental functions:

$$\iint_D [N_\varepsilon(T, P) \Delta N(T, Q) - N(T, Q) \Delta N_\varepsilon(T, P)]\, d\tau = N_\varepsilon(P, Q) - N(P, Q), \qquad d\tau = \text{area element in } T, \tag{2.2}$$

and

$$\iint_D [G_\varepsilon(T, P) \Delta G(T, Q) - G(T, Q) \Delta G_\varepsilon(T, P)]\, d\tau = G_\varepsilon(P, Q) - G(P, Q). \tag{2.3}$$

Using the differential equations (I.1.1) and (2.1) for the fundamental functions, we arrive at

$$N_\varepsilon(P,Q) + \varepsilon \iint_D N_\varepsilon(T,P)\,N(T,Q)\,p(T)\,d\tau = N(P,Q), \tag{2.4}$$

and

$$G_\varepsilon(P,Q) + \varepsilon \iint_D G_\varepsilon(T,P)\,G(T,Q)\,p(T)\,d\tau = G(P,Q). \tag{2.5}$$

These are integral equations for determining N_ε and G_ε in terms of N and G. They yield geometrically convergent series for N_ε and G_ε in powers of ε as long as ε remains in modulus smaller than the least eigenvalue of the homogeneous integral equations

$$\varphi(Q) - \lambda \iint_D N(T,Q)\,p(T)\,\varphi(T)\,d\tau = 0 \tag{2.6}$$

and

$$\psi(Q) - \varkappa \iint_D G(T,Q)\,p(T)\,\psi(T)\,d\tau = 0, \tag{2.7}$$

respectively.

From the singularities and boundary behavior of N and G, it is obvious that the homogeneous integral equations (2.6) and (2.7) can be transformed into eigenvalue problems of partial differential equations. Namely:

$$\Delta\varphi - q\varphi + \lambda p\varphi = 0 \quad \text{with} \quad \frac{\partial\varphi}{\partial\nu} = 0 \quad \text{on } C \tag{2.6'}$$

and

$$\Delta\psi - q\psi + \varkappa p\psi = 0 \quad \text{with} \quad \psi = 0 \quad \text{on } C. \tag{2.7'}$$

It is well known[1] that the eigenvalues λ and $\varkappa$ can be estimated as follows: Let $\omega(z, y)$ be any function of class Ω; then the smallest eigenvalue λ of (2.6′) satisfies the inequality:

$$\lambda \leqslant (E\{\omega\}) \cdot \left(\iint_D p\,\omega^2\,dx\,dy \right)^{-1}. \tag{2.8}$$

[1] See, for example, Courant-Hilbert [13], vol. 1, p. 346.

For the corresponding eigenfunction φ, equality is attained in (2.8), i. e.,

$$\lambda = (\mathrm{E}\{\varphi\}) \cdot \left(\iint_{\mathsf{D}} p \varphi^2 \, dx \, dy \right)^{-1}. \tag{2.9}$$

Now let

$$\alpha = \min q(P), \qquad \beta = \max p(P), \qquad \text{for} \qquad P \in \mathsf{D} + \mathsf{C}. \tag{2.10}$$

We clearly have, in view of (I.2.1) and (2.9):

$$\lambda \geqslant \frac{\alpha}{\beta}. \tag{2.11}$$

Similarly, we can estimate the least eigenvalue $\varkappa$ of (2.7') by an arbitrary function ω_0 of the class Ω^0:

$$\varkappa \leqslant (\mathrm{E}\{\omega_0\}) \cdot \left(\iint_{\mathsf{D}} p \, \omega_0^2 \, dx \, dy \right)^{-1}; \tag{2.12}$$

equality holds again for the corresponding eigenfunction ψ. Clearly, we have $\varkappa \geqslant \lambda$, so that the estimate (2.11) holds for $\varkappa$, too.

Thus, we may assert that as long as $\varepsilon < \alpha/\beta$ the Neumann series for $N_\varepsilon(P, Q)$ and $G_\varepsilon(P, Q)$ will converge geometrically, and for not too large ε this result yields a convenient method for determining the neighboring fundamental functions.

We can make general statements about the functions N_ε and G_ε without entering into any detailed computation. We have assumed $\varepsilon > 0$; from formulas (2.4) and (2.5), and because of the positive character of all fundamental functions, we derive the inequalities

$$N_\varepsilon(P, Q) \leqslant N(P, Q) \qquad \text{for} \qquad \varepsilon > 0, \tag{2.13}$$

$$G_\varepsilon(P, Q) \leqslant G(P, Q) \qquad \text{for} \qquad \varepsilon > 0. \tag{2.14}$$

Thus, we have proved: *Green's and Neumann's functions decrease if the coefficient* $q(P)$ *in* (I.1.1) *is increased.*

Let us next consider the behavior of the kernel $K(P, Q)$ under change of $q(P)$. From (2.4) and (2.5), and because of (II.1.2), we deduce

$$K_\varepsilon(P, Q) + \varepsilon \iint_{\mathsf{D}} [N_\varepsilon(T, P) N(T, Q) - G_\varepsilon(T, P) G(T, Q)] \, p(T) \, d\tau = K(P, Q). \tag{2.15}$$

But by (1.10) each Neumann's function is larger than the corresponding Green's function, whence the inequality

(2.16) $$K_\varepsilon(P,Q) \leqslant K(P,Q) \quad \text{for} \quad \varepsilon > 0$$

i. e., *the kernel decreases with an increase of* $q(P)$.

Let $u(P)$ be a solution of (I.1.1) with prescribed boundary values on C; let $v(P)$ be the solution of (2.1) with the same boundary values as $u(P)$. Consider the identity

(2.17) $$\iint_D [v(T) \triangle G(T,P) - G(T,P) \triangle v] d\tau = v(P) - \int_C v(T) \frac{\partial G(T,P)}{\partial \nu_T} ds_T$$

where G is Green's function with respect to the original equation (I.1.1). Using the differential equations (2.1) and (I.1.1), we may transform (2.17) into

(2.18) $$v(P) + \varepsilon \iint_D p(T) v(T) G(T,P) d\tau_T = u(P)$$

since in view of (I.5.13) and the identity of u and v on the boundary C, the last integral in (2.17) represents exactly $u(P)$. This is again an integral equation for the varied function $v(P)$ in terms of $u(P)$ and the known Green's function with respect to (I.1.1). Our preceding study of the eigenvalues of the corresponding homogeneous integral equation (2.7) determines the range for ε in which the Neumann series for $v(P)$ will converge.

Let us assume, in particular, that the prescribed boundary values of u on C are non-negative. Then $u(P)$ and $v(P)$ are non-negative in D and from (2.18) we read off that

(2.19) $$v(P) \leqslant u(P) \quad \text{for} \quad \varepsilon > 0;$$

i. e., we have proved the theorem: *If a solution of* (I.1.1) *and a solution of* (2.1) *have the same non-negative boundary values, that solution belonging to the larger factor of* u *is smaller in* D.

We are now able to answer an important question which arose in Section (I.3). There we considered the possibility that for a given point $Q \in$ D all functions $u \in \Sigma$ might vanish; a necessary and sufficient condition for this was the vanishing at Q of the function $U \in \Sigma$ which on C has the constant boundary value one.

Suppose that for some differential equation (I.1.1) we have $U(Q) = 0$. In view of the preceding theorem, the corresponding U-functions belonging to differential equations with larger coefficient $q(P)$ would have to be less than or equal to zero at Q; on the other hand, each $U(P)$ is non-negative.

Hence we would have $U(Q) = 0$ for all differential equations (I.1.1) with larger q than that of the equation considered. Let us now assume that the original $q(P)$ satisfied in D the inequality

$$q(P) \leqslant \Lambda^2. \tag{2.20}$$

Then, the $U(P)$-function with respect to the simple equation

$$\Delta u = \Lambda^2 u \tag{2.21}$$

would vanish at the point Q and, hence, so would all solutions of the differential equation (2.21). However, the function $u = e^{\Lambda x}$ satisfies (2.21) and does not vanish at any finite point of the (x, y)-plane. This contradicts the assumption $U(Q) = 0$ for the original differential equation and we have proved: *The function $U(P)$ does not vanish at interior points of* D. Thus, there does not exist a point $Q \in$ D where all functions of the class Σ vanish.

Various similar results may be obtained by the same method. We only indicate here briefly that if R and R_ε are the Robin's functions of D with the same $\lambda(s)$ and belonging to the equations (I.1.1) and (2.1), respectively, we have the identity

$$\iint_{D} \left(R_\varepsilon(T,P)\,\Delta R(T,Q) - \Delta R_\varepsilon(T,P)\,R(T,Q)\right) d\tau = R_\varepsilon(P,Q) - R(P,Q). \tag{2.22}$$

Thus

$$R_\varepsilon(P,Q) + \varepsilon \iint_{D} p(T)\,R_\varepsilon(T,P)\,R(T,Q)\,d\tau = R(P,Q) \tag{2.22'}$$

which is an integral equation for $R_\varepsilon(P,Q)$ and all our above considerations can be repeated. In particular, we conclude from (V.1.3)

$$R_\varepsilon(P,Q) \leqslant R(P,Q) \quad \text{if} \quad \varepsilon > 0. \tag{2.23}$$

Thus, we have shown that all fundamental functions behave similarly under change of the differential equation.

Bergman-Schiffer (B 23).

3. Stability of eigenvalues: In Section III.4 we showed how a knowledge of the lowest eigenvalue λ_1 of the integro-differential equation

$$u_\rho(P) = \lambda_\rho \mathrm{E}\{l(P,Q), u_\rho(Q)\} \tag{3.1}$$

leads to a useful estimate for the approximation of the fundamental functions by means of a given finite set of orthogonal functions. We remarked in

(II.9.14) that the series development for the K-kernel in terms of iterated integrals converges like a geometric series with ratio $\frac{1}{\lambda_1^2}$. Thus, it is important to derive a method for estimating the value of this characteristic quantity; such a method is, in fact, provided by the formulas of the last section.

Let us change the coefficient $q(P)$ in (I.1.1) by an infinitesimal amout δq. In view of (2.4) and (2.5) the Neumann's and Green's functions of the domain D will satisfy the variational equations

$$\delta N(P,Q) = -\iint_{\mathsf{D}} N(T,P)\, N(T,Q)\, \delta q\, d\tau_T, \tag{3.2}$$

$$\delta G(P,Q) = -\iint_{\mathsf{D}} G(T,P)\, G(T,Q)\, \delta q\, d\tau_T. \tag{3.3}$$

If the domain D lies inside of a larger domain D_1, corresponding formulas can be written down for the Neumann's and Green's functions N_1 and G_1 of this domain. Now consider equation (3.1) which can, by (II.4.1), also be brought into the form

$$u_\rho(P) + \lambda_\rho \int_{\mathsf{C}} l(P,Q) \frac{\partial u_\rho}{\partial \nu_Q}\, ds_Q = 0. \tag{3.4}$$

Let us vary the coefficient $q(P)$ of (I.1.1) and ask for the corresponding eigenfunctions and eigenvalues of the differential equation obtained. Since, by definition,

$$l(P,Q) = N(P,Q) + G(P,Q) - N_1(P,Q) - G_1(P,Q) \tag{3.5}$$

the variational equations (3.2) and (3.3) will be sufficient to provide the answer.

It is easily seen that the variations $\delta u_\rho(P)$ and $\delta\lambda_\rho$ of the eigenfunctions and the eigenvalues satisfy the equation

$$\delta u_\rho(P) - \frac{\delta\lambda_\rho}{\lambda_\rho} u_\rho(P) + \lambda_\rho \int_{\mathsf{C}} \delta l(P,Q) \frac{\partial u_\rho}{\partial \nu_Q}\, ds_Q + \tag{3.6}$$
$$+ \lambda_\rho \int_{\mathsf{C}} l(P,Q) \frac{\partial(\delta u_\rho)}{\partial \nu_Q}\, ds_Q = 0.$$

Let us consider this equation for $P \in \mathsf{C}$; multiplying by $\dfrac{\partial u_\rho(P)}{\partial \nu}$ and integrating over C again, because of (3.4) and the normalization $\mathrm{E}\{u_\rho\} = 1$, we obtain

$$\int_{\mathsf{C}} \frac{\partial u_\rho}{\partial \nu}\, \delta u_\rho\, ds + \frac{\delta\lambda_\rho}{\lambda_\rho} + \tag{3.7}$$

$$+ \lambda_\rho \int_{\mathsf{C}}\int_{\mathsf{C}} \delta l\,(P,Q)\, \frac{\partial u_\rho}{\partial \nu_Q}\frac{\partial u_\rho}{\partial \nu_P}\, ds_P\, ds_Q - \int_{\mathsf{C}} u_\rho \frac{\partial(\delta u_\rho)}{\partial \nu}\, ds = 0.$$

Applying Green's identity, we find:

$$\int_{\mathsf{C}} \left(\frac{\partial u_\rho}{\partial \nu}\, \delta u_\rho - u_\rho \frac{\partial(\delta u_\rho)}{\partial \nu} \right) ds = \tag{3.8}$$

$$= \iint_{\mathsf{D}} [\triangle\,(u_\rho + \delta u_\rho)\cdot u_\rho - (u_\rho + \delta u_\rho)\,\triangle\, u_\rho]\, d\tau = \iint_{\mathsf{D}} \delta q\, u_\rho^2 d\tau.$$

Applying equations (3.2), (3.3), and their analogues for the domain D_1, we derive from (3.7) and (3.8):

$$- \frac{\delta\lambda_\rho}{\lambda_\rho} = \iint_{\mathsf{D}} \delta q\, u_\rho^2\, d\tau + \tag{3.9}$$

$$+ \lambda_\rho \int_{\mathsf{C}}\int_{\mathsf{C}} \frac{\partial u_\rho}{\partial \nu_Q}\frac{\partial u_\rho}{\partial \nu_P} \Bigg[\iint_{\mathsf{D}_1} \big(N_1\,(T,P)\, N_1\,(T,Q) + G_1\,(T,P)\, G_1\,(T,Q)\big)\, \delta q\, d\tau$$

$$- \iint_{\mathsf{D}} N\,(T,P)\, N\,(T,Q)\, \delta q\, d\tau \Bigg]\, ds_P\, ds_Q.$$

Let us define

$$\int_{\mathsf{C}} N_1\,(T,Q) \frac{\partial u_\rho}{\partial \nu_Q}\, ds_Q = a_\rho\,(T), \qquad \int_{\mathsf{C}} G_1\,(T,Q) \frac{\partial u_\rho}{\partial \nu_Q}\, ds_Q = b_\rho\,(T); \tag{3.10}$$

in view of (I.5.15) we have

$$- \int_{\mathsf{C}} N\,(T,Q) \frac{\partial u_\rho}{\partial \nu_Q}\, ds_Q = u_\rho\,(T). \tag{3.10'}$$

Thus, (3.9) may be written

$$- \frac{\delta\lambda_\rho}{\lambda_\rho} = (1 - \lambda_\rho) \iint_{\mathsf{D}} \delta q\, u_\rho^2\, d\tau + \lambda_\rho \iint_{\mathsf{D}_1} [a_\rho\,(T)^2 + b_\rho\,(T)^2]\, \delta q\, d\tau. \tag{3.11}$$

In view of (3.4), (3.5), (3.10), and (3.10′), we have for $T \in \mathsf{D}$

$$a_\rho(T) + b_\rho(T) + u_\rho(T) = \frac{1}{\lambda_\rho} u_\rho(T). \tag{3.12}$$

Therefore, putting $a_\rho^2 + b_\rho^2 = \frac{1}{2}(a_\rho + b_\rho)^2 + \frac{1}{2}(a_\rho - b_\rho)^2$, we may bring (3.11) in the form

$$-\frac{\delta\lambda_\rho}{\lambda_\rho} = \frac{1}{2}\left(\frac{1}{\lambda_\rho} - \lambda_\rho\right)\iint_{\mathsf{D}} \delta q\, u_\rho^2\, d\tau + \frac{\lambda_\rho}{2}\iint_{\mathsf{D}} (a_\rho(T) - b_\rho(T))^2\, \delta q\, d\tau + \tag{3.13}$$

$$+ \lambda_\rho \iint_{\mathsf{D}_1 - \mathsf{D}} [(a_\rho(T))^2 + (b_\rho(T))^2]\, \delta q\, d\tau.$$

This leads to the estimate

$$-\frac{\delta\lambda_\rho}{\lambda_\rho^2} \leqslant -\frac{1}{2}\left(1 - \frac{1}{\lambda_\rho^2}\right)\iint_{\mathsf{D}} \delta q\, u_\rho^2\, d\tau, \tag{3.14}$$

if we assume $\delta q < 0$ in D_1. Moreover, let

$$\max_{P \in \mathsf{D}} \frac{|\delta q|}{q} = \delta_\mu; \tag{3.14′}$$

then (3.14) can be weakened to the more convenient inequality

$$-\frac{\delta\lambda_\rho}{\lambda_\rho^2 - 1} \leqslant \frac{\delta_\mu}{2}\iint_{\mathsf{D}} q\, u_\rho^2\, d\tau \leqslant \frac{\delta_\mu}{2} \mathrm{E}\,\{u_\rho\} = \frac{\delta_\mu}{2}. \tag{3.15}$$

This estimate suggests a useful method for the estimation of the lowest eigenvalue λ_1 for a given differential equation (I.1.1) and given domain D and D_1. We consider at first a differential equation

$$\Delta u = \Lambda^2 u \tag{3.16}$$

with a constant coefficient Λ such that $\Lambda > q(P)$ in D_1. We determine the lowest eigenvalue λ_1 in this case. Changing now Λ continuously into $q(P)$ we may estimate the change of λ_1 by means of (3.15). We see that the particularly simple partial differential equation (3.16) yields an estimate of the important functional λ_1 for the general type of equations (I.1.1).

4. Construction of a fundamental singularity: In most constructive procedures developed until now, we have assumed either the knowledge of a complete system of solutions or of a fundamental singularity of the differential equation (I.1.1) in the domain D. The formalism of the last section, however, leads to a series development for fundamental functions of (I.1.1) if fundamental functions of nearby differential equations are known. This is of great practical use, since the fundamental functions or at least fundamental singularities of the differential equation

$$\Delta \varphi = c^2 \varphi, \quad c = \text{const.} \tag{4.1}$$

are easily available. In fact, in the function (II.5.2) we possess a fundamental singularity for (4.1) and may compute for the given domain D all fundamental functions by the methods previously described. We shall utilize this fact to construct a fundamental singularity for an arbitrarily given equation (I.1.1).

In fact, let

$$c^2 = \operatorname{Max} q(P) \quad \text{for} \quad P \in \mathsf{D} + \mathsf{C}. \tag{4.2}$$

We may write equation (I.1.1) in the form

$$\Delta u = [c^2 - (c^2 - q)]\, u, \qquad c^2 - q \geqslant 0 \quad \text{in } \mathsf{D}. \tag{4.3}$$

Denoting the Green's function of D with respect to (4.1) by $\gamma(P, Q)$, we obtain from (2.5) the following integral equation for Green's function $G(P, Q)$ with respect to (I.1.1):

$$G(P,Q) - \iint_{\mathsf{D}} \big(c^2 - q(T)\big)\, G(T,Q)\, \gamma(T,P)\, d\tau = \gamma(P,Q). \tag{4.4}$$

In order to study the convergence of the Neumann series solving this equation, we have to consider the corresponding homogeneous equation

$$\varphi(P) - \lambda \iint_{\mathsf{D}} \big(c^2 - q(T)\big)\, \gamma(T,P)\, \varphi(T)\, d\tau = 0 \tag{4.5}$$

or the corresponding eigenvalue problem in partial differential equations

$$\Delta \varphi - c^2 \varphi + \lambda (c^2 - q)\, \varphi = 0, \qquad \varphi = 0 \text{ on } \mathsf{C}. \tag{4.6}$$

For any eigenfunction of (4.6) we have by Green's identity

$$\iint_{\mathsf{D}} |\operatorname{grad} \varphi|^2\, dx\, dy = \iint_{\mathsf{D}} \varphi^2 \big(\lambda (c^2 - q) - c^2\big)\, dx\, dy. \tag{4.7}$$

In order that the right-hand integral be non-negative, we must clearly require

$$\lambda > 1. \tag{4.8}$$

Hence, the lowest eigenvalue of (4.5) is greater than one and the Neumann series of $G(P, Q)$ in (4.4) converges. Let

$$\Lambda^{(n)}(P, Q) = \iint_D \Lambda^{(1)}(P, T)\,\Lambda^{(n-1)}(T, Q)\,d\tau \tag{4.9}$$

$$\Lambda^{(1)}(P, Q) = \gamma(P, Q)\,[c^2 - q(Q)];$$

then we may write (4.4) in the form

$$G(P, Q) - \iint_D \Lambda^{(1)}(P, T)\,G(T, Q)\,d\tau = \gamma(P, Q). \tag{4.4'}$$

Hence, using the kernel

$$\Lambda^{(-1)}(P, Q) = \sum_{\nu=1}^{\infty} \Lambda^{(\nu)}(P, Q), \tag{4.10}$$

we obtain the usual inversion formula

$$G(P, Q) = \gamma(P, Q) + \iint_D \Lambda^{(-1)}(P, T)\,\gamma(T, Q)\,d\tau = \tag{4.11}$$

$$= \gamma(P, Q) + \iint_D [c^2 - q(T)]\,\gamma(P, T)\,\gamma(T, Q)\,d\tau + \dots.$$

It should be remarked that each term of this series is non-negative and that each approximating step for $G(P, Q)$ leads to an estimate for this function.

If we compare the series development (4.11) for Green's function with the development (II.7.29) for the kernel $K(P, Q)$ certain characteristic advantages of each procedure become obvious. In (4.11) we start with relatively elementary functions and by simple integrations derive the Green's function of (I.1.1), while in (II.7.29) we have to start with a fundamental singularity and at each step perform the rather troublesome E-multiplication. On the other hand, in (II.7.29) we are working with proper integrals and at each step stay within the space of all solutions, while in (4.11) we integrate over infinities of γ and obtain a solution of our differential equation only in the limit. Which method a practical computer should prefer will, therefore, depend on the actual problem in question.

Finally, we shall describe a *series development for Neumann's function* $N(P, Q)$ *in terms of an orthonormal system of functions* $v_\nu(P)$ *which are not necessarily solutions of* (I.1.1). We assume that the $v_\nu(P)$ are a complete set within the class of all functions $f(P)$ which are continuously differentiable in $\mathsf{D}+\mathsf{C}$; i. e., each such function can be approximated in the E-metric arbitrarily by a linear combination of $v_\nu(P)$; in formulas, there exists a set of constants $c_{n\nu}$ such that

$$\mathrm{E}\left\{f(P)-\sum_{\nu=1}^{n} c_{n\nu}\, v_\nu(P)\right\}<\varepsilon \quad \text{for} \quad n>N(\varepsilon). \tag{4.12}$$

The particular function

$$\Phi(P,Q)=N(P,Q)-\Gamma(P,Q), \qquad Q\in \mathsf{D}, \tag{4.13}$$

is of this class, where N is Neumann's function of D with respect to (I.1.1) and $\Gamma(P,Q)$ is Green's function of D for Laplace's equation. In fact, the logarithmic singularities of both functions cancel each other and for fixed $Q\in\mathsf{D}$ the derivatives of Φ are also continuous in $\mathsf{D}+\mathsf{C}$. We may assume without loss of generality that the system $v_\nu(P)$ is orthonormalized in the E-metric, i. e.,

$$\mathrm{E}\{v_\nu, v_\mu\}=\delta_{\nu\mu}. \tag{4.14}$$

We may compute the Fourier coefficients of $\Phi(P,Q)$ with respect to v_ν and, in view of (I.6.1), find

$$c_\nu(Q)=\mathrm{E}\{\Phi(P,Q), v_\nu(P)\}=v_\nu(Q)-\mathrm{E}\{\Gamma(P,Q), v_\nu(P)\}. \tag{4.15}$$

Let us denote

$$-\mathrm{E}\{\Gamma(P,Q), v_\nu(P)\}=h_\nu(P); \tag{4.16}$$

these functions are known and easily computed by means of the v_ν and the known Green's function of Laplace's equation. Thus, Φ has the known Fourier coefficients:

$$c_\nu(Q)=v_\nu(Q)+h_\nu(Q) \tag{4.17}$$

Since the system $\{v_\nu\}$ is complete, we have the following Parseval identity:

$$\mathrm{E}\{\Phi(P,Q), \Phi(P,R)\}=\sum_{\nu=1}^{\infty} c_\nu(Q)\, c_\nu(R)= \tag{4.18}$$

$$=\sum_{\nu=1}^{\infty}[v_\nu(Q)+h_\nu(Q)]\,[v_\nu(R)+h_\nu(R)].$$

But the left-hand side of (4.18) can be easily transformed by means of the definition (4.13) and the identity (I.6.1):

$$\mathrm{E}\{\Phi(P,Q), \Phi(P,R)\}=\Phi(R,Q)-\mathrm{E}\{\Phi(P,Q), \Gamma(P,R)\}. \tag{4.18'}$$

Now, we know from (I.6.7) that we have the identity

$$\mathrm{E}\{N(P,Q), \Gamma(P,R)\} = \Gamma(Q,R) \tag{4.19}$$

even for the singular function Γ. Thus, finally from (4.18), (4.18'), and (4.19):

$$N(Q,R) = 2\Gamma(Q,R) - \mathrm{E}\{\Gamma(P,Q), \Gamma(P,R)\} + \\ + \sum_{\nu=1}^{\infty} [v_\nu(Q) + h_\nu(Q)]\,[v_\nu(R) + h_\nu(R)]. \tag{4.20}$$

We may transform the second right-hand term in order to make it easier to compute:

$$\mathrm{E}\{\Gamma(P,Q), \Gamma(P,R)\} = \Gamma(Q,R) + \iint_{\mathsf{D}} q(P)\,\Gamma(P,Q)\,\Gamma(P,R)\,dx\,dy \tag{4.21}$$

and, hence:

$$N(Q,R) = \Gamma(Q,R) - \iint_{\mathsf{D}} q(P)\,\Gamma(P,Q)\,\Gamma(P,R)\,dx\,dy + \\ + \sum_{\nu=1}^{\infty} \big(v_\nu(Q) + h_\nu(Q)\big)\cdot\big(v_\nu(R) + h_\nu(R)\big). \tag{4.22}$$

This formula permits us to compute the Neumann's function by means of Laplace's Green's function and a complete system of functions $v_\nu(P)$. In this section we have thus shown two methods of constructing fundamental functions without presupposing the knowledge of any solution of (I.1.1).

CHAPTER VI

GENERALIZATIONS

1. Different types of metrics: Thus far, we have considered the linear space Σ of all twice-continuously differentiable solutions of (I.1.1) in $\mathsf{D} + \mathsf{C}$ and introduced a metric based on the Dirichlet product $\mathrm{E}\{u, v\}$. We shall interpret this product in a new way and arrive at the possibility of introducing analogous but different metrics into the linear space Σ.

To each function $u \in \Sigma$ belong two associated functions defined on the boundary C of D which determine u in a unique way; namely, the boundary values $u(P)$ on C and the values of its normal derivative $\frac{\partial u}{\partial \nu}$ on C. We may interpret the scalar product in the Dirichlet metric

$$\text{(1.1)} \qquad E\{u, v\} = -\int_C u \frac{\partial v}{\partial \nu} ds = -\int_C v \frac{\partial u}{\partial \nu} ds$$

as the product of these associated functions along C. One may then generalize this type of scalar multiplication as follows:

Let $u(P)$ and $v(P)$ be two arbitrary elements of Σ; we *define the three following types of scalar products* between them:

$$\text{(1.2)} \qquad (u, v) = \int_C u(P) v(P) ds,$$

$$E\{u, v\} = -\int_C u \frac{\partial v}{\partial \nu} ds = -\int_C v \frac{\partial u}{\partial \nu} ds,$$

$$[u, v] = \int_C \frac{\partial u}{\partial \nu} \frac{\partial v}{\partial \nu} ds.$$

While $E\{u, v\}$ leads to a positive-definite metric only in the case that the coefficient $q(P)$ in (I.1.1) is positive in D + C, it is obvious that (u, u) and $[u, u]$ will always be positive, even if the assumption $q > 0$ is dropped. The two new metrics have, therefore, the advantage over the Dirichlet metric of being more easily generalized to the case of various differential equations of elliptic type.

It is now of great interest to remark that the fundamental solutions of (I.1.1) lead immediately to reproducing kernels in Σ with respect to each of these new metrics. Let us define the kernels

$$\text{(1.3)} \qquad F(P,Q) = [G(R,P), G(R,Q)] = \int_C \frac{\partial G(R,P)}{\partial \nu_R} \frac{\partial G(R,Q)}{\partial \nu_R} ds_R,$$

$$M(P,Q) = (N(R,P), N(R,Q)) = \int_C N(R,P) N(R,Q) ds_R,$$

while observing that in view of (II.1.4) and (II.1.5) the K-kernel satisfies:

$$\text{(1.4)} \qquad K(P,Q) = \int_C N(R,P) \frac{\partial G(R,Q)}{\partial \nu_R} ds_R.$$

We can readily verify that for every solution $u \in \Sigma$ we have

$$(F(P,Q), u(Q)) = u(P), \quad [M(P,Q), u(Q)] = u(P). \tag{1.5}$$

This stands in complete analogy to the reproducing property of the K-kernel

$$\mathrm{E}\{K(P,Q), u(Q)\} = u(P). \tag{1.6}$$

In fact, the function $F(P, Q)$ has, for fixed $P \in \mathsf{D}$, the boundary values $\dfrac{\partial G(P,Q)}{\partial \nu_Q}$ for $Q \in \mathsf{C}$. Hence, the scalar product between F and u in (1.5) can be written in the form

$$(F(P,Q), u(Q)) = \int_{\mathsf{C}} \frac{\partial G(P,Q)}{\partial \nu_Q} u(Q)\, ds_Q = u(P) \tag{1.7}$$

which proves the first identity in (1.5).

Similarly, we have for fixed $P \in \mathsf{D}$

$$\frac{\partial M(P,Q)}{\partial \nu_Q} = -N(P,Q) \quad \text{for} \quad Q \in \mathsf{C}. \tag{1.8}$$

Hence, for any $u(P) \in \Sigma$

$$[M(P,Q), u(Q)] = -\int_{\mathsf{C}} N(P,Q) \frac{\partial u(Q)}{\partial \nu_Q} ds_Q = u(P) \tag{1.9}$$

which proves the second identity in (1.5).

The kernels F and M are symmetric functions of their two argument points. For fixed $Q \in \mathsf{D}$ each of these kernels is an element of Σ with respect to P. The kernels do not belong to Σ as functions of P, however, if the second argument point Q lies on the boundary C of D.

We may construct each kernel in terms of a complete set of functions $u_\nu \in \Sigma$ which are orthonormalized with respect to the corresponding metric. It is very remarkable that there exists one complete set of functions in Σ which is orthogonal with respect to all three metrics defined in (1.2) and which permits, therefore, an elegant representation for all three reproducing kernels. These functions were first introduced by Stekloff in the case of Laplace's equation and are defined in general as follows: They are elements of Σ and on C satisfy the boundary conditions

$$\frac{\partial \chi_\rho}{\partial \nu} = -\varkappa_\rho \chi_\rho. \tag{1.10}$$

There exists a denumerable set of Stekloff functions χ_ρ with corresponding eigenvalues $\varkappa_\rho$ which is complete in Σ. The functions $\chi_\rho(P)$ are defined by the boundary conditions (1.10) only up to a multiplicative constant and this may be disposed of by the requirement

$$(\chi_\rho, \chi_\rho) = \int_C \chi_\rho^2 \, ds = 1. \tag{1.11}$$

The existence of the set of Stekloff functions can again be proved by means of the theory of integral equations. In fact, consider the homogeneous integral equation

$$0 = \vartheta_\rho(P) - \varkappa_\rho \int_C N(P,Q)\, \vartheta_\rho(Q)\, ds_Q, \qquad P, Q \in C. \tag{1.12}$$

In spite of the fact that the kernel $N(P,Q)$ of this equation becomes logarithmically infinite for $P = Q$, the general theory of integral equations with symmetric kernel still remains applicable and we can assert the existence of a set of eigenvalues $\varkappa_\rho$ and eigenfunctions $\vartheta_\rho(P)$. We put

$$\chi_\rho(P) = -\int_C N(P,Q)\, \vartheta_\rho(Q)\, ds_Q, \qquad P \in D, \tag{1.13}$$

and thus obtain a sequence of elements of Σ with the values of the normal derivative on C:

$$\frac{\partial \chi_\rho}{\partial \nu} = \vartheta_\rho(Q). \tag{1.14}$$

In view of (1.12), (1.13), and (1.14), we conclude

$$\frac{\partial \chi_\rho}{\partial \nu} = -\varkappa_\rho \chi_\rho \tag{1.15}$$

which is just the boundary condition (1.10).

Multiplying (1.12) by $\vartheta_\sigma(P)$ and integrating over C, we obtain

$$0 = \int_C \vartheta_\rho \vartheta_\sigma \, ds - \varkappa_\rho \int_C \int_C N(P,Q)\, \vartheta_\sigma(P)\, \vartheta_\rho(Q)\, ds_P\, ds_Q \tag{1.16}$$

and interchanging ρ and σ:

$$0 = \int_C \vartheta_\rho \vartheta_\sigma \, ds - \varkappa_\sigma \int_C \int_C N(P,Q)\, \vartheta_\rho(P)\, \vartheta_\sigma(Q)\, ds_P\, ds_Q. \tag{1.16'}$$

This proves two facts: a) In view of the non-negative character of $N(P, Q)$, we have

$$\varkappa_\rho > 0 \tag{1.17}$$

and b) from (1.16) and (1.16′) we conclude

$$\int_{\mathsf{C}} \vartheta_\rho \vartheta_\sigma \, ds = 0 \qquad \text{for} \qquad \varkappa_\rho \neq \varkappa_\sigma. \tag{1.18}$$

In view of (1.14) and (1.15) we see that we can choose the functions $\chi_\rho(P)$ in such a way that they satisfy the conditions

$$(\chi_\rho, \chi_\sigma) = \frac{1}{\varkappa_\rho{}^2}[\chi_\rho, \chi_\sigma] = \frac{1}{\varkappa_\rho} \mathrm{E}\{\chi_\rho, \chi_\sigma\} = \delta_{\rho\sigma}. \tag{1.19}$$

Thus, we have obtained *a set of functions* $\chi_\rho(P) \in \Sigma$ *which are orthogonal in all three metrics considered.*

Let us show next that the functions $\chi_\rho(P)$ are complete in the linear space Σ. For this purpose, consider the function $M(P, Q)$ defined in (1.3); it may be understood as the iterated kernel of the integral equation (1.12) and is continuous for P and Q on C. Hence, we have the integral equation with symmetric continuous kernel

$$0 = \vartheta_\rho(P) - \varkappa_\rho{}^2 \int_{\mathsf{C}} M(P, Q)\, \vartheta_\rho(Q)\, ds_Q, \qquad P, Q \in \mathsf{C}. \tag{1.12′}$$

In view of (1.14) and (1.19), we have

$$\int_{\mathsf{C}} \vartheta_\rho{}^2 \, ds = \varkappa_\rho{}^2 \tag{1.20}$$

and according to the general theory of integral equations, we may develop $M(P, Q)$ as follows:

$$M(P, Q) = \sum_{\rho=1}^{\infty} \frac{1}{\varkappa_\rho{}^4} \vartheta_\rho(P)\, \vartheta_\rho(Q) = \sum_{\rho=1}^{\infty} \frac{1}{\varkappa_\rho{}^2} \chi_\rho(P)\, \chi_\rho(Q), \tag{1.21}$$

where both sums converge uniformly on C. By Green's formula (I.5.13) we have

$$\begin{aligned} M(P, Q) &= \int_{\mathsf{C}} \int_{\mathsf{C}} M(S, T) \frac{\partial G(S, P)}{\partial \nu_S} \frac{\partial G(T, Q)}{\partial \nu_T} \, ds_S \, ds_T \\ &= \sum_{\rho=1}^{\infty} \frac{1}{\varkappa_\rho{}^2} \chi_\rho(P)\, \chi_\rho(Q) \qquad \text{for} \qquad P, Q \in \mathsf{D}. \end{aligned} \tag{1.22}$$

Thus, we have succeeded in extending the identity (1.21), valid only for points in the boundary C of D, to all values of the two argument points P and Q in D.

Now let $u(P)$ be an arbitrary function of the class Σ. By virtue of the second identity (1.5), we have

$$u(P) = [M(P,Q), u(Q)] = \sum_{\rho=1}^{\infty} \frac{1}{\varkappa_\rho^2} \chi_\rho(P) [\chi_\rho, u]. \tag{1.23}$$

This shows that every element $u \in \Sigma$ can be developed in a Fourier series with respect to the χ_ρ. This proves the completeness of set χ_ρ.

Using the reproducing properties of the kernels in their corresponding metric and the norm conditions (1.19), we obtain the following series development:

$$F(P,Q) = \sum_{\rho=1}^{\infty} \chi_\rho(P) \chi_\rho(Q), \qquad K(P,Q) = \sum_{\rho=1}^{\infty} \frac{1}{\varkappa_\rho} \chi_\rho(P) \chi_\rho(Q), \tag{1.24}$$

$$M(P,Q) = \sum_{\rho=1}^{\infty} \frac{1}{\varkappa_\rho^2} \chi_\rho(P) \chi_\rho(Q).$$

We derive from (1.24) by Schwarz' inequality the estimate

$$(K(P,Q))^2 \leqslant \text{Min}\,\{F(P,P)\, M(Q,Q), F(Q,Q)\, M(P,P)\}. \tag{1.25}$$

The knowledge of the two kernel functions F and M thus permits an estimate for the third kernel K. This result is closely related to the following inequality which is obtained from the definitions (1.2) by means of the Schwarz inequality:

$$(\mathrm{E}\,\{u, v\})^2 \leqslant \text{Min}\,\{(u,u)\,[v,v], [u,u]\,(v,v)\}. \tag{1.26}$$

The Stekloff functions $\chi_\rho(P)$ also yield an elegant representation of the Robin's functions $R_\lambda(P,Q)$, defined in Section I.5, if the coefficient λ is constant on C. For this purpose we introduce the function

$$K_\lambda(P,Q) = R_\lambda(P,Q) - G(P,Q) \tag{1.27}$$

which is symmetric and of the class Σ in each argument. We can easily compute the Fourier coefficients of K_λ with respect to the χ_ρ. By definition, we have

$$(K_\lambda(P,Q), \chi_\rho(Q)) = \int_{\mathrm{C}} R_\lambda(P,Q)\, \chi_\rho(Q)\, ds_Q = -\frac{1}{\varkappa_\rho} \int_{\mathrm{C}} R_\lambda(P,Q) \frac{\partial \chi_\rho}{\partial \nu_Q}\, ds_Q. \tag{1.28}$$

On the other hand, we have in view of (I.5.19)

$$\chi_\rho(P) = -\int_C R_\lambda(P,Q)\left(\frac{\partial \chi_\rho(Q)}{\partial \nu_Q} - \lambda\, \chi_\rho(Q)\right) ds_Q = \tag{1.29}$$

$$= (\varkappa_\rho + \lambda)\big(K_\lambda(P,Q), \chi_\rho(Q)\big).$$

Thus, finally

$$\big(K_\lambda(P,Q), \chi_\rho(Q)\big) = \frac{1}{\varkappa_\rho + \lambda}\, \chi_\rho(P). \tag{1.30}$$

This leads to the Fourier development

$$K_\lambda(P,Q) = R_\lambda(P,Q) - G(P,Q) = \sum_{\rho=1}^{\infty} \frac{1}{\varkappa_\rho + \lambda}\, \chi_\rho(P)\, \chi_\rho(Q). \tag{1.31}$$

We confirm at first that in the limit as $\lambda \to 0$ the above identity gives the representation (1.24) for the kernel $K(P,Q)$ as is to be expected from the relation $\lim_{\lambda \to 0} R_\lambda(P,Q) = N(P,Q)$. We can express all three preceding kernels as limits of the kernel $K_\lambda(P,Q)$; namely

$$F(P,Q) = \lim_{\lambda\to\infty} \lambda\, K_\lambda(P,Q), \qquad K(P,Q) = \lim_{\lambda\to 0} K_\lambda(P,Q) \tag{1.32}$$

$$M(P,Q) = -\lim_{\lambda\to 0} \frac{dK_\lambda(P,Q)}{d\lambda} = -\lim_{\lambda\to 0} \frac{dR_\lambda(P,Q)}{d\lambda}.$$

From (1.31) we derive the interesting identity

$$\big(K_\lambda(T,P), K_\mu(T,Q)\big) = \int_C R_\lambda(T,P)\, R_\mu(T,Q)\, ds_T = \tag{1.33}$$

$$= \sum_{\rho=1}^{\infty} \frac{1}{(\varkappa_\rho + \lambda)(\varkappa_\rho + \mu)}\, \chi_\rho(P)\, \chi_\rho(Q),$$

i. e.,

$$-\int_C R_\lambda(T,P)\, R_\mu(T,Q)\, ds_T = \frac{1}{\lambda - \mu}\{R_\lambda(P,Q) - R_\mu(P,Q)\}. \tag{1.33'}$$

Let us define the kernel

$$V_{\lambda,\mu}(P,Q) = -\frac{R_\lambda(P,Q) - R_\mu(P,Q)}{\lambda - \mu} = \sum_{\rho=1}^{\infty} \frac{\chi_\rho(P)\, \chi_\rho(Q)}{(\varkappa_\rho + \lambda)(\varkappa_\rho + \mu)}. \tag{1.34}$$

For every Stekloff function $\chi_\rho(Q)$ we have

$$\begin{aligned}(1.35)\qquad & [V_{\lambda,\mu}(P,Q),\chi_\rho(Q)]+\\ &+(\lambda+\mu)\,\mathrm{E}\,\{V_{\lambda,\mu}(P,Q),\chi_\rho(Q)\}+\lambda\mu\big(V_{\lambda,\mu}(P,Q),\chi_\rho(Q)\big)=\chi_\rho(P).\end{aligned}$$

Since the $\{\chi_\rho(P)\}$ form a complete basis in the space Σ, we can conclude that the kernel $V_{\lambda,\mu}(P,Q)$ reproduces for the metric based on the scalar product

$$u\times v=[u,v]+(\lambda+\mu)\,\mathrm{E}\,\{u,v\}+\lambda\mu\,(u,v). \tag{1.36}$$

In particular, the derivatives of the Robin's functions with respect to the parameter λ

$$V_{\lambda\lambda}(P,Q)=-\frac{\partial R_\lambda(P,Q)}{\partial\lambda} \tag{1.37}$$

will be reproducing kernels with respect to the metric

$$[u,v]+2\lambda\,\mathrm{E}\,\{u,v\}+\lambda^2(u,v). \tag{1.37'}$$

Obviously, $M(P,Q)=V_{00}(P,Q)$ appears as a special case in this result.

The considerations of this section show how many metrics can be used for the study and the construction of fundamental solutions. It should be pointed out, however, that some of these metrics play a distinguished role in the theory. The Dirichlet metric which was used throughout most of our exposition has the advantage of permitting us to express all metric integrals as integrals over the domain D and to stay away from the boundary C of the domain. This fact enables us to perform operations of closure in Σ with great ease and to apply the theory of Hilbert space without difficulty. It is probably the most convenient metric in the case of the differential equation (I.1.1) with $q(P)>0$. It becomes inapplicable if the definite character of $q(P)$ is not assumed, while the metrics based on (u,v) and $[u,v]$ remain definite. Thus, these two metrics are useful for a generalization of the theory of orthogonal solutions to the most general case of an elliptic differential equation of second order in two variables.

Bergman [6], Hilbert [22], Ch. 9, Schiffer (S 5), Stekloff (S 12), Szegö (S 13),

2. Further generalizations: The preceding formal considerations may be generalized in various ways. There is no necessity for restricting the reasoning to differential equations in two independent variables or to the standard form (I.1.1). One can also treat the case of Laplace's equation and obtain a theory of conformal mapping in two independent variables and a powerful method for potential theory in space. The theory of conformal mapping can be made particularly simple by use of complex variables and consideration of kernels within the space of analytic functions. In fact, this type of kernel was the first to be studied systematically and to be used for practical problems. The consideration of kernels within the class of harmonic functions, however, made all results of the original theory more significant and permitted the extension to the theory of partial differential equations in the generality treated there.

There is also an easy extension of the methods presented in this book to all types of equations which may be considered as variational equations for extremum problems with positive-definite quadratic functionals of a function $\varphi(x, y)$. It is clear that all such equations are necessarily linear in the unknown function, but may be integral or integro-differential equations as well as differential equations. The assumption on the linearity of the problem, however, is very essential in the kernel theory which is specifically adapted to this case. Nevertheless, the kernel method may also be of use in non-linear cases, if one attacks such problems by successive approximations in which each step is reduced to a linear problem. In this case, a short and easy method for solving the auxiliary linear questions may be of decisive importance, and here kernel methods may prove powerful.

LIST OF SYMBOLS AND NOTATIONS USED IN PART B

$$\mathrm{E}\{u\} = \iint_{\mathsf{D}} [u_x^2 + u_y^2 + q\,u^2]\, dx\, dy \tag{I.2.1}$$

$$\mathrm{E}\{u, v\} = \iint_{\mathsf{D}} [u_x v_x + u_y v_y + q\,u\,v]\, dx\, dy \tag{I.2.2}$$

Ω: linear space of twice continuously differentiable functions in $\mathsf{D} + \mathsf{C}$

Σ: linear subspace of solutions of (I.1.1)

Ω_0: linear subspace of functions which vanish on the boundary

$\Gamma(P, Q)$: Green's function of the domain D with respect to the Laplace equation

$H(P, Q)$: Neumann's function of the domain D with respect to the Laplace equation

$$\gamma(P, Q) = \Gamma(P, Q) - \frac{1}{2\pi} \log \frac{1}{r(P, Q)} \tag{I.4.4}$$

$$\eta(P, Q) = H(P, Q) - \frac{1}{2\pi} \log \frac{1}{r(P, Q)} \tag{I.4.4}$$

$S(P, Q)$: fundamental singularity of equation (I.1.1)

$$s(P, Q) = S(P, Q) - \frac{1}{2\pi} \log \frac{1}{r(P, Q)} \tag{I.5.2}$$

$G(P, Q)$: Green's function of the domain D with respect to (I.1.1)

$N(P, Q)$: Neumann's function of the domain D with respect to (I.1.1)

$$g(P, Q) = G(P, Q) - S(P, Q) \tag{I.5.11}$$

$$n(P, Q) = N(P, Q) - S(P, Q) \tag{I.5.14}$$

$R_\lambda(P, Q)$: Robin's function for (I.1.1)

$$r_\lambda(P, Q) = -S(P, Q) + R_\lambda(P, Q) \tag{I.5.17}$$

$$\mathrm{E}_\lambda\{u, v\} = \mathrm{E}\{u, v\} + \int_{\mathsf{C}} \lambda(s)\, u\, v\, ds \tag{I.6.4}$$

Ω_λ linear space under metric E_λ

$K(P,Q) = N(P,Q) - G(P,Q) = n(P,Q) - g(P,Q)$, kernel function (II.1.2), (II.1.3)

$K_\lambda(P,Q) = R_\lambda(P,Q) - G(P,Q)$ (II.1.22)

$$I(P,Q) = \int_C S(T,Q) \frac{\partial S(T,P)}{\partial \nu_T} ds_T \qquad \text{(II.4.4)}$$

$l(P,Q) = n(P,Q) + g(P,Q)$ (II.5.8)

$\lambda(P,Q) = \gamma(P,Q) + \eta(P,Q)$ (II.6.3)

$$K(Q,T) = \frac{\partial (K(T,Q) - 4I(T,Q))}{\partial \nu_T} \qquad \text{(II.7.3)}$$

$$u_1(T) = \mathrm{E}\{N_1(Q,T), u(Q)\} = -\int_C \frac{\partial N_1(Q,T)}{\partial \nu_Q} u(Q)\, ds_Q \qquad \text{(II.7.10)}$$

$M^{(n)}(P,Q) = \mathrm{E}\{M(T,P), M^{(n-1)}(T,Q)\}$,

$M^{(1)}(P,Q) = M(P,Q) = K(P,Q) - 4I(P,Q)$ (II.7.24)

$\mathbf{K}^{(-1)}(Q,T) = \mathbf{K}(Q,T) - \mathbf{K}^{(2)}(Q,T) + \mathbf{K}^{(3)}(Q,T)\ldots$ (II.7.27)

$i^{(\nu)}(P,Q) = \mathrm{E}\{i^{(\nu-1)}(P,T), i^{(1)}(T,Q)\}, \qquad i^{(1)}(P,Q) = 4I(P,Q)$ (II.7.31)

$T_u(P) = \mathrm{E}\{l(R,P), u(R)\}$ (II.8.2)

λ_ν, $u_\nu(P)$: eigenvalues and eigenfunctions of equation

$$u_\nu(P) = \lambda_\nu T_{u_\nu}(P) \qquad \text{(II.8.5)}$$

$\omega_\nu(Q) = M^{(2\nu)}(Q,Q)/M^{(2\nu-2)}(Q,Q)$ (II.8.9)

$$M^{(-1)}(P,Q);\lambda) = \sum_{\nu=1}^{\infty} \lambda^\nu M^{(\nu)}(P,Q) \qquad \text{(II.8.12)}$$

$$\mathbf{K}^{(-1)}(Q,R;\lambda) = \frac{\partial M^{(-1)}(R,Q;\lambda)}{\partial \nu_R}, \qquad R \in \mathsf{C} \qquad \text{(II.8.13)}$$

$M_1(P,Q) = M(P,Q) - u_1(P)\, u_1(Q)/\lambda_1^2$ (II.8.20)

$$L_n(P,Q) = l(P,Q) - \sum_{\nu=1}^{n} \frac{u_\nu(P)\, u_\nu(Q)}{\lambda_\nu} \qquad \text{(II.8.29)}$$

$$\mathbf{\Delta}(P,Q) = M(P,Q) - \sum_{\nu=1}^{\infty} \frac{u_\nu(P)\, u_\nu(Q)}{\lambda_\nu^2} \qquad \text{(II.8.32)}$$

$\Sigma^\blacktriangle$ Hilbert space, the completion of Σ

$$\mathfrak{M}(P,Q) = \sum_{\rho=0}^{\infty} M^{(\rho)}(P,Q) = \sum_{\nu=1}^{\infty} \left(1 - \frac{1}{\lambda_\nu^2}\right)^{-1} u_\nu(P)\, u_\nu(Q) \qquad \text{(II.9.3)}$$

$$K_n(P,Q) = \sum_{\rho=0}^{n} \mathrm{E}\{4I(R,Q), M^{(\rho)}(R,P)\} = \sum_{\nu=1}^{\infty}\left(1-\frac{1}{\lambda_\nu^{2n+2}}\right) u_\nu(P)\, u_\nu(Q)$$ (II.9.8), (II.9.9)

$$\mathfrak{K}(P,Q) = 2\,\frac{\partial S(P,Q)}{\partial \nu_Q}, \qquad P,Q \in \mathsf{C}$$ (II.9.29)

$$\varphi_\rho(P) = u_\rho(P), \quad \psi_\rho(P) = \frac{\partial u_\rho(P)}{\partial \nu}$$ (II.9.30), (II.9.31)

$$K_1(P,Q) = N_1(P,Q) - G_1(P,Q), \qquad L_1(P,Q) = N_1(P,Q) + G_1(P,Q)$$ (III.1.1), (III.1.2)

$\mathrm{E}_i\{u, v\}$: the subscript i indicates that the integration is carried out over the domain D_i

$\mathrm{E}_\Delta\{u, v\}$, $\mathrm{E}_{\mathsf{D}-\Delta}\{u, v\}$, etc., indicate that the integration is carried out over $\mathbf{\Delta}$, $\mathsf{D}-\mathbf{\Delta}$, etc.

D_1 is a domain including D

$$\mathsf{D}_0 = \mathsf{D}_1 - \overline{\mathsf{D}}$$ (III.1.6)

Σ_i: the set of all solutions of (I.1.1) which are twice differentiable in $\mathsf{D}_i + \mathsf{C}_i$

Σ^*: the set of functions of class Σ in D and of class Σ_0 in D_0.

$$B(P,Q) = \mathrm{E}_0\{L_1(R,P), L_1(R,Q)\}$$ (III.1.11)

$$T_u(P) = \mathrm{E}\{l(P,Q), u(Q)\}, \; S_u(P) = \mathrm{E}\{K_1(P,Q), u(Q)\}, \; u \in \Sigma$$ (III.1.14)

$$T_u(P) = u(P) - \mathrm{E}_1\{L_1(P,Q), u(Q)\}, \qquad u \in \Sigma^*$$ (III.1.26)

$$S_u(P) = \mathrm{E}_1\{K_1(P,Q), u(Q)\}, \qquad u \in \Sigma^*$$ (III.1.27)

$$l(P,Q) = \begin{cases} L(P,Q) - L_1(P,Q) & \text{for } P \in \mathsf{D},\; Q \in \mathsf{D} \\ -L_1(P,Q) & \text{for } P \in \mathsf{D},\; Q \in \mathsf{D}_0 \text{ or } P \in \mathsf{D}_0,\; Q \in \mathsf{D} \\ L_0(P,Q) - L_1(P,Q) & \text{for } P \in \mathsf{D}_0,\; Q \in \mathsf{D}_0 \end{cases}$$ (III.1.28)

$$k(P,Q) = \begin{cases} K(P,Q) - K_1(P,Q) & \text{for } P \in \mathsf{D},\; Q \in \mathsf{D} \\ -K_1(P,Q) & \text{for } P \in \mathsf{D},\; Q \in \mathsf{D}_0 \text{ or } P \in \mathsf{D}_0,\; Q \in \mathsf{D} \\ K_0(P,Q) - K_1(P,Q) & \text{for } P \in \mathsf{D}_0,\; Q \in \mathsf{D}_0 \end{cases}$$ (III.1.30)

$$\gamma_\mu^+ = T_u + S_u \quad \text{and} \quad \gamma_\mu^- = S_u - T_u$$ (III.1.38)

$[f]$ denotes the saltus of f across C

$$\mathrm{E}_{\mu,\lambda}\{u, v\} = \mathrm{E}_1\{u, v\} + \int_{\mathsf{C}_1} \lambda(s)\, u\, v\, ds + \int_{\mathsf{C}} \mu(s)\, [u\, v]\, ds,$$

$$\lambda(s) > 0, \quad \mu(s) > 0, \quad u, v \in \Sigma^*$$ (III.1.52)

$\mathfrak{R}_\lambda$: Robin's function for the class Σ_1

$$\mathfrak{T}_u(P) = u(P) + 2 \int_{\mathsf{C}} \left(\mu(s)\, \mathfrak{R}_\lambda(P,Q) - \frac{\partial \mathfrak{R}_\lambda(P,Q)}{\partial \nu_Q} \right) [u(Q)]\, ds_Q \qquad \text{(III.1.53)}$$

d_ν, $\varkappa_\nu$: eigenfunctions and eigenvalues of (III.3.1)

$$K_N(P,Q) = \sum_{\nu=1}^{N} u_\nu(P)\, u_\nu(Q) \qquad \text{(III.4.1)}$$

$$F_N(P,Q) = K(P,Q) - K_N(P,Q) \qquad \text{(III.4.2)}$$

$$g(P,Q) = \begin{cases} G(P,Q) - G_1(P,Q) & \text{for } P, Q \in \mathsf{D} \\ -G_1(P,Q) & \text{for } P \in \mathsf{D},\ Q \in \mathsf{D}_0 \text{ or } P \in \mathsf{D}_0,\ Q \in \mathsf{D} \\ G_0(P,Q) - G_1(P,Q) & \text{for } P, Q \in \mathsf{D}_0 \end{cases} \qquad \text{(III.5.3)}$$

$$n(P,Q) = \begin{cases} N(P,Q) - N_1(P,Q) & \text{for } P, Q \in \mathsf{D} \\ -N_1(P,Q) & \text{for } P \in \mathsf{D},\ Q \in \mathsf{D}_0 \text{ or } P \in \mathsf{D}_0,\ Q \in \mathsf{D} \\ N_0(P,Q) - N_1(P,Q) & \text{for } P, Q \in \mathsf{D}_0 \end{cases} \qquad \text{(III.5.7)}$$

$$\mathfrak{G}(P,Q) = \frac{\partial^2 G(P,Q)}{\partial \nu_P\, \partial \nu_Q}$$

$$\left.\begin{aligned} (u, v) &= \int_{\mathsf{C}} u(P)\, v(P)\, ds, \\ \mathrm{E}\{u, v\} &= -\int_{\mathsf{C}} u \frac{\partial v}{\partial \nu}\, ds = -\int_{\mathsf{C}} v \frac{\partial u}{\partial \nu}\, ds, \\ [u, v] &= \int_{\mathsf{C}} \frac{\partial u}{\partial \nu} \frac{\partial v}{\partial \nu}\, ds \end{aligned}\right\} \qquad \text{(VI.1.2)}$$

χ_ρ: the Stekloff functions which satisfy (VI.1.10)

BIBLIOGRAPHY

Books

[1] P. Appell, Traité de mécanique rationelle, vol. 3, Paris, 1928.

[2] H. Bateman, Partial differential Equations of Mathematical Physics, New York, 1944.

[3] S. Bergman, Partial Differential Equations, Advanced Topics, Brown University, Providence, R. I., 1941.

[4] —, Sur les fonctions orthogonales de plusieurs variables complexes avec les applications à la théorie des fonctions analytiques, Mémorial des Sciences Mathématiques, vol. 106, 1947.

[5] —, Sur la fonction-noyau d'un domaine et ses applications dans la théorie des transformations pseudo-conformes, Mémorial des Sciences Mathématiques, vol. 108, 1948.

[6] —, The Kernel Function and Conformal Mapping, Mathematical Surveys No. 5, New York, 1950.

[7] L. Bieberbach, Theorie der Differentialgleichungen, Berlin, 1930.

[8] —, Lehrbuch der Funktionentheorie, vols. 1 and 2, Leipzig and Berlin, 1921—1927, New York, 1945.

[9] O. Bolza, Vorlesungen über Variationsrechnung, Leipzig and Berlin, 1909.

[10] U. Cisotti, Idromeccanica piana, vols. 1 and 2, Milan, 1921.

[11] L. Collatz, Eigenwertprobleme und ihre numerische Behandlung, New York, 1948.

[12] R. Courant, Dirichlet's Principle, Conformal Mapping, and Minimal Surfaces, New York, 1950.

[13] R. Courant and D. Hilbert, Methoden der mathematischen Physik, vol. 1, 2nd revised edition, Berlin, 1931, vol. 2, Berlin, 1937.

[14] P. Frank and R. v. Mises, Die Differential- und Integralgleichungen der Mechanik und Physik, vols. 1 and 2, New York, 1943.

[15] M. Fréchet, Les espaces abstraites, Paris, 1928.

[16] E. Goursat, Cours d'analyse mathématique, vol. 3, Paris, 1927.

[17] N. M. Gunther, La théorie du potentiel et ses applications aux problèmes fondamentaux de la physique mathématique, Paris, 1934.

[18] J. Hadamard, Leçons sur le calcul des variations, Paris, 1910.

[19] —, Lectures on Cauchy's Problem, New Haven, 1923.

[20] G. Hamel, Integralgleichungen, Berlin, 1937.

[21] E. Hellinger and O. Toeplitz, Integralgleichungen und Gleichungen mit unendlich vielen Unbekannten, *Enzyklopädie der mathematischen Wissenschaften*, vol. II, 3, II.

[22] D. Hilbert, Grundzüge einer allgemeinen Theorie der linearen Integralgleichungen Leipzig and Berlin, 1912.

[23] A. Hurwitz and R. Courant, Vorlesungen über allgemeine Funktionentheorie und elliptische Funktionen, vols. 1 and 2, revised and enlarged edition, Berlin, 1925.

[24] J. H. Jeans, The Mathematical Theory of Electricity and Magnetism, Cambridge, 1908.

[25] H. and B. S. Jeffreys, Methods of Mathematical Physics, Cambridge, 1946.

[26] G. Julia, Introduction mathématique aux théories quantiques, vols. 1 and 2, Paris, 1936—1938.

[27] S. Kaczmarz and H. Steinhaus, Theorie der Orthogonalreihen, Warsaw and Lwów, 1935.

[28] L. V. Kantorovitch and V. I. Kriloff, Approximation Methods in Higher Analysis, Moscow and Leningrad, 1950. (In Russian.)

[29] T. Kármán and M. A. Biot, Mathematical Methods in Engineering, New York, 1940.

[30] O. D. Kellogg, Foundations of Potential Theory, New York, 1929.

[31] G. Kirchhoff, Vorlesungen über mathematische Physik, vol. 1 (Mechanik), Leipzig, 1883.

[32] A. Kneser, Die Integralgleichungen, Braunschweig, 1911.

[33] N. E. Kochin, I. A. Kibel, N. B. Rose, Theoretical Hydrodynamics, Moscow, 1948. (In Russian.)

[34] G. Kowalewski, Integralgleichungen, Berlin and Leipzig, 1930.

[35] H. Lamb, Hydrodynamics, 5th edition, Cambridge, 1924.

[36] —, Hydrodynamics, New York, 1945.

[37] M. A. Lavrentieff and B. V. Shabat, Methods in the Theory of Functions of a Complex Variable, Moscow and Leningrad, 1951. (In Russian.)

[38] P. Lévy, Leçons d'analyse fonctionelle, Paris, 1922.

[39] A. Lichnerowicz, Algèbre et analyse linéaires, Paris, 1947.

[40] L. Lichtenstein, Grundlagen der Hydromechanik, Berlin, 1929.

[41] —, Neuere Entwicklungen der Theorie partieller Differentialgleichungen zweiter Ordnung vom elliptischen Typus, *Enzyklopädie der mathematischen Wissenschaften*, vol. II, 3, II.

[42] —, Neuere Entwicklung der Potentialtheorie, *Enzyklopädie der mathematischen Wissenschaften*, vol. II, 3, I.

[43] A. E. H. Love, A Treatise on the Mathematical theory of Elasticity, Cambridge, 1944.

[44] W. V. Lovitt, Linear Integral Equations, New York, 1924.

[45] H. Margenau and G. M. Murphy, The Mathematics of Physics and Chemistry, New York, 1948.

[46] J. C. Maxwell, A Treatise on Electricity and Magnetism, Oxford, 1881.

[47] S. Mikhlin, Integral Equations and Their Application to Problems in Mechanics, Moscow, 1949. (In Russian.)

[48] L. M. Milne-Thomson, Theoretical Hydrodynamics, London, 1938.

[49] —, Theoretical Aerodynamics, New York, 1947.

[50] R. v. Mises, Notes on Mathematical Theory of Compressible Fluid Flow, 2d edition, Cambridge, 1949.

[51] R. v. Mises and K. O. Friedrichs, Fluid Dynamics (mimeographed notes), Brown University, Providence, R. I., 1941.

[52] H. Müntz, Integral Equations, Leningrad, 1934. (In Russian.)

[53] F. D. Murnaghan, Introduction to Applied Mathematics, New York, 1948.

[54] N. I. Muskhelishvili, Some Fundamental Problems of the Mathematical Theory of Elasticity, Moscow, 1949. (In Russian.)

[55] A. Nádai, Die elastischen Platten, Berlin, 1925.

[56] J. v. Neumann, Mathematische Grundlagen der Quantenmechanik, Berlin, 1932.

[57] F. Ollendorff, Potentialfelder der Elektrotechnik, Berlin, 1932.

[58] J. Pérès, Cours de mécanique des fluides, Paris, 1936.

[59] I. G. Petrovsky, Lectures on the Theory of Partial Differential Equations, Moscow, 1949. (In Russian.)

[60] E. Picard, Traité d'analyse, vol. 2, Paris, 1922—1928.

[61] M. Planck, The Mechanics of Deformable Bodies, London, 1932.

[62] J. Plemelj, Potentialtheoretische Untersuchungen, Leipzig, 1911.

[63] H. Poincaré, Théorie du potential newtonien, Paris, 1899.

[64] G. Pólya and G. Szegö, Aufgaben und Lehrsätze aus der Analysis, vols. 1 and 2, Berlin, 1925.

[64 a] G. Pólya and G. Szegö, Isoperimetric Inequalities in Mathematical Physics, Annals of Mathematics Studies, No. 27, Princeton University Press, 1951,

[65] J. W. S. Rayleigh Baron, The Theory of Sound, New York, 1945.

[66] B. Riemann and H. Weber, Die partiellen Differentialgleichungen der mathematischen Physik, vols. 1 and 2, Braunschweig, 1900.

[67] R. Sauer, Theoretische Einführung in die Gasdynamik, Berlin, 1943.

[68] M. Schiffer and D. Spencer, Functionals on Finite Riemann Surfaces, Princeton, 1953.

[69] V. I. Smirnoff, Course of Higher Mathematics, Moscow, 1941. (In Russian.)

[70] I. S. Sokolnikoff, Mathematical Theory of Elasticity, New York, 1946.

[71] A. Sommerfeld, Partial Differential Equations in Physics, New York, 1949.

[72] —, Mechanics of Deformable Bodies, New York, 1950.

[73] —, Randwertaufgaben in der Theorie der partiellen Differentialgleichungen, *Enzyklopädie der mathematischen Wissenschaften*, vol. II, 1, I.

[74] R. V. Southwell, An Introduction to the Theory of Elasticity for Engineers and Physicists, London, 1941.

[75] —, Relaxation Methods in Theoretical Physics, Oxford, 1946.

[76] W. Sternberg, Die Theorie der Randwertaufgaben im Gebiete der partiellen Differentialgleichungen, Repertorium der höheren Mathematik, vol. I, 3, Chapter 22, Leipzig and Berlin, 1929.

[77] W. Sternberg and T. L. Smith, The Theory of Potential and Spherical Harmonics, Toronto, 1944.

[78] M. H. Stone, Linear Transformations in Hilbert Space and Their Applications to Analysis, Colloquium Publications, vol. 15, American Mathematical Society, New York, 1932.

[79] G. Szegö, Orthogonal polynomials, Colloquium Publications, vol. 23, American Mathematical Society, New York, 1939.

[80] J. D. Tamarkin and W. Feller, Partial differential equations, Providence, R. I., 1941.

[81] S. Timoshenko, Theory of Plates and Shells, New York and London, 1940.

[82] E. C. Titchmarsh, The Theory of Functions, Oxford, 1932.

[83] G. Valiron, Cours d'analyse mathématique, vols. 1 and 2, Paris, 1945—1948.

[84] H. Villat, Leçons sur l'hydrodynamique, Paris, 1929.

[85] H. Villat, Leçons sur la théorie des tourbillons, Paris, 1930.

[86] V. Volterra, Leçons sur les fonctions de lignes, Paris, 1913.

[87] —, Theory of Functionals, London, 1931.

[88] V. Volterra and J. Pérès, Théorie générale des fonctionelles, vol. 1, Paris, 1936.

[89] A. G. Webster, Partial Differential Equations of Mathematical Physics, New York, 1947.

[90] A. Webster and G. Szegö, Partielle Differentialgleichungen der mathematischen Physik, Leipzig and Berlin, 1930.

Articles

(A 1) E. Almansi, Sull'integrazione dell'equazione differenziale $\Delta^{2n} = 0$, *Annali di matematica pura ed applicata*, Series III, vol. II (1898—99), pp. 1—51.

(A 2) N. Aronszajn, La théorie des noyaux reproduisants et ses applications, Première partie, *Proceedings of the Cambridge Philosophical Society*, vol. 39 (1943), pp. 133—153.

(A 3) —, Reproducing and pseudo-reproducing kernels and their application to the partial differential equations of physics, Studies in Partial Differential Equations, Technical Report 5, Harvard Engineering School, Cambridge, Mass. (1948), 31 pages.

(A 4) —, Theory of reproducing kernels, *Transactions of the American Mathematical Society*, vol. 68 (1950), pp. 337—404.

(B 1) S. Bergman, Über die Entwicklung der harmonischen Funktionen der Ebene und des Raumes nach Orthogonalfunktionen, *Mathematische Annalen*, vol. 86 (1922), pp. 238—271.

(B 2) —, Über die Bestimmung der Verzweigungspunkte eines hyperelliptischen Integrals aus seinen Periodizitätsmoduln mit Anwendungen auf die Theorie des Transformators, *Mathematische Zeitschrift*, vol. 19 (1923), pp. 8—25.

(B 3) —, Über die Bestimmung der elastischen Spannungen und Verschiebungen in einem konvexen Körper, *Mathematische Annalen*, vol. 98 (1927), pp. 248—263.

(B 4) —, Zwei Sätze über Funktionen von zwei komplexen Veränderlichen, *Mathematische Annalen*, vol. 100 (1928), pp. 399—410.

(B 5) —, Mehrdeutige Lösungen bei Potentialströmungen mit freien Grenzen, *Zeitschrift für angewandte Mathematik und Mechanik*, vol. 12 (1932), pp. 95—121

(B 6) —, Zur Theorie der Funktionen, die eine lineare partielle Differentialgleichung befriedigen, *Recueil mathématique*, nouvelle série, vol. 2 (44) (1937), pp. 1169—1198.

(B 7) —, The approximation of functions satisfying a linear partial differential equation, *Duke Mathematical Journal*, vol. 6 (1940), pp. 537—561.

(B 8) —, The hodograph method in the theory of compressible fluids, supplement to Fluid Dynamics by von Mises and Friedrichs, Brown University (1942), pp. 1—40.

(B 9) —, A formula for the stream function of certain flows, *Proceedings of the National Academy of Sciences of the U.S.A.*, vol. 29 (1943), pp. 276—281.

(B 10) —, Linear operators in the theory of partial differential equations, *Transactions of the American Mathematical Society*, vol. 53 (1943), pp. 130—155.

(B 11) —, On two-dimensional flows of compressible fluids, *Technical Note* 972, National Advisory Committee for Aeronautics, Washington D. C. (1945), pp. 1—81.

(B 12) S. Bergman, Certain classes of analytic functions of two real variables and their properties, *Transactions of the American Mathematical Society*, vol. 57 (1945), pp. 299—331.

(B 13) —, On supersonic and partially supersonic flows, *Technical Note* 1096, National Advisory Committee for Aeronautics, Washington D. C. (1946), pp. 1—85

(B 14) —, Construction of a complete set of solutions of a linear partial differential equation..., *Quarterly of Applied Mathematics*, vol. IV (1946), pp. 233—245.

(B 15) —, Functions satisfying certain partial differential equations of elliptic type and their representation, *Duke Mathematical Journal*, vol. 14 (1947), pp. 349—366.

(B 16) —, Punch-card machine methods applied to the solution of the torsion problem, *Quarterly of Applied Mathematics*, vol. V (1947), pp. 69—81.

(B 17) —, Two-dimensional subsonic flows of a compressible fluid and their singularities, *Transactions of the American Mathematical Society*, vol. 62 (1947), pp. 452—498.

(B 18) —, Operator methods in the theory of compressible fluids, *Proceedings of Symposia in Applied Mathematics*, vol. 1, (1949), pp. 19—40.

(B 19) —, Determination of axially symmetric flow patterns of a compressible fluid, *Journal of Mathematics and Physics*, vol. 29 (1950), pp. 133—145.

(B 20) —, Determination of subsonic flows around profiles, *Proceedings of the first United States National Congress of Applied Mechanics* (1952), pp. 705—713.

(B 21) S. Bergman and M. Schiffer, A representation of Green's and Neumann's functions in the theory of partial differential equations of second order, *Duke Mathematical Journal*, vol. 14 (1947), pp. 609—638.

(B 22) —, On Green's and Neumann's functions in the theory of partial differential equations, *Bulletin of the American Mathematical Society*, vol. 53 (1947), pp. 1141—1151.

(B 23) —, Kernel functions in the theory of partial differential equations of elliptic type, *Duke Mathematical Journal*, vol. 15 (1948), pp. 535—566.

(B 24) —, The theory of kernel functions in conformal mapping, *Construction and Applications of Conformal Maps*, National Bureau of Standards Applied Mathematics Series 18, Washington, D. C. (1952), pp. 199—206.

(B 25) —, Kernel functions and conformal mapping, *Compositio Mathematica*, vol. 8 (1951), pp. 205—249.

(B 26) —, Some linear operators in the theory of partial differential equations, *Proceedings of the National Academy of Sciences of the U.S.A.*, vol. 36 (1950), pp. 742—746.

(B 27) —, Various kernels in the theory of partial differential equations, *Proceedings of the National Academy of Sciences of the U.S.A.*, vol. 36 (1950), pp. 559—563.

(B 28) L. Bers and A. Gelbart, On a class of differential equations in mechanics of continua, *Quarterly of Applied Mathematics*, vol. 1 (1943), pp. 168—188.

(B 29) —, On a class of functions defined by partial differential equations, *Transactions of the American Mathematical Society*, vol. 56 (1944), pp. 67—93.

(B 30) S. Bochner, Über orthogonale Systeme analytischer Funktionen, *Mathematische Zeitschrift*, vol. 14 (1922), pp. 180—207.

(C 1) C. Carathéodory, Untersuchungen über die konformen Abbildungen von festen und veränderlichen Gebieten, *Mathematische Annalen*, vol. 72 (1912), pp. 107—144.

(D 1) P. J. Daniell, Orthogonal potentials, *Philosophical Magazine and Journal of Science*, (7), vol. 2 (1926), pp. 247—258.

(D 2) P. Davis, An application of doubly orthogonal functions to a problem of approximation in two regions, *Transactions of the American Mathematical Society*, vol. 72 (1952), pp. 104—137.

(D 3) J. B. Diaz and A. Weinstein, Schwarz' inequality and the methods of Rayleigh-Ritz and Trefftz, *Journal of Mathematics and Physics*, vol. 26 (1947), pp. 133—136.

(D 4) —, The torsional rigidity and variational methods, *American Journal of Mathematics*, vol. 70 (1948), pp. 107—116.

(F 1) O. Farrell, On approximation to analytic functions by polynomials, *Bulletin of the American Mathematical Society*, vol. 40 (1934), pp. 908—914.

(F 2) W. Feller, Über die Lösungen der linearen partiellen Differentialgleichungen zweiter Ordnung vom elliptischen Typus, *Mathematische Annalen*, vol. 102 (1930), pp. 633—649.

(F 3) G. Fichera, Risultati concernenti la risoluzione delle equazioni funzionali lineari dovuti all'istituto Nazionale per le applicazioni del calcolo, *Memorie della reale accademia nazionale dei Lincei* (*Classe di scienze fisiche, matematichi e naturali*), Series VIII, vol. III (1950), pp. 1—81.

(F 4) I. Fredholm, Sur les équations de l'équilibre d'un corps solide élastique, *Acta Mathematica*, vol. 23 (1900), pp. 1—42.

(F 5) —, Sur une classe d'équations fonctionelles, *Acta Mathematica*, vol. 27 (1903), pp. 365—390.

(F 6) K. Friedrichs, Die Randwert- und Eigenwertprobleme aus der Theorie der elastischen Platten, *Mathematische Annalen*, vol. 98 (1928), pp. 205—247.

(F 7) —, Über ein Minimumproblem für Potentialströmungen mit freiem Rande, *Mathematische Annalen*, vol. 109 (1933), pp. 60—82.

(G 1) B. G. Galerkin, Contribution à la solution générale du problème de la théorie de l'élasticité dans le cas de trois dimensions, *Comptes rendus de l'academie des sciences*, vol. 190 (1930), pp. 1047—1048.

(G 2) —, Contribution à la solution du problème de la théorie de l'élasticité dans le cas de trois dimensions à l'aide des fonctions des tensions et des déplacements, *Comptes rendus de l'academie des sciences, U.S.S.R.*, (1931), pp. 281—286. (In Russian.)

(G 3) P. R. Garabedian, A new proof of the Riemann mapping theorem, *Construction and Applications of Conformal Maps*, National Bureau of Standards Applied Mathematics Series 18, Washington, D. C. (1952), pp. 207—214.

(G 3a) P. R. Garabedian, H. Lewy, and M. Schiffer, Axially symmetric cavitational flow, *Annals of Mathematics*, vol. 56 (1952), pp. 560—602.

(G 4) P. R. Garabedian and M. Schiffer, Identities in the theory of conformal mapping, *Transactions of the American Mathematical Society*, vol. 65 (1949), pp. 187—238.

(G 5) P. R. Garabedian and M. Schiffer, On existence theorems of potential theory and conformal mapping, *Annals of Mathematics*, vol. 52 (1950), pp. 164—187.

(G 5a) —, Variational problems in the theory of elliptic partial differential equations, *Journal of Rational Mechanics and Analysis*, vol. 2 (1953), pp. 138—171.

(G 6) P. R. Garabedian and D. C. Spencer, Extremal methods in cavitational flow, *Journal of Rational Mechanics and Analysis*, vol. 1 (1952), pp. 359—409.

(G 7) A. Gelbart, On subsonic compressible flows by a method of correspondence, I. Methods for obtaining subsonic circulatory compressible flows about two-dimensional bodies, *Technical Note* 1170, National Advisory Committee for Aeronautics, Washington, D. C. (1947), pp. 1—35.

(H 1) J. Hadamard, Mémoire sur le problème d'analyse relatif à l'équilibre des plaques élastiques encastrées, *Mémoires présentés par divers savants a l'académie des sciences de l'institut de France*, (2), vol. 33, No. 4 (1908), p. 128.

(H 2) G. Hamel, Über einen hydrodynamischen Unitätssatz des Herrn Weinstein, *Résumé des conférences du deuxième congrès international de mécanique appliqué*, Zürich (1926), pp. 489—494.

(H 3) E. Hopf, Bemerkungen zum ersten Randwertproblem der Potentialtheorie im Raume, *Sitzungsberichte der Berliner Mathematischen Gesellschaft*, vol. 26 (1927), pp. 43—48.

(H 4) —, Elementare Bemerkungen über die Lösungen partieller Differentialgleichungen zweiter Ordnung vom elliptischen Typus, *Sitzungsberichte der Preussischen Akademie der Wissenschaften, Berlin*, vol. 19 (1927), pp. 147—152.

(J 1) C. Jacob, Sur la détermination des fonctions harmoniques conjuguées par certaines conditions aux limites, *Mathematica*, vol. 11 (1935), pp. 58—175.

(J 2) G. Julia, Sur une équation aux dérivées fonctionelles liée à la représentation conforme, *Annales de l'école normale* (3), vol. 39 (1922), pp. 1—28.

(K 1) T. v. Kármán, Druckverteilung an Luftschiffkörpern, *Abhandlungen aus dem Aerodynamischen Institut an der Technischen Hochschule, Aachen*, vol. 6 (1927), pp. 1—17.

(K 2) —, The engineer grapples with non-linear problems, *Bulletin of the American Mathematical Society*, vol. 46 (1940), pp. 615—683.

(K 3) A. Korn, Über die Lösung des Grundproblems der Elastizitätstheorie, *Mathematische Annalen*, vol. 75 (1914), pp. 497—544.

(K 4) J. Kravtchenko, *Comptes rendus de l'académie des sciences*, vol. 200 (1935), p. 208; vol. 200 (1935), p. 1832; vol. 202 (1936), p. 276; vol. 203 (1936), p. 426; vol. 205 (1937), p. 1203.

(K 5) —, Sur le problème de représentation conforme de Helmholtz; théorie des sillages et des proues, *Journal de mathématiques pures et appliqués*, vol. 20 (1941), pp. 35—303.

(K 6) —, Sur l'existence des solutions du problème de représentation conforme de Helmholtz, *Annales de l'école normale*, vol. 62 (1945), pp. 233—268; vol. 63 (1946), pp. 161—184.

(L 1) G. Lauricella, Sur l'integration de l'équation rélative à l'équilibre des plaques élastiques encastrées, *Acta Mathematica*, vol. 32 (1909), pp. 201—256.

(L 2) M. A. Lavrentieff, Über eine extremale Aufgabe aus der Tragflügeltheorie, *Cent. Aero-Hydrodyn. Inst.*, No. 155 (1934), pp. 1—40.

(L 3) —, Sur certaines propriétés des fonctions univalentes et leurs applications à la théorie des sillages, *Recueil mathématique* (*Mat. Sbornik*), vol. 4 (1938), pp. 391—458.

(L 4) P. D. Lax, A remark on the method of orthogonal projections, *Communications on Pure and Applied Mathematics*, vol. 4 (1951), pp. 457—464.

(L 5) O. Lehto, Anwendung orthogonaler Systeme auf gewisse funktionentheoretische Extremal- und Abbildungsprobleme, *Annales Academiae Scientiarum Fennicae*, Series AI, No. 59, (1949), pp. 1—51

(L 6) J. Leray, Sur la validité des solutions du problème de la proue, Volume du Jubilé de M. M. Brillouin (1935), p. 246.

(L 7) —, Les problèmes de représentation conforme de Helmholtz, *Commentarii Mathematici Helvetici*, vol. 8 (1935—1936), pp. 149—180 and 250—263.

(L 8) J. Leray and J. Schauder, Topologie et équations fonctionelles, *Annales de l'école normale*, vol. 51 (1934). pp. 45—78.

(L 9) T. Levi-Cevita, Scie e leggi di resistenza, *Rendiconti del circlo mathematico di Palermo*, vol. 23 (1907), pp. 1—37.

(L 10) L. Lichtenstein, Über die zweite und dritte Randwertaufgabe in der Theorie der partiellen Differentialgleichungen, *Sitzungsberichte der Berliner Mathematischen Gesellschaft*, vol. 9 (1909), pp. 19—28.

(L 11) —, Zur Theorie der gewöhnlichen Differentialgleichungen und der partiellen Differentialgleichungen zweiter Ordnung, Rendiconti del circolo Matematico di Palermo, vol. 28 (1909), pp. 267—306.

(L 12) —. Randwertaufgaben der Theorie der linearen partiellen Differentialgleichungen zweiter Ordnung vom elliptischen Typus, I., *Journal für Mathematik*, vol. 142 (1913), pp. 1—40.

(L 13) —, Randwertaufgaben der Theorie der linearen partiellen Differentialgleichungen zweiter Ordnung vom elliptischen Typus, II., *Journal für Mathematik*, vol. 143 (1913), pp. 51—105.

(L 14) —, Zur Theorie der linearen partiellen Differentialgleichungen zweiter Ordnung vom elliptischen Typus, *Acta Mathematica*, vol. 36 (1913), pp. 345—386.

(L 15) —, Zur Theorie der linearen partiellen Differentialgleichungen zweiter Ordnung vom elliptischen Typus, *Sitzungsberichte der Berliner Mathematischen Gesellschaft*, vol. 15 (1916), pp. 123—130.

(L 16) —, Über die erste Randwertaufgabe der Elastizitätstheorie, *Mathematische Zeitschrift*, vol. 20 (1924), pp. 21—28

(L 17) —, Mathematisches über die Gestalt des Weltmeeres, *Sitzungsberichte der Leipziger Akademie*, vol. 79 (1927), pp. 197—214.

(L 18) —, Über ein spezielles Problem der Variationsrechnung, *Sitzungsberichte der Leipziger Akademie*, vol. 79 (1927), pp. 137—144.

(L 19) C. C. Lin, On an extension of the von Kármán-Tsien method to two-dimensional subsonic flows with circulation around closed profiles, *Quarterly of Applied Mathematics*, vol. 4 (1946), pp. 291—297.

(L 20) —, On the subsonic flow through circular and straight lattices of airfoils, *Journal of Mathematics and Physics*, vol. 28 (1949), pp. 117—130.

(L 21) O. Lokki, Über Existenzbeweise einiger mit Extremaleigenschaft versehenen analytischen Funktionen, *Annales Academiae Scientiarum Fennicae*, Series AI, No. 76 (1950), pp. 1—75.

(L 22) G. S. S. Ludford, The behavior at infinity of the potential function of a two-dimensional subsonic compressible flow, *Journal of Mathematics and Physics*, vol. 30 (1951), pp. 117 —130.

(M 1) J. H. Michell, The flexure of a circular plate, *Proceedings of the London Mathematical Society*, vol. 34 (1902), pp. 223—228.

(M 2) R. v. Mises, Zur Theorie des Tragflächenauftriebes, *Zeitschrift für Flugtechnik und Motorluftschiffahrt*, (1920).

(M 3) R. v. Mises and M. Schiffer, On Bergman's integration method in two-dimensional compressible fluid flow, *Advances in Applied Mechanics*, vol. 1 (1948), pp. 249—285.

(N 1) Z. Nehari, The kernel function and construction of conformal maps, *Construction and Applications of Conformal Maps*, National Bureau of Standards Applied Mathematics Series 18, Washington, D. C. (1952), pp. 215—224.

(N 2) H. Neuber, Ein neuer Ansatz zur Lösung räumlicher Probleme der Elastizitätstheorie, *Zeitschrift für angewandte Mathematik und Mechanik*, vol. 14 (1934), pp. 203—212.

(P 1) P. F. Papkovitch, Solution générale des équations différentielles fondamentales de l'élasticité exprimé par trois fonctions harmoniques, *Comptes rendus de l'académie des sciences*, vol. 195 (1932), pp. 513—515.

(P 2) O. Perron, Eine neue Behandlung der ersten Randwertaufgabe für $\Delta u = 0$, *Mathematische Zeitschrift*, vol. 18 (1923), pp. 42—54.

(P 3) M. Picone and G. Fichera, Neue funktionalanalytische Grundlagen für die Existenzprobleme und Lösungsmethoden von Systemen linearer partieller Differentialgleichungen, *Monatshefte für Mathematik und Physik*, vol. 54 (1950) pp. 188—209.

(P 4) J. Plemelj, Ein Ergänzungssatz zur Cauchyschen Integraldarstellung analytischer Funktionen, Randwerte betreffend, *Monatshefte für Mathematik und Physik*, vol. 19 (1908), pp. 205—210.

(P 5) G. Pólya, A minimum problem about the motion of a solid through a fluid, *Proceedings of the National Academy of Sciences of the U.S.A.*, vol. 33 (1947), pp. 218—221.

(P 6) —, Torsional rigidity, principal frequency, electrostatic capacity and symmetrization, *Quarterly of Applied Mathematics*, vol. 6 (1948), pp. 267—277.

(P 7) G. Pólva and G. Szegö, Approximations and bounds for the electrostatic capacity and similar physical quantities, Potential Theory and Variational Methods, Technical Report, Stanford University, Stanford, California (1949), 278 pages. (Incorporated in [64 a].)

(P 8) G. Pólya and A. Weinstein, On the torsional rigidity of multiply connected cross sections, *Annals of Mathematics*, vol. 52 (1950), pp. 154—163.

(P 9) J. J. Privaloff, Cauchy's integral, *Reports of the Faculty of Physics and Mathematics at the University of Saratow* (1919), pp. 1—96. (In Russian.)

(R 1) E. Reissner, Über die Biegung der Kreisplatte mit exzentrischer Einzellast, *Mathematische Annalen*, vol. 111 (1935), pp. 777—780.

(R 2) R. Reynolds, The Dirichlet problem for multiply-connected domains, *Journal of Mathematics and Physics*, vol. 30 (1951), pp. 11—22.

(S 1) M. Schiffer, Sur la variation de la fonction de Green de domaines plans quelconques, *Comptes rendus de l'académie des sciences*, vol. 209 (1939), pp. 980—982.

(S 2) —, The kernel function of an orthonormal system, *Duke Mathematical Journal*, vol. 13 (1946), pp. 529—540.

(S 3) —, Hadamard's formula and variation of domain-functions, *American Journal of Mathematics*, vol. 68 (1946), pp. 417—448.

(S 4) —, An application of orthonormal functions in the theory of conformal mapping, *American Journal of Mathematics*, vol. 70 (1948), pp. 147—156.

(S 5) —, Various types of orthogonalization, *Duke Mathematical Journal*, vol. 17 (1950), pp. 329—366.

(S 6) M. Schiffer and G. Szegö, Virtual mass and polarization. *Transactions of the American Mathematical Society*, vol. 67 (1949), pp. 130—205.

(S 7) E. Schmidt, Mathematische Abhandlung, Hermann Amandus Schwarz gewidnet, Berlin (1914), pp. 365—383.

(S 8) K. Schröder, Zur Theorie der Randwertaufgaben der Differentialgleichung $\Delta \Delta u = 0$, *Mathematische Zeitschrift*, vol. 48 (1942), pp. 553—675.

(S 9) G. S. Shapiro, Three-dimensional problems of elasticity, *Mechanics in U.S.S.R. during Thirty Years* (1950), pp. 165—191. (In Russian.)

(S 10) D. I. Sherman, On solutions of the plane problem of the theory of elasticity in the case of given exterior forces, *Comptes rendus de l'academie des sciences U.S.S.R.*, vol. 28 (1940). pp 28—31.

(S 11) M. Shiffman, On free boundaries of an ideal fluid, *Communications on Applied Mathematics*, vol. 1 (1948), p. 89—99, vol. 2 (1949), pp. 1—11.

(S 12) W. Stekloff, Sur la théorie des fonctions fondamentales, *Comptes rendus de l'académie des sciences*, vol. 128 (1899), pp. 984—987.

(S 13) G. Szegö, Über orthogonale Polynome, die zu einer gegebenen Kurve der komplexen Ebene gehören, *Mathematische Zeitschrift*, vol. 9 (1921), pp. 218—270.

(T 1) G. I. Taylor, The Energy of a Body Moving in an Infinite Fluid, with an Application to Airships, *Proceedings of the Royal Society (London)*, Series A, vol. 120 (1928), pp. 13—21.

(T 2) O. Tedone, Allgemeine Theoreme der mathematischen Elastizitätslehre, *Enzyklopädie der mathematischen Wissenschaften*, vol. IV—4, pp. 55—124.

(T 3) E. Trefftz, Ein Gegenstück zum Ritzschen Verfahren, *Proceedings of the Congress of Applied Mechanics*, Zürich (1926), p. 131—137.

(V 1) H. Villat, Sur la résistance des fluides, *Annales de l'école normale*, vol. 28 (1911), pp. 203—311.

(V 2) —, Aperçus théoriques sur la résistance des fluides, *Collection Scientia*, No. 38, Paris (1920), pp. 7—101.

(W 1) A. Weinstein, Zur Theorie der Flüssigkeitsstrahlen, *Mathematische Zeitschrift*, vol. 31 (1929), pp. 424—433.

(W 2) —, Les conditions aux limites introduites par l'hydrodynamique, *L'enseignement mathématique*, vol. 35 (1936), pp. 107—125

(W 3) —, Non-linear problems in the theory of fluid motion with free boundaries, *Proceedings of Symposia in Applied Mathematics*, vol. 1 (1949), pp. 1—18.

(W 4) —, New methods for the estimation of torsional rigidity, *Proceedings of Symposia in Applied Mathematics*, vol. 3 (1950), pp. 141—161.

(W 5) H. Weyl, Das asymptotische Verteilungsgesetz der Eigenwerte linearer partieller Differentialgleichungen, *Mathematische Annalen*, vol. 71 (1911), pp. 441—479.

(W 6) —, Strahlbildung, nach der Kontinuitätsmethode behandelt, *Nachrichten der Gesellschaft der Wissenschaften zu Göttingen* (1927), pp. 227—237.

(W 7) W. Wirtinger, Zur formalen Theorie der Funktionen von mehr komplexen Veränderlichen, *Mathematische Annalen*, vol. 97 (1927), pp. 357—375.

(Z 1) S. Zaremba, L'équation biharmonique et une classe remarquable de fonctions fondamentales harmoniques, *Bulletin internationale de l'académie des sciences de Cracovie* (1907), pp. 147—196.

(Z 2) —, Sur le calcul numérique des fonctions demandées dans le problème de Dirichlet et le problème hydrodynamique, *Bulletin internationale de l'académie des sciences de Cracovie* (1909), pp. 125—195.

Author Index

Subject Index

W